ADVANCES IN EXTRACTIVE METALLURGY AND REFINING

Advances in extractive metallurgy and refining

Proceedings of an international symposium, organized by the Institution of Mining and Metallurgy, held in London from 4 to 6 October 1971

Edited by M. J. Jones

The Institution of Mining and Metallurgy, London

Library of Congress Catalog Card Number: 72–79461

SBN 900488 06 9

Contents

Organizing Committee

Dr. D. A. Temple (*Chairman*)
G. N. Boulter
A. L. Guise Brown
M. J. Cahalan
J. A. Charles
G. E. Davies
Dr. E. F. Emley
Dr. T. W. Farthing
A. W. Fletcher

P. M. J. Gray
I. C. Herbert
Dr. A. W. D. Hills
Dr. J. E. Hughes
Dr. S. C. Pearce
N. J. B. Pocock
Dr. A. J. Robinson
L. R. Verney

Foreword

Before the proceedings of the Symposium commenced on Monday, 4 October, 1971, the Eighth Sir Julius Wernher Memorial Lecture,* 'The case for continuity in extractive metallurgy', was delivered by Dr. J. H. Chesters, O.B.E., F.I.M., F.R.S., lately Director, BISRA—The Corporate Laboratories, British Steel Corporation, in the Lecture Hall of the Institution of Electrical Engineers, Savoy Place, London. Dr. Chesters' lecture was a fitting introduction to the Symposium.

Following a recommendation by its Metallurgy Committee, the Institution Council gave approval for a Symposium on 'advances in extractive metallurgy and refining' to be run on similar lines to that held in April, 1967,† which had proved highly successful. It was intended to include the development, improvement and control of metallurgical processes in the papers, and authors were asked to give careful consideration to the needs for increasing production capacity and for treating low-grade, complex and refractory raw materials, including secondary materials. Aspects of the reduction of operating costs, both by the extended employment of automation and improved materials-handling techniques, were sought, and as many details of the operational economics as possible were requested. Similarly, the effects of changes in the cost patterns of energy sources on extractive and refining processes by the use of advanced heating techniques and alternative fuels were to be included.

The Organizing Committee was formed in January, 1970; its members were most resourceful and influential in arranging a programme of high quality and interest. The Committee included representatives from all facets of the extractive metallurgy industry, both ferrous and non-ferrous. Thirty papers, by authors in 13 countries, were selected from a large number submitted in response to the request for manuscripts.

The technical sessions commenced after Dr. Chesters' lecture in the afternoon of 4 October and continued until the afternoon of Wednesday, 6 October. Approximately 250 registrants from 22 countries attended the technical sessions. Records of the discussions are published in this volume.

The Organizing Committee considered that the opportunity should be taken to include an additional session on the control of environmental pollution in metallurgical operations. This informal discussion meeting was held on the evening of Tuesday, 5 October; Sir Frederick Warner acted as Chairman and the topic was introduced by Mr. E. C. Mantle and Mr. D. G. Fowler. The report of an interesting discussion follows this Foreword.

* CHESTERS J.H. The case for continuity in extractive metallurgy. *Bull. Instn Min. Metall.* no. 781, Dec. 1971, 13–28; *Trans. Instn Min. Metall.*, **80**, 1971, 52–67.
† Proceedings published in *Advances in extractive metallurgy* (London: Institution of Mining and Metallurgy, 1968), 1023 p.

A large committee is seldom suited to execute all the necessary arrangements and, consequently, a small working group—Archie Fletcher, Phil Gray and Michael Jones—gallantly became actively involved in the detailed decisions required to implement the broad principles outlined by the Committee.

The Institution offers its sincere thanks to the authors, to the sessional chairmen, to the referees, to the contributors to the discussion, to those who attended the meeting and, especially, to the editorial staff of the Institution, who, following established practice, ensured that the papers were preprinted and distributed before the Symposium, thus allowing the maximum time for discussion.

DEREK TEMPLE
Chairman, Organizing Committee

Control of environmental pollution in metallurgical operations

Report of an informal discussion meeting (Chairman: Sir Frederick Warner) held on 5 October 1971

The Chairman said that only air and water pollution would be considered. In the United Kingdom, although river pollution was an offence, certain discharges from abandoned mines and discharges of heavy metals from industrial operations constituted problems. In the case of copper and zinc, very low concentrations were toxic to fish. Discharge into the sea ameliorated that problem, however, since the sea had a considerable buffering action, with precipitation of heavy metals as carbonates.

With regard to air pollution, the existing Alkali Act had recently been considerably extended to include fluoride, chloride and all other types of metallurgical works. Sulphur dioxide was a major air pollutant, and its control depended either on its conversion to sulphuric acid or its efficient dispersal by techniques based on model studies. Experience which was becoming available from Anglesey and Invergordon of the long-term effects of fluorides would assist in the development of control techniques.

Mr. E. C. Mantle* confined his remarks to air pollution, and demonstrated that the non-ferrous metals industry was not a major polluter of the atmosphere on a global scale. Out of an estimated total world man-made sulphur dioxide emission of 126×10^6 tons per annum (United Kingdom, 6×10^6 tons per annum), only about 9.5% would be emitted to the atmosphere by copper, zinc and lead production if no recovery of sulphur were made. In practice, however, much of the sulphur dioxide was recovered as sulphuric acid.

Similarly, for fluorine, production from coal burning was very much greater than that discharged from aluminium smelting. With regard to particulate emissions, figures for the U.S.A. indicated that the non-ferrous metals industry contributed only 3.3% of the total of 18 000 000 tons per annum.

Pollution from smelting was primarily a local problem, requiring the limitation of ground level concentrations to below harmful levels. Although those levels were very difficult to determine, the U.S.A. Environmental Protection Agency had set standards to be met by 1975. The primary standards were designed to protect public health and the secondary standards to conserve the environment. For sulphur dioxide the primary standard was 80 $\mu g/m^3$ annual mean concentration, with a maximum 24-h figure of 365 $\mu g/m^3$ not to be exceeded more than once per year. By present United Kingdom figures those standards were unrealistic, since current average concentrations were about 200 $\mu g/m^3$ in Inner London, 150 $\mu g/m^3$ in Greater London and 80 $\mu g/m^3$ in southeast

* Deputy Director, BNFMRA, London.

England, excluding London. A costly wholesale change in the U.S.A. to low-sulphur fuel would be required since present emissions were some four times greater than those in the United Kingdom. A primary standard also existed for particulates, stipulating 75 μg/m^3 and 260 μg/m^3 as annual mean and maximum 24-h concentrations, respectively.

In the United Kingdom no such standards existed. Legislation consisted of the Clean Air Act, which limited smoke production, and the Alkali Act, which now applied to a large proportion of industry. The Alkali Inspectorate used the 'best practicable means' approach for controlling pollution, and usually stipulated a maximum emission and an accompanying stack height to ensure dispersion. That generally ensured a maximum ground level concentration of a pollutant of not more than one-fortieth of the level permitted for eight hours' exposure in a factory.

The 'best practicable means' approach frequently involved severe restrictions on emissions. For example, sulphuric acid plants based on pyrites burning must convert 96% sulphur to acid with a total acidity of tail gases less than 8 g/m^3. In many cases emission of particulates was limited to 0·1 g/m^3 and lower for certain toxic materials. For example, a lead plant discharging 283 m^3/min must have a lead concentration less than 0·02 g/m^3 and a mass emission of less than 450 kg per week. The United Kingdom regulations were strictly enforced, whereas apparently more severe legislation elsewhere often was not.

Sulphur dioxide was not a dangerous gas in low concentrations nor was it persistent in the atmosphere. Emissions had been kept low in many smelters, such as modern zinc plants, where up to 99% conversion of concentrate sulphur to acid was obtained. Acid production was, however, an operation of doubtful economics for many remote smelters. Nevertheless, the employment of tall stacks, as in the power industry, should have been more widespread to avoid the local spoliation caused by low-level discharges. For comparison, a 4000-MW coal-fired power station, which would discharge 1200 tons of sulphur dioxide a day through tall stacks, was being constructed in Yorkshire. That was equivalent to a smelter producing 400 000 tons of zinc per year, all sulphur dioxide being emitted to atmosphere.

The eventual solution to the pollution problem must lie with alternative non-thermal extraction processes. An industry handicapped by heavy pollution control costs for existing plants was, however, unlikely to develop them, and therefore a gradual programme for containment of pollution was required.

Mr. D. G. Fowler* discussed the economics of pollution control: the technology was available for almost any kind of pollution control, but he wondered if society was willing to pay for it. Public bodies and industry should jointly explain the situation to the public and justify the price increases which additional pollution control would require. Too much ignorant criticism of industry had been published.

The cost to industry of anti-pollution measures was exemplified by the

* Partner, Fowler Davies & Co., Industrial Hygiene Consultants, Horsham, Surrey.

case of a small U.S. steel plant, which had closed down recently because the required expenditure to meet local standards would have equalled its capital. The United Kingdom was fortunate that tall stacks were permitted for sulphur dioxide dispersal. In the U.S.A. that was certainly not true for smelters and, for example, a West Coast smelter recently was denied permission to build a 1000-ft stack.

The Chairman pointed out that the British approach was the employment of 'best practicable means'. That only meant tall stacks and dispersion in the case of power stations, where the 0·8% SO_2 gas could not be treated otherwise.

The 100-year history of pollution control in the United Kingdom enabled the setting up of models to enable further control to be effective. The level of atmospheric pollution in the United Kingdom was lower than in many other countries and it was steadily diminishing. For example, the hours of sunshine in London in winter had doubled in the last 10 years. In the application of control, local conditions were considered rather than the laying down of rigid overall rules.

Discussion

Contributors to the discussion dealt mainly with the subject of pollution and its control within their own countries. The discussion is therefore summarized on a geographical basis.

Sweden

The total annual emission of sulphur in Sweden was stated to be 500 000 tons, mainly from fossil fuels. Boliden, the largest non-ferrous smelter, recovered more than 90% of the sulphur in gases as sulphuric acid.

No legislation existed to control pollution, but the following provisional guidelines had been laid down for SO_2:

$\frac{1}{2}$ hour average	25 pphm*
1 week average	10 pphm
1 month average	2 pphm

The use of low-sulphur fuel oil was mandatory in several large cities.

It was stated that of the 200 000 000–250 000 000 tons of sulphur dioxide entering the atmosphere each year, the majority was accounted for by natural phenomena, such as volcanoes. Emitted sulphur dioxide usually came down again within 4–5 days as sulphuric acid.

The problem of pollution was a global one and should be tackled as such. It was suggested that the prevailing winds carrying sulphur dioxide from the United Kingdom, because of its tall stacks policy, could be responsible for the increase in acidity of Swedish lakes from pH 7 to pH 5·5 in the last 10 years. That suggestion was disputed by several speakers and it was pointed out

* Parts per hundred million.

that if all the sulphur dioxide produced by the United Kingdom went direct into the lakes of Sweden, it would only produce a pH change of one-tenth. The change in Swedish lakes must be attributable to more local factors.

U.S.A.

Copper, zinc and lead smelters accounted for only 12% of the sulphur dioxide emitted in the U.S.A., the major source of emission being power stations. The smelters were, however, more obvious polluters and had attracted special legislation. This legislation was not uniform, however, since states which were particularly affected had drawn up their own, which could be more severe than the Federal standards. Standards existed which not only restricted emissions but stated that only 10% of the input sulphur could be emitted. Under those regulations copper smelting with reverberatory furnaces was impossible and it was doubtful whether the Noranda or Outokumpu process would give a 90% recovery of sulphur when the tail gases from acid plants were taken into account. In any case, disposal of product acid represented a great problem.

The copper industry had estimated costs of more than $500 000 000 to meet proposed standards—compared with government estimates of $100 000 000.

Australia

There had been some discussion in Australia regarding pollution legislation, particularly regarding ground level concentrations. Fortunately, the major ore deposits and smelters were located away from centres of population, but the public was becoming more concerned about the effects of such industries. The importance of public activities was stressed and reference was made to a recent symposium,* which had brought common sense to an emotional situation. The Australasian Institute of Mining and Metallurgy was encouraging public dialogue between its members and critics of the industry.

Belgium

In 1920 the combination of smelter sulphur dioxide discharges and a temperature inversion caused the deaths of 20 people in Liège. Legislation was then passed such that sulphur dioxide discharged must not exceed 0·1% by volume if the stack were 100 m high. Most Belgian smelters had improved on that requirement and up to 95% recovery of sulphur was obtained.

It was considered to be the responsibility of managers to ensure that equipment worked properly and that pollution was minimized.

South Africa

Expenditure on pollution control during the last 10 years had amounted to 0·3% of sales value. The problem of solid wastes around Johannesburg was

---

* A seminar 'Progress—mining and environment', organized by the Australasian Institute of Mining and Metallurgy in conjunction with the Australian Mining Industry Council, was held in Melbourne from 19 to 21 April 1971.

largely under control. Grass was being grown on old tailings dams and acid mine water drainage was being checked.

In the recent Water Act the 'best practicable means' approach had been adopted after consultations with the Chief Alkali Inspector in the United Kingdom.

United Kingdom

Variation in pollution control standards throughout the world had adverse effects on companies subject to stringent standards. Companies had to bear the costs of anti-pollution measures, while often producing products at international prices. An example of the costs of anti-pollution measures was the Avonmouth zinc smelter, where more than £2 000 000 of the total cost of £14 000 000 was spent on ventilation and effluent treatment systems.

In the case of lead, a conflict existed between trying to maintain a suitable working atmosphere and minimizing discharges from the plant. In that context it was questioned whether the United Kingdom limit of 450 kg per week was realistic. It was stated that particulate pollution was very local to a works. Carbon monoxide and carbon dioxide represented greater problems than sulphur dioxide since they tended to accumulate in the upper atmosphere and cause a greenhouse effect. That suggestion was disputed, however, since world temperatures were decreasing.

General

It was considered that the marketing problem for sulphuric acid required the development of elemental sulphur production processes to overcome sulphur dioxide pollution. Although the Noranda and Outokumpu processes were attractive in that respect, since they provided high-strength gas, the problem of obtaining a suitably priced reductant remained. Alternative hydrometallurgical processes were receiving a great deal of attention, but the possibility of exchanging one pollution problem for another must be guarded against.

It was suggested that the session had concentrated unduly upon sulphur dioxide. Other pollutants, such as heavy metals, pickle liquors and ferric oxide, were equally important. That suggestion was reinforced by the expression of an opinion that persistent pollutants were the important ones so far as international control was concerned.

A. W. FLETCHER
R. W. LEE

Session 1

Continuous processing

Chairman
Professor T. R. A. Davey

Production of copper by the Noranda process

N. J. Themelis B.Eng., Ph.D.

Engineering Division, Noranda Research Centre, Pointe Claire, Quebec, Canada

G. C. McKerrow B.Sc.

Noranda Mines, Ltd., Noranda, Quebec, Canada

669.012.49:669.333.3

Synopsis

A new process for the continuous smelting and converting of copper concentrates has been developed by Noranda Mines, Ltd., and tested in a pilot plant of smelting capacity of 100 tons concentrate/day. The pilot plant has been in operation at the Noranda, Quebec, smelter since May, 1968, and during its first three years of operation smelted nearly 50 000 tons of concentrates. On the basis of this work an 800 ton/day plant is being built at the Noranda, Quebec, smelter.

The basic unit of the Noranda process is a horizontal, cylindrical reactor, which, in some aspects, resembles a Peirce–Smith converter. The reactor bath consists of layers of slag, high-grade matte and metallic copper. Pelletized copper concentrates and flux are distributed, by means of a slinger-belt feeder, on the surface of the bath in the smelting and converting zone, which is strongly agitated by air injected through a series of tuyères.

The low-silica, high-copper slag produced during converting passes through a settling zone before it is tapped. The slag is treated by milling to yield a high-grade concentrate, which is recycled to the pelletizer, and a low-copper tailing, which is discarded. Large-scale milling trials have shown that the tailing loss for a 25% Cu concentrate was 1·6% of the input copper, which corresponds to a 0·37% copper slag from a conventional reverberatory furnace.

The copper produced during converting settles in a sump near the middle of the reactor, and it is tapped intermittently. It contains 1–1·5% sulphur, and can be processed to anode copper by conventional methods, a longer than usual oxidation period being used.

The process generates a continuous flow of sulphur dioxide gas which (after sufficient dilution with air to produce the required O_2/SO_2 ratio) is suitable for the manufacture of sulphuric acid.

Despite the fact that the first patent on the continuous smelting and converting of copper was published in 1898,[1] it is only in recent years that concerted efforts have been made towards the development of such a process.[2-6] The subject of

3

this paper is the Noranda process, which has been under development in Canada since 1964,[7, 8, 9] and has now reached the stage where an 800 ton/day plant is scheduled to be operating in March, 1973.

In order to describe the principles and advantages of the Noranda process, we shall first examine briefly the conventional process of reverberatory smelting. In the reverberatory furnace copper concentrates and flux are melted to form a matte layer and a slag which is relatively low in copper content and can be discarded.

The matte is transferred to a converter and, in the first stage of the converting operation, the iron sulphide component is oxidized with air and fluxed with silica to form a high-copper slag, which is recirculated to the reverberatory for cleaning. In the second stage of converting the accumulated copper sulphide is oxidized to metallic copper. The division of the converting process into two stages is imposed by chemical thermodynamics since, in an equilibrium system, it is not possible to produce metallic copper without first oxidizing nearly all the iron sulphide in the matte.

A disadvantage of reverberatory smelting is that a large amount of fuel is used for smelting in the reverberatory, and an excess of heat is produced by the exothermic reactions in the converter. Also, the reverberatory flue gases have a low sulphur dioxide content and are not economically amenable to the manufacture of sulphuric acid, thus posing a serious problem in areas where the emission of sulphur dioxide into the atmosphere is restricted.

The Noranda process

In the Noranda process pelletized concentrates are smelted and converted simultaneously in a single reactor (Fig. 1), which is a horizontal cylindrical

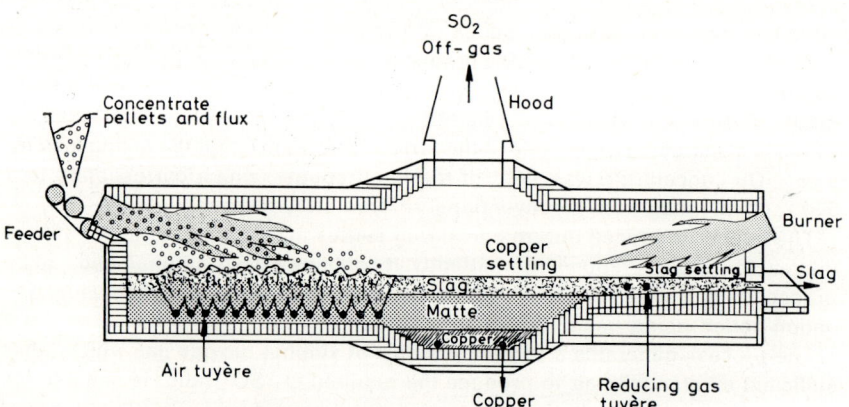

Fig. 1 Schematic drawing of Noranda process reactor

furnace with a raised hearth at one end and a sump-like depression near the middle. A series of air tuyères is located along the reactor in a smelting and converting zone. The reactor can be rotated to bring the tuyères out of the bath. A hood is provided for off-gases. Other design features are burners at each end, a feed port for charging copper concentrate and flux by means of a belt-slinger, and separate tapholes for tapping slag and copper.

The reactor bath consists of layers of slag, high-grade matte and metallic copper. Pelletized copper concentrates and silica flux are distributed on the surface of the bath in the smelting and converting zone, which is strongly agitated by air, or oxygen-enriched air, injected through the tuyères.

The bath in the smelting and converting zone of the Noranda process reactor may be described as a system in which a 'dynamic equilibrium' condition exists. Concentrate is smelted to matte, and, in the same general zone, white metal is converted to copper, despite the fact that, on average, the molten matte contains more iron than an equilibrium system.

The air injected through the tuyères forms a highly turbulent jet in the bath. In the upward flow of this jet there is an exchange of momentum between the gas and the surrounding matte, which is entrained in the jet cone. The jet acts as a powerful mixing device, pushing the sulphide phase through the slag layer— from where it settles by gravity again into the copper sulphide layer. The energy of the jets is not dissipated entirely in mixing the bath. Particles of liquid are carried with the gas above the surface of the bath in the form of liquid spouts and droplets.

The intense mixing action of the air jets maintains the bath in turmoil, and thus provides the required high heat-transfer rate from the copper sulphide matte, where heat is generated by the converting reactions to the slag phase and to the concentrate charge on the surface of the bath. The additional process heat required is supplied by the burners.

The concentrate pellets and flux are continuously distributed widely over the surface of the molten bath by means of a belt-slinger, and substantially remain as individual lumps until they are absorbed into the molten bath. The large surface area per unit volume of charge therefore contributes to the high smelting rate of the reactor.

Under normal operating conditions the rate at which air is blown through the tuyères and the rate of concentrate addition to the reactor are controlled closely to the stoichiometric ratio so that all the input sulphur and iron is oxidized to produce copper and slag, the volume of matte in the reactor remaining constant. At the same time the rate of flux addition is controlled proportionally to the air and concentrate input rates.

The molten copper and the slag are tapped off intermittently or continuously so that the levels of the molten copper, matte and slag remain within the desired operating levels in the reactor.

By introducing the air at a sufficient depth below the surface of the matte, 95–100% (generally approaching 100%) of the oxygen reacts with the matte. Consistent high utilization of oxygen makes it possible to predict accurately the amount of air required for each ton of concentrate of a particular composition.

The slag produced during converting flows through a settling zone before it is tapped from the reactor. Initially, the process was envisaged to incorporate a reducing treatment of the slag in the reactor in order to decrease its copper content to acceptable levels. In present practice, however, a low-silica, high-copper slag is produced which can be treated by milling to yield a high-grade concentrate. The concentrate is recycled to the reactor, and the low-copper tailing is discarded.

Results of pilot-plant work

After four years of research at Noranda Research Centre, which included small pilot furnace and model tests (Figs. 2 and 3), a 100 ton/day pilot plant (Fig. 4)

Fig. 2 Small pilot converter (2·5-ft internal diameter) used at Noranda Research Centre during development

Fig. 3 Model of pilot-plant reactor used in feed distribution tests at Noranda Research Centre

was built at the smelter of Noranda Mines, Ltd., Noranda, Quebec. The pilot plant went into operation in May, 1968, and since then has smelted nearly 50 000 tons of concentrates and has provided enough data to confirm the economic feasibility of the process. As a result of this work, in March, 1971, it was decided

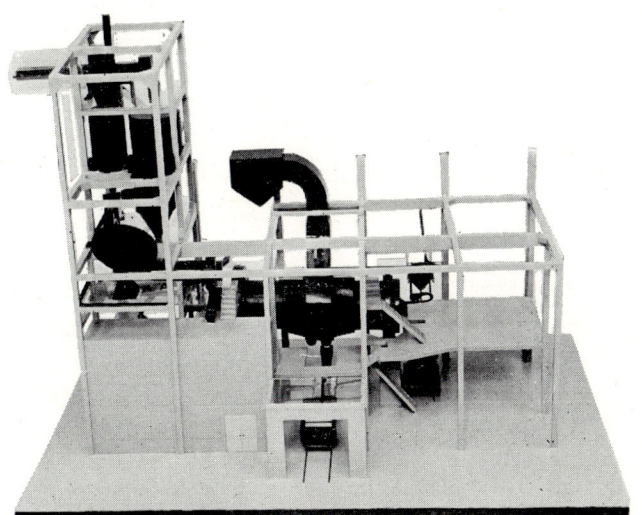

Fig. 4 Engineering model of 100 ton/day pilot plant

to build an 800 ton/day industrial plant at the Noranda, Quebec, smelter of Noranda Mines, Ltd. The plant is expected to go into operation early in 1973.

Description of pilot plant

The pilot plant adjoins the converter aisle of the Noranda smelter. This location permits the plant to be linked to existing utilities, charge handling facilities, flues and Cottrell. Slag and blister copper produced in the pilot plant can also be handled by the converter aisle cranes.

A flowsheet of the pilot plant is shown in Fig. 5. Copper concentrate is received

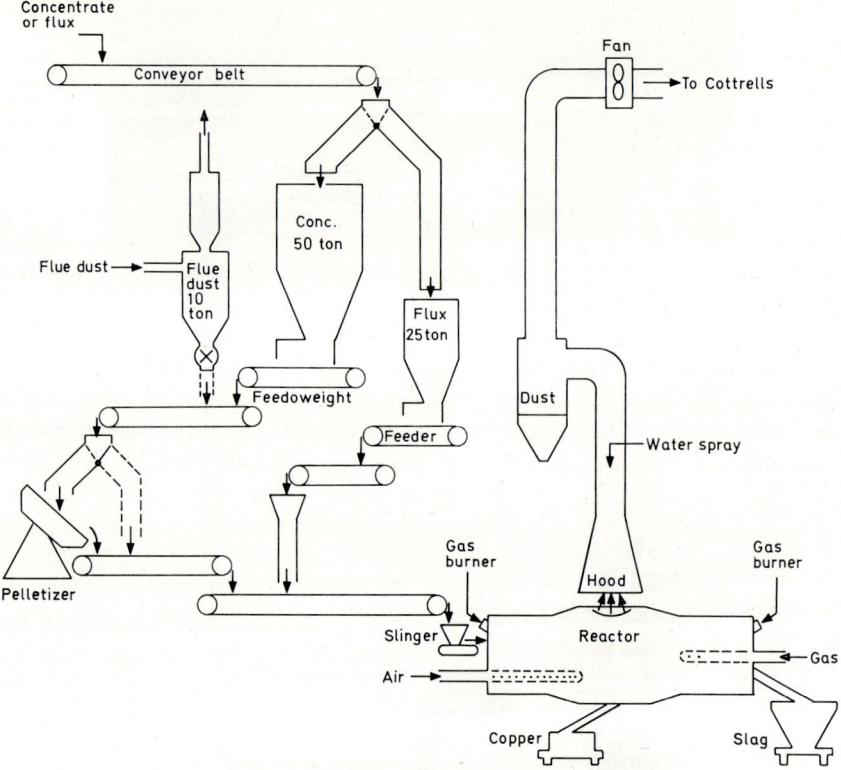

Fig. 5 Schematic diagram of pilot-plant equipment

and stored in a 50-ton bin. A constant weight feeder feeds the concentrate to a 10-ft pelletizing disc. Flue dust can be added to the concentrate prior to pelletizing from a 10-ton bin provided with a star feeder. Concentrate pellets are discharged on to a belt and join the silica flux ($\frac{1}{2}$–1 in), which is drawn from a 25-ton bin by a volumetric feeder. The mixture of pellets and flux is thrown into the reactor through a feed port in the end wall by a belt-slinger.

The cylindrical reactor (Fig. 1) has an inside length of 32·5 ft, with a 7-ft internal diameter at the feed end. Near the middle the reactor diameter widens out to form a copper sump. Two copper tapholes, 1 in in diameter, are located at the bottom of the sump. A small gas-fired furnace is mounted on the outside of the reactor around the opening of each taphole. The mouth of the reactor is above the sump. Beyond the sump a raised hearth slopes upwards to a level 48 in above the bottom of the sump at the slag taphole in the end wall. The reactor is lined with burned or fused chrome–magnesite brick, and at high wear areas there are water-cooled blocks or panels.

A gas burner with a rating of 15×10^6 Btu/h is positioned in the feed end wall beside the feed port. This burner can be automatically controlled via a radiation pyrometer sighting through the hood in the reactor. A small burner with a rating of 5×10^6 Btu/h is located in the slag end wall.

There are thirteen standard converter 2-in air tuyères at 6-in centres in the smelting and converting zone of the reactor. As few as four and as many as 12 of these tuyères have been used at times. Normally, eight tuyères blowing at 450–500 Sft³/min (15 lb/in² gauge air at 160°F) are sufficient for a throughput of 100 tons of concentrate per day. The reactor can be rotated through an angle of 54° to bring the tuyères out of the bath. The burners operate continuously, and therefore the hood of the reactor was designed to cover the mouth when the tuyères were in or out of the bath.

At the slag end of the reactor there are tuyères which can be fitted to blow either air or natural gas.

Flue gases leave the reactor through a water-cooled hood and are then cooled with water sprays and exhausted through a fan to a Cottrell precipitator. Coarse flue dust is collected in a settling box in the flue and can be returned to the process.

In order to enable all possible data to be collected, the pilot plant is highly instrumented and is controlled from a central control room (Fig. 6). Operation

Fig. 6 Control room of pilot plant

of the reactor requires instrumentation for the control, recording and integration of the concentrate and flux feed rates, the converting air flow rate, burner inputs and bath temperature. Ratio controllers which maintain fixed air/concentrate and air/flux ratios are essential features of the process. Other instruments installed for data-collection purposes measure the draught, the composition and temperature of the flue gas, refractory temperatures, individual tuyère air flows and running times of various pieces of equipment.

The pilot plant is operated in three shifts by seven-man crews. Each crew is led by a technician, with high-school education, who controls the operating parameters, conducts tests and collects data. A reactor operator assists in the pilot-plant operation and looks after the crew of tapper, tapper's helper, puncher, feed preparation man and sampler. The sampler collects and prepares the many samples taken in the pilot plant, but would not be necessary in an industrial plant. On the other hand, an industrial plant would require additional men to attend to the Cottrells and for the slag casting operation.

Bath level control

The copper level in the pilot reactor is allowed to rise to 10–12 in above the bottom of the sump before it is tapped down to 4–5 in. If the copper is allowed to rise too high, punching of the tuyères becomes more difficult. On the other hand, if copper is tapped out completely, some matte may be also tapped.

The matte level is normally maintained at a thickness of 29–34 in. The tuyères are located so that air enters the molten bath in the lower portion of the matte phase. The depth of the slag layer is maintained at 12–15 in.

In order to ensure that the air/concentrate charge ratio is properly maintained, the levels of slag, matte and copper in the reactor are measured every hour by dipping an iron bar into the bath through a porthole on top of the reactor. Any variation in level can be compensated by adjusting the air/concentrate ratio and the frequency of tapping copper and slag.

Reactor temperature

The temperature in the reactor is measured by a radiation pyrometer located in the hood and sighted on the slag surface. The temperature is maintained at 2250°F by means of automatic control of the feed end burner. Slag is tapped at 2200–2230°F and copper at 2180–2200°F.

Refractory wear

In the first two years of operation of the pilot plant the main areas of refractory wear occurred around the slag line of the reactor and around the feed end burner. This was minimized through the use of fused chrome–magnesite bricks at the slag line and a water-cooled panel near the feed end burner.

The most recent campaign of the reactor (Nov., 1970–March, 1971) lasted 146 days and incorporated a five-week period during which oxygen-enriched air was used. The campaign was ended because of refractory wear at the tuyère line.

Slag composition

Slags are fluxed to yield a Fe/SiO_2 ratio of 1·5–1·9, which, for the concentrates smelted at Noranda, corresponds to a slag content of 22–25% SiO_2. A low-silica slag is chosen in order to produce less slag per ton of concentrates smelted and to facilitate the subsequent grinding of the slag.

The slag contains 10–12% copper, most of which is present as metal globules, and 20–30% magnetite. At higher silica concentrations the magnetite in the slag is reduced, but this offers no special advantage in the subsequent milling operation.

If the slag is allowed to stagnate in the slag zone, a mushy layer forms on the surface, presumably due to the heat loss by radiation to the water-cooled hood. The mushy layer is of the same composition as the fluid slag underneath, and it must be stirred to prevent it from interfering with tapping. Normally, the slag zone is stirred by injecting natural gas through lances inserted through portholes in the roof. Tuyères blowing either natural gas or air into the slag at the settling zone have also been used for this purpose.

The silica flux used in the pilot plant contains about 69% SiO_2 and 10–12% Al_2O_3. In February, 1971, a limited test was carried out with high-silica flux containing 95% SiO_2. The slags produced during this period were very fluid and did not require the use of tuyères or lances in the slag zone. The copper content of these slags was about 10–11% Cu, but flotation tests indicated that lower tailing losses (0·45% Cu in the tailing) could be expected.

Copper produced

Copper containing 1–1·5% S is tapped through one of two tapholes, which are fitted with small gas-fired furnaces to facilitate opening the taphole with an oxygen lance. At the end of the tap the hole is closed with a clay stopper. The copper is cast into cakes.

Table 1 Typical analysis of concentrates, copper and slag

| | Composition, % | | | | | | |
	Cu	Fe	S	Zn	Pb	SiO_2	Fe_3O_4
Concentrate 1	23·7	28·6	27·6	0·4	0·9	8·2	
Concentrate 2	22·5	32·3	27·8	1·4	0·17	7·0	
Concentrate 3	23·5	28·5	33·6	5·9	1·23	3·3	
Concentrate 4	28·2	27·5	33·6	7·2	0·52	2·4	
Copper 1	97·4	0·3	1·50	0·1	0·08		
Copper 2	97·4	0·2	1·80	<0·1	0·03		
Copper 3	97·7	0·1	1·50	0·1	0·15		
Copper 4	97·5	0·1	1·30	<0·1	0·10		
Slag 1	7·9	39·3		1·1	0·33	25·4	19·7
Slag 2	9·2	40·5		0·9	0·11	24·5	20·0
Slag 3	10·7	35·5		5·5	0·57	22·0	22·8
Slag 4	11·0	32·8		7·8	0·61	24·8	26·0

Experimental work on the oxidation and subsequent deoxidation of Noranda process copper has shown that it can be processed readily to anode copper. The impurity levels in the copper tapped from the reactor and in the anode copper are well within the range encountered in conventional smelting. Typical analyses of concentrates smelted and copper and slag produced are shown in Table 1.

Reactor flue gas

The reactor flue gases, before dilution with air, contain 7–8% SO_2. The flue dust represents 5% of the charge input to the reactor and is recirculated to the reactor by incorporation in the concentrate pellets.

Fuel requirements

The fuel oil consumption in the pilot plant has been about 5 000 000 Btu/ton of concentrate smelted. This is relatively high owing to the high heat losses associated with the small size of the pilot-plant reactor.

Natural gas was used until February, 1970, when conversion was made to Bunker C fuel oil. It was found that this resulted in a decrease of 10–15% in the fuel consumption.

Slag milling

In the original concept of the Noranda process it was proposed to produce a 30–32% silica slag which could be cleaned pyrometallurgically in the reactor proper. This was not achieved in the pilot plant, however, and it was therefore decided to produce a low-silica, high-copper slag which could be cleaned by milling.

The slag is highly oxidized and contains 20–30% Fe_3O_4 in soluble and entrained form and 8–12% copper. Microscopic examination of rapidly quenched slag (granulated slag) indicates that the soluble copper represents nearly two-thirds of this amount. These results are in agreement with thermodynamic studies on the solubility of copper in slags equilibrated with metallic copper.[11, 12, 13]

Open-circuit flotation tests were carried out initially to establish the feasibility of slag milling and determine the required fineness of grind and flotation reagents. It was found[14] that a fine grind (about 90% −325 mesh) was essential to produce an acceptable low-copper tailing. The optimum combination of reagents was 0·20 lb/ton slag of sodium isopropyl xanthate and an equal quantity of Z-200 (isopropyl ethyl thionocarbamate); pine oil and MIBC (methyl isobutyl carbinol) were found to be suitable frothers.

Pilot-plant tests were conducted at the Noranda, Quebec, concentrator at grinding and flotation rates of 200 lb slag/h. This work was then followed by a full-scale milling test at the same plant during which 1500 tons of slag was milled at the rate of 15 ton/h. The overall results of this test showed that a tailing of 0·5% Cu had been produced at a concentration ratio of 4·5:1 (Table 2). A recent test of autogenous grinding and flotation of 62 tons of Noranda

Table 2   Milling tests on Noranda process slags[14]

	Fineness of grind, % −325 mesh	% Copper in Head slag	Concentrate	Tailing	Concentration ratio, head slag/concentrate	% Recovery
Slag cooled in 150-lb mould, laboratory standard test	93·8	13·8	62·2	0·53	5·05	97·3
Large-scale milling (1430 tons slag milled), ball-mill grinding	91·1	11·4	51·5	0·50	4·54	96·5
Large-scale milling (365 tons slag milled), autogenous grinding	90·0	11·7	52·1	0·53	4·74	96·3

process slag (12·1% Cu) at Lakefield Research, Lakefield, Ontario, has corroborated the milling results at Noranda: at a grind of 95% −325 mesh, the tailings contained 0·45% Cu and the concentrate 47·2% Cu.

The slag for the milling tests was cast in beds of flux, in cakes of 4–6 ft in diameter and about 1·5 ft in thickness. Laboratory studies have shown that it is very important to cool the slag slowly in order to allow for the precipitation and growth of copper particles (Fig. 7).

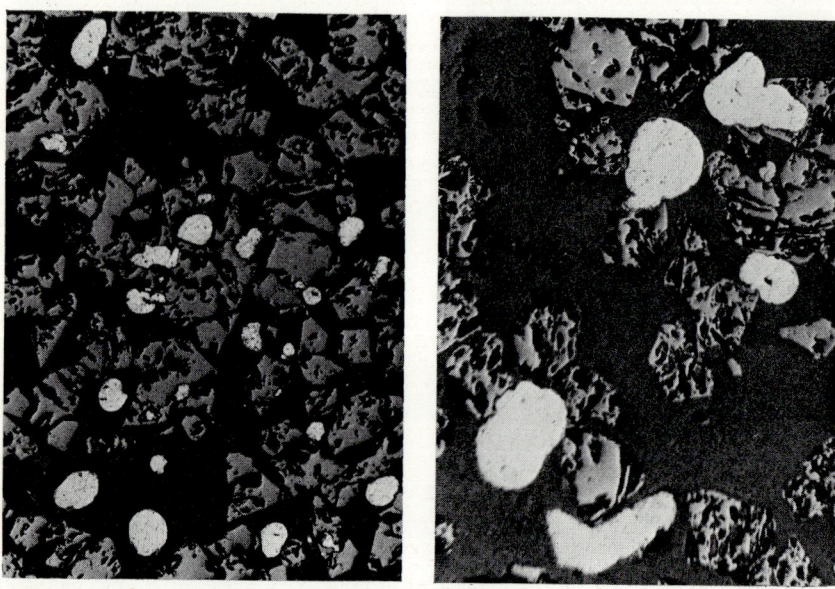

Fig. 7 Photomicrographs of Noranda process slags cooled to 1000°C in *(a)* *(left)* 39 min and *(b) (right)* 227 min.[14] Magnification, ×160

As was noted earlier, the slag produced in the Noranda process reactor is highly oxidized and contains 20–30% Fe_3O_4. The magnetite content can be reduced to the 10–12% Fe_3O_4 level and the copper to 2–3% by subjecting the slag to a reducing treatment with copper concentrates or a reducing agent, e.g. coal or natural gas.

Tests of this nature were carried out mainly in crucibles; magnetite was reduced to about 6% and there was an attendant decrease in the copper content of the slag from 10 to 1·2%. Subsequent milling of these low-magnetite, low-copper slags, however, did not result in a significant improvement in copper recovery (Table 3).

In another test in the pilot-plant reactor addition of coal in the slag zone resulted in a slag containing 12·3% Fe_3O_4 and 2·3% copper. Flotation of this slag yielded a tailing containing 0·54% copper, which is nearly the value obtained by milling high-copper, high-Fe_3O_4 slags.

Table 3 Milling of Noranda process slags of different magnetite content[1,4]

Description of slag	% Fe_3O_4 in slag	% Copper in Head	Concentrate	Tailing	Concentration ratio, head/concentrate	Copper loss in the tailing as % of input to reactor
Slag milled in large-scale test (ball-mill grinding)	20–26	11·4	51·5	0·50	4·54	1·47
Slag milled in large-scale test (autogenous grinding)	20–26	11·7	52·1	0·53	4·74	1·58
Slag deoxidized by anthracite addition in pilot-plant reactor	12	2·2	19·8	0·54	11·70	1·71
Slag deoxidized by silicon carbide in a crucible	6	1·4	6·1	0·44	6·10	1·25

Grind, 90% −325 mesh.

Acknowledgment

The authors wish to thank the management of Noranda Mines, Ltd., for permission to publish this paper. The contributions of J. N. Anderson, A. G. Balogh, W. H. Gauvin, G. D. Hallett, P. J. Mackey, L. A. Mills, A. B. Neil, P. R. Schmidt, P. Spira, K. N. Subramanian, P. Tarassoff, J. A. Vogt and A. J. Weddick to the development of the Noranda process are gratefully acknowledged.

References

1. GARRETSON O. S. U.S. Patent 586 991, 1898.
2. DIOMIDOVSKII D. A. *et al.* Continuous conversion of mattes. *Tsvet. Metally, Mosk.*, **32**, no. 2 1959, 27–34. (Russian text).
3. SEHNÁLEK F. HOLÉCZY J. AND SCHMIEDL J. Continuous converting of copper mattes. *J. Metals, N.Y.*, **16**, 1964, 416–20.
4. HOLÉCZY J. SCHMIEDL J. AND SEHNÁLEK F. U.S. Patent 3 459 415, 1969.
5. WORNER H. K. REYNOLDS J. O. AND ANDREWS B. S. WORCRA copper smelting. In *Copper metallurgy* EHRLICH R. P. ed. (New York: AIME, 1970), 198–219.
6. WORNER H. K. U.S. Patent 3 326 671, 1967.
7. THEMELIS N. J. AND SPIRA P. Canadian Patent 758 020, 1967; U.S. Patent 3 437 475, 1969.
8. Noranda pilots continuous copper smelting. *Engng Min. J.*, **169**, May 1968, 85–7.
9. THEMELIS N. J. AND TARASSOFF P. Canadian Patent 833 475, 1970.
10. THEMELIS N. J. MCKERROW G. C. TARASSOFF P. AND HALLETT G. D. The Noranda process for continuous smelting and converting of copper concentrates. Paper presented at AIME Centennial Meeting, New York, 1971.
11. KORAKAS N. Magnetite formation during copper matte converting. *Trans. Instn Min. Metall.*, **72**, Oct. 1962, 35–53.
12. TOGURI J. M. AND SANTANDER N. H. The solubility of copper in fayalite slags at 1300°C. *Can. Metall. Q.*, **8**, 1969, 167–71.
13. JOHANSEN E. B. ROSENQVIST T. AND TORGERSEN P. T. On the thermodynamics of continuous copper smelting. *J. Metals, N.Y.*, **22**, Sept. 1970, 39–47.
14. SUBRAMANIAN K. N. AND THEMELIS N. J. Recovery of copper from slags by milling. Paper presented at AIME Centennial Meeting, New York, 1971.

Developments in WORCRA smelting–converting

Howard K. Worner D.Sc., Hon. D.Sc., A.B.S.M., F.I.M., M.A.I.M.E.,
M.Aus.I.M.M., F.R.A.C.I., M.I.M.M.
J. O. Reynolds B.Sc., M.Aus. I.M.M., M.A.I.M.E.
B. S. Andrews B.Sc., A.M.Aus.I.M.M.
A. W. G. Collier B.E., A.M.Aus. I.M.M.

All of Conzinc Riotinto of Australia, Ltd., Melbourne, Australia

669.012.49 : 669.33

Synopsis

The principles involved in, and the results of, early pilot-plant trials on WORCRA continuous integrated smelting–converting were discussed in 1967; the present paper outlines experiences over the past three years with a semi-commercial WORCRA furnace built at Port Kembla, Australia, and designed to smelt copper or nickel concentrates at the rate of 3 ton/h.

The promise of the earlier pilot furnace copper smelting trials has been realized. The one furnace is able to produce continuously and directly from concentrates blister copper suitable for refining to anodes, throwaway slag and high-tenor SO_2 gas well suited to sulphur recovery.

WORCRA smelting–converting offers the potential for a significant contribution to the control of atmospheric pollution. Unlike present copper smelters, a WORCRA furnace produces in a single gas stream of steady high SO_2 tenor all of the sulphur from the smelter charge, other than the minor residual amounts in the throwaway slag and blister product. This gas is low in oxygen and well suited to economic processing.

Engineering feasibility studies point to reductions in capital costs over established copper and nickel smelters in the range 25–30%. It is also expected that production costs will be less, the amount depending on local factors. Where restrictions in sulphur emissions are enforced, the capital and operating savings are likely to be even greater. Several elements of WORCRA copper and nickel technology show promise of profitable application in established smelting practices.

The principles of WORCRA continuous smelting and refining technology in both the ferrous and non-ferrous fields have been discussed in several earlier papers.[1-6] Experience gained from the smelting–converting of sulphide copper concentrates in a semi-commercial WORCRA smelter built by Conzinc Riotinto of Australia, Ltd., in the works of the Electrolytic Refining and Smelting Co. of Australia, Ltd. (E.R. & S.), Port Kembla, New South Wales, is summarized in this paper. The smelter was commissioned in July, 1968, and three campaigns aggregating 23 months of continuous operation have been completed.

19

For ten weeks during campaign no. 1 the furnace operated with considerable promise on nickel concentrates, producing simultaneously a high-grade nickel matte and throwaway slags.

The ability of the WORCRA process to generate in a single high-strength gas stream all sulphur released during smelting and converting is discussed. This feature has attracted considerable interest because of the worldwide concern for the reduction of environmental pollution from non-ferrous smelters.

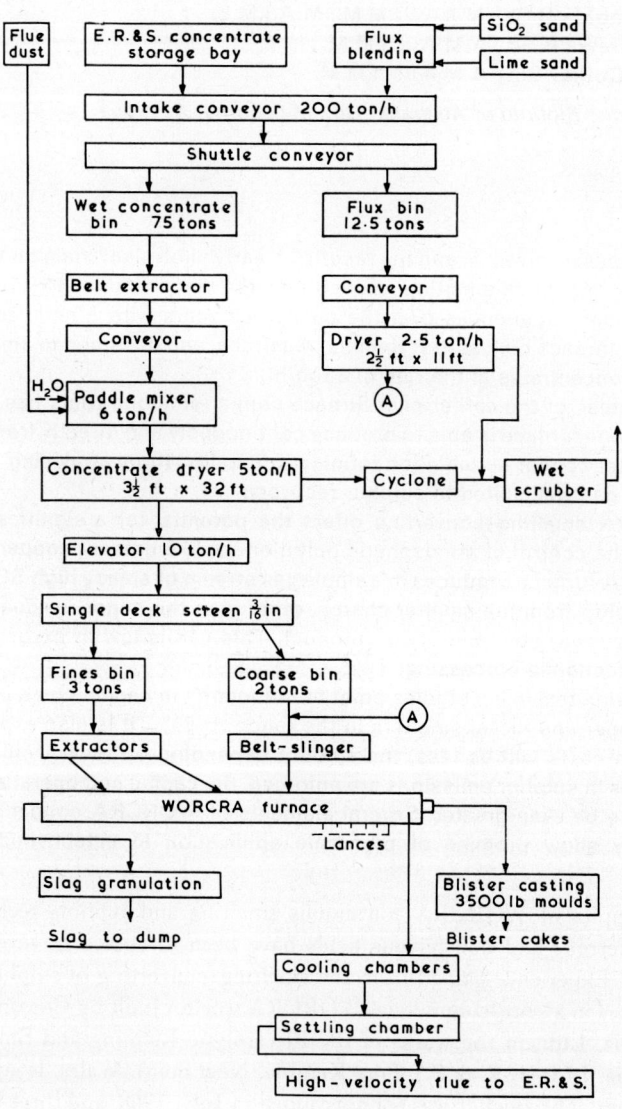

Fig. 1 Materials-handling flowsheet

Novel equipment designs and operating practices developed in the furnace at Port Kembla are applicable in present-day smelters as a means of improving metal recovery and increasing production.

Semi-commercial plant

Feed system

A flowsheet of materials handling in the Port Kembla plant, designed for a throughput of 3 long tons of dry concentrates per hour, is shown in Fig. 1. Two feed streams, one for concentrate and a second for flux, were incorporated in the plant. Concentrates received from the storage bays of the E.R. & S. smelter entered the WORCRA building (Fig. 2) from an inclined conveyor discharging

Fig. 2 WORCRA smelter building, Port Kembla, Australia

via a shuttle conveyor into a storage bin of 75-ton capacity. The wet concentrates were continuously fed by a belt extractor and conveyor into a single-shaft paddle mixer.

Moisture adjustments were made in the mixer, and the material was partially nodulized before passing to a co-current direct oil-fired rotary drier. Return flue dust and a small quantity of a binder were found to aid conditioning, which, together with the drying operation, was developed to optimize micro-pelletization of the concentrates. The dryer discharge gases passed through a cyclone and a wet scrubber.

The concentrates from the dryer, at virtually zero moisture content, were elevated to a single-deck vibrating screen, with $\frac{3}{16}$-in aperture, and the products were collected in two separate small-capacity bins. Three belt extractors delivered the undersize material to charge the furnace continuously at two points in the smelting zone and at one point in the slag-cleaning zone. The oversize concentrates, limited to a maximum size of approximately $\frac{3}{4}$ in, were fed to the converting zone of the furnace by means of a belt-slinger positioned to operate along the centre line of the converting zone, and throwing over the smelting zone.

A flux blend of high silica content sand, obtained from local beaches, and lime sand was extracted from a storage bin and conveyed into a countercurrent direct oil-fired drier. The gases from this drier joined the off-gases from the concentrate drier and were exhausted via the wet scrubber. The dried flux was elevated and charged to the furnace continuously through a chute on to the same belt-slinger which fed oversize concentrate to the converting zone. All flux was thereby delivered to the area of the furnace in which most of the iron was oxidized.

Furnace shape and zones

After various furnace shapes had been tested at the small pilot scale at Cockle Creek, New South Wales,[1] a U-shaped furnace was decided upon as being compact and well suited to the space available at Port Kembla. It also permitted concentrates and flux to be fed at one end of the furnace and copper and slag to be tapped, separately, at the other. A diagrammatic plan view of the furnace is shown in Fig. 3. The sections marked *A*, *B*, *C*, *D* and *E* served the following functions.

A—the converting zone Copper was generated continuously by air lancing in this zone and flowed through an underpass in the end *riser wall* to the *copper well* to the lower right of Fig. 3. Copper was surface tapped from the well (Fig. 5).

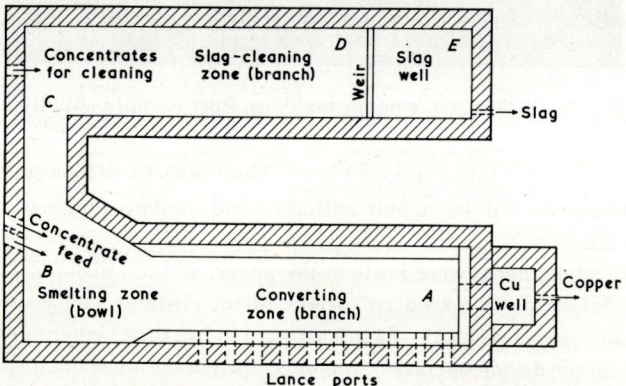

Fig. 3 Plan view of U-shaped **WORCRA** furnace built at Port Kembla, Australia

Slag was also formed continuously in the converting zone by reaction between the added silica flux and the freshly generated FeO. The slag flowed in a relatively shallow layer, countercurrent to the matte, away from the riser wall, into and through the other zones. The furnace gases were removed in an offtake at the end of the converting zone. The offtake is the structure in the left centre of Fig. 4.

Fig. 4 View inside **WORCRA** smelter building showing absence of heavy cranes. Furnace gas off-take can be seen in left centre

B—the smelting zone (also called the 'bowl') The major proportion of concentrates, injected by feeder lances, was smelted in this area of the furnace and, simultaneously, a substantial proportion of the entrained copper was washed from the counterflowing slag by a multitude of fine droplets of newly formed matte. *C—the slag-cleaning zone* Slag entered the relatively quiescent slag-cleaning zone at this point. Fine concentrates were also continuously fed to the bath here—to complete the washing of the slag. Matte underlying the slag in the major part of this zone flowed slowly by gravity along the downward-sloping hearth to the smelting zone.

Fig. 5 Copper running from copper well via a curved launder into moulds of 3500-lb capacity

D—After some settling the slag overflowed the *weir*, just past this point, to enter the slag well on the right.

E—the slag well   Final settling was achieved in the slag well section of the furnace, where an adequate depth of slag was maintained to allow continuous tapping, without matte carryover (Fig. 6). The matte collected in the well was tapped occasionally and reverted to the furnace proper.

Fig. 6   Continuous slag tapping into granulating launder

Some development of an airlift pump for the slag well matte was carried out in 1966, but when it was realized that the amount of matte collected was so small, the development was discontinued.

Salient design features in the furnace

The furnace was designed on the basis of parameters calculated from operating data obtained on the smaller pilot furnace at Cockle Creek.[1] Specifically, a smelting zone absorption intensity of 60 lb/ft^2/h and a converting zone lancing intensity of 20 ft^3 of air/ft^2/min were assumed.

Allowing for a proportion of the concentrates to be fed to the converting zone and some to the slag-cleaning zone, and taking into consideration the best information then available on matte settling rates in slag, the following dimensions inside the brickwork were selected: smelting zone, 10-ft 'diameter'; converting zone, 6 ft in width at liquid line and 28 ft in length; slag-cleaning zone, 8 ft in width and 31 ft in length; combustion-free space above liquid level, 9 ft in converting zone down to 4·5 ft in slag-cleaning zone; and bath depth, 4 ft at the riser wall in converting zone, sloping upwards continuously to the slag weir.

During operations it was established that intensities far greater than those quoted could be realized. All zones of the furnace were larger than necessary for the throughput of 72 tons of concentrates per day.

The brickwork lining throughout the furnace was direct bonded magchrome. The continuously sloping hearth in all areas was in the form of an inverted arch and was supported on basic castable refractory backed with lightweight castable. The foundation was of solid concrete, and included air-cooling ducts. The roof in the smelting and converting areas was suspended, and in the slag-cleaning zone it was a sprung arch.

Water-cooled copper blocks were located behind bricks at the slag line in all parts of the furnace. These blocks were designed to increase the rate of heat extraction from the hot face of the bricks and to contribute to the establishment and maintenance of an eventual stable wall profile. The converting zone riser wall, forming the underflow passage for removal of copper from the furnace, included both water- and air-cooling devices within sections of the brickwork. The liquid level in the furnace was determined by the fluid-cooled weir towards the outlet end of the slag-cleaning zone.

To provide efficient sealing, as a means of assisting control of furnace atmosphere, all door jambs and ports were water cooled and all doors were mild steel. The tapping breasts for blister copper and slag were also water-cooled. After some minor modifications these gave virtually no trouble and tapping procedures were such that no significant deterioration of the blocks occurred.

Refractory wear

Erosion of the furnace lining was significant in restricted areas of the furnace at or above the liquid line. In particular, wear occurred in areas where there was a *combination* of high temperature, neutral or reducing atmosphere (as in the path of flames) and gas-borne liquid droplets. These conditions were largely confined to the smelting zone centre wall area and the wall immediately adjacent to it at the beginning of the converting zone.

Fig. 7 shows a view inside the converting zone after the drain out at the end of campaign no. 3. This part of the furnace, which was subjected to considerable turbulence and splash, was, nevertheless, in good condition. Two large side-wall lances still *in situ* can be seen on the right-hand side. Close inspection of the whole furnace brickwork at the end of the three campaigns, coupled with additional experimental work, has led to a much better understanding of the causes and location of the brickwork erosion. It has also pointed up some errors of judgment in the design and operation of the Port Kembla furnace. This experience has indicated the nature of modifications which it is planned to incorporate in a straight-line prototype commercial furnace (see later).

Roof wear was minimal for the full length of the furnace and no problems were encountered with the later designs of slag weir and riser wall.

Some changes were made to the furnace structure between campaigns. These related to three aspects of design: (1) the lateral dimensions of water-cooled blocks were increased to allow the hot face of each to retain its position with service connexions readily accessible; (2) the *crossover* section of the furnace between the smelting and slag-cleaning zones was widened; and (3) the brick-

B*

Fig. 7   View inside converting branch after drain-out at end of campaign no. 3. Two large lances still *in situ* can be seen on right-hand side

work thickness was reduced in some parts of the furnace to allow increased heat loss and, thereby, diminish wall erosion.

Feeder lances

The concentrates, partly agglomerated to micro-pellets in the drier, were injected at an angle into the bath via two feeder lances. This method made possible a high rate of smelting per unit of bath area and caused a sustained circulatory flow pattern of the liquids. It also achieved a highly efficient slag-cleaning action.

Although the design of the feeder lances retained elements from the early small-scale test work, they were progressively improved both in construction and performance over the three campaigns. At the end of the development the flame intensity had been greatly increased and, as a consequence, bath absorption was significantly improved and approached levels double that of the original design smelting intensity. It was possible to achieve the necessary 'bowl' feed rate via only one feeder lance.

Lances

The decision to employ lances rather than tuyères (both were covered in the original WORCRA patents) was based on three contentions: (1) lances are more appropriate in a fixed furnace; (2) by introducing the oxygen-containing converting gas remote from the walls, furnace life could be increased; and (3) lancing would be better if future trends were towards oxygen smelting–converting.

An adequate lance performance provides the key to viable WORCRA converting. This equipment is required to withstand severe thermal, chemical and mechanical conditions in its function of introducing air (or oxygen) below the bath surface. No satisfactory designs for this duty previously existed. A suitable lance was evolved from concepts tested at an early stage of small-scale pilot-plant operations and progressively improved by exhaustive test work in the Port Kembla furnace over two years. More than fifty design stages were involved. This lance specification development was by far the most significant achievement of the three furnace campaigns.

As an indication of the progressive improvement achieved, the data in Table 1

Table 1 Lance performance—all designs

Campaign no.	Lance life, h	
	Average	Best
1	20	85
2	23	156
3	86	415
3 (Best design, 15 lances)	264	415

may be quoted. It is now confidently predicted that lance lives *averaging* two weeks will be achieved and, ultimately, lances lasting more than a month may be commonplace. Cost calculations indicate that the minimum acceptable lance life in a commercial furnace will be of the order of five days.*

Supply air pressure to the most successful lances was in the range 14–20 lb/in^2 gauge, although higher pressure lances were also tested. During short trials with supplemental oxygen (see later) line pressures were between 25 and 40 lb/in^2 gauge.

Three sequential increases in lance size took place during the operations at Port Kembla. The aim was to up-rate the volume delivered by an individual lance, high oxygen efficiency being retained in the converting reactions. Towards the end of the third campaign, in order to evaluate lancing techniques applicable to commercial-scale operation, several large lances, each delivering 1200 $Nft^3/$ min, were successfully tested. There was no evidence that this was the largest size which could have been used efficiently in the furnace.

* The improved lance design is protected by patent applications.

Operating experience

Concentrates used

Concentrates smelted in the furnace were from Cobar in New South Wales and Mt Lyell, Tasmania. Typical assays are shown in Table 2 (dry weight basis).

Table 2   Composition of concentrates smelted

	Cobar, %	Mt Lyell, %
Cu	23·7	26·0
Fe	30·6	30·5
S	32·9	35·0
SiO_2	3·7	3·6
Al_2O_3	0·7	0·1
CaO	0·1	0·1
Zn	5·0	0·1
Pb	2·2	0·1

Capacity

The furnace, designed to treat 72 long tons per day of dry concentrates, operated for extended periods at this capacity, and for some days at a time this production was exceeded. Restrictions to throughput, however, were often present owing to difficulties with ancillary equipment.

In the early stages of operations deficiencies in the feed conditioning plant imposed a restriction. Later difficulties with gas-handling curtailed production rates. There were a few periods when furnace conditions limited feed rate; as a general rule it was found that with increased production rate, performance was improved. Table 3 lists a set of throughput data for a month when the furnace was in continuous and relatively steady operation, apart from two days (19 and 20) when the plant was put on standby to permit work on the gas-handling system. During the 30-day period for which totals have been calculated, the recovery of metallic copper in the cast 'cakes' was 97·8% of the actual Cu in the feed concentrates.

The weight of copper tapped in any particular day did not necessarily correspond closely with the copper fed in that 24-h period. The furnace acted like a 'surge tank', and it was found to be possible to operate with copper levels in the deep end of the converting zone varying between as little as 10 in and as much as 25 in. This was equivalent to a copper-in-furnace 'flexibility range' of approximately 14 tons.

Table 3   Throughput and production data for a representative period of relatively steady operation

| Day no. | Concentrate fed | | 'Blister' Cu tapped |
	Dry long tons	Contained Cu (based on daily assay), long tons	Long tons
1	67·7	17·0	19·4
2	79·7	19·5	12·2
3	85·7	21·6	11·3
4	76·1	19·2	18·3
5	81·1	19·3	20·3
6	76·3	19·1	24·9
7	64·8	15·2	12·4
8	60·2	14·4	23·8
9	66·7	16·6	10·8
10	69·6	17·9	13·1
11	66·0	16·3	20·2
12	68·2	16·6	12·5
13	75·8	18·3	23·3
14	66·5	16·3	18·6
15	66·7	16·0	18·7
16	53·8	13·4	10·9
17	76·1	18·3	13·7
18	58·6	14·5	17·1
19*	37·4	9·2	10·9
20*	0	0	9·4
21	78·7	18·4	18·7
22	96·7	23·8	21·8
23	82·8	19·7	20·2
24	88·6	21·3	23·4
25	45·8	10·8	20·3
26	74·2	18·2	9·4
27	85·4	20·7	4·7
28	48·7	12·4	12·4
29	79·2	19·1	18·7
30	91·2	23·2	20·2
31	98·2	24·8	18·3
32	82·8	21·2	19·1

For the 30-day period, day 2 to day 31, inclusive:
                    Copper in feed concentrates, tons 514·1
                'Blister' output, tons 509·6
                 Average 'blister' assay, % 98·7 Cu
* Plant on standby for day and a half.

Conditions in different furnace zones

The WORCRA process is unique in the sense that in one furnace there are three distinct zones in a horizontal plane, each having its own characteristic functions and metallurgy. The compositions of both the matte–metal and the slag phases change as the liquids flow in opposite directions from one zone to the next simply under the action of gravity. Data to illustrate this, taken from the operating furnace, are shown in Table 4. Samples of slag existing in the

Table 4 Typical copper and magnetite values in slag in different furnace positions

		(a) Steady		(b) Unsteady	
	Position (see Fig. 3)	% Cu	% Fe_3O_4	% Cu	% Fe_3O_4
A	Copper end of converting zone	14·0*	26	18*	33
B	Smelting zone	3·5	16	5	23
C	Entry to slag-cleaning zone	1·2	8	3·5	12
D	Before weir in slag-cleaning zone	0·45	2	1·5	4
E	Slag well	0·35	1	0·85	2

* Virtually an emulsion of Cu_2S and Cu in slag.

various zones of the furnace were assayed for copper and magnetite. The two sets of data relate to steady conditions with high feed rate and unsteady (over-oxidizing) conditions with low feed rate.

Matte assays (samples taken well below slag layer) were found during campaign no. 3 to be within the following ranges:

Smelting zone	70–75% Cu
Slag-cleaning zone	45–65% Cu
Slag well	35–45% Cu

It might be expected that it would be difficult to achieve low copper-in-slag values over matte ranging between 45 and 65% copper in the slag-cleaning zone; however, although these relatively high copper values existed in the matte *underneath* the slag layer, the slag itself was continually being 'washed' with a shower of droplets of freshly melted concentrates. This 'new' matte would range in copper values from only 28 to 35%.

Control

Process control was achieved by balancing the mass flow rates of *input*—air, concentrates and flux—and *output*—copper. Simple calculation was required to set up the theoretical balance. Variations arose, however, in practice, and periodic corrections to one or more of these four factors was necessary. The need for such correction was indicated by variation from target levels in the depths of copper and slag in the furnace. These depths were readily measured and the quantitative corrections were determined by reference to simple charts. Instrumentation requirements were not unusual. Control of the process was undertaken by a normally trained operator.

The process exhibited surprising stability, despite the upsets which caused marked deviation from target conditions. On a number of occasions, particularly in the early stages of operation, unsteady conditions were experienced when, for periods, the smelting rate was out of balance with the lancing rate, this condition usually having arisen from the failure of experimental lances. Unfortunately, during each of the three campaigns there were also a number of power failures, some of which lasted as long as two hours. Although these disturbed the balance of the furnace metallurgy, on each occasion the effects were soon rectified.

Throwaway slag produced

As operators gained experience, and as engineering difficulties with the feed and gas systems were progressively mastered, it was confirmed that the scaled-up process was capable of producing throwaway slags simultaneously with the production of blister copper, as had been demonstrated in the smaller pilot plant at Cockle Creek. In this achievement, as far as is known from published information, the WORCRA process is unique.

Data given in Table 5 show assays of copper in slag tapped from the furnace for a continuous 30-day period during campaign no. 3, when the daily concentrate input ranged between 40 and 85 (dry) long tons. These analyses were ob-

Table 5 Daily average weighted copper assays in slag tapped for a continuous 30-day period during campaign no. 3

Day	% Cu	Day	% Cu	Day	% Cu
1	0·53	11	0·34	21	0·40
2	0·50	12	0·63	22	0·65
3	0·63	13	0·53	23	0·58
4	0·56	14	0·80	24	0·57
5	0·43	15	0·41	25	0·81
6	0·38	16	0·46	26	0·57
7	0·64	17	0·70	27	0·55
8	0·56	18	1·00*	28	0·47
9	0·32	19	0·48	29	0·55
10	0·70	20	0·43	30	0·62

* Some matte carryover.

tained from weighted composite samples taken by probe from granulated slag prior to cartage to the dump. Each assay represents the average content of *all* slag tapped during the 24-h operating periods.

In Table 6 assays of routine samples taken from the slag launder at two-hourly intervals are listed. These are typical of results obtained during the 30-day period referred to in Table 5 and relate to days 11–13.

Table 6   Routine spot samples of slag taken at the slag launder at 2-h intervals, days 11-13

Day	% Cu	Day	% Cu	Day	% Cu
11	0·26	12	0·56	13	0·48
	0·29		0·58		0·30
	0·22		0·87		0·30
	0·40		0·72		0·42
	0·43		0·56		0·80
	0·43		0·86		0·68
	0·39		0·72		0·64
	0·40		1·30*		0·66
	0·28		0·82		0·61
	0·27		0·69		0·56
	N.S.		0·42		0·38
	N.S.		0·68		0·35

N.S., No sample.
* Some matte carryover.

Slag copper assays have been correlated with prevailing furnace conditions and a measure of understanding of relevant factors has been achieved. In the development programme, however, it was not always easy to isolate the individual parameters which may have determined the level of slag copper losses. Factors known to have affected these losses include (*a*) feed continuity; (*b*) burner firing in the slag-cleaning zone; (*c*) draft control; (*d*) liquid mobility in the furnace crossover section between the smelting and slag-cleaning zones; and (*e*) evenness of the frozen layer on the slag weir.

Contrary to earlier expectations[2] that WORCRA slags would need to contain about 38% SiO_2, it was found that low slag losses were achieved with silica in the range 28–32%. During campaign no. 3 slag contained on the average 29·3% SiO_2 and 7·5% CaO. Lime sand additions were made in the belief that CaO in the slag would widen the acceptable composition range and, hence, provide a more satisfactory basis for development of the process. The value of the lime, if any, remained uncertain at the end of the campaign.

Metal product composition

Being in dynamic equilibrium with white metal (Cu_2S) above it in the converting zone, the metal which flowed through the underpass into the copper well contained a little more than 1% of sulphur. Some of this S was removed under the oxidizing flame used to keep the metal hot in the 'well'. It was customary to tap metal with between 0·5 and 0·8% S and cast it into 3500-lb cakes, which went direct to the E.R. & S. anode furnace. Although colloquially called 'blister', this metal rarely blistered in the same way as metal blown in a batch converter; it contained little or no oxygen.

The average copper analysis (%) for campaign no. 3 when Cobar concentrates were being smelted was: copper, 98·75; sulphur, 0·74; iron, 0·15; lead, 0·06; and zinc, 0·01.

Zinc and lead eliminations from concentrate *to fume* during the campaign averaged 55 and 89%, respectively. A high recovery of precious metals, along with the copper, was achieved.

Offtake gas quality

All sulphur contained in the charge materials, except for the minor residual amounts in slag and blister copper, was contained in the gas emitted via the single integral offtake from the converting end of the furnace. In the semi-commercial plant furnace gases, with an average dust loading equivalent to 4% of the concentrates fed, passed through two cooling chambers in series, into a final settling chamber and then along a high-velocity flue to the E.R. & S. waste gas handling system.

With the relatively small furnace at Port Kembla, burning considerably more oil per ton of feed concentrate than would be required in a commercial plant, the SO_2 levels in the exit gas ranged between 5 and 8% for normal air lancing. (As is pointed out later, the SO_2 is expected to range between 9 and 14% in gases from air-lanced commercial scale WORCRA furnaces, the actual level depending principally on the percentage of sulphur in the feed concentrates.) Oxygen determinations in the offtake gave values in the range 0·5–1·0%.

Conversion efficiency

It is believed that the efficiency of oxidation of *bath* matte by air (or oxygen) introduced through the lances was similar to that achieved in conventional converters. It is clear, however, that further oxidation took place in the lance splash *above the bath* by reaction of the matte droplets with residual oxygen in the gases passing into the converting zone from the smelting zone.

The oxygen efficiency related to the quantity of air (or oxygen) blown through the lances was, in fact, usually above 100%. Draught control was, of course, important.

Supplementary oxygen

During the development programme at Port Kembla sufficient work was done with supplementary oxygen to indicate the considerable potential which exists for upgrading, by this means, both the metal production rate and the SO_2 level in furnace gases.

For limited periods oxygen was used in either or both the smelting zone and the converting zone. Such usage raised the SO_2 tenor by reducing (a) the 'ballast' nitrogen blown into the furnace and (b) the amount of carbonaceous fuel burnt in the smelting zone. It is of significance that when supplemental oxygen was employed in both the feeder lances and the converting lances, the oxygen level in the furnace off-gases remained within the range 0·5–1·5%. In other words, oxygen utilization efficiency remained at a high level.

Development of prototype commercial plant

The operations of the semi-commercial plant have provided the bases for designs for commercial furnaces. Overall metallurgical performance criteria (smelting capacity, lancing rates, metal recovery and fuel consumption) have been delineated for different concentrate compositions and throughout capacities. It is envisaged that the next stage of WORCRA copper smelting should be a commercial prototype plant to produce between 25 000 and 40 000 ton/year of copper, but there do not appear to be any basic reasons why a furnace should not ultimately be designed to produce up to 100 000 ton/year.

It is already apparent that it is possible to achieve feeding and lancing intensities far higher than was envisaged when the semi-commercial plant was designed. As a consequence, relative heat losses will be reduced and gas strength increased. Calculations indicate that, for an air-lanced furnace producing 80 000 ton/year of copper from normal chalcopyritic concentrates, the fuel consumption will be less than 2 500 000 Btu/ton of dry charge—a figure which could be greatly reduced by the use of supplemental oxygen.

Depending on the sulphur level in the feed concentrates, the sulphur dioxide tenor in the exit gas is expected to be within the range 9–14% for an air-lanced furnace: it will, of course, be higher if supplemental oxygen is employed. Free oxygen in the furnace gas is expected to be in the range 0·5–1·0%, and, thus, the WORCRA process offers considerable attraction for linking, in due course, with direct reduction operations for the production of elemental sulphur.

There is evidence from earlier pilot-plant trials[2] that the process is capable of treating a wide range of sulphide copper concentrates from those high in sulphur and pyritic iron to other types containing significantly lower sulphur and iron values (e.g. less than 25% each of S and Fe). It is believed that all types of concentrates now smelted in reverberatory furnaces may be treated in a WORCRA smelter and, in this respect, the range will be wider than that of flash-smelters. It has also been demonstrated that it is possible to smelt concentrates containing more than 7% zinc.

Refractory consumption on the semi-commercial U-shaped furnace was, admittedly, relatively high. As has already been pointed out, it is now appreciated why certain areas of the walls above bath level were subject to wear, and the design criteria are available for either avoiding such erosion or providing for adequate protection or rapid replacement of the affected lining.

In the light of experience gained at Port Kembla it is expected that hot patching or demountable panel replacement in some sections of the furnace walls (above bath level) may be necessary within the first nine to twelve months of operation of a commercial WORCRA furnace. The remainder of the wall, the hearth and the roof should give at least two years' service.

For a number of reasons, including the problem of refractory wear, it has been decided that the prototype commercial furnace should be of a straight-line form, such as is shown diagrammatically in Fig. 8. It is now appreciated that this

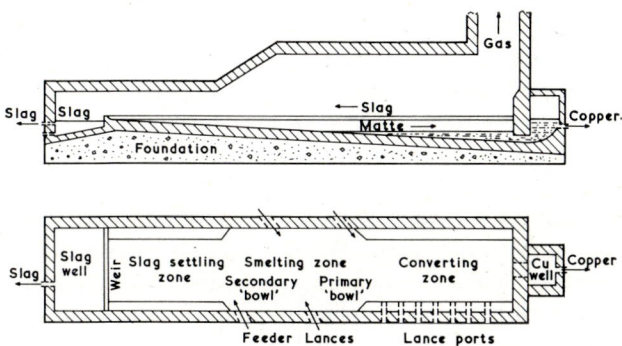

Fig. 8 Diagrammatic sectional plan and elevation of proposed straight-line commercial **WORCRA** furnace

shape offers structural and geometrical advantages over the U-shaped furnace, and from recent large model studies and other experiments it is believed that the straight-line form offers greater potential for operating reliability and further reduction of copper losses in slags. Much of the wall erosion in the relatively small Port Kembla furnace was attributable to burner flames impinging directly on to the brickwork. And, as has already been pointed out, relatively more fuel had to be burnt in this furnace because of the high heat losses attributable to the large surface to volume ratio.

Reference has already been made to the important contribution which the countercurrent flow of slag and matte make to overall metallurgical efficiency, and, particularly, to the recovery of copper from the oxidized slag generated in the converting zone. The prototype commercial furnace has been designed to ensure that there will be the maximum of mixing of the backward-flowing slag with hot concentrates and freshly formed matte injected into the bath by the several feeder lances. There will be repeated 'washing' actions and the well reduced slag will flow into the final settling section after being in contact with low-grade matte. It will, in effect, emerge from the WORCRA furnace as if it were leaving a reverberatory furnace producing matte in the range 30–35% copper.

The ability of the WORCRA process to generate throwaway slags in the same furnace chamber as the copper itself is produced is probably its most novel feature. This, of course, eliminates the necessity for the slag-reverting or slow cooling–milling–flotation or electric furnace cleaning practised in existing copper metallurgy.

The copper product from commercial scale WORCRA furnaces is expected to be generally similar to that produced at Port Kembla, i.e. to contain between 0·5 and 0·8% sulphur. This sulphur can readily be reduced to any desired level in an anode furnace ahead of casting. Currently, investigations are in hand on the vacuum refining of WORCRA metal.

On the basis of the experience gained so far, and with the knowledge that in all other new pyrometallurgical processes, particularly the pneumatic types, considerable further improvements take place after the pilot-plant proving stage, it is confidently expected that the prototype commercial furnace will yield a performance superior to conventional copper smelting processes.

Pollution control

Non-ferrous smelters are currently being severely criticized for their contribution to atmospheric pollution. When copper is extracted from sulphide concentrates, it is difficult to imagine any process, whether pyro- or hydrometallurgical, which has useful sulphur by-products other than sulphuric acid, liquid sulphur dioxide or elemental sulphur.

The WORCRA process offers the possibility of considering the production of any one of these three by-products, and particularly so if supplemental oxygen is used to lift the level of SO_2 in the steadily emitted one-furnace gas.

It is possible in the most modern copper smelters (fluidized-bed roasters–reverberatory–converter complexes and flash-smelter–converter combinations) to collect about 90% of the feed sulphur in gases amenable to further processing. A comparison of the WORCRA process, however, with these more conventional modern smelters will show that (a) the potential for recovery of the sulphur contained in the WORCRA gas is significantly higher than is now achieved in modern smelters—about 97% of the sulphur entering a WORCRA furnace leaves in the one gas stream; (b) the necessity for blending of the gases from intermittently blown converters with the roaster or flash smelter gas is eliminated; (c) there are substantial cost savings in the flues and waste-heat recovery systems needed to cool and treat the gas prior to entry to the treatment/recovery plant. As a comparison, the single fixed-flue system from the WORCRA furnace can be set against the multiplicity of boilers, cyclones and precipitators used in modern calcine-fed reverberatory smelters, where separate roaster and converter gases are treated for the production of sulphuric acid; in addition, of course, special 'hooding' or 'siphon' offtakes are required on the conventional tiltable converters; and (d) the cost of sulphuric acid or other sulphur recovery facilities should be lower because of the higher and more consistent gas tenor, together with a steady, and smaller, gas volume.

Economics of WORCRA smelting

Capital cost

Capital cost estimates for commercial scale WORCRA smelters have been made as the development programme progressed. These estimates have been based on detailed design criteria and engineering feasibility studies for various locations. Seven such studies have been completed for copper smelting and five for WORCRA nickel smelting. It has been estimated for different cases that, compared with conventional modern pyrometallurgical processes, capital savings of between 25 and 35% may be expected with WORCRA plants.

The following is a short list of summarizing conclusions drawn when the contents of the WORCRA estimates are compared with those for a hot-charged reverberatory smelter in the same locality treating an identical quantity of copper concentrates: (*a*) a smaller area is required for the WORCRA smelter; (*b*) site development costs are lower, the amount being dependent on the nature of the terrain; (*c*) the cost of buildings and supporting steel structures to house the smelter is less, owing to the compact nature of the furnace and the absence of heavy ladle-carrying cranes and a converter aisle; (*d*) the cost of furnace and ancillaries is less, particularly when it is considered necessary, as is usual, to provide standby batch converting capacity in the case of the reverberatory smelter; and (*e*) as was referred to earlier, there are substantial cost savings in the plant needed for the collection, handling and treatment of furnace gases and the recovery of waste heat.

Direct operating costs

A worthwhile comparison of direct operating costs can be made only when the nature of concentrates and fluxes is assessed, the availability and quality of the work force are determined, and local costs for fuel, power and supplies are specified. The following general considerations have, however, emerged from the operating cost estimates made in conjunction with the feasibility studies completed to date.

(1) Labour requirements are expected to be lower for a WORCRA smelter. The savings are due to the simplified flowsheet, the potential for compact design of plant, the absence of batch processing and the avoidance of transfer operations between smelting and converting units.

(2) Fuel requirements are likely to be lower as a result of the benefit obtained by carrying out the exothermic converting reactions in the same furnace chamber as the heat-absorbing smelting operations. (It will be recalled that a significant proportion of the concentrates, as well as the flux, is charged direct to the converting zone, where the reactions are predominantly exothermic and, for most concentrates, are able to supply all the heat required for the melting of such feed materials.)

(3) Maintenance and cost of supplies are expected to be lower because of the absence of multiple units and batch processing and the lower initial value of plant.

(4) Metal recovery is improved as a result of lower in-plant handling losses. More important, it is expected that operations will show that because WORCRA slag leaves the furnace in a condition chemically dominated by freshly melted concentrates rather than semi-processed matte, the copper loss will be less than that which occurs in present-day smelters.

'Spin-off' from WORCRA technology

There is evidence that the new equipment used in the WORCRA furnace and the novel methods employed in the metallurgical operations can be applied with benefit to present-day smelters. The types of operations already subjected to trial in commercial smelters involve the use of WORCRA feeder lances to increase production rates and/or to reduce slag copper losses. This work will be the subject of a separate paper.

Acknowledgment

The authors wish to thank the Directors of Conzinc Riotinto of Australia, Ltd., for permission to publish this paper. They also gratefully acknowledge the sterling contribution to the development project of many colleagues at Port Kembla and Cockle Creek, including officers of the Electrolytic Refining and Smelting Company of Australia, Ltd.

References

1. WORNER H. K. Continuous smelting and refining by the WORCRA processes. In *Advances in extractive metallurgy* (London: Institution of Mining and Metallurgy, 1968), 245–63; discussion, 287–313.
2. WORNER H. K. WORCRA smelting–converting. Paper presented at UNIDO symposium on modernisation and expansion of plants in the copper industry, Vienna, 1967, 28 p.
3. WORNER H. K. *et al.* Continuous steelmaking. *J. Metals, N.Y.*, **21,** June 1969, 51–6.
4. WORNER H. K. Reynolds J. O. AND ANDREWS B. S. WORCRA copper smelting. In *Copper metallurgy* EHRLICH R. P. ed. (New York: AIME, 1970), 198–219.
5. WORNER H. K. AND BAKER F. H. WORCRA steelmaking. Paper presented at international conference on the science and technology of iron and steel, Tokyo, 1970.
BAKER F. H. AND WORNER H. K. WORCRA iron- and steelmaking. In *Alternative routes to steel* (London: Iron and Steel Institute, 1972), 99–106.
6. WORNER H. K. Developments in WORCRA copper-smelting–converting. Paper presented at UNIDO symposium on copper production, Moscow, 1970.

Slags from continuous copper production

F. Sehnálek Doc. Ing., C. Sc.
I. Imriš Ing.

Both of the Department of Chemical Principles of Metallurgy, Technical University, Košice, Czechoslovakia

669.046.584:669.33–932

Synopsis

Lower energy consumption, lower capital investment and production costs and the possible automation of the production cycle are the main advantages of continuous copper production over conventional technology utilizing reverberatory or blast-furnace and converter.

The problem common to both the new and the conventional technology of copper production is the copper loss in slags, which may be divided into mechanical and physico-chemical losses.

Physico-chemical losses are considered specifically as they represent a substantial part of the copper lost in slags in continuous units. A literature survey of the new methods of continuous copper production and systems describing pyrometallurgical copper production is followed by a discussion on the forms of copper losses.

Based on the values of the standard free energies of reactions taking place during copper production, isothermal diagrams for the system Cu–Fe–S–O–SiO$_2$ at silica saturation were calculated at 1200 and 1300°C. These permit a description of the process of copper production in conventional and continuous units, taking into account physico-chemical losses of copper in slags. The system Cu–Fe–S–O–SiO$_2$ was experimentally verified in the region of coexistence of matte and silica-saturated slag in N$_2$–S$_2$–SO$_2$ atmosphere and in the region of coexistence of white matte and slag saturated with silica and magnetite in a N$_2$–SO$_2$ atmosphere at 1200°C.

On the assumptions that slag behaves as an ideal ionic solution and that matte is an ideal solution, and the values found experimentally, the relationship between physico-chemical losses in silica-saturated slags at 1200°C and the matte grade was calculated:

$$\% \ \mathrm{Cu_{in \ slag}} = 0{\cdot}046 \ \sqrt{\frac{N_{\mathrm{Cu_2S}}}{1 - N_{\mathrm{Cu_2S}}}} + 0{\cdot}3368 \ \sqrt{N_{\mathrm{Cu_2S}}}$$

The first term represents copper losses in slags arising from Cu$_2$O solubility, which, at constant temperature and silica saturation, is only a function of matte

39

grade and FeO activity in slag. The second term represents copper lost in slag owing to Cu_2S dissolution, which, under the conditions given, depends only on the matte grade. The relationship established is in a good agreement with laboratory results by various workers as well as with data from various smelters.

Applying the equation to the continuous copper production, it is concluded that 40% of physico-chemical losses of copper with slags are created by Cu_2S dissolution. This important fact should be taken into account in the search for methods of lowering the copper losses in slags.

The technology of copper production from sulphide concentrates consists of the production of matte in a reverberatory or blast-furnace and its subsequent blowing in a Peirce–Smith converter to obtain blister copper. Industrial units such as reverberatory or blast-furnaces, horizontal converters and auxiliary equipment have now attained a high degree of technical perfection and further substantial improvements in these units cannot be expected. The disadvantages of conventional copper production technology, the lack of continuity, with consequent low energy efficiency, the high costs of modern large-capacity units, in particular those for the cleaning and utilization of waste gases, and the relatively low yield of copper owing to copper losses in the waste slags—coupled with the advantages of the possible automation of the entire production cycle and increased productivity—have led to a search for new methods of copper production. Specifically, the following should be mentioned: lower energy consumption—autogeneous smelting of sulphide concentrates (flash-smelting,[1] INCO process[2] and treatment of pellets in the converter[3]); lower capital investment—intensifying the exploitation of the furnace space—cyclone smelting (Tonkonogii et al.[4] and Kadlec[5]); and automation of the process with lower production costs and capital investment—continuation of the manufacture of the blister copper (Konti,[6] WORCRA,[7] Noranda[8] and Brittingham[9] processes).

With the solution of the problem of the continuous converting of copper mattes,[10-13] attention was directed at the continuous production of blister copper from the sulphide concentrates. Various reports on four different methods of direct treatment of concentrates by the continuous method have been published.

The first such unit, Konti[6] (Fig. 1), was developed on the pilot-plant scale in 1962 at the Technical University, Košice. The capacity of the unit was 6 tons of copper concentrates per day. In 1963 and 1964 the WORCRA unit was developed in Australia,[14] the pilot plant (Fig. 2) being built in 1967 at Port Kembla. Production is 6000 t of copper per year. In 1968 the results of the research by Noranda Mines, Ltd. Quebec, were published;[8] based on that work, the unit presented in Fig. 3 has been constructed. In 1966 Brittingham[9] published a proposal for the continuous production of blister copper from sulphide concentrates (Fig. 4).

For comparison, technical and economic data relating to copper production by conventional and continuous methods are summarized in Table 1,[15] Table 2 and Table 3.[16] The superiority of the continuous methods for the direct pro-

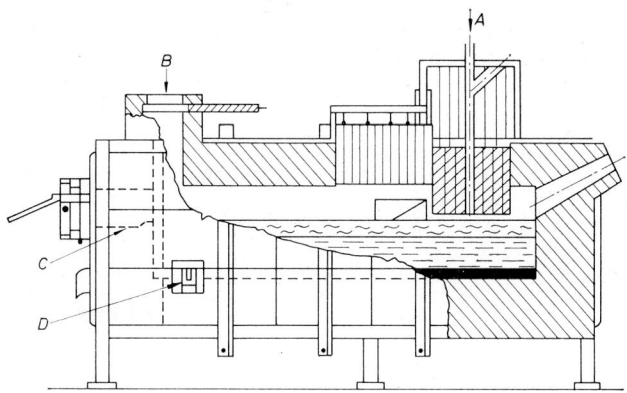

Fig. 1 Diagrammatic representation of Konti unit.[6] *A*, pressure air inlet and charge hole; *B*, gas outlet; *C*, slag discharge hole; *D*, copper taphole

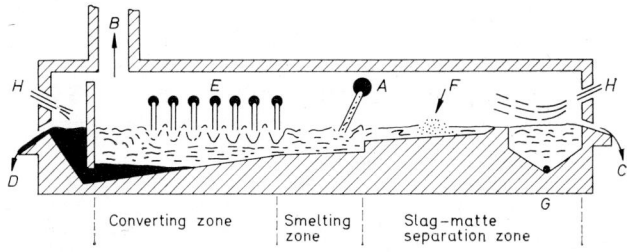

Fig. 2 Diagrammatic representation of **WORCRA** unit.[7] *A*, charging concentrate and flux; *B*, gas outlet; *C*, slag discharging; *D*, copper discharging; *E*, air inlet; *F*, charging of pyrite; *G*, tapping of matte; *H*, burners

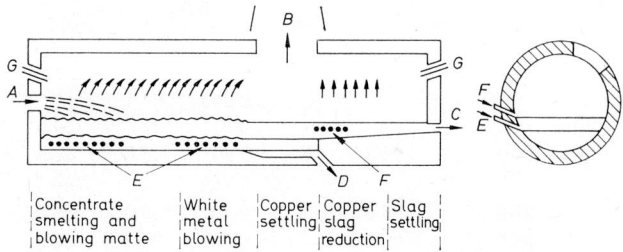

Fig. 3 Diagrammatic representation of Noranda unit.[8] *A*, charging of concentrate and flux; *B*, gas outlet; *C*, slag discharging; *D*, copper discharging; *E*, air inlet; *F*, inlet of reduction gas; *G*, burners

duction of copper from concentrates is apparent. Although the data presented in Table 1 also favour continuous methods, the problems of copper extraction cannot be considered to have been completely solved. The yields of copper may be increased by lowering the copper content of the waste slags.

The problem of copper losses in slags has often been considered,[11, 17, 18]

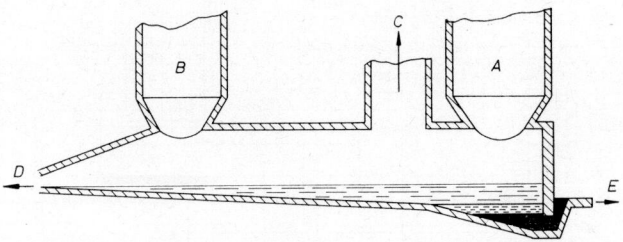

Fig. 4 Diagrammatic layout of Brittingham's unit.[9] *A*, main reaction shaft; *B*, secondary reaction shaft; *C*, gas outlet; *D*, slag discharging; *E*, copper discharging

Table 1 Chemical compositions and copper yields[15]

Copper production	Cu content in concentrate, wt %	Copper, wt %		Slag, wt %			Yield, %
		Cu	S	Cu	Fe	SiO$_2$	
Reverberatory	20·0	97·0	—	0·45*	—	—	98·0
Flash-smelting, Harjavalta	21·0	—	—	0·20†	—	—	—
Flash-smelting, Ashio	21·2	—	—	1·16	39·0	31·4	
				0·55†	36·0	34·0	96·5
INCO, Canada	31·5 (CuNi)	—	—	0·74 (CuNi)	—	—	—
				0·48‡ (CuNi)	—	—	—
Autogenous smelting, Hitachi	15·7	—	—	5·00	—	—	—
				0·38§	49·7	—	98·2
Cyclone smelting	2·62	—	—	0·27	22·7	34·8	95·1
Konti	14·0	97·3	0·9	0·90*	45·6	32·9	95·8††
				0·28§	—	—	98·3††
WORCRA	21·0	98·8	0·9	0·40‡	39·0	38·0	98·5††
Noranda	26·0	98·6	—	0·35**	35·1	30·0	98·8††
Brittingham	27·0	—	—	0·10‡	56·0	24·0	—

* Favourable result.

†Decopperizing in electrical furnace.

‡Washing with pyrite.

§ Decopperizing by flotation.

** Blowing reducing gas.

†† Values calculated from copper balance.

special attention being paid to the slags originating at the matte production stage. Neither slags originating in a continuous converter nor those coming from the converting of copper mattes have yet been sufficiently studied.

In conventional smelting the melting of the charge, consisting of ore or copper concentrates and the flux, is followed by a formation of the three phases matte, slag and gas. In continuously operating units the number of the phases in coexistence is greater because of the presence of the metallic copper. Ignoring

Table 2   Heat requirements

Copper production	Theoretical Cu content in concentrate, wt%	Heat required for I-ton concentrate, kcal	References
Reverberatory Flash-smelting,	25·0	$1·2 .10^6$	12,13
Harjavalta	20·0	$1·0 .10^6$	12
INCO, Canada	20·0	$0·8 .10^6$	12
WORCRA process	25·0	$0·18.10^6$	13
Noranda process	26·0	$0·7 .10^6$	8

Table 3   Investment and production costs[26]

Copper production	Capital costs		Treatment costs	
	30 000 t Cu per annum	80 000 t Cu per annum	30 000 t Cu per annum	80 000 t Cu per annum
Reverberatory	100	100	100	100
Blast-furnace	90	110	130	150
Flash-smelting	92	93	110	105
WORCRA process	85	85	72	75

the minor components of the charge, for example, Zn, Ni, Sb, etc., the equilibrium between matte slag and gas can be represented by the $Cu-Fe-S-O-SiO_2$ system, which has not yet been studied as a whole. Some studies of the partial binary and ternary systems involved have, however, been made—the results of which, given here, describe the matte and slag phases. Some thermodynamic and laboratory studies of the $Cu-Fe-S-O-SiO_2$ system are also mentioned, followed by a discussion on the copper losses with slags and their possible treatment to decrease the copper content.

Slags

If the presence of minor components in the slags, such as CaO, MgO, Al_2O_3, etc., is ignored, these can be described as the system $Fe-O-SiO_2$. In this

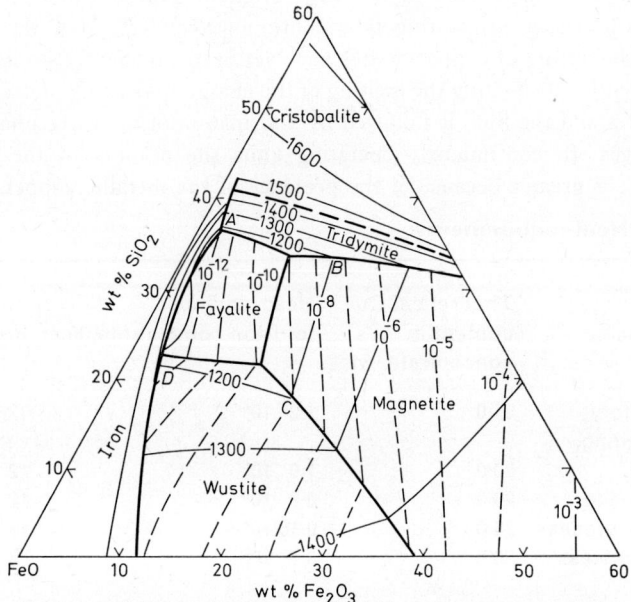

Fig. 5 Liquidus diagram and oxygen isobars for system FeO–Fe$_2$O$_3$–SiO$_2$[21]

system iron may exist either as Fe^0, Fe^{2+} or Fe^{3+}, depending mainly on the partial pressure of oxygen in the gaseous phase, as there is equilibrium between slag and atmosphere. In pyrometallurgical copper production the partial

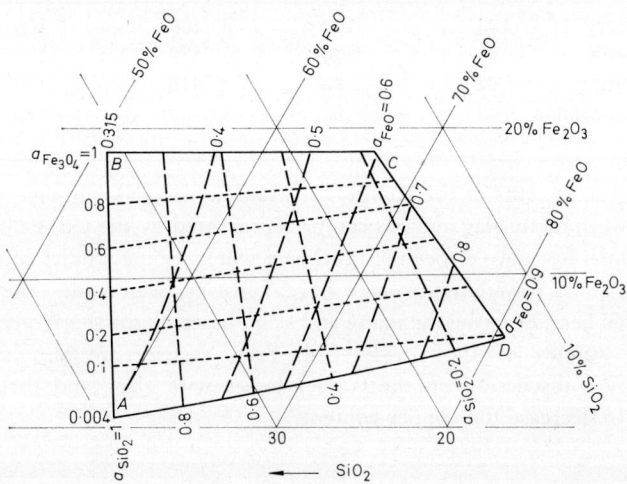

Fig. 6 FeO, SiO$_2$ and Fe$_2$O$_3$ *iso*-activity lines in system FeO–Fe$_2$O$_3$–SiO$_2$ at 1300°C[22]

pressure of oxygen is too high for metallic iron to exist in slag. Silicate slags can therefore be described as the system $FeO-Fe_2O_3-SiO_2$.

The liquidus diagram for the system $FeO-Fe_2O_3-SiO_2$ was studied by Schuhmann, Powell and Michal.[20] Oxygen isobars above the melt in the range between 10^{-10} and 1 atm were established by the equilibrium study of this system in a CO_2-H_2 atmosphere by Muan.[21] The ternary diagram for this system with the oxygen isobars established by the above authors is given in Fig. 5. Based on experimental data, Yazawa[22] calculated *iso*-activity lines for FeO, Fe_2O_3 and SiO_2 in the region of the homogeneous melt at 1300°C (Fig. 6) and Korakas[23] calculated the activities of FeO and Fe_3O_4 at 1200°C (Fig. 7).

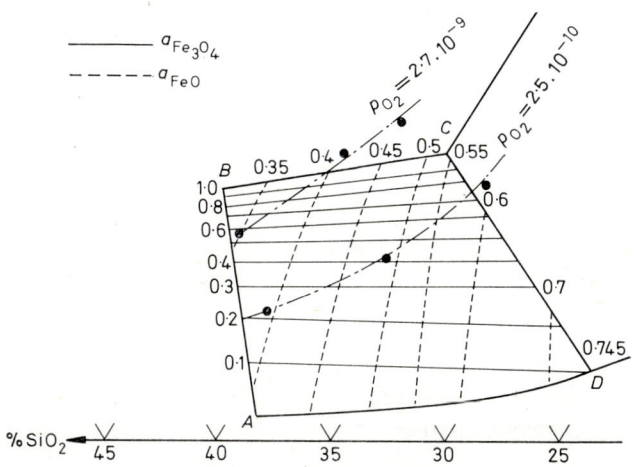

Fig. 7   FeO and Fe_3O_4 *iso*-activity lines in system $FeO-Fe_2O_3-SiO_2$ at 1200°C[23]

The composition of the slags from the reverberatory or blast-furnace is near to the silica saturation point, i.e. in Figs. 6 and 7 it is in the vicinity of the line *AB*. The converter slags, however, are by their composition near magnetite saturation, i.e. near the line *CB*.

Mattes

If the minor constituents of matte, such as Zn, Pb, As, etc., are ignored, it may be described as the system Cu–Fe–S–O. Matte is often considered as a simple eutectic system (Cu_2S-FeS). Schlegel and Schüller[24] confirmed this view by their study of the ternary system Cu–Fe–S, the results of which are summarized in Fig. 8. They concluded that $Cu_2S-FeS_{1.08}$ forms a quasi-binary system (Fig. 9). Krivsky and Schuhmann[25] concluded from a study of the activities of this system that the behaviour of the Cu_2S-FeS system at 1350°C is nearly ideal, similar conclusions being reached by Nagamori,[26] who studied activities in this system by the equilibrium method at 1200°C. It is known that the actual sulphur content of the matte is lower than that calculated stoichiometrically. Yazawa

and Kameda[27] explained this phenomenon by reference to the presence of the
oxygen, the content of which varies from 6% for pure iron sulphide to zero for
white metal coexisting with silica-saturated slag. The same authors discovered

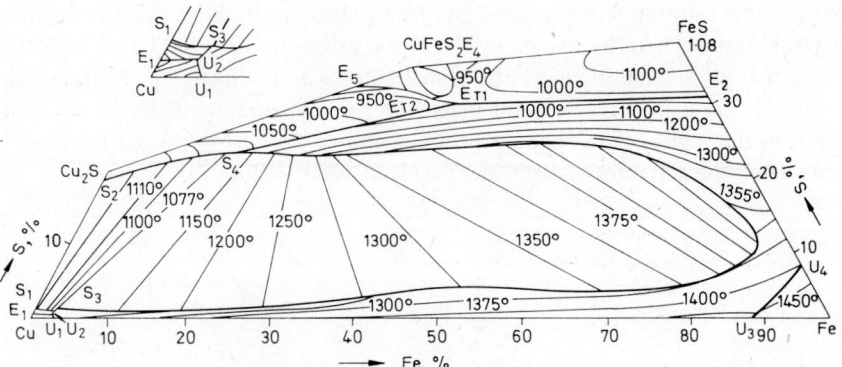

Fig. 8 Equilibrium diagram for system Cu–Fe–S [24]

that the presence of the dissolved oxygen in the matte leads to the crystallization
of wustite or magnetite on cooling, depending on the matte grade.

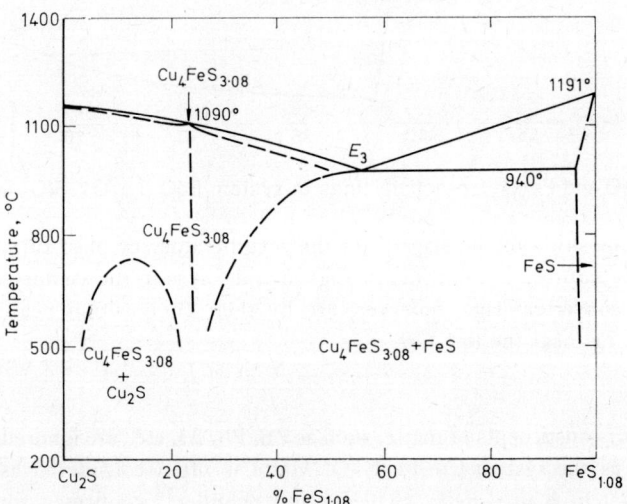

Fig. 9 Equilibrium quasi-binary diagram Cu_2S–$FeS_{1.08}$ [24]

A comprehensive investigation of the matte necessitates an understanding of
the systems Cu_2S–FeS–FeO and Cu_2S–FeO–Fe_2O_3; only the former has been
investigated. The partial liquidus diagram of the quasi-ternary system Cu_2S–
FeS–FeO was studied by Yazawa and Kameda,[27] the results of their experiments
being given in Fig. 10.

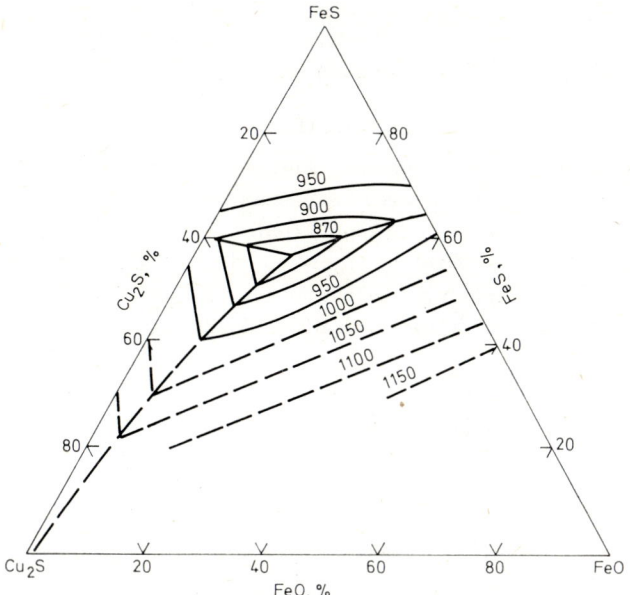

Fig. 10   Equilibrium diagram for system $Cu_2S–FeS–FeO$ [27]

Detailed study of the equilibrium between rich mattes and slags, i.e. of the two liquidus phases that coexist in the continuously operating units, necessitates a discussion of the Cu–S–O system. Kuxmann and Benecke[28] studied the

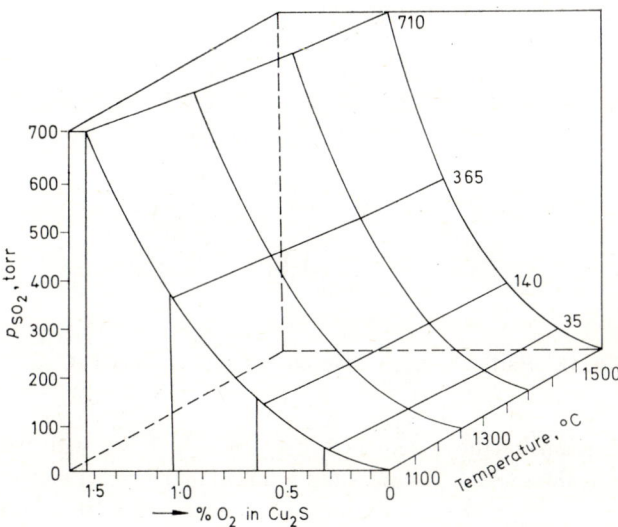

Fig. 11   Equilibrium SO_2 pressure above melts in system $Cu_2S–Cu_2O–Cu$ [28]

region of coexistence of the liquid phase Cu_2S-Cu_2O with copper as a function of partial pressure of SO_2 in the temperature range 1100–1500°C, the results of their experiments being summarized in Fig. 11.

Equilibrium between slag and matte

In reverberatory and blast-furnaces, continuous converters, etc., slag coexists with matte: it is therefore necessary to discuss the behaviour of these two phases from the standpoint of the phase equilibrium.

The results obtained from the study[29] of the $FeS-FeO-SiO_2$ system are of great importance, despite the fact that the system does not comprise copper as a component (the results of this study are summarized in Fig. 12, where a partial

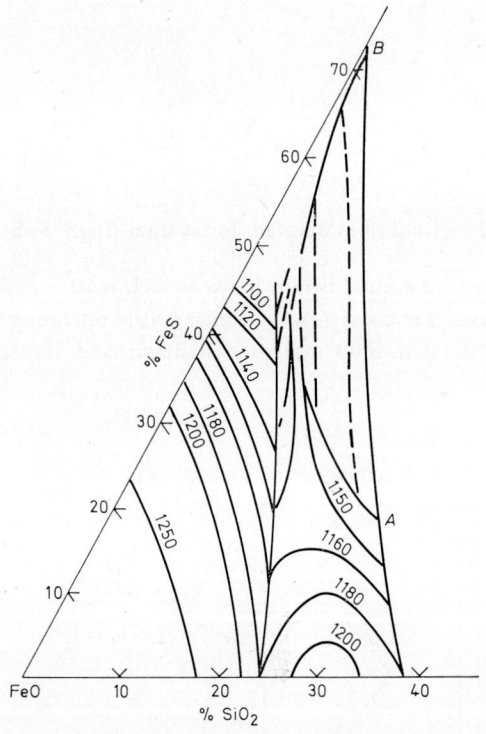

Fig. 12 Partial liquidus diagram for system $FeS-FeO-SiO_2$[29]

liquidus diagram for the system $FeS-FeO-SiO_2$ is shown with the miscibility gap in the liquidus state). If some silica is added to the binary system $FeS-FeO$, which is miscible in the whole range of concentration, separation into two liquid phases takes place. By increasing the amount of silica, the distribution becomes more nearly perfect, until silica saturation is reached and two liquid phases, representing slag and matte, attain the composition given by points *A* and *B*, respectively, in Fig. 12.

Yazawa and Kameda[30] studied the dissolution of copper and sulphur in silica-saturated slags coexisting with mattes, the results of their experiments being given in Fig. 13 as copper and sulphur contents in slag against matte

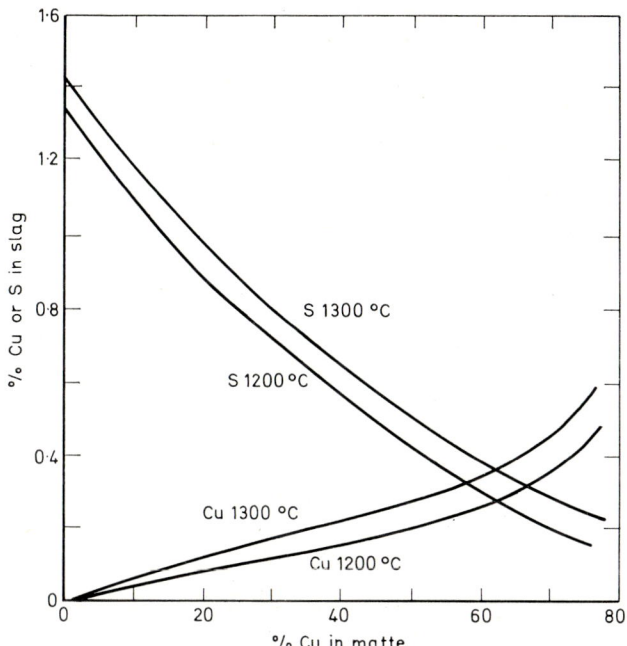

Fig. 13 Effect of matte grade on copper and sulphur contents of silica-saturated slag at 1200 and 1300°C[30]

grade. The curve for copper dissolution is almost linear up to 60% Cu in matte; the ratio of copper contents of matte and slag is approximately 0·42 and 0·55 for 1200 and 1300°C, respectively. Results for sulphur contents in mattes show that if the copper content of the matte is increased from zero, i.e. pure FeS up to 80%, i.e. pure Cu_2S, the sulphur content decreases correspondingly from 26% for FeS to 20% for pure Cu_2S.

Among others who have contributed to the study of the equilibrium between silica-saturated slag and matte, Rosenqvist,[31] Ruddle and co-workers,[32] Vanyukov and Zaytsev[33] and Spira and Themelis[34] should be mentioned.

Thermodynamics of the Cu–Fe–S–O–SiO₂ system

With regard to the thermodynamic study of the equilibrium between matte, slag and gaseous phase, the $Cu–Fe–S–O–SiO_2$ system has been considered. For simplicity of calculation, the system was divided into the two partial systems

C

Table 4   Standard free energy values for reactions considered in Figs. 14 and 15

	ΔG°_T, cal/mol	$\log K_{1473}$	$\log K_{1573}$
1 $4Cu_{(l)}+S_{2(g)} = 2Cu_2S_{(l)}$	$\Delta G^{\circ}_T = -\ 50\ 920 + 6{\cdot}00\ T$	6·245	5·764
2 $4Cu_{(l)}+O_{2(g)} = 2Cu_2O_{(l)}$	$\Delta G^{\circ}_T = -\ 57\ 840 + 16{\cdot}52\ T$	4·972	4·426
3 $2Cu_2S_{(l)}+O_{2(g)} = 2Cu_2O_{(l)}+S_{2(g)}$	$\Delta G^{\circ}_T = -\ 6\ 920 + 10{\cdot}52\ T$	−1·273	−1·338
4 $2Fe_{(\gamma)}+SiO_{2(s)}+O_{2(g)} = 2FeO.SiO_{2(l)}$	$\Delta G^{\circ}_T = -124\ 900 + 26{\cdot}50\ T$	12·742	11·563
5 $2Fe_3O_{4(s)}+3SiO_{2(s)} = 3(2FeO.SiO_2)_{(l)}+O_{2(g)}$	$\Delta G^{\circ}_T = 154\ 500 - 71{\cdot}70\ T$	−7·254	−6·793
6 $2FeS_{(l)}+O_{2(g)}+SiO_{2(s)} = 2FeO.SiO_{2(l)}+S_{2(g)}$	$\Delta G^{\circ}_T = -\ 64\ 700 + 10{\cdot}10\ T$	7·393	6·783
7 $2Fe_{(\gamma)}+S_{2(g)} = 2FeS_{(l)}$	$\Delta G^{\circ}_T = -\ 60\ 200 + 16{\cdot}40\ T$	5·348	4·781
8 $3FeS_{(l)}+2O_{2(g)} = Fe_3O_{4(s)}+3/2S_{2(g)}$	$\Delta G^{\circ}_T = -174\ 300 + 51{\cdot}00\ T$	14·717	13·073
9 $\tfrac{1}{2}S_{2(g)}+O_{2(g)} = SO_{2(g)}$	$\Delta G^{\circ}_T = -\ 86\ 200 + 17{\cdot}26\ T$	9·019	8·205

Cu–O–S and Fe–S–O–SiO$_2$. Based on knowledge of the standard free energies for the reactions listed in Table 4, the stability regions for the different phases

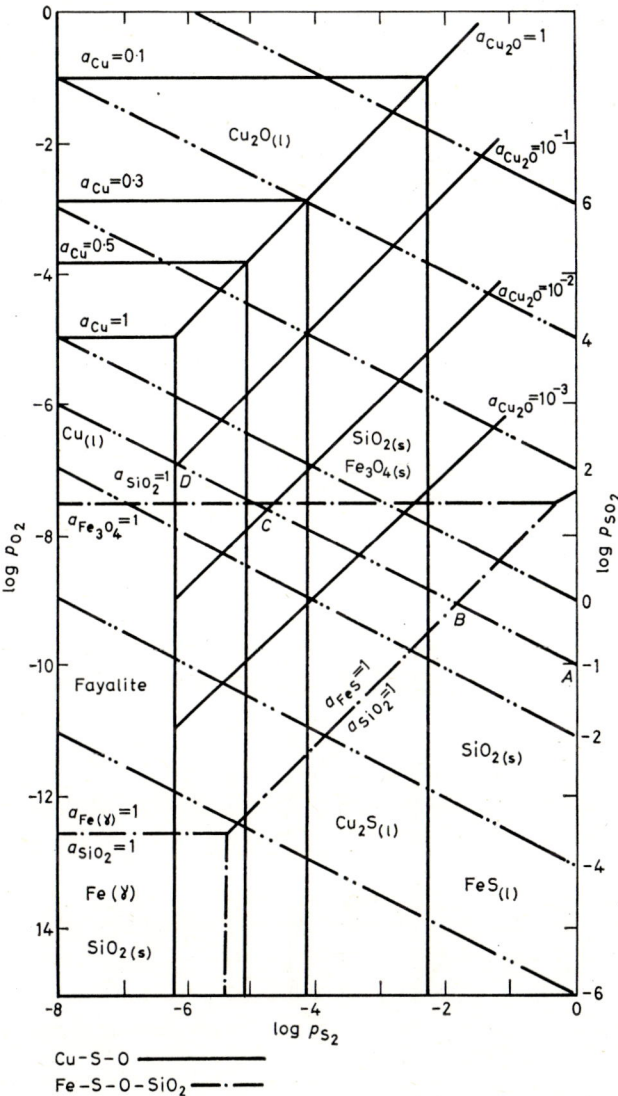

Fig. 14   System Cu–Fe–S–O–SiO$_2$ at 1200°C

have been calculated at 1200 and 1300°C. The system Fe–S–O–SiO$_2$ was considered to be silica-saturated. The results of the calculations are plotted in Figs. 14 and 15: in the calculations of *iso*-activity lines the assumption was made that the activities in equations 1 and 2 (Table 4) equal unity. Similarly, for the *iso*-activity lines of Cu_2O in the region of stability of Cu_2S, the value of the activity of Cu_2S was taken as unity for equation 3. From equation 9 isobars of

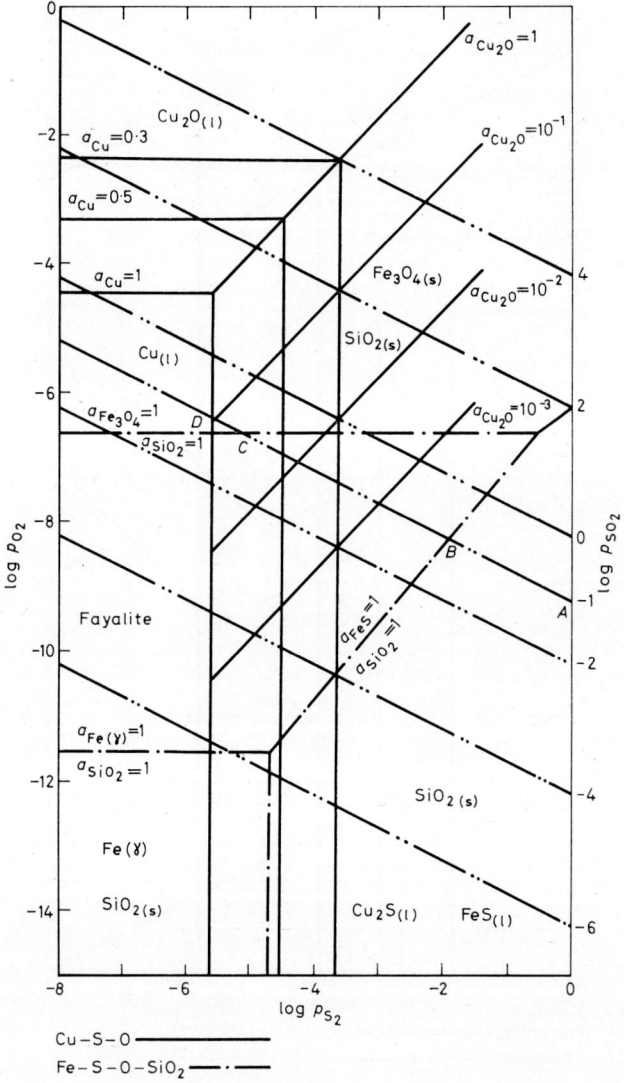

Fig. 15   System $Cu-Fe-S-O-SiO_2$ at 1300°C

the partial pressure of SO_2 have been calculated which, together with oxygen and sulphur, represent the gaseous phase in the system $Cu-Fe-S-O-SiO_2$.

If it is assumed that, on melting, the partial pressure of sulphur dioxide in the furnace is of the order of 10^{-1} atm, the equilibrium between slag and matte can be represented by the isobar of sulphur dioxide in Figs. 14 and 15 (points A, B, C and D). Point A represents fresh charge in a furnace, consisting of the sulphide concentrates and siliceous flux; point B corresponds to the condition of coexistence of matte and slag in a reverberatory or blast-furnace; point C represents the coexistence of white metal with the slag saturated with magnetite and silica at the end of the first period of converting; and point D represents the conditions in a continuously operating converter, where copper, white metal and silica and magnetite-saturated slag coexist with the furnace atmosphere.

Experimental

During the experimental stage some equilibrium studies in the Cu–Fe–S–O–SiO$_2$ system were made by the equilibrium method at 1200°C in the region of coexistence of the white metal and silica-saturated slag with the furnace atmosphere. Saturation with silica resulted in a decrease in copper losses and in a lowering of the number of degrees of freedom to two for the system matte–silica-saturated slag–gas and to one for the system white metal–slag saturated with silica and the magnetite–gaseous phase.

In the study of the equilibrium in the system matte–silica-saturated slag–gaseous phase, N_2–S_2–SO_2 atmosphere was used to fix two degrees of freedom. The application of this atmosphere permitted the stabilization of p_{O_2} and p_{S_2}. Synthetic samples (2–3 g) of the slag and matte, prepared by melting the pure compounds FeO, SiO$_2$, FeS and Cu$_2$S, were used. They were melted in the furnace for 24–30 h at 1200°C under constant partial pressures of oxygen and sulphur. When the experiments were complete, samples were taken from the slag and matte for microscopic examination and chemical analysis to discover the copper, iron, oxidic Fe^{2+} and Fe^{3+}, sulphur and silica contents. The amount of iron in the form of FeS was then calculated from the difference between the oxidic cations Fe^{2+} and Fe^{3+} and the total iron content. Matte was analysed for copper. The results of the chemical analyses are presented in Tables 5 and 6.

For the investigation of the equilibrium between white metal, slag saturated with silica and the magnetite and gaseous phase the N_2–SO_2 atmosphere was used in order to fix one degree of freedom. The experiments were made with the synthetic slags and Cu$_2$S by the same method as that described above. Slags were chemically analysed for total copper, copper in sulphidic form, oxidic Fe^{2+}, Fe^{3+}, silica and sulphur. The percentage of the oxygen in the slag and matte phases was analysed by use of a chromatograph. The results of the analyses are summarized in Table 7.

Copper osses in slags

Despite the contradictory opinions regarding the forms of copper losses in slags which have appeared recently, the two forms considered here are mechanical losses and physico-chemical losses. In the first group can be included particles of

Table 5 Chemical composition of mattes and slags at 1200°C in N_2–S_2–SO_2 atmosphere at constant $p_{O_2} = 5.10^{-9}$ atm

No.	p_{S_2}, atm	Slag, wt %								Matte, wt %
		Cu	Fe_s^{2+}	Fe^{2+}	Fe^{3+}	Fe_T	SiO_2	S	O	Cu
310	$6.4.10^{-5}$	0·39	4·52	39·47	8·81	52·80	29·50	2·78	30·84	75·51
311	$6.4.10^{-5}$	0·55	3·94	38·93	7·90	50·77	31·00	2·40	31·09	74·90
312	$6.4.10^{-5}$	0·64	3·69	40·64	8·95	53·28	28·70	2·27	30·80	76·12
391	$4.0.10^{-4}$	0·34	5·22	39·63	8·32	53·17	28·20	3·17	29·98	66·13
392	$4.0.10^{-4}$	0·49	5·92	38·23	7·69	51·84	29·30	3·50	29·90	65·85
393	$4.0.10^{-4}$	0·34	5·34	41·03	7·41	53·78	28·60	3·14	30·20	65·11
471	$1.0.10^{-3}$	0·30	7·82	39·08	6·08	52·98	28·70	4·55	29·13	58·13
472	$1.0.10^{-3}$	0·14	7·06	38·60	6·71	52·37	29·10	4·08	29·50	57·82
512	$4.9.10^{-1}$	0·07	8·84	38·15	5·66	52·65	28·80	5·08	28·74	15·84

mechanically entrained or floated unsedimented matte which coexist with slag; physico-chemical losses, on the other hand, are caused by solubility of copper in slag in the form of sulphide or oxide. The problem of minimizing copper losses has been discussed in various papers: it has been suggested that mechanical losses can be lowered by settling of the matte particles,[37] or by high-temperature flotation,[38] centrifuging[39] or flotation of the finely powdered slag after cooling.[3]

Solution of the problem of physico-chemical losses remains unresolved, and wide disagreement exists as to the forms of the copper losses.

Table 6 Chemical composition of mattes and slags at 1200°C in N_2–S_2–SO_2 atmosphere at constant $p_{S_2} = 9.10^{-4}$ atm

No.	p_{O_2}, atm	Slag, wt %								Matte, wt %
		Cu	Fe_s^{2+}	Fe^{2+}	Fe^{3+}	Fe_T	SiO_2	S	O	Cu
530	$9.0.10^{-10}$	0·33	5·79	40·87	5·87	52·53	30·40	3·39	30·46	62·38
401	$3.6.10^{-9}$	0·42	3·63	41·26	8·32	53·21	27·70	2·18	30·18	68·21
402	$3.6.10^{-9}$	0·30	4·64	40·72	6·43	51·79	31·30	2·74	31·13	67·13
403	$3.6.10^{-9}$	0·38	4·33	41·96	7·20	53·49	28·60	2·56	30·38	67·05
441	$8.0.10^{-9}$	0·41	1·97	42·97	9·09	54·03	28·90	1·23	31·64	72·11
442	$8.0.10^{-9}$	0·47	1·72	42·27	9·23	53·22	28·90	1·10	31·50	72·98
443	$8.0.10^{-9}$	0·44	2·80	42·58	8·60	53·98	28·30	1·71	31·00	71.80
481	$1.3.10^{-8}$	0·59	0·68	41·34	10·00	52·02	29·80	0·54	32·04	77·63
482	$1.3.10^{-8}$	0·62	0·52	42·81	10·55	53·88	26·80	0·46	31·12	77·00

Table 7 Chemical composition of mattes and slags melted at 1200°C in N_2–SO_2 atmosphere

No.	p_{SO_2}, atm	Slag, wt %									Matte, wt %			
		Cu_T	Cu_S	Fe_s^{2+}	Fe^{2+}	Fe^{3+}	Fe_T	SiO_2	S	O	Cu	Fe	S	O
31	1·00	7·95	3·65	1·08	16·76	34·20	52·04	18·78	1·55	29·49	78·00	0·36	18·95	0·828
32	1·00	9·30	4·13	0·52	16·76	34·21	51·49	19·56	1·59	30·43	78·20	0·35	18·90	0·878
52	0·21	6·31	3·59	0·82	27·20	18·15	46·17	21·20	1·37	28·41	77·92	0·28	19·25	0·570
53	0·21	5·89	3·04	0·24	30·22	20·94	51·40	20·11	0·88	28·72	78·00	0·30	19·82	0·695
41	0·11	4·80	3·01	0·73	29·32	18·84	48·89	29·40	1·18	32·16	78·20	0·19	19·78	0·493
71	0·03	3·10	2·70	0·67	32·81	17·82	51·30	30·92	1·05	33·58	79·00	0·21	19·54	0·127
73	0·03	3·95	2·83	1·04	36·30	13·26	50·60	28·72	1·30	30·00	78·87	0·17	19·20	0·086
61	0·01	2·27	1·35	0·58	39·37	8·02	47·97	36·58	0·45	34·30	78·60	0·18	19·59	0·063
63	0·01	2·18	1·30	0·62	39·50	9·06	49·18	35·60	0·47	34·16	78·90	0·21	19·32	0·078

Table 8   Forms of copper losses

	Dissolved sulphide Copper, %	Dissolved oxide Copper, %	Suspension, %
Blast-furnace slag	60	—	40
Reverberatory furnace slag	25	50	25
Converter slag	12·5	12·5	75

The ratio of mechanically entrained and dissolved copper is given in Table 8,[22] but the values for the reverberatory furnace differ from those of Kammel and co-workers,[40] who claimed that the form in which copper appears in slags is mainly dissolved and partly segregated sulphide. Similar conclusions were reached by Barker and co-workers[41] and Utkin and co-workers,[42] who studied slags from the reverberatory furnace. Other workers determined that in a slag containing about 0·4% copper, some 50% of its content was in the dissolved form.[43] These workers claimed that converter slags contain as much as 0·5% of the dissolved copper. The same view was expressed by Vanyukov and Zaytsev,[33] who subscribe to the ionic theory of slags and therefore distinguish electro-chemical and mechanical copper losses. They found that in slags from a rever-beratory or blast-furnace some 20–30% of copper is lost electrochemically, whereas in those from the converter it was between 50 and 60%.

Ruddle and co-workers[32] suggested that the dissolution of copper in slags follows the reaction

$$2Cu_{(l)} + Fe_2O_3 = 2FeO_{(l)} + Cu_2O \qquad (10)$$

where the activity of copper in matte is less than unity. This view differs from that of Yazawa and Kameda,[30] who claimed that copper is dissolved in slags mainly as Cu_2S, although it is in a good agreement with the findings of Toguri and Santander,[44] who investigated the equilibrium between ferro-silicate slags and Cu–Au alloys at 1300°C and at various oxygen partial pressures.

Based on thermodynamic calculations (see Figs. 14 and 15), it can be assumed that copper is to be found in slags both as Cu_2S and Cu_2O. Moving along the iso-activity lines in the Cu_2S stability region, it can be seen that if matte is produced in a reverberatory or blast-furnace (corresponding to point B), the activity of Cu_2O is smaller than 10^{-3}, i.e. it is dissolved Cu_2S that prevails in the silica-saturated slags. This is in accord with other workers' findings[40,41,42] for a reverberatory furnace and with the data summarized in Table 8 for a blast-furnace. If the copper content of the slags is higher than 70–75% (corresponding to points C and D in Figs. 14 and 15), the activity of Cu_2O approaches 10^{-1}. This is, however, in disagreement with the results of Yazawa and Kameda,[30] according to which the oxygen content of the white metal is zero, whereas Ruddle and co-workers[32] reported that high-grade matte (containing 79·1–80% Cu) co-existing with silica-saturated slag contains between 0·155 and 0·403% oxygen. Kuxmann and Benecke[28] established that white metal contained approximately 0·35% oxygen. Similarly, Spira and Themelis[34] considered that, with regard to the coexistence of silica-saturated slag with high-grade matte, the latter contained some oxygen. This was confirmed by Johansen and co-workers,[45] who studied the equilibrium between copper, white metal and silica-saturated slag at temperatures between 1331 and 1383°C in an atmosphere of SO_2. The composition of the slag was 5·8–6·6% Cu and 0·15–0·1% S, which means that a substantial part of copper existed in the form of dissolved oxide.

This was further confirmed by experimental work in the system Cu–Fe–S–O–SiO_2, the results of which are presented in Tables 5–7.

Table 5, in which the results of a study of the system matte–silica-saturated slag–gaseous phase are given for constant oxygen partial pressure and different values of sulphur partial pressure, shows that an increase in the latter causes the fall in the copper content of the matte and slag, whereas the content of Fe_2O_3 and SiO_2 in the slag remains almost constant. The copper and sulphur contents of the slags found by chemical analysis and also by microscopic examination suggested that copper existed there mainly as Cu_2S.

From the results of the experiments with the system matte–silica-saturated slag–gaseous phase at constant sulphur partial pressures and different oxygen pressures, summarized in Table 4, it can be concluded that if the oxygen pressure is increasing, the copper contents of the matte and of the slag will increase. The Fe_2O_3 content of the slag also increased with increased oxygen pressure and a simultaneous fall in the concentration of the silica and ferrous sulphide. On the basis of the copper and sulphur contents in the slag, it can be assumed that copper is contained in the slag in the form of cuprous sulphide.

Table 7, which gives the results of the experiments in the system matte–slag saturated with silica and magnetite–gaseous phase, shows that at constant copper content in matte both the oxygen content of the matte and the copper content of the slag increase with increase of p_{SO_2}. There is good agreement between the oxygen contents of the white metal and the experimental results of Kuxmann and Benecke.[28] The higher the p_{SO_2} value, the more Fe_2O_3 the slag will contain, whereas the SiO_2 and FeO contents fall. The FeS content remained nearly constant. The analysis of the slags for sulphur and Cu_2S suggested that, with increase in p_{SO_2}, there is growth of the total copper content of the slag and of the copper in the form of Cu_2O.

It is possible to conclude from the above literature survey, thermodynamic considerations and experimental results that the copper losses arising from solubility of Cu_2S and Cu_2O in ferro-silicate slags saturated with silica are mainly a function of matte grade. The partial pressure of oxygen in the furnace atmosphere influences the copper content of the matte according to

$$[FeS] + 3/2O_2 = (FeO) + SO_2 \qquad (11)$$

c*

Assuming that the behaviour of the melted slag is that of an ideal ionic solution, copper losses due to solubility phenomena can be expressed by reactions 12 and 13

$$[Cu_2S] = 2(Cu^+) + (S^{2-}) \tag{12}$$
$$[Cu_2O] = 2(Cu^+) + (O^{2-}) \tag{13}$$

for which the equilibrium constants are given by

$$K_{12} = \frac{a^2_{Cu^+} \cdot a_{S^{2-}}}{a_{Cu_2S}}$$

$$K_{13} = \frac{a^2_{Cu^+} \cdot a_{O^{2-}}}{a_{Cu_2O}}$$

If, as an approximation, we suppose that the activities of the O^{2-} and S^{2-} ions are constant at constant temperature, and that the copper content of the slag corresponds to the concentration of a diluted solution

$$a_{Cu_2S} = K'_{12} \cdot \% \, Cu_1^2 \tag{14}$$
$$a_{Cu_2O} = K'_{13} \cdot \% \, Cu_2^2 \tag{15}$$

where $\% \, Cu_1$ is the equilibrium copper concentration in the slag in the Cu_2S form and $\% \, Cu_2$ is the equilibrium copper concentration in the slag in the Cu_2O form, a_{Cu_2S} is the activity of Cu_2S in the matte and a_{Cu_2O} is the activity of Cu_2O in the matte.

Supposing, further, that the behaviour of the matte is that of the ideal solution composed mainly of Cu_2S and FeS, i.e.

$$N_{Cu_2S} + N_{FeS} \simeq 1$$

and if the following reaction is taking place in the matte

$$[Cu_2O] + [FeS] = [Cu_2S] + (FeO) \tag{16}$$

for which the equilibrium constant is

$$K_{16} = \frac{a_{FeO}}{a_{Cu_2O}} \cdot \frac{a_{Cu_2S}}{a_{FeS}}$$

the activity of Cu_2O can be expressed as a function of the copper content in the matte and the activity of FeO in the slag at a constant temperature

$$a_{Cu_2O} = \frac{a_{FeO}}{K_{16}} \cdot \frac{N_{Cu_2S}}{1 - N_{Cu_2S}} \tag{17}$$

Finally, for the total copper losses in the slag due to the solubility of Cu_2O and Cu_2S, the following equation is valid:

$$\% \, Cu_{in \, slag} = \% \, Cu_{Cu_2O} + \% \, Cu_{Cu_2S} \tag{18}$$

Substituting equations 14, 15 and 17 in equation 18

$$\% \; Cu_{in\;slag} = A \sqrt{\frac{N_{Cu_2S}}{1-N_{Cu_2S}}} + B \sqrt{N_{Cu_2S}} \tag{19}$$

where

$$A = \sqrt{\frac{u_{FeO}}{K_{16}} \cdot \frac{1}{K'_{13}}}$$

$$B = \sqrt{\frac{1}{K'_{12}}}$$

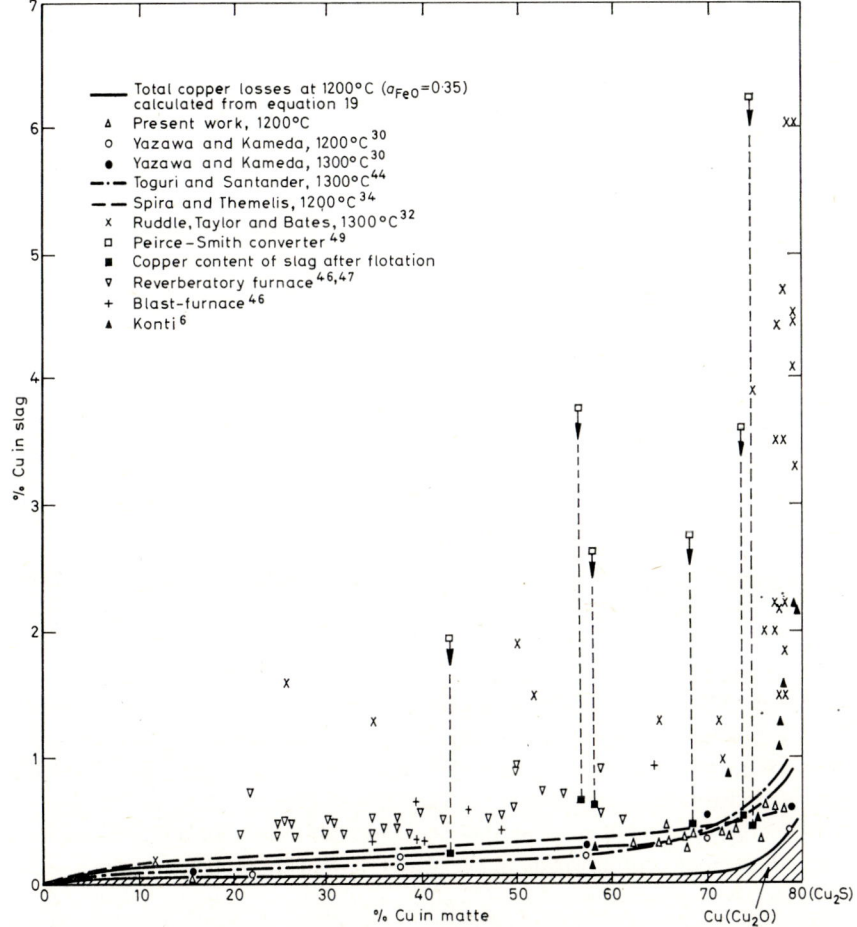

Fig. 16 Solubility of copper in silica-saturated slags as function of matte grade

Equation 19 signifies that copper losses in slags arising from the solubility phenomena of Cu_2O depend not only on the copper content in the matte and temperature but also on the FeO activity in the slag, whereas those due to dissolution of Cu_2S are only a function of the matte grade.

Based on the experimental results given in Table 8 and the value of the equilibrium constant of reactions 3 and 9 (Table 4) at 1200°C, the activities of Cu_2O in white metal were calculated for different values of p_{SO_2} on the assumption that the activity of Cu_2S in white metal is unity and the partial pressure of sulphur 10^{-6} atm. If the value of a_{FeO} in the region of a homogeneous melt saturated with silica is 0·35 (Fig. 7) and the equilibrium constant of reaction 16 is 8.10^3, the value of coefficient A in equation 19 could be calculated: for 1200°C it equals 0·046. From the analyses of the total copper content in the slag summarized in Tables 5–7 and the calculated coefficient A, the mean value of the coefficient B for equation 19 was calculated to be 0·3368 at 1200°C.

The calculated copper losses from equation 19 at 1200°C are plotted in Fig. 16 as a function of the matte grade, together with results obtained by other workers.[30, 32, 34, 44, 46, 47, 49] It is clear that if a matte contains between 30 and 50% copper, i.e. a matte obtained in a reverberatory or blast-furnace, approximately 80% of the dissolved copper present in the slag is in the Cu_2S form—which is in a good agreement with thermodynamic calculations and literature data. If the copper content of the matte is approximately 80%, which corresponds to conditions in continuous units, the physico-chemical losses of copper in the form of dissolved Cu_2S will represent only 40% at the relatively higher total content of dissolved copper in the slags.

Conclusions

From the above thermodynamic considerations, which have been confirmed quantitatively by experimental work in the $Cu–Fe–S–O–SiO_2$ system, it can be stated that slags from the reverberatory and blast-furnaces contain mainly dissolved Cu_2S, whereas those from the continuous converter contain Cu_2O.

It is possible to decrease the copper losses in slags originating from reverberatory or blast-furnaces by flotation of a slowly cooled slag—this method was used by Davčeva and co-workers,[48] who, thereby, decreased the copper content of the slag from 0·55 to 0·15%.

The copper content of slags from the continuous converter can be decreased by washing with pyrite, where Cu_2O is transformed to Cu_2S, which, together with pyrite, forms low-grade matte. This method is employed in the WORCRA process, where the copper content of the waste slag is decreased to 0·4%.

The other method of cleaning the slags from the continuous units is based on the reduction of cuprous oxide in the slag, followed by cooling and flotation to decrease the copper content to 0·28%.[49]

References

1. The Outokumpu flash smelting method. *Outokumpu News*, no. 1 1969, 3–8.
2. THE STAFF. The oxygen flash smelting process of the International Nickel Company. *Trans. CIM*, **58**, 1955, 158–66.

3. Kubota Y. and Nagayama S. Flotation of copper converter slag at Hitachi mine. *Fusen*, no. 7 1962, 45–9. (Japanese text)

4. Tonkonogii A. V. *et al.* Cyclone smelting of sulfide copper concentrates. *Tsvet. Metally, Mosk.*, **33**, no. 3 1960, 20–8; *Tsvet. Metally, N.Y.*, **1**, no. 3 1960, 24–32.

5. Kadlec F. Cyklonove tavenie. Medzinárodné kolokvium o neželezných kovoch 1966. *Sbor. prednášok VÚK Panenske Březany*, 7–17.

6. Sehnálek F. Holéczy J. and Schmiedl J. Priama výroba medzi koncentrátov v kontinuálne pracujúcom konvertore. Medzinárodné kolokvium o neželezných kovoch 1966. *Sbor. prednášok VÚK Panenske Březany*, 170–83.

7. Worner H. K. Continuous smelting and refining by the WORCRA processes. In *Advances in extractive metallurgy* (London: Institution of Mining and Metallurgy, 1968), 245–63.

8. Noranda pilots continuous copper smelting. *Engng Min. J.*, **69**, May 1968, 85–7.

9. Brittingham G. J. Review of efficiency of copper recovery. *Trans. Instn Min. Metall.* (*Sect. C: Mineral Process. Extr. Metall.*), **75**, 1966, C65–73.

10. Diomidovskii D. A. *et al.* Continuous converting of matte. *Tsvet. Metally, Mosk.*, **32**, no. 2 1959, 27–34. (Russian text)

11. Sehnálek F. Holéczy J. and Schmiedl J. A new process—continuous converting of copper mattes. *J. Metals, N.Y.*, **16**, 1964, 416–20.

12. Kuxmann U. Gedanken zur schmelzmetallurgischen Gewinnung von Kupfer. *Z. Erzbergb. Metallhüttenw.*, **19**, 1966, 549–54.

13. Pawlek F. Arbeitsverfahren und Entwicklungstendenzen bei den Kupferverhüttung. *Z. Erzbergb. Metallhüttenw.*, **22**, 1969, 413–8.

14. Worner H. K. The WORCRA smelting process. *C.R.A. Gazette*, **3**, Sept. 13 1968.

15. Sehnálek F. and Imriš I. Development trends in the pyrometallurgy of copper. Copper slags. I. *Hutn. Listy*, **25**, 1970, 570–5. (Czech text)

16. Worner H. K. WORCRA smelting–converting, a new approach to continuous direct copper production. Paper presented at UNIDO symposium of Expert consulting Group on the copper industry, Vienna, 1967, 28 p.

17. Ruddle R. W. *The physical chemistry of copper smelting* (London: Institution of Mining and Metallurgy, 1953), 156 p.

18. Toguri J. M. Themelis N. J. and Jennings P. H. A review of recent studies on copper smelting. *Can. metall. Q.*, **3**, 1964, 197–220.

19. Imriš I. and Sehnálek F. Copper wastes in slags. *Hutn. Listy*, **26**, 1971, 59–66. (Czech text)

20. Schuhmann R. Jr. Powell R. G. and Michal E. J. Constitution of the FeO–Fe$_2$O$_3$–SiO$_2$ system at slagmaking temperatures. *Trans. Am. Inst. Min. Engrs*, **197**, 1953, 1097–104.

21. Muan A. Phase equilibria in the system FeO–Fe$_2$O$_3$–SiO$_2$. *Trans. Am. Inst. Min. Engrs*, **203**, 1955, 965–76.

22. Yazawa A. Equilibrium relations between matte and slag in copper metallurgy. *Internal Rep. Noranda Res. Centre.* no. 151, 1969, 29 p. (Typescript)

23. Korakas N. Etude thermodynamique de l'équilibre entre scories ferro-siliceuses et mattes de cuivres. Thesis, University of Liège, 1964.

24. Schlegel H. and Schüller A. Die Schmelz- und Kristallisationsgleichgewichte im System Kupfer–Eisen–Schwefel und ihre Bedeutung für die Kupfergewinnung. *Freiberger ForschHft B*, no. 2 1952, 32 p.

25. Krivsky W. A. and Schuhmann R. Jr. Thermodynamics of the Cu–Fe–S system at matte smelting temperatures. *Trans. Am. Inst. Min. Engrs*, **209**, 1957, 981–8.

26. Nagamori M. Some studies on the thermodynamics of iron and copper sulphides. University of Trondheim, 1967.

27. Yazawa A. and Kameda M. Fundamental studies on copper smelting (III). *Technol. Rep. Tohoku Univ.*, **19**, 1955, 239–50.

28. Kuxmann U. and Benecke T. Untersuchungen zur Löslichkeit von Sauerstoff in Kupfersulfid-Schmelzen. *Z. Erzbergb. Metallhüttenw.*, **19**, 1966, 215–21.

29. Yazawa A. and Kameda M. Fundamental studies on copper smelting (I). *Technol. Rep. Tohoku Univ.*, **18**, 1953, 40–58.

30. Yazawa A. and Kameda M. Fundamental studies on copper smelting (II). *Technol. Rep. Tohoku Univ.*, **19**, 1954, 1–22.

31. ROSENQVIST T. Some studies on the thermodynamics of iron–copper mattes and their equilibrium with iron silicate slags. Unpublished report.
32. RUDDLE R. W. TAYLOR B. AND BATES A. P. The solubility of copper in iron silicate slags. *Trans. Instn Min. Metall.* (*Sect. C: Mineral Process. Extr. Metall.*), **75,** 1966, C1–12.
33. VANYUKOV A. V. AND ZAYTSEV V. *Slaki i stejny svetnoj metallurgii* (Moskva: Metallurgiya, 1969).
34. SPIRA P. AND THEMELIS N. J. The solubility of copper in slags. *J. Metals, N.Y.*, **21,** April 1969, 35–42.
35. SCHUHMANN R. JR. A survey of the thermodynamics of copper smelting. *Trans. Am. Inst. Min. Engrs*, **188,** 1950, 873–84.
36. ST. PIERRE G. R. AND CHIPMAN J. Sulfur equilibria between gases and slags containing FeO. *Trans. Am. Inst. Min. Engrs*, **206,** 1956, 1474–83.
37. YAZAWA A. AND KAMEDA M. Experiments on decopperizing of converter slag. *Bull. Res. Inst. Miner. Dress. Metall. Tohoku Univ.*, **19,** no. 1 1963, 79–90.
38. VANYUKOV A. V. AND ZAYTSEV V. YA. Surface forces at the matte–slag–gas boundary and reduction of loss of metals with slag. *Izv. vyssh. uched. Zaved. Tsvetnaya Metall.*, **6,** no. 1 1963, 48–57. (Russian text)
39. WIESE W. Über die Löslichkeit von Sulfiden in Schlacken. *Z. Erzbergb. Metallhüttenw.*, **16,** 1963, 377–86.
40. KAMMEL R. SAMANS R. AND WINTERHAGER M. Elektronenstahl-Mikroanalyse von Metallverlusten in Schlacken der NE-Metallurgie. Technische Hochschule, Aachen, 1966.
41. BARKER I. L. JACOBI J. S. AND WADIA B. H. Some notes on Oroya copper slags. *Trans. Am. Inst. Min. Engrs*, **209,** 1957, 774–80.
42. UTKIN I. N. DERGACHEV N. M. AND ANAN'EV F. M. Copper, nickel and cobalt losses in reverberatory smelting slags. *Tsvet. Metally, Mosk.*, **39,** no. 1 1966, 49–51; *Tsvet. Metally, N.Y.*, **7,** no. 1 1966, 53–5.
43. NORANDA MINES, LTD. British Patent 1 176 655, 1970.
44. TOGURI J. M. AND SANTANDER N. H. The solubility of copper in fayalite slags at 1300°C. *Can. metall. Q.*, **8,** 1969, 167–71.
45. JOHANSEN E. B. ROSENQVIST T. AND TORGERSEN P. T. On the thermodynamics of continuous copper smelting. *J. Metals, N.Y.*, **22,** Sept. 1970, 39–47.
46. VERNEY L. R. Fluxing in copper reverberatory furnaces and copper losses in slag. *Trans. Instn Min. Metall.* (*Sect. C: Mineral Process. Extr. Metall.*), **78,** 1969, C28–42.
47. LATHE F. E. AND HODNETT L. Data on copper converter practice in various countries. *Trans. Am. Inst. Min. Engrs*, **212,** 1958, 603–17.
48. DAVČEVA N. G. RAZUMOV K. A. AND MASLENICKIJ I. N. Investigation of crystallization and flotation of metallurgical copper-bearing slags. *Rudy*, **18,** no. 3–4, 1970, 107–8. (Czech text)
49. SEHNÁLEK F. *et al.* Flotačné ochudobnovanie konvertorových trosiek. Výskumná správa KCHZH VŠT Košice, 1968.

DISCUSSION

Professor M. G. Fleming, in opening the Symposium, said that Dr. J. H. Chesters' lecture* had provided a particularly appropriate introduction and, lest he be accused of interrupting the continuity of extractive metallurgy, he must not take up their time with any formal preamble. He would, however, not be denied the pleasure of welcoming registrants to the Symposium and of saying how gratifying it was to have so many authors and participants from abroad. The meeting followed the Symposium *Advances in extractive metallurgy* held by the Institution in 1967—an extremely successful symposium, he might say, that encouraged the planning, after a lapse of four years, of another gathering that would highlight and record changes, inventions and developments in the important and complex field of extractive metallurgy. The response that they had had from authors and the presence of so many distinguished registrants promised another successful symposium with fruitful discussions and valuable exchanges of knowledge, views and opinions.

He wanted to thank Dr. D. A. Temple and the Organizing Committee for the time and thought and work that they had put into the preparation of the programme. Their Institution depended largely on the voluntary efforts of such busy men to fulfil the obligations imposed by their Charter to collect and disseminate the specialized knowledge of its subjects. For Mr. B. W. Kerrigan, Mr. M. J. Jones and the other members of the Institution's permanent staff those meetings provided a heavy additional burden. It was a burden that they willingly and, indeed, eagerly accepted, but he wanted them to know that their efforts and also their attitude to that extra work were very warmly appreciated.

It was his pleasure and privilege to declare open the Symposium *Advances in extractive metallurgy and refining.* He would ask Professor T. R. A. Davey to take the Chair for the first session.

Dr. N. J. Themelis introduced his joint paper summarizing its principal contents and conclusions.

Dr. Howard K. Worner introduced his joint paper by showing a colour film, which depicted the principles and operation of the WORCRA furnace.

I. Imriš introduced his joint paper, summarizing its principal contents and conclusions.

The Chairman, in opening the discussion, first congratulated the organizers of the Symposium on the excellent programme that they had put together, the international flavour of which was well pointed up by the four people on the

---

* On the occasion of the Symposium the Institution of Mining and Metallurgy arranged the Eighth Sir Julius Wernher Memorial Lecture, which was delivered by Dr. J. H. Chesters, O.B.E., F.R.S. (CHESTERS J. H. The case for continuity in extractive metallurgy. *Bull. Instn Min. Metall.* no. 781, Dec. 1971, 13–28; *Trans. Instn Min. Metall.,* **80,** 1971, 52–67.)

platform; Dr. Themelis, Dr. Worner and he were all wild colonial boys, and when they went through Passport Control at London airport they found that they were, like Mr. Imriš, all foreigners!

Most people knew that Dr. Worner named the WORCRA process by choosing the first three letters of his name, followed by the initial letters, CRA, of his Company, Conzinc Riotinto, Australia. He felt that they should all be grateful that Dr. Worner had not chosen the second three letters of his name, followed by the initial letters, RTZ, of the parent Company, Rio Tinto–Zinc Corporation!

Mark Twain had suggested that it was better to keep one's mouth shut and appear stupid than to open it and remove all doubt. He would, however, take the risk and draw attention to a difficulty he had with equations 12–19 (pp. 58–9) in the paper by Sehnálek and Imriš. He did not think that equation 18 could be accepted by anyone who believed that slags were ionic in nature, since that equation regarded the total copper content of the slag as being comprised of Cu(I), dissolved as copper sulphide, added to Cu(II), dissolved as copper oxide. He felt that the copper ions dissolved in the slag would not know whether they were supposed to be there as oxide or sulphide, and so could not be distinguished, unless, of course, they were complexed in different forms in the solution, for which he believed there was no evidence. If the copper ions could not be distinguished as belonging to either oxide or sulphide, then the correct form of equation 19 would seem to be derived as followed (accepting all other assumptions of Sehnálek and Imriš):

$$(Cu_2O)_{slag} + [FeS]_{matte} = [Cu_2S]_{matte} + (FeO)_{slag} \qquad (16)$$

$$K_{16} = \frac{a_{FeO}}{a_{Cu_2O}} \cdot \frac{a_{Cu_2S}}{a_{FeS}}$$

$$a_{Cu_2O} = K'_{13} \cdot \%Cu^2 \qquad (15)$$

$$\%Cu_{in\ slag} = A \sqrt{\frac{N_{Cu_2S}}{1 - N_{Cu_2S}}}$$

where

$$A = \sqrt{\frac{a_{FeO}}{K_{16}}} \cdot \frac{1}{K'_{13}}$$

The copper in slag could be considered as *either* Cu$_2$O *or* Cu$_2$S, but not both as separate species. Since some S existed in solution in the slag, it could be considered as affecting the activity coefficient of the Cu in the slag—which entered into K'_{13}.

J. B. W. Bailey* asked the authors if they had considered recovering the copper from the Noranda process slag by reducing the molten slag rather than by slow cooling and milling. It should be possible to reduce the copper content of the

* Department of Minerals Engineering, University of Birmingham.

slag to below 0·5 per cent by the addition of coke, in a process similar to that described by Banks,* thus producing a discardable slag.

In the operation of the furnace itself he asked if the smelting rate could be improved by pelletizing the flux with the concentrates rather than adding it separately; but, possibly, that would make the control of flux additions too difficult.

F. A. Garner† said that for the calculation of the stability regions in Fig. 15 (p. 52) Sehnálek and Imriš had assumed the equilibrium p_{SO_2} value to be of the order of 10^{-1} atm. That was higher than the maximum obtained by workers in his own Department, which was of the order of 10^{-2} atm for mattes containing no copper, and decreased appreciably with increasing matte grade.

In order to correlate that experimental work with their own data they would appreciate more details of the experimental methods used, with particular reference to the essential precautions required to ascertain the establishment of equilibrium.

In Tables 5, 6 and 7 (pp. 54 and 55) the slag compositions when totalled came to approximately 110%. Could the authors indicate where that error was likely to have arisen?

The authors, in deriving the copper dissolution equation, assumed the slag to be an ideal ionized melt and then postulated two reactions (equations 12 and 13, p. 58) to produce the ionic species. They then differentiated between the activities of copper ions from the sulphide and oxide sources, which was a contradiction of the assumption of the ideal ionized state in which the activity of copper ions would be the same in both cases. That made the derivations of equations 14 and 15 (p. 58) meaningless.

Dr. P. J. Bowles,‡ speaking on the paper by Sehnálek and Imriš, asked the authors to give full details of the analytical technique for the determination of Cu, Fe^{2+} and Fe^{3+} in slags, mentioned on page 53. Reference 49 was not readily available in the United Kingdom: perhaps the authors would give details of the method of cuprous oxide reduction.

Dr. J. H. E. Jeffes§ said that both the Noranda and WORCRA processes used fuel. If air enriched to 30–40% O_2 were used in concentrate processing, no fuel was necessary. Had the use of oxygen-enriched air been considered for those processes? The off-gas SO_2 content would be higher and, thus, more readily removed.

* Banks C. C. Recovery of non-ferrous metals from secondary copper smelter slags. This volume, pp. 551–64.
† Department of Minerals Engineering, University of Birmingham.
‡ Warren Spring Laboratory, Department of Trade and Industry, Stevenage, Hertfordshire.
§ Department of Metallurgy, Imperial College, London.

No mention had been made of problems caused by the formation of magnetite. In most processes that caused difficulties, and he asked if that were not so with the two processes under discussion.

J. S. Jacobi* said that the paper by Themelis and McKerrow described a very remarkable achievement in practical extraction metallurgy. What were the economics of milling the slag? How did its hardness or grinding index compare with, say, a normal hard siliceous ore? It was a pity that the elegant process of continuous smelting had to be followed by a less elegant batch cooling of slag at the end, or did the authors expect to put that on a continuous basis also? One would certainly agree that slow cooling of slags would give better grinding and flotation results, but he wondered if the difference were very marked.

Work carried out in South America some years ago had convinced him that even rapidly quenched converter slags were quite amenable to cleaning by milling with high operating efficiency. Also, he believed that recovery of copper values by physical means was possible from granulated slags, even in the absence of a matte phase.

J. A. Holmes,† speaking on the papers by Themelis and McKerrow and Worner *et al.*, asked the authors to comment on the handling of scrap materials— in particular, tankhouse scrap. If they envisaged remelting scrap in their furnaces, he wondered if they foresaw any difficulties in superimposing a somewhat intermittent scrap charging operation on their continuous process, or whether they would advocate separate remelting of scrap. In the latter event additional capital and working costs must be included in any comparison of their processes with conventional methods.

Kauko Kaasila‡ said that in Table 2 (p. 43) of the Sehnálek and Imriš paper the heat required for 1 ton of concentrate in the flash-smelting process at Harjavalta was given as $1\cdot0 \times 10^6$ kcal. That figure was excessive; the process required only $0\cdot30$–$0\cdot35$ kcal for 1 ton of concentrate on average, the heat requirement depending on unit size, concentrate composition, matte grade, temperature of preheated air, etc.

In the paper by Worner *et al.* flash-smelter–converter combinations were included in the group of processes where it was possible to collect about 90% of the feed sulphur in gases for further processing. He would like to point out that in most flash-smelters more than 95% of the feed sulphur could be collected in gases.

Contributed remarks
A. Vega§ I shall be grateful for comments by Themelis and McKerrow and

* IMI Refiners, Ltd., Walsall, Staffordshire.
† Anglo American Corporation (Central Africa), Ltd., Lusaka, Zambia.
‡ Outokumpu Oy, Helsinki, Finland.
§ Ministry of Mining and Metallurgy, Havana, Cuba.

Worner *et al.* on the following questions. (1) What would be the minimum recommended capacity for the Noranda and WORCRA processes? Information on the consumption of raw materials and fuel and on copper recovery would be very valuable. (2) Can the processes be applied to, for example, lead, zinc, etc? (3) Is a second furnace (refining) required prior to electrorefining?

N. E. Brown* The Noranda process appears to have a distinct advantage over the WORCRA process from the point of view of thermal efficiency, this coming from the smelting and converting to metal in one zone. Would it not be possible to dispense with the smelting bowl of the WORCRA process by transferring the bulk of the concentrates to the conversion zone. The metal could be tapped from this zone and the slag could pass through a cleaning zone, where the remainder of the concentrates would be added. This modification should reduce the amount of fuel required and, if oxygen enrichment of the converting gases is used, the process may become autogenous.

It is stated that, from pilot-plant trials, the WORCRA process is capable of treating sulphide copper concentrates containing less than 25% each of iron and sulphur. I should be interested to know (*a*) the maximum concentration of oxidic copper that may be smelted by this process and (*b*) the extent to which oxidic copper concentrates alter the operational characteristics of the WORCRA process.

G. J. Brittingham† The group of papers dealing with continuous smelting and converting forms an interesting contribution to the literature on this extremely important subject.

The paper by Sehnálek and Imriš provides a general review, supported by some published data and results of experimental work. It constitutes an important contribution to the literature.

There can be no doubt that, viewed from the theoretical aspect, the simplest system in smelting and converting which can be considered is complex, comprising Cu, Fe, O, S and Si (or SiO_2). In practice, to these must be added CaO, Al_2O_3 plus any other metals present. Much has already been written on this subject, but it would seem that too little attention has been given to the fundamentals, which are self-evident, but should not be ignored.

Slags and mattes in this system are produced together, exist together and are immiscible liquids. They should therefore be expected to conform with the behaviour of conjugate solutions, which, in detail, means that when the composition of one of the pair of conjugates varies, that of the other will vary in accordance with their phase rule relationship. This fact is not even acknowledged in most of the discussions of the solubility of copper in slags.

Slags and mattes are also ionic liquids; the elements of the ionic forms present in both phases will be as above—Cu, Fe, O, S and Si. The slag carries

* Department of Minerals Engineering, University of Birmingham.
† Consulting Metallurgical Engineer, Broadbeach, Queensland, Australia.

the great bulk of the Si as SiO_2, and, in addition, carries Fe in an oxidized condition. All slag analyses in this system indicate that the oxygen present is more than sufficient to provide stoichiometrically for all of the Si as SiO_2 (plus CaO, etc.) and Fe as FeO. The extra oxygen can be conveniently regarded as Fe_2O_3, although there is no evidence to support the presence of this grouping in the molten slag. Since Fe is the only element present capable of existing in two states of valency under the conditions obtaining, however, it is convenient to regard the extra oxygen in this way.

When such a slag is allowed to solidify with a relatively high 'extra' oxygen content, the first solid to crystallize out is almost invariably magnetite, or Fe_2O_3.FeO. To provide some quantitative measure for the presence of this extra oxygen it becomes appropriate to speak of oxygen potential, where this represents the ratio of ferric oxide present to ferrous oxide. For this specification the oxygen potential of magnetite is 1, and that of any slag formed during copper smelting processes will be less than unity.

Mattes are also composed of the same elements, Cu, Fe, S, O and Si, but the last must be very small in amount in the presence of the amount of O in the slag. Once again when the matte composition is reduced to stoichiometric relationships between Cu and S, Fe and S, and Fe and O, it is found that for most mattes there is an excess of O above that required to provide for the remaining Fe as FeO if the order of satisfying the S is as indicated. This at once indicates that there is 'extra' O, which can be very logically regarded as Fe_2O_3, which is also known to be present in the conjugate slag. Thus mattes also do exhibit this phenomenon of oxygen potential. Strong evidence in support of the theory that mattes do contain ferric oxide has been provided by Drummond[1] and others.

Ruddle and co-workers[2] and Korakas[3] provided much evidence to establish that the presence of this 'extra' oxygen in slag, as indicated by a high oxygen potential, was invariably accompanied by copper solubility in the slag, this varying with the oxygen potential, among other factors. Notably, when the oxygen potential was low, so also was the copper solubility.

Korakas[3] also showed very clearly that to obtain a conjugate solution relationship between white metal and slag required a high oxygen potential in the slag phase, but that this equilibrated with a sulphide phase of very low oxygen content. When this sulphide phase was subjected to further oxidation, copper metal appeared quickly as a result of the Cu_2S–Cu relationship. That is, to produce copper metal in any continuous smelting and converting process it will be essential to obtain a higher oxygen potential in the slag than would be present at the termination of a normal batch process converter blow.

This is a fundamental point in any continuous smelting and converting process; it will be essential to have a sulphide phase present in conjugate solution relationship with copper metal on the one hand and slag on the other. For convenience, this sulphide phase, which is essentially Cu_2S carrying some extra copper in solution, will be referred to as enriched white metal.

The amount of oxygen present in a slag in conjugate relationship with such an enriched white metal would probably be equivalent to some 25–35% Fe_3O_4 if the slag were allowed to solidify, and this would be an oxygen potential of 0·4–0·5.

From a study of the work of Ruddle and co-workers[2] this would be expected to correspond with a slag copper tenor of about 4–5%; the figure for a converter slag skimmed from contact with white metal, as in normal practice, is 2·5–3·0%.

The earlier BNFMRA work,[4] in which sulphur was not a component of the system, indicated that even higher copper tenors for slag of this composition were to be expected, since here the conjugate solution relationship was one between slag and metal, and not slag and sulphide phase. This may well be relevant to the copper in slag analyses recorded for the high oxygen potential slags in both the Noranda and WORCRA processes. When air is injected into a sulphide phase overlain by slag, it is inevitable that there will be contact between slag and metal as well as between slag and sulphide phase. This probably requires a higher copper tenor in the slag, as instanced in these results (Noranda 8–12% and WORCRA 14–18%).

Turning now to the other extreme, the conjugate solution relationships between matte and slag where the oxygen potential of the slag was reduced to the minimum possible by contact with metallic iron, this system was investigated for typical silica-saturated slags by Yazawa and Kameda.[5] Sehnálek and Imriš reproduce Fig. 6 of that paper as Fig. 13 (p. 49). This shows that for mattes of less than 15–20% Cu the copper tenor of the slag in equilibrium is less than 0·1%. The original work records a matte of 22% grade in equilibrium with a slag of 0·098% Cu, with lower values for lower grades.

The work of Yazawa and Kameda[5] links up very well with that of Richardson and Billington,[6] who indicated a solubility of only 0·05% Cu in a sulphur-free slag under non-oxidizing conditions. This appears to be the limit of neutral copper solubility.

It has been shown that in any continuous smelting and converting system it is essential to produce a high oxygen potential slag if copper metal is to be produced.

The Noranda process acknowledges this and simply removes this slag from the melting system at a copper tenor of 8–12%, allows it to solidify slowly and then recovers this copper as far as possible by mineral dressing techniques to provide a concentrate of metallic material and matte. The residue from this operation contains at least 0·5% Cu.

These results are exactly what could be expected when the conjugate relationships of the system, coupled with the copper solubility induced by the necessary oxygen potential and iron content of the slag, are considered. When slow cooling of such a slag is employed the main phenocrysts to solidify preferentially would be magnetite, thus steadily reducing the oxygen potential of the slag as this material separates. Copper, primarily, and then matte of a composition controlled by the oxygen potential of the slag at the moment of rejection of the copper, will be precipitated, and this will continue until the ternary eutectic SiO_2–FeO–Fe_2O_3, as modified by the presence of other components, freezes. As the liquid concerned in this final stage of solidification still does have an appreciable oxygen potential, it still does have solubility for copper. When this eutectic liquid does solidify, the copper remaining in solution can be expected to be precipitated as an extremely finely divided matte of relatively low grade, and it will be so sub-microscopic in size as to be irrecoverable by flotation.

The Noranda process is stated to produce 7·5 tons of metallic copper, 7·5 tons of 50% copper concentrate, which is recovered from the retreatment of the slag, 1·7 tons of flue dust of unspecified copper tenor, and a loss of 0·124 tons of copper in slag tailings. The copper in the recirculated concentrates and flue dust is then one-half of the amount of copper produced directly, and must, of course, be recirculated for recovery, involving additional costs for heat energy in particular.

The recovery claimed under this system approximates 98·3%—comparable with the recovery available from existing technology.

The WORCRA process treats the slag from the converter zone by recycling it through the smelting zone primarily and then through the relatively quiescent slag-treatment zone. The materials in the converting and smelting zones are kept thoroughly agitated by lance action, and therefore should reflect the conjugate relationships between the phases, and in the converter zone it must be recalled that the oxygen is maintained at a value such that copper metal can be produced.

In the smelting zone conjugates will represent a slightly lower oxygen potential in the slag, because of the reducing action of the iron and sulphur contents of the new concentrates charged. In the slag-cleaning zone 'Fine concentrates were also continuously fed to the bath here—to complete the washing of the slag' (p. 23).

Table 4 (p. 30) substantiates these differing conjugate solution relationships, but the slag well copper tenor of 0·35% claimed here does not appear to be confirmed by the values recorded in Table 5 (p. 31). The figures given in Table 3 (p. 29) appear more consistent with those of Table 5 than of Table 4, and from Table 3 the recovery is 97·8%.

Neither of these processes (Noranda or WORCRA) attempts to employ the conjugate solution relationships between mattes and slag as fully as they might. Both produce, and indeed there is no alternative, a high oxygen potential slag which is so necessary for contact with both metallic and sulphide phases.

It has been quite clearly established that copper solubility in slags is controlled by the slag oxygen potential coupled with the iron content, and each grade of matte requires a slag of a certain minimum oxygen potential in equilibrium with it; if it is a high-grade matte, it must be a high oxygen potential slag, but lower oxygen potentials suffice for contact with lower-grade mattes. Both slags and mattes have solubility for extra oxygen, which gives rise to their oxygen potential, and if this is lowered in both phases simultaneously, the oxygen potential of the slag is reduced, and so is its solubility for copper.

This point was very well illustrated by Yazawa and Kameda,[5] recorded as Fig. 13 in the Sehnálek and Imriš paper, but it is also set out more fully in their own publication. This means that by equilibrating a slag with a low-grade, low oxygen potential matte the oxygen potential of the slag can be reduced below the concentration of Fe_2O_3 corresponding to the ternary eutectic in the system SiO_2–FeO–Fe_2O_3 and, consequently, a slag of 0·1% Cu or less must be obtained if the conjugate solution relationships are fully and properly employed.

Mention is now made of Fig. 4 (p. 42)[7] and of the reference to the process indicated there in Table 1 (p. 42). Fig. 1 is perhaps a slightly more detailed

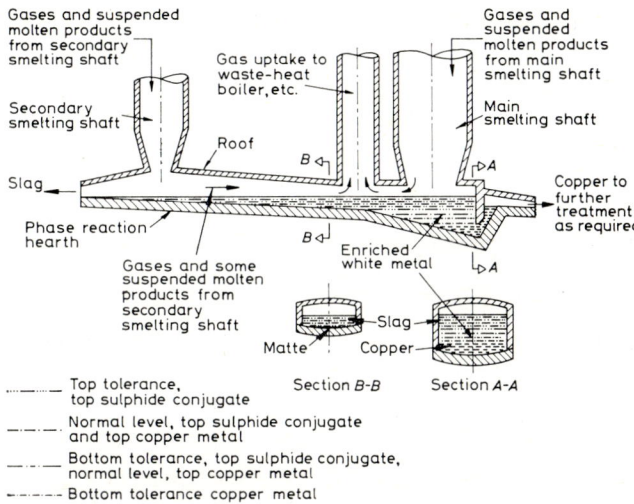

Fig. 1 Diagrammatic section of proposed furnace

diagrammatic representation of the furnace in sectional elevations. The secondary reaction shaft has been proposed as one method of producing a low oxygen potential, low-grade matte from a low-grade copper, pyrite or pyrrhotite concentrate by flash-smelting in a controlled atmosphere; this takes rather more cognisance of the phase relationship than 'washing the slag with pyrite', as suggested in Table 1.

This low-grade matte is added in just sufficient quantity to reduce, by means of its iron and sulphur contents, the oxygen potential of the slag to its minimum value—thereby reducing its copper solubility to a minimum. The grade of this matte and its oxygen potential are the factors that will determine the residual solubility of the slag for copper.

As the amount of extra oxygen introduced into the slag to permit of the production of copper metal will be more, only slightly more, than needs to be reduced from the slag, there will be no call to add excess low-grade matte. This arises because the slag, even at the point of incipient presence of metallic iron, still carries a small concentration of ferric oxide.

The results reported by Yazawa and Kameda[5] were for a typical smelter slag of relatively high silica and lime. It may well be that for a slag containing less silica and no added lime a lower-matte grade than was indicated in their results will be needed to reduce the copper tenor in the slag to 0·1%; but, obviously, this can be done even if the slag composition must be varied by flux additions at this point.

No successful continuous smelting and converting system can afford to ignore the basic conjugate solution relationships between matte and slag: a successful system will use them to the fullest possible extent. The use of such a phase exchange hearth in any system for matte smelting of copper or nickel is the subject of patents in a number of countries—typically, Australian Patent 273,006, 1967.

References

1. DRUMMOND P. R. On the constitution of mattes. *Trans. Can. Inst. Min. Metall.*, **43,** 1940, 627–52.
2. RUDDLE R. W. TAYLOR B. AND BATES A. P. The solubility of copper in iron silicate slags. *Trans. Instn Min. Metall. (Sect. C: Mineral Process. Extr. Metall.*), **75,** 1966, C1–12.
3. KORAKAS N. Magnetite formation during copper matte converting. *Trans. Instn Min. Metall.*, **72,** Oct. 1962, 35–53.
4. BRITISH NON-FERROUS METALS RESEARCH ASSOCIATION. The solubility of copper in slags produced during the smelting of copper. I. The equilibrium between pure copper and iron silicate slags saturated with silica. *BNFMRA Res. Rep.* A1063, 1954, 43 p.
5. YAZAWA A. AND KAMEDA M. Fundamental studies on copper smelting (II). *Technol. Rep. Tohoku Univ.*, **19,** 1954, 1–22.
6. RICHARDSON F. D. AND BILLINGTON J. C. Copper and silver in silicate slags. *Trans. Instn Min. Metall.*, **65,** April 1956, 273–97.
7. BRITTINGHAM G. J. Review of efficiency of copper recovery. *Trans. Instn Min. Metall. (Sect. C: Mineral Process. Extr. Metall.*), **75,** 1966, C65–73.

AUTHORS' REPLIES

Dr. N. J. Themelis and G. C. McKerrow　With respect to the question by Mr. J. B. W. Bailey (pp. 64–5), the milling process has been selected for the recovery of copper from the slag to be produced in the 800 ton/day plant which is under construction at Noranda. Experimental work at the Noranda Research Centre has shown, however, that the Noranda process slags may also be treated pyrometallurgically by reduction and settling in separate furnaces. Coming to the second question, there is no evidence that the smelting rate would be increased by incorporating the flux in the concentration pellets; most of the converting reaction takes place after the pellet has smelted and separated into its matte and slag components.

In answer to the question by Dr. J. H. E. Jeffes (pp. 65–6), extended tests have been carried out in the Noranda process pilot plant with oxygen-enriched air. Some of the results of this work were presented in an earlier paper.* As Dr. Jeffes surmised, the use of oxygen minimized the fuel consumption, but, the major advantage would be in producing a flue gas of higher SO_2 concentration for use in the manufacture of sulphuric acid or for reduction to elemental sulphur.

With regard to the question by Mr. J. S. Jacobi (p. 66), the cost of slag milling is estimated at about $2.75–3.00/ton of slag milled. An advantage of clearing the slag by milling is that one can produce a slag of much lower silica content than reverberatory slag. Thus, the amount of silica flux required in the Noranda process is less than in conventional smelting and compensates, from the point of view of fuel consumption, for the recirculation of slag concentrates to the reactor.

The difference in milling results between cooling the slag in pits or in moulds is not substantial: however, if the slag is rapidly quenched, the copper loss increases markedly. It is possible that in the South American converter slags referred to by Mr. Jacobi most of the copper was in the form of matte globules. With respect to the question of hardness, the Noranda process slags are roughly twice as hard to grind as low-grade chalcopyrite ore.

In answer to the question by Mr. J. A. Holmes (p. 66), operating experience at the pilot plant has shown that large quantities of material (e.g. concentrates, flux) can be added intermittently through the hood without any noticeable effect on the operation of the reactor. The fuel burners automatically compensate for any heat imbalance in the bath. Therefore, no difficulty is envisaged in melting scrap in the 800 ton/day reactor.

Mr. A. Vega (pp. 66–7) enquired the minimum recommended capacity for a Noranda process reactor. As was stated in the paper, a 100 ton/day (of concentrates) reactor has been operated at Noranda, Quebec, for a number of years. Of course, the cost of production per ton in such a small reactor is greater than in the 800 ton/day reactor which is under construction. Some information on fuel consumption, etc., was presented in the paper. The Noranda smelter welcomes visitors at the pilot plant and would provide information on specific applications. With respect to the second question by Mr. Vega, the Noranda process could be applied to lead, but only a limited amount of experimentation has been done in this direction.

Dr. Howard K. Worner, J. O. Reynolds, B. S. Andrews and A. W. G. Collier In reply to Dr. J. H. E. Jeffes (pp. 65–6), extensive studies with supplemental oxygen were carried out during both the pilot and semi-commercial stages of the WORCRA development. These studies included enrichment of lance air at various levels up to 40%, operation of lances with commercially pure oxygen, enrichment of feeder lance combustion air and operation with oxy-fuel flames. Equipment for operation under all these conditions was successfully developed.

* See reference 10 on page 18.

Economic studies have indicated that at this stage of development of the process it is desirable to continue to use a small amount of fuel in the smelting and slag-cleaning zones in order to ensure that part of the concentrate feed is melted under slightly reducing conditions, thereby supplying the chemical reduction potential necessary to convert Fe_3O_4 to FeO and also to provide low-grade matte to 'wash' prills of copper or rich matte out of the backward-flowing slag.

Clearly, there are technical benefits associated with the use of oxygen. The desirability of using this technology commercially will depend on the availability of cheap oxygen, relative prices of electricity and fossil fuel, composition of the concentrate and the sulphur recovery method and equipment proposed.

WORCRA process operators are fully conscious of the significance of magnetite formation, and regular monitoring of the level around the furnace has been practised. It can be seen from Table 4 (p. 30), however, that under steady conditions the magnetite level falls as slag passes through the furnace; it is found that sufficient agitation exists in each zone to counter the tendency for magnetite to settle in that zone.

The problem of handling scrap copper into the WORCRA furnace, raised by Mr. J. A. Holmes (p. 66), has been considered. It is feasible to feed such material, including tankhouse scrap. Some size reduction of large lumps of such material may be desirable. Small-size scrap was fed to the WORCRA semi-commercial plant for short periods without problems.

In reply to Mr. A. Vega (pp. 66–7), it is not possible to define the minimum capacity of a WORCRA plant in general terms because the economic threshold depends on so many local factors. However, some simplifications can be made in a small plant, and it is believed that for any specific location and set of conditions a WORCRA plant in the small-size range (15 000–25 000 ton/year) as well as the large (50 000–100 000 ton/year) is likely to be of lower capital cost than alternative processes designed to produce the same quantity of copper.

The basic principles (continuous single-furnace operation, direct smelting–converting of fine particulate concentrate and countercurrent 'washing' of slag) can be applied to lead smelting. Indeed, all of the work in the first eight months of 1963, when WORCRA concepts were first tested in small pilot-scale furnaces, was carried out with lead concentrates. Despite the promise with WORCRA lead smelting–converting, this particular application of the technology has not been developed beyond small pilot scale because, since September, 1963, we have been preoccupied with the application of these principles to the continuous production of copper, nickel and steel.

The technology is not directly applicable to zinc concentrates, but much of the zinc present in either lead or copper concentrates smelted in WORCRA furnaces comes off as fume and can be collected from the gas stream.

At this stage of the development of WORCRA copper smelting we think it best to use an anode casting facility similar to that employed in existing modern smelters.

In reply to Mr. N. E. Brown (p. 67), the partition of concentrate feed between the converting zone and the smelting zone in a WORCRA furnace is determined by the heat balance. In a commercial furnace with normal chalcopyritic concentrate and cold air lancing as much as 50% of the concentrate can be fed to the converting zone.

In the absence of supplemental oxygen, the overall amount of fuel used is not greatly reduced by putting more feed into the converting zone. If converting air is enriched with oxygen (or some lances deliver oxygen), however, the proportion of concentrate fed to the converting zone can be increased and fuel saved. The limit is set by the necessity to feed some fine concentrate into the backward flowing slag in the smelting–slag-cleaning zones.

We have demonstrated that low-copper slags can be produced even when 50% of the concentrate is fed to the converting zone. This leaves considerably more concentrate than is theoretically required for reduction in the smelting and slag cleaning zones. Mechanisms for increasing the washing efficiency are currently being investigated. At some future date it may be possible to use a smaller proportion of the concentrate for washing and, in this case, the operation will become more nearly autogenous. At this stage, however, it is considered that the cost penalties associated with use of a small amount of fuel are more than offset by the production of throwaway slags in one and the same furnace.

Oxidic ores (up to 15% of the total concentrate fed) were, in fact, added successfully to the converting zone in one of the pilot furnace runs.

Heat balance considerations would, of course, set a limit to the amount of oxidic material which could be fed beneficially with cold air lancing. Beyond this limit it would be necessary to use one or more of the following: preheated lancing air, oxygen enrichment and/or more fuel.

We are interested in Mr. G. J. Brittingham's suggestion (see pp. 67–72) that because slags and mattes exist together as immiscible liquids in the smelting and converting of copper concentrate, they 'should therefore be expected to conform with the behaviour of conjugate solutions'. In the WORCRA countercurrent system the fullest use is made of the fact that low-copper slags can be generated when they are intimately mixed with low-grade mattes.

In the smelting zone and the early part of the slag-settling zone the backward-flowing slag is subjected to a sequence of vigorous 'injections' of fine concentrate. The concentrate particles melt either just before or just after entering the top layers of the circulating slag and form a large surface area of low-grade matte within the slag. Relatively rapid reduction of the oxygen level in the slag takes place and a vertical composition gradient as well as a horizontal gradient is established and maintained. In this manner the slag flows through the settling zone and out from the furnace dominated by the lowest-grade (high FeS content) matte that can be generated from the particular concentrate being used.

It is, however, important to remember that, apart from conditions determining the copper in solution in the slag phase, entrainment of fine prills of matte and/or metal is an important factor in determining the level of copper losses in slag. Washing with freshly melted concentrates, together with the generation of conditions suitable for coalescence and settling, is essential in order to achieve low copper-in-slag values.

With reference to the data recorded in Tables 5 and 6 (pp. 31 and 32), we would point out that those slag copper figures were obtained while we are still in the relatively early stages of the development of this new process. Every pyrometallurgical process with which we are familiar improved its performance characteristics as experience was gained. Work carried out subsequent to the writing of the paper has increased our confidence that a straight-line WORCRA furnace of the type shown in Fig. 8 (p. 35) will be capable, after a few years of operation, of recoveries at least as high as any of the two- or three-stage processes currently in use.

Dr. F. Sehnálek and I. Imriš We would like, first, to thank the organizers, and, in particular, Dr. D. A. Temple, for enabling us to participate in the Symposium.

We would reply to Professor T. R. A. Davey (pp. 63–4) by way of an example. Let us imagine a glass of water, to which amounts of NaCl and NaBr are added. Suppose that the water represents slag and the NaCl and NaBr crystals represent matte. If NaCl is being dissolved in water, the water will contain both Cl^- and Na^+ ions, the concentration of which is $C_{NaCl}^{Na^+}$ If NaBr only is dissolved in water, then the water will contain Br^- and Na^+ ions, the concentration of which is $C_{Na^+}^{NaBr}$. In fact, NaCl and NaBr are dissolved simultaneously, so the water contains Na^+, Br and Cl^- ions. One part of the Na^+ ions belongs to NaCl and the other to NaBr: hence, the total concentration of Na^+ ions will be given by

$$C_{Na^+} = C_{Na^+}^{NaCl} + C_{Na^+}^{NaBr}$$

The validity of this equation may be verified by measurement of the concentration of Cl^- and Br^- ions in the same way as the oxygen and sulphur contents in the slag were analysed.

In reply to Mr. F. A. Garner (p. 65), the experiments were made on the apparatus shown schematically in Fig. 2. Three crucibles containing samples of matte and slag were placed in the furnace, each containing matte and slag of different chemical composition. After 24 or 30 h the chemical composition of both phases was the same, which indicated the establishment of equilibrium in the system. The composition of the gaseous phase also became steady. During the experiment analyses for atmospheric SO_2 content were made simultaneously.

In Tables 5, 6 and 7 the SiO_2 contents are given—not those of Si: this is why one part of the oxygen content was included twice in the total arrived at by Mr. Garner.

Based on the ionic theory of slags it follows that for the ideal ionic solution the following equation is valid:

$$a_{Cu^+} = N_{Cu^+}$$

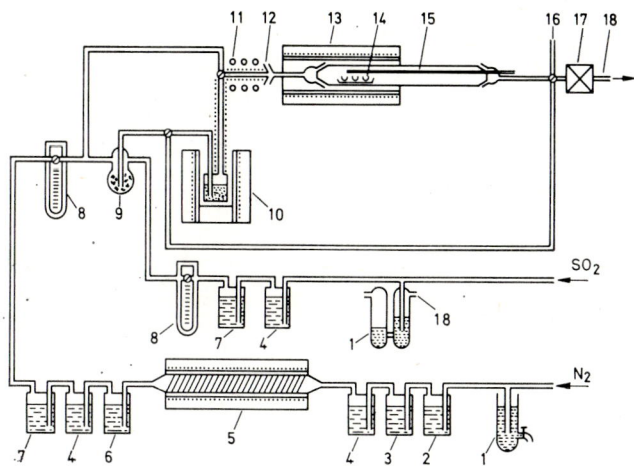

Fig. 2 Schematic diagram of apparatus: 1, manostat; 2, pyrozalol; 3, sulphuric acid; 4, silica gel; 5, copper turnings; 6, calcium chloride; 7, P_2O_5, 8, flow meter; 9, mixer; 10, sulphur evaporizer; 11, cooling; 12, heating; 13, reaction furnace; 14, samples; 15, thermocouple; 16, vacuum; 17, SO_2 analyser; 18, to atmosphere

If both Cu_2S and Cu_2O are being dissolved in slag, we may write:

$$N_{Cu^+} = N_{Cu^+}^{Cu_2S} + N_{Cu^+}^{Cu_2O}$$

from which it is clear that a_{Cu^+} for K_{12} and K_{13} are different. The O^{2+} and S^{2+} activities were considered to be constant as their concentration changes were negligible in comparison with variation in Cu content.

The analytical methods used, queried by Dr. P. J. Bowles (p. 65), were the same as those employed by Korakas.*

With regard to the reduction of Cu_2O in slag, the best results were obtained when commercial quality pyrite was added, followed by slow cooling of the melted slag.

* See reference 23 on page 61.

Session 2

Equilibrium/kinetic studies

Chairman
J. A. Charles

Equilibrium studies concerning the copper matte smelting process

J. B. W. Bailey B.Sc., Stud. I.M.M.
N. E. Brown A.R.I.C., Stud. I.M.M.
F. A. Garner B.Sc., C. Eng., A.M.I.M.M.
S. G. Ward M.Sc., Ph.D., C. Eng., M.I.M.M.

All of the Department of Minerals Engineering, University of Birmingham

669.046.582.2:669.333.4

Synopsis

Factors affecting the equilibria between iron silicate slags and copper metal or mattes have been investigated. For slags equilibrated with copper, copper losses were found to be dependent on the partial pressure of oxygen in the system and the iron content of the slag. A linear relationship between the iron and copper contents of the slag at constant oxygen pressure is postulated.

The influence of oxygen pressure and matte grade on the activity of ferrous sulphide in mattes equilibrated with silica-saturated iron silicate melts was determined, and it was found that for mattes containing no copper the equilibrium limits of the attendant atmosphere were 3×10^{-12} atm and $2\cdot3 \times 10^{-8}$ atm oxygen. This range decreased with increasing matte grade, and with an approximate copper content of 48% the system becomes invariant at the lower limit.

The maximum activity of magnetite in the equilibrium system was found to be 0·22 at an oxygen pressure of $2\cdot3 \times 10^{-8}$ atm.

The significance of the results is discussed.

In the pyrometallurgical extraction process for the recovery of copper an overall smelting loss of the order of 3% is incurred, mainly in the slags from the reverberatory furnace.

Two schools of thought with regard to the nature or mechanism of slag copper losses have appeared during the last few decades. The earlier was concerned with a physical mechanism, the loss of copper by entrainment of metal or matte in the slag phase. Entrainment of the matte phase arises from several factors, the more important of which are insufficient settling time in the furnace, insufficient heat from the burners to produce fluid slags and incorrect fluxing, producing viscous slags. In the extreme these factors can lead to floating matte masses on top of the slags, which are tapped to waste with the slags. Thus, early research was concerned with the chemical nature of slags with a view to optimizing their physical properties such that losses were minimized.

D   81

The second school of thought considered that a major cause of slag copper losses was by dissolution of the metal into the slag, and research was concerned with determining the relationship between slag composition and the solubility of copper in slags. Results reported in the literature, however, are inconsistent, and much of the work may be criticized on the grounds that, since atmosphere control was not practised, the results were not obtained under defined equilibrium conditions or under conditions pertaining to industrial plant practice.

Some years ago new interest was stimulated within the Department of Minerals Engineering at the University of Birmingham, and work was initiated to re-examine the factors influencing the loss of copper by dissolution into the slag. This paper reviews some of the work concerned with the influence of the oxygen pressure of the system and of the iron content of the slag on the solubility of copper in sulphur-free iron silicate melts, and with the influence of oxygen pressure on matte–slag equilibria in sulphur-containing systems.

In its simplest form copper matte smelting may be regarded as a three-phase process in which reactions occur between the slag, matte and the attendant atmosphere.

The major constituents of most copper smelting slags are silica and the oxides of iron. Lime and alumina are usually present, but together they rarely exceed 20% of the whole. For this reason the bulk of the thermodynamic studies of copper smelting slags have been based on the simple iron silicate system. This system has now been studied in considerable detail and a modified form of the partial liquidus diagram produced by Muan[1] is given in Fig. 1. At 1300°C the homogeneous slag region falls within the area $ABCD$, and most copper matte smelting slags may be regarded as being chemically similar to the silica-saturated compositions represented by the curve AD. These vary from melts at point A, in equilibrium with iron and silica with an equilibrium partial pressure of oxygen of 3×10^{-12} atm, to those at point D, in equilibrium with silica and magnetite, which exert an oxygen partial pressure of 1×10^{-6} atm approximately. Accordingly, the studies concerned with sulphur-free iron silicate melts were carried out by equilibrating the slags with copper metal at 1300°C under flowing atmospheres in which the partial pressure of oxygen could be accurately controlled within the limits stated above.

The thermodynamic properties of the matte phase have not been studied in such detail as have those of the slag. In their simplest form, however, copper mattes may be regarded as members of the quaternary copper–iron–sulphur–oxygen system—a non-condensed system in which the attendant oxygen and sulphur partial pressures influence the composition of the melt. The lower limit of oxygen pressure for the matte phase is zero—a condition obtained when ferrous and cuprous sulphides are melted under an oxygen-free atmosphere. Consequently, for a matte–slag system the lowest oxygen pressure at which equilibrium can be attained is that set by the slag phase, i.e. 3×10^{-12} atm approximately.

The maximum equilibrium oxygen pressure that can be exerted by a matte is not defined in the literature. It will, however, be a function of the composition of the matte and dependent on the copper–iron ratio of the matte. Hence, for the slag–matte system one of three conditions will prevail, depending on the maximum equilibrium oxygen pressure that the matte phase can sustain: (1) if this pressure is greater than 1×10^{-6} atm, the equilibrium limits of the system are defined by the slag phase as between 3×10^{-12} and 1×10^{-6} atm; (2) if this pressure lies between 3×10^{-12} and 10^{-6} atm, the lower equilibrium limit is defined by the slag as 3×10^{-12} atm and the upper limit is the maximum oxygen pressure that the matte can sustain; or (3) if this pressure is less than 3×10^{-12} atm, equilibrium between matte and slag is impossible.

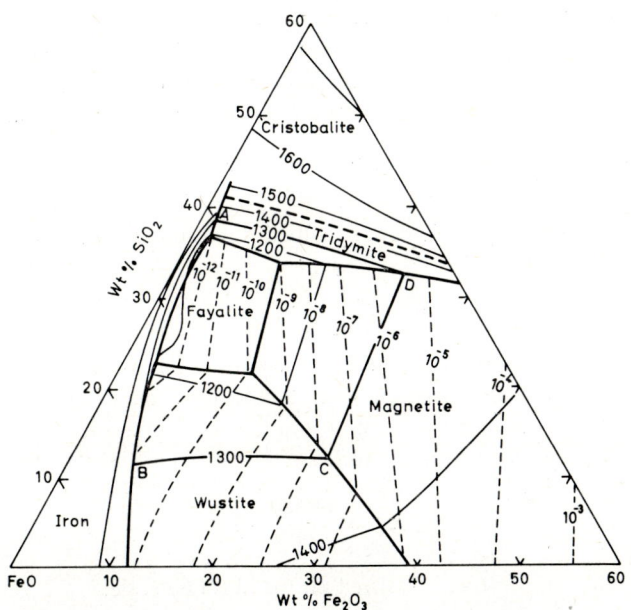

Fig. 1   Partial liquidus diagram for system $FeO–Fe_2O_3–SiO_2$. Dotted lines are oxygen isobars

In the absence of information on the relevant oxygen and sulphur pressures, work on the sulphur-containing system has been carried out by equilibrating synthetic mattes of various compositions with synthetic silica-saturated iron silicate slags under a recirculating atmosphere, thereby allowing a mutual approach to equilibrium of the three phases.

Sulphur-free systems

Experimental

The studies of copper solubility in sulphur-free iron silicate melts were made by equilibrating the slags with copper for periods of at least 14 h each under flowing atmospheres of mixtures of carbon monoxide and carbon dioxide of known oxygen pressure.

In the earlier experiments the charge was supported on a refractory rod introduced through the base of a vertical tube furnace. After equilibration, this rod was removed to quench the charge in a metal container at the bottom of the work tube. For more recent work the charge was suspended from a refractory rod, resting in two holes near the base of a refractory tube which was fixed to the top of the furnace and extended to just above the hot zone (Fig. 2). At the completion of the required heating time this rod was broken to allow the crucible to drop into the quench tank situated below the furnace. The quench tank and the tube connecting it to the furnace were flushed with the controlled gas mixtures to prevent oxidation of the slag surface as it was quenched.

The control of oxygen partial pressure by mixtures of carbon dioxide and carbon monoxide depends on the reaction between the two gases at elevated temperatures, which liberates a very small concentration of oxygen according to

$$CO + \tfrac{1}{2}O_2 \rightleftharpoons CO_2 \tag{1}$$

The concentration of oxygen for a particular CO_2/CO ratio can thus be calculated from relevant thermodynamic data by substitution in the equation

$$p_{O_2} = \left[\frac{1}{K_1} \cdot \frac{p_{CO_2}}{p_{CO}} \right]^2 \tag{2}$$

where K_1 is the equilibrium constant for reaction 1. The value of K_1 is temperature-dependent, but its variation with temperature may be calculated from thermodynamic data, and this relationship can be represented by equation 3, which has been used by several workers.[2,3]

$$\log K_1 = \frac{14\,550}{T} - 4 \cdot 405 \tag{3}$$

where T is the temperature measured on the absolute scale.

This simplified equation is only accurate over a limited range of temperatures, so for much of this work a more comprehensive equation was derived, i.e.

$$\log K_1 = \frac{14\,888}{T} + 0 \cdot 101 \log T + 6 \cdot 8 \times 10^{-5} T - \frac{19\,126}{T^2} - 5 \cdot 0451 \tag{4}$$

Although mixtures of carbon monoxide and carbon dioxide are suitable for atmosphere control at elevated temperatures, they cannot be used during the initial warming-up period as carbon may be precipitated at temperatures below 800°C. Therefore oxygen-free nitrogen was used to flush air from the furnace at the start of each experiment, and this was replaced by the CO_2–CO mixture when the furnace temperature had reached 1000°C.

The required gas mixtures were produced by a gas train similar to those used by Ruddle and co-workers[4] and Larson and Chipman,[3] but including modifications developed by previous workers in this Department[2,5,6] and the present authors. These modifications enable more precise control of the gas mixtures over long periods of time to be obtained.

The furnace gases were analysed by gas chromatography by a method developed for these studies,[7] which proved to be more sensitive and reliable than the absorption techniques used by earlier workers.

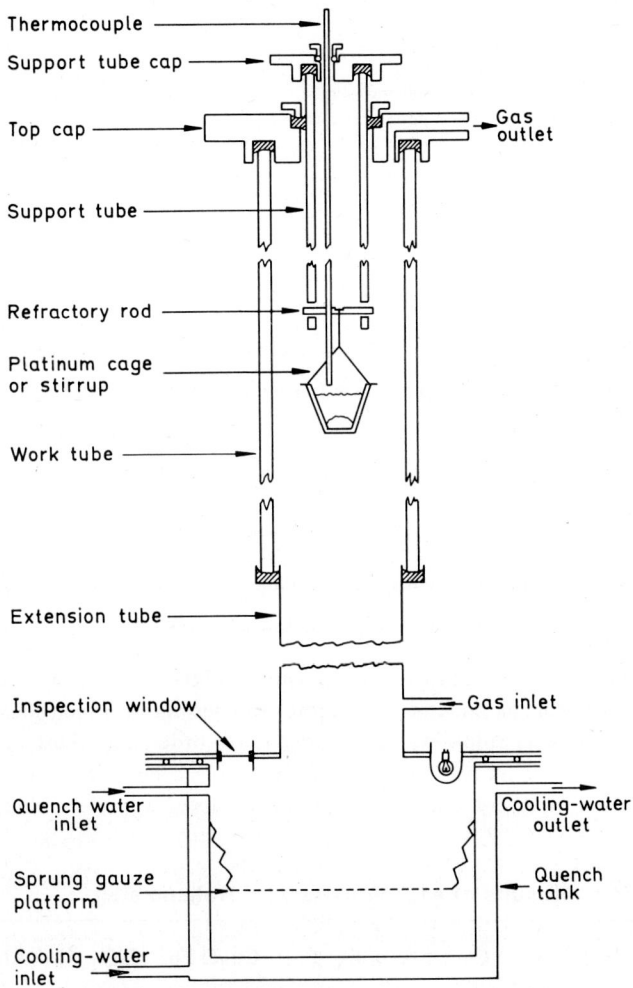

Thermocouple

Support tube cap

Top cap

Gas outlet

Support tube

Refractory rod

Platinum cage or stirrup

Work tube

Extension tube

Inspection window

Gas inlet

Quench water inlet

Cooling-water outlet

Sprung gauze platform

Quench tank

Cooling-water inlet

Fig. 2 Furnace used for sulphur-free systems

Results

Ruddle and co-workers[4] established a relationship between the equilibrium oxygen pressure and the solubility of copper in synthetic silica-saturated iron silicate melts and demonstrated that, at oxygen pressures of 1×10^{-6} atm and a temperature of 1300°C, i.e. at silica and magnetite saturation, the dissolved copper content (expressed as percentage Cu_2O) was as high as 8. Mihalop,[5] working with slags of very similar compositions, achieved higher solubilities of about 10% Cu_2O under the same operating conditions. The results of both studies were not, however, well defined at the extremes of the slag composition (Fig. 3).

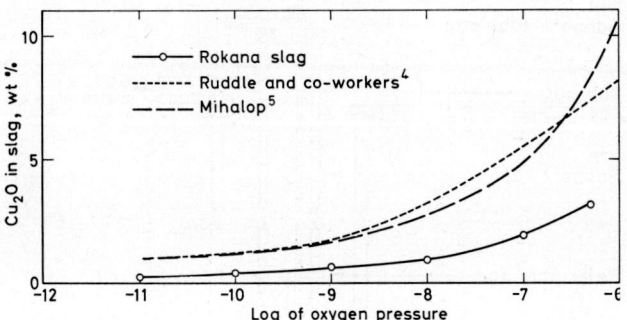

Fig. 3 Copper in slag versus oxygen pressure

Mihalop gave the relationship between N, the mole fraction of Cu_2O, and oxygen pressure as

$$\log N_{Cu_2O} = 0.217 \log p_{O_2} - 0.0176 \qquad (5)$$

which is in close agreement with that developed by Ruddle and co-workers, i.e.

$$\log N_{Cu_2O} = 0.22 \log p_{O_2} - 0.05 \qquad (6)$$

Recent work with an industrial slag sample obtained from a reverberatory furnace at the Rokana smelter in Zambia, the results of which are shown in Table 1, gave copper solubility figures of a lower order than those obtained by Ruddle and co-workers and by Mihalop; but, as can be seen from Fig. 3, the shapes of the copper content–oxygen pressure curves were very similar.

Table 1   Results of experiments with Rokana slag

Code	$\log p_{O_2}$	Cu_2O, %	Fe, %	Cu_2O/Fe	SiO_2, %	Al_2O_3, %
21	−7	1·94	15·2	0·127	37·7	16·28
25	−8	0·95	16·4	0·058	38·7	16·55
26	−9	0·63	16·6	0·038	38·5	17·38
28	−10	0·20	16·2	0·013	38·5	n.d.
29	−11	0·39	15·2	0·026	38·4	17·19
30	−6·3	3·23	15·2	0·216	37·4	16·77

The major difference in composition between the industrial slag and the synthetic iron silicate slags was that the iron content of the former type was considerably lower than that of the latter, although it also contained appreciable amounts of lime, alumina and potash (Table 2). Consequently, to assess the

Table 2 Approximate composition (%) of slags

	Synthetic slags[4,5]	Rokana slag (after equilibration)
SiO_2	35	38
Fe	43	16
CaO	0	19
Al_2O_3	0	17
K_2O	0	4

influence of iron content on the solubility of copper in the slags, values of $\%Cu_2O/\%Fe$ in slag versus log p_{O_2} were plotted (Fig. 4). These values fall on one curve, suggesting that, to a first approximation, the solubility of copper in an iron silicate slag is, at any particular oxygen pressure, directly related to its iron content, and that the minor slag constituents do not significantly alter this relationship. As most of the experimental data available are concerned with

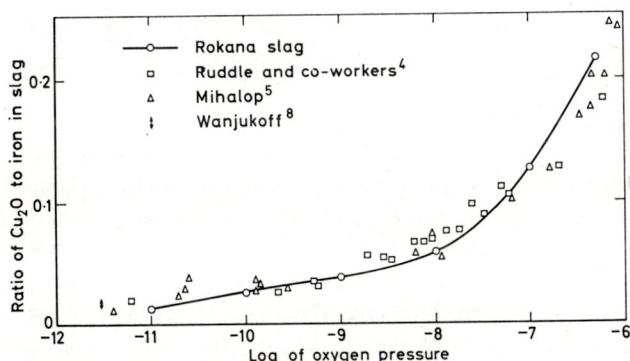

Fig. 4 Ratio of copper to iron in slag versus oxygen pressure

silica-saturated iron silicate melts, however, further work on high-iron iron silicate melts is essential to establish the validity of this relationship.

Results of earlier workers have been examined to determine if they could be included in this analysis; but, almost without exception, this has proved impossible because either equilibrium had not been established or no atmosphere control was practised. The results of Wanjukoff,[8] however, who in 1912 carried out an assessment of the effects of various slag additives on dissolved copper losses, are of interest. By adding lime the iron contents of his slags were varied between 54 and 6%, and as his tests were carried out in graphite crucibles it is reasonable to assume that the oxygen pressure of the system would approximate to that obtained when an iron silicate melt is buffered with iron, i.e. an oxygen pressure of 3×10^{-12} atm. The copper contents of the resultant slags varied from 1·16% to nearly zero, but in all cases the Cu_2O/Fe ratio is virtually constant between 0·015 and 0·020. All the values so derived fall within the arrowed line in Fig. 4 and tend to confirm the importance of the postulated Cu_2O/Fe ratio.

Sulphur-containing systems

Experimental

In comparison with the data now available on the properties of iron silicate slags, information on the properties of copper mattes is extremely sparse. The major problems encountered in equilibrium studies on the matte phase are caused by the presence of sulphur in the system, which would be stripped progressively from the melt if the experiments were carried out under the flowing CO/CO_2 atmospheres used in the previously reported work.

Initially, thought was given to the construction of a gas train to produce mixtures of three gases i.e. $CO/CO_2/SO_2$; but, owing to the lack of thermodynamic data, it was found impossible to specify the proportion of sulphur dioxide in the gas stream necessary for the attainment of equilibrium conditions. Consequently, a closed-circuit system was adopted in which a given volume of gas within the furnace was allowed to recirculate over the melt. In this way the gases were brought to equilibrium with the melt and could then be analysed by gas chromatography.

A section of the vertical tube furnace assembly used is shown in Fig. 5. A metal well was sealed to the top of the furnace tube, into which the top cap was fitted and sealed with Woods metal. In addition to containing clamps to support the crucible suspension, gas sampling unit and thermocouple sheath, the top cap also contained a water-cooled 'cold finger'. This device was essential to eliminate thermal segregation of the gases contained in the furnace by inducing convection currents within the system. Preliminary analyses of gas samples taken from the top, bottom and centre of the furnace proved that thermal segregation effects were virtually eliminated.

After the slag–matte sample had been suspended in the furnace, the system was flushed with a CO–CO_2 mixture to eliminate all air. The outlet was then closed off and the inlet was connected to an oil-filled constant pressure device to allow the escape of gases from the system as the temperature was raised, without permitting the ingress of air.

A heating time of at least 14 h at a temperature of 1300°C was required for the system to approach an equilibrium where successive gas samples were of the same composition. When this state was attained, it was considered that equilibrium was established between all phases present.

The gas samples were analysed by gas chromatography for CO_2, CO, SO_2 and COS, from which the oxygen and sulphur pressures were calculated by use of the relevant thermochemical data for equation 1 and equations 7 and 8.

$$SO_2 \rightleftharpoons \tfrac{1}{2}S_2 + O_2 \tag{7}$$

$$COS \rightleftharpoons CO + \tfrac{1}{2}S_2 \tag{8}$$

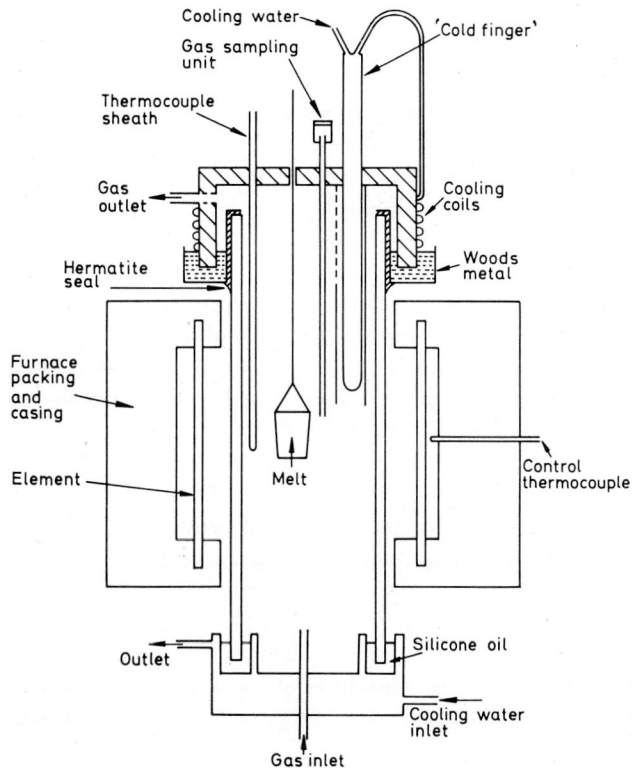

Fig. 5 Furnace used for sulphur-containing systems

At the completion of the required heating time the crucible was lowered to the bottom of the furnace, where it was cooled in a stream of nitrogen gas. Subsequently, the matte phase was analysed for iron, copper, sulphur and oxygen.

Results

From the determined equilibrium oxygen and sulphur dioxide pressures the activities of ferrous sulphide and magnetite were calculated by use of

$$3Fe_3O_4 + FeS \rightleftharpoons 10FeO + SO_2 \tag{9}$$

and

$$Fe_3O_4 \rightleftharpoons 3FeO + \tfrac{1}{2}O_2 \tag{10}$$

D*

for which the equilibrium constants are given by

$$K_9 = \frac{a_{FeO^{10}} \cdot p_{SO_2}}{a_{Fe_3O_4} \cdot a_{FeS}} \tag{11}$$

and

$$K_{10} = \frac{a_{FeO^3} \cdot p_{O_2}^{\frac{1}{2}}}{a_{Fe_3O_4}} \tag{12}$$

respectively, and have values of $K_9 = 1\cdot33 \times 10^{-2}$ and $K_{10} = 3\cdot226 \times 10^{-5}$.[9,10]

The values for the activity of FeO were taken from the data of Michal and Schuhmann[11] for silica-saturated iron silicate slags, from which a graph of $\log a_{FeO}$ versus $\log p_{O_2}$ was constructed.

Table 3 contains gas analyses and corresponding values of equilibrium oxygen pressure and ferrous sulphide activity for three series of tests on iron sulphide–copper sulphide mattes containing 0, 10 and 20% copper, respectively. Plots of these corresponding values indicated that a linear relationship exists and, hence, the lines of best fit were determined by regression analysis (Fig. 6).

As is to be expected, at any particular oxygen pressure the activity of ferrous sulphide increases with decreasing matte grade: hence, the maximum oxygen pressure that can exist in equilibrium with a matte in the presence of a silica-saturated iron silicate slag is that obtained for a copper-free matte when the activity of ferrous sulphide is zero, i.e. an oxygen pressure of $2\cdot3 \times 10^{-8}$ atm.

The minimum equilibrium oxygen pressure for the system has been defined previously as that below which the slag cannot exist as a single phase. This is represented by point A in the equilibrium diagram (Fig. 1), where the slag may coexist with silica and iron as separate phases and where the oxygen pressure is approximately 3×10^{-12} atm. Fig. 7 contains a plot of matte grade versus activity of ferrous sulphide at this minimum oxygen pressure, and results obtained to date suggest that a linear relationship exists, and, by extrapolation, the maximum grade of a matte that can coexist in equilibrium with the slag is of the order of 48% copper.

Fig. 8 contains a plot of the calculated activity of magnetite versus partial pressure of oxygen, from which the maximum activity of magnetite was found to be $0\cdot22$ at the maximum oxygen pressure of $2\cdot3 \times 10^{-8}$ atm. Thus, the concept of magnetite saturation of a matte or of a matte–slag system is not viable when an equilibrium system is envisaged. This observation was confirmed when attempts were made to fuse ferrous sulphide in magnetite-coated crucibles. In each case foaming occurred and continued until one of the phases was consumed.

From theoretical considerations it is to be expected that the maximum dissolved oxygen content of a matte will be obtained for those containing no copper. Fig. 9 is a plot for this series of dissolved oxygen in matte versus equilibrium oxygen pressure, from which the maximum content is found to be $6\cdot7\%$ dissolved oxygen at the maximum partial pressure of $2\cdot3 \times 10^{-8}$ atm oxygen. Above this value a matte will break down, with the evolution of sulphur dioxide.

Table 3 Results of experiments on matte–slag systems

Gas analysis, atm			Values calculated from gas analysis	
p_{CO_2}	p_{CO}	p_{COS}	p_{O_2}, atm	a_{FeS}
Mattes containing 0% copper				
0·096	0·544	$4·6 \times 10^{-4}$	$6·5 \times 10^{-12}$	0·41
0·240	0·489	$1·7 \times 10^{-3}$	$5·0 \times 10^{-11}$	0·30
0·290	0·511	$8·4 \times 10^{-4}$	$6·7 \times 10^{-11}$	0·23
0·450	0·460	$1·3 \times 10^{-4}$	$2·0 \times 10^{-10}$	0·22
0·650	0·259	$5·4 \times 10^{-4}$	$1·3 \times 10^{-9}$	0·06
0·538	0·040	$2·6 \times 10^{-5}$	$3·7 \times 10^{-8}$	0·003
Mattes containing 10% copper				
0·081	0·692	$3·6 \times 10^{-4}$	$2·8 \times 10^{-12}$	0·33
0·114	0·657	$4·4 \times 10^{-4}$	$6·3 \times 10^{-12}$	0·27
0·145	0·722	$5·6 \times 10^{-4}$	$7·4 \times 10^{-12}$	0·31
0·174	0·684	$6·4 \times 10^{-4}$	$1·3 \times 10^{-11}$	0·29
0·360	0·380	$6·8 \times 10^{-4}$	$1·9 \times 10^{-10}$	0·14
0·460	0·469	$1·5 \times 10^{-3}$	$2·0 \times 10^{-10}$	0·25
0·315	0·291	$7·6 \times 10^{-4}$	$2·5 \times 10^{-10}$	0·14
0·436	0·354	$8·8 \times 10^{-4}$	$3·2 \times 10^{-10}$	0·15
0·372	0·226	$7·8 \times 10^{-4}$	$5·6 \times 10^{-10}$	0·15
0·350	0·422	$8·2 \times 10^{-4}$	$9·0 \times 10^{-10}$	0·07
Mattes containing 20% copper				
0·090	0·720	$3·0 \times 10^{-4}$	$3·2 \times 10^{-12}$	0·25
0·124	0·642	$3·2 \times 10^{-4}$	$7·7 \times 10^{-12}$	0·20
0·142	0·640	$1·8 \times 10^{-4}$	$1·0 \times 10^{-11}$	0·10
0·380	0·508	$4·4 \times 10^{-4}$	$2·9 \times 10^{-11}$	0·18
0·222	0·572	$5·8 \times 10^{-4}$	$3·1 \times 10^{-11}$	0·20
0·242	0·524	$6·4 \times 10^{-4}$	$4·5 \times 10^{-11}$	0·21
0·383	0·498	$5·6 \times 10^{-4}$	$1·3 \times 10^{-10}$	0·11
0·451	0·279	$7·8 \times 10^{-4}$	$5·5 \times 10^{-10}$	0·10
0·479	0·220	$5·4 \times 10^{-4}$	$9·8 \times 10^{-10}$	0·08
0·460	0·194	$4·4 \times 10^{-4}$	$1·2 \times 10^{-9}$	0·07
0·536	0·186	$5·0 \times 10^{-4}$	$1·7 \times 10^{-9}$	0·07

Discussion and conclusions

Copper matte smelting is a multi-phase process in which reactions occur between the slag, matte and attendant atmosphere, the individual compositions of which significantly influence the loss of copper by dissolution into the slag.

The influence of the oxygen pressure of the system established by Ruddle and co-workers and Mihalop has been confirmed, and it has been demonstrated that a similar relationship exists for the more complex industrial reverberatory furnace slag obtained from Zambia, although the copper tenor of the slag at any

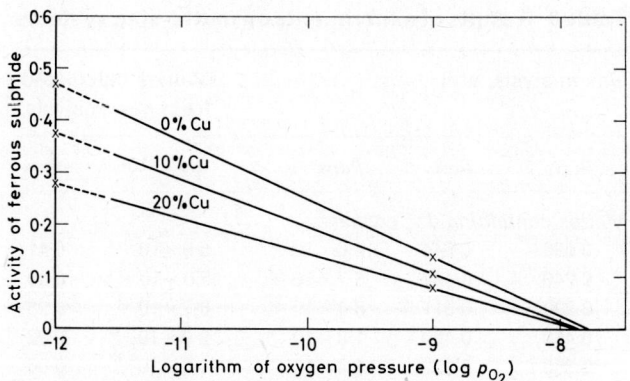

Fig. 6   Activity of ferrous sulphide versus log P_{O_2}

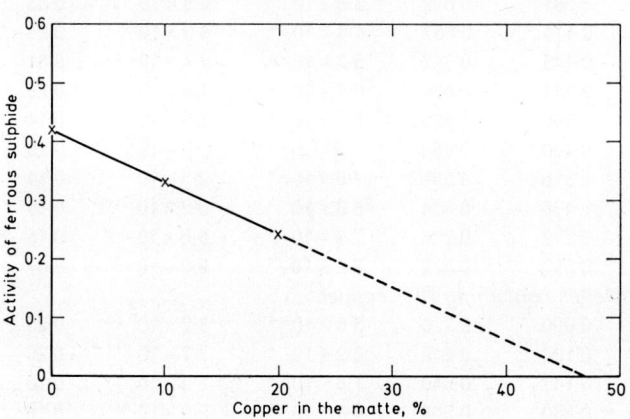

Fig. 7   Percentage copper in matte versus activity of ferrous sulphide at partial pressure of 3.0×10^{-12} atm

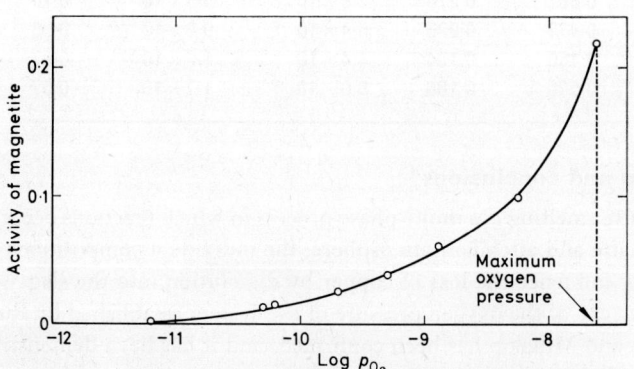

Fig. 8   Activity of magnetite in copper-free matte at 1300°C

particular oxygen pressure was lower than that obtained with the synthetic silica-saturated iron silicate melts.

The importance of the iron content of the slag has also been demonstrated, and for the results at present available it can be shown that at any particular oxygen pressure the ratio of dissolved copper to iron content of the slag is a constant which increases with increasing oxygen pressure.

Ruddle and co-workers and Mihalop postulated that for their synthetic silica-saturated melts a linear relationship could be established between the ferric and copper contents of the slags. The variation of the copper to iron ratio with oxygen pressure would support such a postulation, but confirmation has not yet been obtained owing to the inherent inaccuracies of all the methods of ferrous and ferric analyses tested when applied to complex silicate slags. Consequently, no mechanism for the dissolution of copper into the slag is proposed.

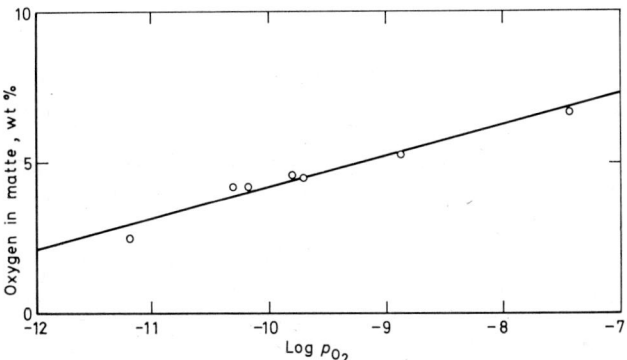

Fig. 9   Oxygen content of matte versus oxygen pressure for system at 1300°C

The copper/iron ratio will be valuable to the study of the effect of minor slag constituents on the solubility of copper in slags. The addition of one particular constituent necessarily decreases the concentration of another and, hence, difficulties are encountered in isolating each particular effect. If the postulated ratio is confirmed by subsequent work, the effects of other slag constituents can be assessed by relating their concentrations to variations in this ratio at a particular oxygen pressure.

Experimental work on synthetic mattes equilibrated with silica-saturated iron silicate slags has demonstrated that the maximum equilibrium oxygen pressure for the system is $2 \cdot 3 \times 10^{-8}$ atm for melts containing no copper. As the matte grade is increased, the value of this maximum oxygen pressure decreases until for an approximate matte grade of 48% copper it equals 3×10^{-12} atm, which is the minimum pressure at which the slag can exist as a single phase. At this point the system is invariant. An increase in the oxygen pressure of the attendant atmosphere will result in the oxidation of the matte, accompanied by the evolution of sulphur dioxide and the precipitation of a copper-rich phase, whereas a decrease in the oxygen pressure will result in the reduction of the slag phase, with the precipitation of iron.

It is of interest to consider industrial copper smelting practice in Zambia, where the matte grade is frequently higher than this limiting value. Under these conditions equilibrium is impossible and copper will form a separate phase in the system, i.e. continuous smelting must occur. Consequently, copper losses by dissolution approach a maximum, since the activity of copper in the matte must tend to unity. It is suggested that when high-grade concentrates are smelted, losses will be reduced if the residence time in the furnace of the slag and matte phases is reduced to a minimum, provided that sufficient time is available for the physical separation of the phases.

The formation of magnetite as a separate phase in the reverberatory furnace has been a topic for discussion for many years, but it is not the intention of the authors to speculate on this formation. The data obtained, however, indicate that the activity of magnetite reaches a maximum of 0·22 for copper-free mattes. It is therefore improbable that, even with the non-equilibrium conditions of the industrial furnace, magnetite can be precipitated from the matte phase.

Acknowledgment

The authors wish to acknowledge Anglo American Corporation (Central Africa), Ltd., for their financial support and technical interest in this project, and Mr. D. A. Rae for his analytical work.

References

1. MUAN A. Phase equilibria in the system $FeO-Fe_2O_3-SiO_2$. *Trans. Am. Inst. Min. Engrs*, **203, 2**, 1955, 965–76.
2. BURCHER M. G. The effect of low oxygen pressures on the viscosity of iron silicate melts. Ph.D. thesis, University of Birmingham, 1969.
3. LARSON H. AND CHIPMAN J. Oxygen activity in iron oxide slags. *Trans. Am. Inst. Min. Engrs*, **197**, 1953, 1089–96.
4. RUDDLE R. W. TAYLOR B. AND BATES A. P. The solubility of copper in iron silicate slags. *Trans. Instn Min. Metall.* (*Sect.C: Mineral Process. Extr. Metall.*), **75**, 1966, C1–12.
5. MIHALOP P. B. The solubility of copper in smelting slags. Ph.D. thesis, University of Birmingham, 1969.
6. REEVE D. A. Studies in the system $CaO-FeO-Fe_2O_3$. Ph.D. thesis, University of Birmingham, 1966.
7. BAILEY J. B. W. BROWN N. E. AND PHILLIPS C. V. A method for the determination of carbon monoxide, carbon dioxide, sulphur dioxide, carbonyl sulphide, oxygen and nitrogen in furnace gas atmospheres by gas chromatography. *Analyst, Lond.*, **96**, 1971, 447–51.
8. WANJUKOFF W. Untersuchungen über die beim Steinschmelzen den Eintritt des Kupfers in die Schlacken beeinflussenden Umstände, über die Verbindungsform des Kupfers innerhalb der Schlacken, und über die Verminderung der Kupferverluste durch Verschlacken. *Metallurgie*, **9**, 1912, 1–27.
9. KORAKAS N. Magnetite formation during copper matte converting. *Trans. Instn Min. Metall.*, **72**, 1962–63, 35–53.
10. SCHUHMANN R. JR. A survey of the thermodynamics of copper smelting. *Trans. Am. Inst. Min. Engrs*, **188**, 1950, 873–84.
11. MICHAL A. J. AND SCHUHMANN R. JR. Thermodynamics of iron-silicate slags: slags saturated with solid silica. *Trans. Am. Inst. Min. Engrs*, **194**, 1952, 723–8.

Oxidation of zinc vapour*

J. V. Stott

Research Department, Imperial Smelting Corporation, Ltd., Avonmouth

D. J. Fray Ph.D., D.I.C., B.Sc., A.R.S.M., A.M.I.M.M.

Formerly Research Department, Imperial Smelting Corporation, Ltd., Avonmouth
(now Department of Metallurgy, University of Cambridge)

542.943:546.47.011.4

Synopsis

A study of the oxidation kinetics of zinc vapour in CO–CO_2 mixtures in a silica apparatus has shown that the mean rate constant is 0.200 ± 0.018 atm^{-1} sec^{-1} cm^{-2} at 805°C, rising to 0.825 ± 0.218 atm^{-1} sec^{-1} cm^{-2} at 930°C. The oxidation was found to be controlled by a chemical reaction occurring on the walls of the reactor and, in the gas mixtures used, there was no apparent nucleation and growth of oxide particles in the gas phase.

In an Imperial Smelting furnace carbon monoxide and carbon dioxide are produced in the tuyère zone by the reaction of air with coke.[1] As the gas mixture passes up the furnace shaft, zinc oxide in the form of sinter is reduced according to reaction 1 to form zinc vapour. This reaction

$$ZnO + CO = Zn_{(v)} + CO_2 \qquad (1)$$

is readily reversible and proceeds farther to the left with decrease in temperature. It is, therefore, important that after the zinc oxide has been reduced, the temperature of the furnace should be maintained above the reoxidation temperature of the gas mixture—otherwise, some of the zinc vapour will be reoxidized. Near the top of the furnace, however, this is not possible, owing to the introduction of the sinter. Heat is transferred to the sinter from the gas, resulting in some reoxidation of the zinc vapour and the generation of additional heat from the exothermic back reaction. If this mixture were led directly to the condensers, further cooling would occur, giving considerable deposition of oxide at the top of the furnace and in the crossovers to the condensers. In order to prevent this, top air, which has been preheated, is added to combust some of the carbon monoxide to carbon dioxide, raising the temperature by 200°C, but only increasing the

---

* This project was undertaken by J. V. Stott as part of his B.Sc. course in chemical engineering at Bath University.

reoxidation temperature by 50°C to approximately 950°C.[1] The gas that finally leaves the furnace has the approximate composition 7·5–8·8% zinc vapour, 7·5–14% carbon dioxide and 16–25% carbon monoxide, the remainder being nitrogen.

On entering the condensers, the gas meets an intense shower of molten lead droplets, which absorb the zinc vapour before significant amounts of reoxidation can take place.[2] Under favourable conditions approximately 95% of the zinc vapour entering the condenser is absorbed, the remainder collecting as a dross and as blue powder scrubbed from the exhaust gases.

The amount of reoxidation of the zinc vapour in the condensers is controlled by the rate of absorption and by the kinetics of the reoxidation reaction. Gases containing up to 13% CO_2 have been satisfactorily condensed, but there is no plant evidence to indicate that this figure is the maximum CO_2 content tolerable. It is important to minimize the quantity of dust, fume, sulphides and other particulate matter carried over in the gas stream—these have been observed to greatly increase the dross formation.[2] This indicates that the reoxidation reaction takes place preferentially on a solid surface. Fortunately, the amount of carryover can be controlled to a certain extent by the quality of the charge and the velocity of the gas leaving the charge.

For a complete understanding of the Imperial Smelting process and, in particular, the condensation mechanism of zinc vapour, accurate rates for the reoxidation reactions are needed. Very few studies have been made on the oxidation of metal vapours, the data being restricted to the work of Polanyi,[3] Frommer and Polanyi[4] and other workers[5] on the reactions of sodium vapour with halogens and halides, and the more recent investigations of the oxidation kinetics of magnesium[6, 7] and cadmium.[8] Except for the cadmium study, most of the other measurements were made by use of the dilute diffusion flame technique, where a carrier gas, such as argon, is saturated with the vapour of the metal and is diffused through a nozzle into an atmosphere of the other reactant at a slightly greater pressure. The two reactants interpenetrate and react to yield a spherical dilute flame. From the intensity or the shape of the flame it is possible to derive the rate of oxidation; but, unfortunately, the results obtained by this method do not appear to be particularly reproducible. Breakspere and Gregg[6] and Markstein[7] investigated the oxidation of magnesium vapour at approximately the same temperatures, the results obtained differing by two orders of magnitude, and in neither case could an activation energy be derived on account of the considerable scatter of the results. Similarly, there is little agreement as to whether the oxidation is homogeneous or heterogeneous.[6] Breakspere and Gregg[8] also investigated the reaction of cadmium vapour with oxygen by use of Polanyi's original method[3] by flowing the gases countercurrent through a glass tube. The oxide was deposited on the wall and an approximate rate constant was calculated.

From the above it is apparent that the results obtained for metal vapour–oxygen reactions are only accurate, at the very best, to an order of magnitude. As no data are available, however, on the oxidation of any metal vapour in

CO–CO_2 mixtures, it was considered worth while to investigate this system by use of zinc vapour.

Experimental procedure

In the techniques for metal vapour oxidation, described in the introduction, the reactions were studied to completion, whereas, during the Imperial Smelting process, the oxidation of the zinc vapour by the CO–CO_2 mixture only progresses to a small extent. It was, therefore, considered that a more informative experiment would be one in which the oxidation reaction did not go to completion. A survey of the possible experimental methods showed that a flow technique would be most suitable.

The apparatus (Fig. 1) consisted of a resistance furnace, approximately 1 m in

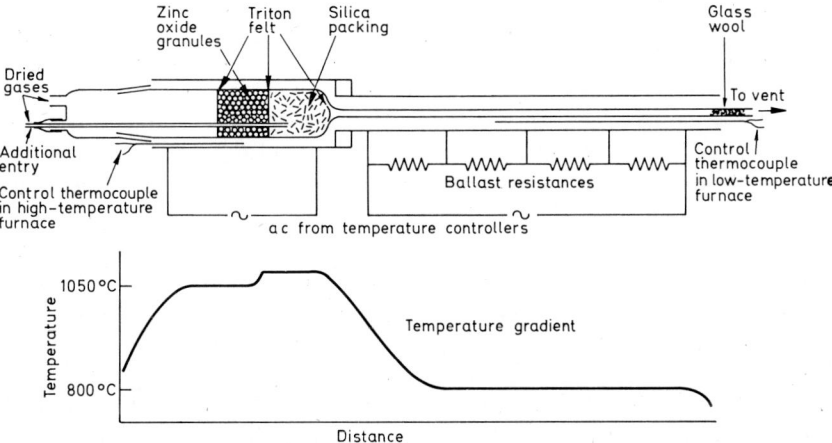

Fig. 1 Schematic diagram of apparatus

length, wound in two portions to give regions of different temperature. The high-temperature region was maintained at 1050°C, and the low-temperature section was varied between 800 and 930°C. A silica tube reactor, 5·5 cm in diameter and 46 cm long, with a 60/46 cone on one end containing zinc oxide plus silica packing and joined to a 1-cm internal diameter, 1·2-cm external diameter tube, was inserted into the furnace. Carbon monoxide, carbon dioxide, nitrogen or a mixture of these could be passed from the gas train, which monitored and dried the gases, into the reactor. An additional entry into the reactor by means of a 4-mm internal diameter tube leading into the SiO_2 packing allowed dilution of the gases after reaction with the zinc oxide.

The general procedure adopted was as follows: with a weighed quantity of zinc oxide and the silica packing in position, the temperature of the two zones would be adjusted and the apparatus filled with the required gas mixture.

The gases at a known flow rate passed through the reactor and entered the 1-cm diameter tube, where reoxidation occurred and oxide was deposited on the walls of the tube. Any zinc vapour which was not reoxidized was deposited as small globules at the cold end of the silica tube. There was some carryover of fine particles into the exit tubes, which, on analysis, proved to be zinc. As no zinc oxide was detected beyond the reoxidation tube, it was assumed that all the oxide collected on the walls of the tube. When a run had been allowed to proceed for a predetermined time, the gas flow was stopped and the tube and reactor were back-flushed with nitrogen to prevent further reaction during removal from the furnace. The zinc oxide and silica packing were reweighed and the weight of zinc adhering to the cold end of the tube was determined by weighing that portion of the tube and then dissolving the zinc in acid, washing and drying the tube and then reweighing. The remainder of the reaction tube was sectioned into 2-cm segments by use of a tungsten carbide knife and the amount of zinc oxide was determined by weighing the segments, dissolving off the zinc oxide in acid, drying and reweighing. As some of the zinc was lost from the system, the amount of condensed zinc was only used as a rough check on the mass balance.

The temperature of the reactor zone was measured with a Pt/Pt–13% Rh thermocouple inserted between the reactor vessel and the furnace wall. Prior to each run a temperature profile was determined in the 1-cm diameter silica tube to ensure that a satisfactory even-temperature zone was present. The thermocouple was withdrawn before the run started. In order to check that the temperature did not change when the gases passed along the tube, a suction pyrometer was used to confirm that the gas temperature coincided with the temperature given by the thermocouple. As the reaction is exothermic, and is thought to proceed on the solid surfaces, thermocouples were welded into the walls of the silica tube and the temperatures were monitored throughout the run. It was found that there was negligible variation in the wall temperature.

The zinc oxide used in the experiments was Pharmakon grade and was pelletized by ball-milling with water until 6-mm spheres were formed; these were then fired at 800°C. Initial experiments showed that when the oxide spheres were reduced at 1050°C, fine particles of oxide were liberated, which travelled into the reoxidation zone and formed nuclei upon which the reaction could proceed. As the amount of oxide carried over is not likely to remain constant, and is certainly a function of flow rate, this led to variable results. It was not easy to find a filter to remove micron-size particles at 1050°C and, in order to overcome this problem, a region of silica packing held at 1075°C was inserted between the zinc oxide and the start of the 1-cm diameter tube. In this way any oxide particles in the gas stream were reduced before entering the reoxidation zone. It was found that 15–20 cm of silica packing was necessary for adequate removal of the oxide particles.

Preliminary experiments showed that the results varied from one batch of tubes to another and, also, between the clear transparent tubes and the satin-finish silica tubes. This indicates that the rate of reaction depends on the surface condition of the silica. The variability of the results was eliminated by soaking the tubes in chromic acid for several hours, washing thoroughly and drying.

In order to confirm that the reaction occurs on a solid surface rather than in the bulk gas phase, the surface available for reaction was varied by inserting an open tube 0·6 cm in external diameter and 0·4 cm in internal diameter into the 1-cm diameter tube, thereby doubling the available surface area. At the end of the experiment both tubes were sectioned and the zinc oxide was determined in the normal way.

From the amount of zinc oxide reduced and the quantity of gas fed into the system it is possible to determine the gas composition as it enters the reoxidation tube. The weight of zinc oxide collected on the walls allows calculation of the rate of reaction, together with the change in gas composition along the tube.

Results

The basic data from the experiment give the partial pressure of the gases leaving the high-temperature reactor and the weight of zinc oxide deposited per square centimetre of wall surface. It is possible that the deposited zinc oxide offers a higher surface area than the bare silica tube, but as the rate did not appear to be dependent on the amount of deposited zinc oxide, the surface area of the tube was considered sufficiently accurate. The gas composition remained approximately constant throughout each run, and, as the weight of zinc oxide varied slightly along the even-temperature plateau, the total weight of zinc oxide was divided by the surface area upon which the reaction occurred to give the zinc oxide deposited in moles/cm^2. In all calculations it has been assumed that the gases behave ideally.

Discussion

The temperature in the reoxidation zone was maintained to within $\pm 4°C$ over 25 cm as measured by a sheathed thermocouple. This temperature corresponded to the temperature of the gas, as measurements with a suction pyrometer had shown them to be identical. Similarly, by sealing thermocouples into the wall of the silica tube it was found that there was no difference in temperature between the wall and the gas. The quantity of zinc oxide deposited along the tube, however, varied irregularly by $\pm 50\%$. In a very few experiments a greater variation than three was obtained, and these results were discarded. During the initial experiments, where there was no silica packing, sectioning of the tube showed that pronounced peaks occurred in the zinc oxide distribution. These peaks varied in size, but were sometimes greater than the initial deposit by a factor of 100 and, generally, occurred farther down the tube with increase in flow rate. It was concluded that this phenomenon was due to particles of ZnO being carried through from the reduction tube and acting as nucleation centres for the zinc vapour oxidation. These particles then grow and, when they reach a sufficient size that they cannot be carried in the gas sheath, deposition on the walls occurs. At the higher flow rates the greater is their size before deposition and,

Table 1

Run	Time of run, min	Initial gas flow (NTP)/min	Average gas composition, atm				ZnO deposited, mole/cm^2
			Zn	CO$_2$	CO	N$_2$	
Zinc vapour–carbon dioxide–carbon monoxide at 805°C							
1	15	1·291	0·0689	0·0689	0·8622	—	0·247 × 10^{-5}
2	11	1·748	0·1083	0·1083	0·7834	—	0·214 × 10^{-5}
3	15	1·291	0·1203	0·1203	0·7594	—	1·19 × 10^{-5}
4	11	0·925	0·1858	0·1858	0·6284	—	1·92 × 10^{-5}
5	15	0·919	0·1656	0·1656	0·6688	—	1·55 × 10^{-5}
6	18	0·916	0·1317	0·1317	0·7366	—	0·8 × 10^{-5}
7	18	0·923	0·147	0·147	0·706	—	1·011 × 10^{-5}
8	13	1·289	0·1193	0·1193	0·7614	—	0·743 × 10^{-5}
9*	15	0·931	0·1309	0·1309	0·7382	—	0·724 × 10^{-5}
10	20	0·931	0·0784	0·1146	0·253	0·554	0·714 × 10^{-5}
11	20	0·931	0·101	0·191	0·438	0·270	1·24 × 10^{-5}
Zinc vapour–carbon dioxide–carbon monoxide at 885°C							
12	10	0·92	0·1698	0·1698	0·6604	—	0·851 × 10^{-5}
13	15	0·92	0·1687	0·1687	0·6626	—	2·82 × 10^{-5}
14	15	0·924	0·1649	0·1649	0·6702	—	1·79 × 10^{-5}
15	17	0·926	0·1141	0·1141	0·7718	—	0·265 × 10^{-5}
16	30	0·931	0·0844	0·0844	0·8312	—	0·459 × 10^{-5}
17	15	0·931	0·1106	0·1106	0·7788	—	0·438 × 10^{-5}
18	16	0·929	0·1596	0·1596	0·6808	—	2·46 × 10^{-5}
19	15	0·935	0·1234	0·1234	0·7532	—	1·17 × 10^{-5}
Zinc vapour–carbon dioxide–carbon monoxide at 930°C							
20	15	0·931	0·0936	0·0936	0·8128	—	0·069 × 10^{-5}
21	15	0·926	0·1565	0·1565	0·6870	—	1·82 × 10^{-5}
22	15	0·930	0·1731	0·1731	0·6538	—	8·15 × 10^{-5}
23	15	0·925	0·1614	0·1614	0·6772	—	3·78 × 10^{-5}

* Surface area doubled by inserting inner tube into reoxidation tube.

Table 2 Calculation of rate constants

Run	Pressure term, atm^2	Rate, $atm\ sec^{-1}\ cm^{-2}$	Rate constant, $atm^{-1}\ sec^{-1}\ cm^{-2}$	Mean rate constant, $atm^{-1}\ sec^{-1}\ cm^{-2}$
805°C				
1	0·0036	0·000904	0·251	
2	0·0107	0·00102	0·096	
3	0·0135	0·00412	0·310	
4	0·0337	0·00907	0·269	
5	0·0265	0·00554	0·209	
6	0·0164	0·00249	0·152	0·200 ± 0·018
7	0·0207	0·00306	0·148	
8	0·0132	0·00230	0·174	
9	0·0162	0·00266	0·164	
10	0·0088	0·00208	0·236	
11	0·0187	0·00353	0·189	
885°C				
12	0·0254	0·00447	0·176	
13	0·025	0·00989	0·396	
14	0·0237	0·00631	0·266	
15	0·0090	0·000873	0·097	0·276 ± 0·039
16	0·0028	0·000886	0·315	
17	0·0082	0·00164	0·200	
18	0·0219	0·00818	0·373	
19	0·0113	0·00433	0·382	
930°C				
20	—	0·000252	—	
21	0·0167	0·00674	0·405	0·826 ± 0·218
22	0·0225	0·0296	1·315	
23	0·0183	0·0139	0·759	

therefore the peak occurs farther along the tube. This confirms plant observations[2] that dust and fume increase the oxide formation and emphasizes the importance of reducing the amount of particulate matter entering the condensers. The introduction of 15–20 cm of silica packing held at a higher temperature than the reduction zone essentially eliminated this problem. The slight variations in oxide deposition that occurred when the silica packing was present are probably due to either small particles of zinc oxide still penetrating the reoxidation tube or small pieces of oxide breaking off after deposition and acting as sites for growth farther down the tube. These observations indicate that the reoxidation reaction is heterogeneous. The type of deposit was also characteristic of a surface reaction in that it was hard and very adherent to the walls of the tube. On one occasion the tube had a small hole in it and the zinc vapour escaped into the air to form a fine flocculant oxide very similar to that observed in the magnesium vapour oxidation studies of Markstein,[7] who assumed that this type of oxide was formed by nucleation of small particles in the gas phase and their subsequent growth. It was also observed that when the tubes were not chromated before use variable results were obtained: this was thought to be due to surface grease and adhering dust particles and, after chromation, reproducible results were obtained, which were the same for satin-finish silica tubes and clear transparent silica tubes. From the above evidence it was concluded that in the $Zn_{(v)}$–CO–CO_2 mixtures examined in these experiments the oxidation reaction requires a solid surface before it can proceed and that, as far as could be ascertained, very little nucleation and growth of oxide particles occurred in the gas phase. In the following discussion it is assumed that the reaction takes place in the walls of the silica tube.

The overall oxidation reaction can be divided into five steps: (1) transport of reactants to reaction site; (2) adsorption of reactants; (3) reaction to form products; (4) desorption of products; and (5) transport of products away from reaction site.

In practice, it is not easy to separate steps (2), (3) and (4), and it is usual, therefore, to regard the reaction on the surface giving the products in their final form as a single step. The type of reaction considered here differs from many other heterogeneous reactions in that one of the products is a solid phase on which subsequent reaction occurs.

The flow rates used in these experiments were kept relatively low—in order to maintain the gas and the tube in thermal equilibrium; and in every case fully developed streamline flow occurred. If the rate were transport-controlled, it would be a linear function of the difference in concentration between the gas and the equilibrium concentration at the wall and nearly independent of temperature. In order to have a rate which can be related directly to the partial pressure, the moles of zinc oxide/cm^2 were converted to atm/cm^2 by use of equation 2 of the Appendix together with the data given in Table 1 and the thermodynamic data of Coughlin.[9] A plot of $d\rho_{Zn}/dt$ versus $\rho_{Zn}-\rho_{(e)Zn}$ is given in Fig. 2; the majority of the points lie on two curves, depending on the temperature—

indicating that the reaction is not transport-controlled. There were too few results at 930°C to have a meaningful curve drawn through them, and these have not been included in the plot. Moreover, approximate calculations show that if the reaction were transport-controlled, the quantity of zinc oxide deposited for a 15-min run at 805°C and a partial pressure of zinc of 0·1 atm would be $3·7 \times 10^{-3}$ mole/cm², which is much larger than the amount of zinc oxide obtained during these experiments. It is, therefore, very likely that the oxidation of zinc vapour in CO–CO_2 mixtures is a chemically controlled reaction occurring on a solid surface. For this type of reaction the rate of zinc reacted can be expressed by

$$\frac{d\rho_{Zn}}{dt} = -k_1 \, \rho_{Zn} \, \rho_{CO_2} + k_{-1} \, \rho_{CO} \tag{3}$$

where ρ_{Zn}, ρ_{CO_2} and ρ_{CO} are the partial pressures, and k_1 and k_{-1} are the rate constants. k_{-1} is the rate constant for the back reaction, and the term $k_{-1} \, \rho_{CO}$ must be included in the rate expression as the oxidation reaction does not go to completion at the temperatures investigated in these experiments.

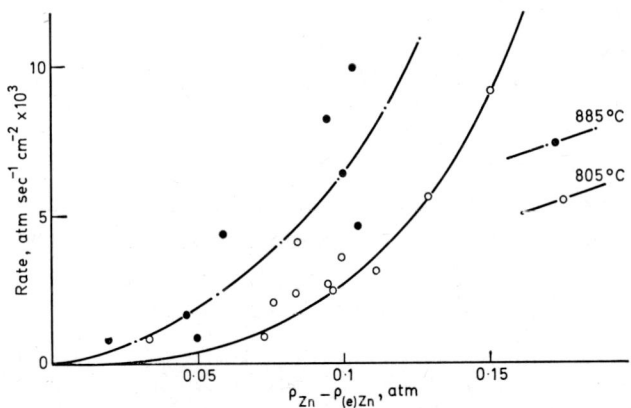

Fig. 2 Rate versus $\rho_{Zn}-\rho_{(e)Zn}$

At equilibrium

$$k_1 \, \rho_{(e)Zn} \, \rho_{(e)CO_2} = k_{-1} \, \rho_{(e)CO} \tag{4}$$

where $\rho_{(e)}$ signifies the equilibrium partial pressure at the reoxidation temperature.

$$k_{-1} = \frac{k_1 \, \rho_{(e)Zn} \rho_{(e)CO_2}}{\rho_{(e)CO}}$$

$$\frac{d\rho_{Zn}}{dt} = -k_1 \left(\rho_{Zn} \, \rho_{CO_2} - \frac{\rho_{(e)Zn} \rho_{(e)CO_2} \, \rho_{CO}}{\rho_{(e)CO}} \right) \tag{5}$$

If preferential adsorption of the reactants or products occurred, this would affect equation 5; but, owing to the scatter of the results, adsorption effects

are not likely to be detected. Plotting $\dfrac{d\rho_{Zn}}{dt}$ against $\left(\rho_{Zn}\,\rho_{CO_2} - \dfrac{\rho_{(e)Zn}\,\rho_{(e)CO_2}\,\rho_{CO}}{\rho_{(e)CO}} \right)$,
as in Fig. 3, shows that within the experimental error the points fall on two distinct straight lines, depending on the temperature. The rate constants, together with the mean rate constants and the standard errors of the mean, are presented in Table 2. It can be seen that these results are more accurate than those of Breakspere and Gregg[6] and Markstein,[7] whose rate constants varied by an order of magnitude and only agreed within two orders of magnitude. The accuracy obtained in these experiments is similar to that attained by Frommer and Polanyi[4] and Fairbrother and Warhurst[5] in their investigations of the kinetics of sodium vapour reaction with chlorine and chlorine-containing compounds at moderate temperatures and low pressures.

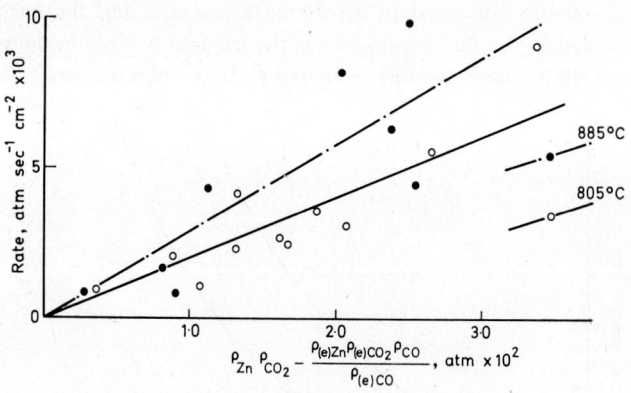

Fig. 3   Rate versus pressure term

For a reaction occurring on a solid surface the rate might be expected to be dependent on the type of surface. In this case, where one of the products of the oxidation reaction is a solid, the substrate is soon separated from the reacting species by an oxide layer, and the rate, provided that oxide can initially deposit, should not be a function of the type of surface. This hypothesis has, however, only been proved for two types of silica, and further experimentation is required.

The oxidation of zinc vapour in the CO–CO_2–N_2 mixtures investigated during these experiments only proceeds on existing solid surfaces, negligible nucleation and growth occurring in the gas phase. The rate of oxidation is controlled by a chemical reaction between zinc vapour and carbon dioxide to form solid zinc oxide, which acts as a surface for subsequent reaction, and carbon monoxide.

Acknowledgment

Thanks are due to Dr. S. E. Woods, Mr. J. Lumsden, Dr. F. G. S. Benatt,

Dr. N. A. Warner and Dr. A. W. Richards for helpful discussions throughout the course of this work.

References

1. MORGAN S. W. K. The production of zinc in a blast furnace. *Trans. Instn Min. Metall.*, **66**, 1956–57, 533–65; **67**, 1957–58, 127–38.
2. MORGAN S. W. K. AND WOODS S. E. Avonmouth zinc blast furnace demonstrates its versatility. *Engng Min. J.*, **159**, Sept. 1958, 95–9.
3. POLANYI M. *Atomic reactions* (London: Williams and Norgate, 1932), 64 p.
4. FROMMER L. AND POLANYI M. A new method for measuring the rate of high velocity gas reactions. *Trans. Faraday Soc.*, **30**, 1934, 519–29.
5. FAIRBROTHER F. AND WARHURST E. The velocity of reaction of sodium atoms with chloro-, bromo- and iodo-benzene. *Trans. Faraday Soc.*, **31**, 1935, 987–98.
6. BREAKSPERE R. J. AND GREGG S. J. Reaction of vaporous magnesium with oxygen and nitrogen. *J. chem. Soc. A*, 1969, 1613–7.
7. MARKSTEIN G. H. Magnesium–oxygen dilute diffusion flame. In *9th Symp. (Int.) on combustion, Cornell University, 1962* (London, New York: Academic Press, 1963), 137–47.
8. BREAKSPERE R. J. AND GREGG S. J. A study of the reaction of cadmium vapour with oxygen by the highly dilute flame method. *J. chem. Soc. A*, 1970, 1468–9.
9. COUGHLIN J. P. Contributions to the data on theoretical metallurgy. XII. Heats and free energies of formation of inorganic oxides. *Bull. U.S. Bur. Mines* 542, 1954, 80 p.

Appendix

For the reaction

$$ZnO + CO = Zn_{(v)} + CO_2$$

the number of moles of each species is given by

$$CO:(n^o{}_{CO} - n_{Zn})$$
$$CO_2:(n^o{}_{CO_2} + n_{Zn})$$
$$Zn:n_{Zn}$$

where n^o signifies the initial composition of the gas prior to reaction.

$$\rho_{Zn} = \frac{n_{Zn}P}{(n^o{}_{CO_2} + n^o{}_{CO} + n^o{}_{N_2} + n_{Zn})} \qquad (1)$$

and

$$\frac{d\rho_{Zn}}{dt} = \frac{(n^o{}_{CO_2} + n^o{}_{CO} + n^o{}_{N_2})P}{(n^o{}_{CO_2} + n^o{}_{CO} + n^o{}_{N_2} + n_{Zn})^2} \frac{dn_{Zn}}{dt} \qquad (2)$$

P is the total pressure and remains equal to the atmospheric pressure throughout the run.

From the experiment the number of moles of zinc reacted/sec cm^2 are obtained and, therefore, $d\rho_{Zn}/dt$, atm/sec cm^2, can be derived from equation 2, where $n^o{}_{CO_2}$, etc., is taken as the number of mole/cm^2 of tube surface.

Principles of refining by slag–metal reactions

G. M. Willis M.Sc., F.I.M., A.M.Aus.I.M.M.

Department of Metallurgy, University of Melbourne, Victoria, Australia

669.054.1 : 669.046.582

Synopsis

Refining by selective oxidation in a slag–metal system can be treated as an analogue of other separations, such as those in distillation or solvent extraction. Jänecke coordinates are convenient to use for the equilibrium compositions of the slag and metal phases in systems of two metals and oxygen (or similar non-metal). Equilibrium relations can be combined with materials balances, and the characteristics of batch refining, with one or more slags, refining with continuous removal of slag, and the possibilities of countercurrent slag–metal reactions can be described.

All of these have analogies in distillation, etc., e.g. continuous removal of slag as it is formed can be described by the Rayleigh equation for distillation. Oxygen is the 'separating agent' which causes the separation into two phases of differing composition.

If the solutions have simple thermodynamic properties, expressions can often be derived for the changes in composition and amount of the slag and metal phases as oxygen is progressively added. Provided that the slag and metal equilibria are known, graphical methods analogous to those used in other mass-transfer operations can be used for more complex relations. These yield considerable insight into the course of the reactions.

The amount of oxygen used by each metal as oxidation proceeds can be followed. It depends on the initial composition of the metal, the slag–metal equilibria and the extent to which oxidation has occurred. There is a more or less well defined end-point separating a region in which oxidation of the base metal predominates from one in which practically only the noble metal is being slagged. The latter region is easy to deal with theoretically, as both solutions are dilute, but refining is quite inefficient under these conditions. There is no sharp boundary between these regions, but if log p_{O_2} is used, a typical end-point is found.

The methods can be extended to cover the use of the oxide of the noble metal instead of oxygen.

The results obtained are compared with those of other workers, who treated the oxide as forming a dilute solution in a slag which has been produced separately. Here, the slag is assumed throughout to consist of the oxides of the two metals.

The different methods of refining are compared, and some practical implications are described.

Introduction

Preferential or selective reactions in which the impurities are concentrated in a second phase (slag, matte or molten salt) are used for the refining of a large number of metals. Although there is a great deal of information on slag–metal equilibria in the literature, little attention has been given to the details of these reactions, such as the changes in composition of metal and slag as oxidation proceeds. The possibilities of the various methods of refining by use of slag–metal reactions do not appear to be generally recognized.

Kootz[1] and Baukloh[2] gave curves for the changes in metal composition during oxidation, with and without slag–metal interaction, but no derivations were given. Oeters[3] calculated the course of a slag–metal reaction as oxidation proceeded, but it is not immediately clear whether his approximation of taking the same atomic weights for iron and manganese is essential to his derivation. Only Kootz has considered any methods other than oxidation of a single batch of metal.

Assumptions

The following assumptions have been used throughout: (1) the temperature is constant; (2) only two metals are present; (3) metal and slag phases are both homogeneous liquids; (4) the equilibrium relations are known; (5) the slag consists of the oxides of the two metals only; no fluxes are added. This is an important difference from the assumptions made by Schenck and his colleagues.[4,5,6] They assumed that the oxide formed was dissolved in a slag which had already been formed and which served as a diluent, and that the weight of impurity transferred was small in that the weights of metal and slag remained practically constant. The following treatment allows for changes in the quantities of metal and slag.

Chiotti[7] dealt with metal–molten salt reactions in which the metals were dissolved in a solvent metal, and the chlorides produced were dissolved in a molten salt. The assumption that the slag consists of the oxides of the two metals drastically changes results such as those of Schenck et al. and of Chiotti.

Simple slag–metal reactions

One of the simplest reactions is

$$[B] + (AR) = [A] + (BR) \tag{1}$$

where A and B are present in a liquid alloy and AR and BR form a liquid slag. R may be oxygen, sulphur, chlorine, etc. (For simplicity, A, B and R have been assumed to have the same valency.) The phase relations shown in Fig. 1(a) illustrate the requirements for the removal of B in the non-metallic phase. An alloy of composition C_1 on treatment with sufficient R to bring the overall composition to C_2 will consist of alloy C_3 and the non-metallic phase C_4 in proportions given by the lever rule—$C_2 C_4 / C_2 C_3 = $ metal/slag.

Further oxidation with R *lowers* the concentration of B in both phases, and, if carried to completion, the A/B ratio in the slag will be the same as in the original alloy. As a rule, it is desired to bring the concentration of the impurity metal below a certain value such as that set by a specification; however, both the amount and composition of the slag may be of importance if it has to be treated again. Loss of the metal A by oxidation may have to be considered, as it will have to be recovered by treatment of the slag—a process which often results in circulating loads of A and B, and excessive handling and labour costs.

Analogy with other separation processes

The simple refining operation just outlined is analogous to other separation processes, such as distillation and solvent extraction. In distillation addition of heat to the liquid results in the formation of a new phase (the vapour) in which the more volatile component is concentrated. In solvent extraction the solvent forms a second liquid phase in which the solute is concentrated. In preferential oxidation the addition of oxygen produces a second phase, generally liquid, in which the more readily oxidized element is concentrated. These analogies are summarized in Table 1, which is an extension of that given by Treybal[8] for distillation and solvent extraction. In principle, it is not necessary for the oxide phase to be liquid; the main advantage of the liquid is its ease of handling at high temperatures.

The analogy is emphasized if the phase diagram is plotted by use of Jänecke coordinates[9] instead of on the usual triangle of Fig. 1(a). Fig. 1(b), which represents the same relation as Fig. 1(a), is analogous to the Ponchon–Savarit diagram for distillation, where enthalpy per mole is plotted against mole fraction.

To avoid confusion with symbols the rest of this discussion will be restricted to oxidation, although the relations can be used for sulphides, halides, etc. In Fig. 1(b) the abscissae used are $X = B/(A+B)$ for the concentration of metal B in the metal phase, and $Y = B/(A+B)$ for the slag phase, rather than the mole fractions $B/(A+B+O)$. For convenience, B always refers to the metal which tends to concentrate in the oxide phase. A and B indicate the quantities of the appropriate metals, e.g. in mass or moles; X and Y are then mass or mole fractions for the metal and slag phases. For the oxygen concentration the ratio $O/(A+B)$ is plotted as the ordinate.

With these 'metal fractions' the total weight of slag or metal is not used but the total weight of *metal* in metal or slag phase, i.e. $A + B$. In effect, all quantities are taken relative to the total quantity of metal. With these 'oxygen-free' fractions and quantities it can be shown that the so-called 'lever rule' applies to diagrams such as Fig. 1(b).

Although pure O_2 cannot be represented, this is no disadvantage in practice. Oxidation or reduction is represented by movement of the point representing the overall composition of the system vertically up or down, respectively. The

Table 1 Comparison of separation processes

Extraction	Distillation	Slag–metal reaction
Addition of solvent	Addition of heat	Addition of oxygen (S, Cl_2, etc.)
Removal of solvent	Removal of heat	Removal of oxygen by reduction
Two-phase liquid mixture	Mixture of liquid and vapour	Metal and slag phases
Selectivity	Relative volatility	Relative stability of oxide
Change of temperature	Change of pressure	Change of temperature or slag additions
Solvent mixer	Reboiler	Furnace for oxidation of metal
Solvent separator	Condenser	Furnace for reduction of slag
Solvent-rich solution saturated with solvent	Vapour at boiling point	Slag in equilibrium with metal
Solvent-rich solution with more solvent than needed for saturation	Superheated vapour	Slag more oxidized than for equilibrium with metal
Solvent-lean solution saturated with solvent	Liquid at boiling point	Metal in equilibrium with slag
Solvent-lean solution with less solvent than needed to saturate it	Liquid below boiling point	Metal phase with less oxygen than needed for saturation

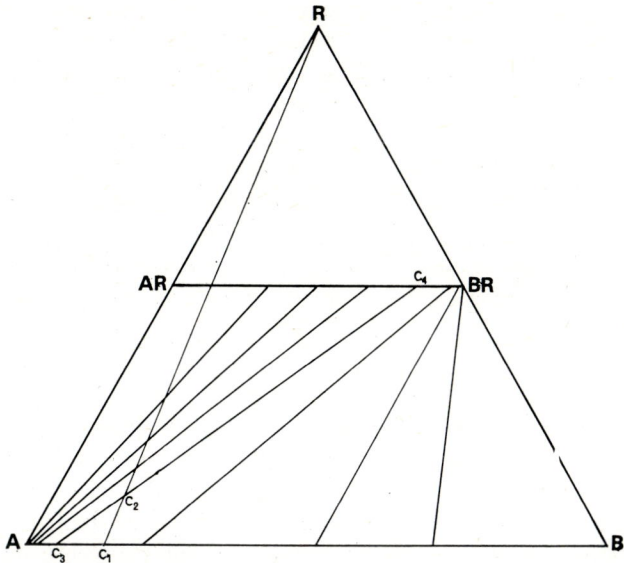

Fig. 1(a)   Equilibrium between metal and slag in a ternary system; $K=100$; both solutions ideal; A, B and R of equal valency

slope of a tie-line shows immediately whether or not a metal is concentrated in the slag.

Binary phases of the systems A–O and B–O are plotted on the ordinates at $X=0$ and $X=1$, respectively. It is not necessary to use the same scales for

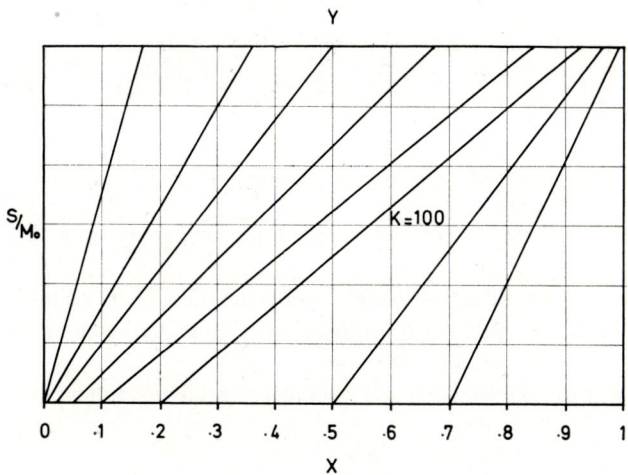

Fig. 1(b)   As for (a) but on Jänecke coordinates; X and Y are $B/(A+B)$ for metal and slag, respectively: $S/M_0 = R/(A+B)$

ordinate and abscissa, which is an advantage if small concentrations of B are of interest, as will often be the case in refining.

As with other separation processes, it is necessary to consider the final concentration of impurity reached, the quantity and composition of the slag produced and the amount of oxygen needed. It may be worth removing a first slag and then producing a second one, or even removing slag continuously. Counter-current methods, batch or continuous, are possibilities if handling problems can be overcome.

Each method of operation has characteristic features, generally analogous to those in distillation or solvent extraction separations. Some of these will be described below.

Equilibrium considerations

It will be assumed that equilibrium measurements are available for the system. In a ternary system with metal, slag and gas phases, at constant temperature, only one degree of freedom remains, so if the composition of metal or that of slag or p_{O_2} is fixed, so are the others. The most important practical consequence is that, at a fixed termperature, there is a one to one relation between metal and slag composition, so it is not possible to choose a metal and slag composition independently.

The equilibrium between metal and slag may be represented in several ways. If both metals have the same valency, then for reaction 1

$$K = a_{[A]} \cdot a_{(BO)} / a_{[B]} \cdot a_{(AO)} \qquad (2)$$

If both metal and slag are ideal solutions, the activities a may be replaced by the mole fractions N. Thus

$$K = N_{[A]} \cdot N_{(BO)} / N_{[B]} \cdot N_{(AO)} \qquad (3)$$

Using X and Y to represent the 'metal fraction' of the less noble metal (here taken to be B) in the metal and slag, respectively, equation 3 becomes

$$K = (1 - X) Y / X (1 - Y) \qquad (4)$$

or

$$Y = KX / (1 + X(K - 1)) \qquad (5)$$

Fig. 2 shows the relation between X and Y for ideal solutions with $K = 10$ and 100.

Equations 3–5 may be solved readily by a nomogram, or by a simple graphical method given by Chiotti[7] which can be adapted to the more complicated forms found when the valencies are not the same.

If the metal and slag contain B and its oxide, respectively, at low concentrations, so that

$$X \ll 1, \; Y \ll 1$$

equations 4 and 5 become

$$Y = K'X \qquad (6)$$

which is analogous to the Nernst distribution law. K' will be used for equation 6 throughout in order to distinguish it from the K of equations 2–5.

If the solutions are dilute enough for Henry's law to apply to the solution of B in the metal and its oxide in the slag, and the other two activities are approximately unity, equation 6 will still apply. Often, equation 6 will be a useful empirical relation.

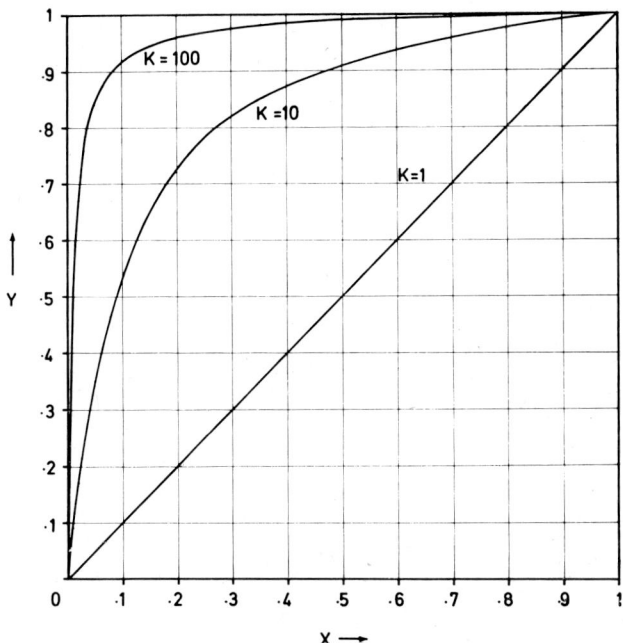

Fig. 2   The relation between slag and metal compositions from equation 5

Although equation 4 is simple, it is an idealized description of most systems, which are rarely ideal. If the metals are of different valency, the expressions become comparatively unwieldy. A more non-committal way of describing the equilibria is to use experimental equilibrium values to give the 'metal' fractions X and Y. Any complications due to variations in the oxygen to metal ratio, or differing valency, are thus avoided. A plot of Y against X gives a convenient way of interpolating between tie-lines when experimental points are widely spaced. When equilibrium 'constants' are far from constant, and analytical methods therefore become complicated, the graphical method is adequate for practical purposes.

Equilibrium with one slag from a batch of metal

If a batch of metal of initial composition X_0 is to be refined to X, say, then the weight of metal in the slag S and the weight of oxygen needed are fixed.

E

The following materials balances are independent of equilibrium considerations: let M_o be the original weight of metal, M the weight of metal left, S the weight of metal oxidized into slag and Y, X equal $B/(A+B)$ for slag and metal, respectively. Then we have

$$M_o = S + M \tag{7}$$

$$X_o \cdot M_o = Y \cdot S + X \cdot M \tag{8}$$

$$X_o \cdot M_o = Y \cdot S + X \cdot (M_o - S)$$

or

$$M_o (X_o - X) = S(Y - X)$$

or

$$M(X_o - X) = S(Y - X_o) \tag{9}$$

The ratio S/M_o is the fraction of the original weight of metal which has been oxidized. Although equation 9 has a simple geometrical interpretation, which is shown in Fig. 3, it is not particularly useful.

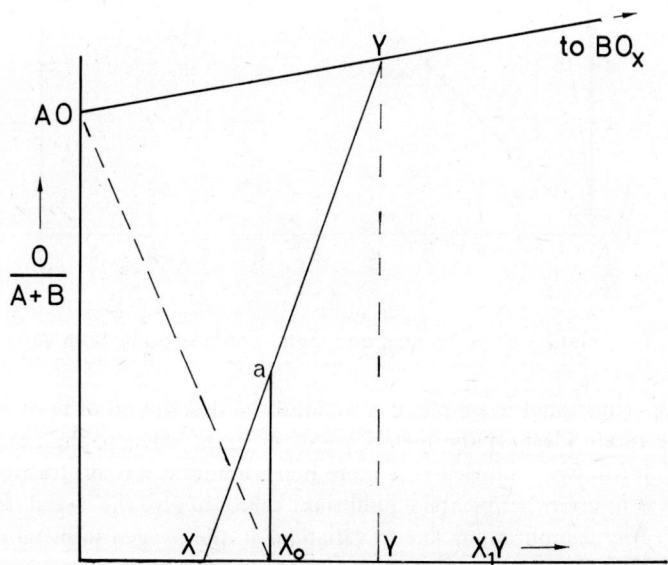

Fig. 3 Oxidation of X_o to give metal X and slag Y. From lever rule
$$(Y - X_o)/(X_o - X) = aY/aX = M/S$$
Broken line shows overall changes in composition if pure **AO** is used for oxidation

The materials balance of equation 9 can be rearranged to give

$$Y = X_o(M_o/S) - X(M/S) \tag{10}$$

which gives a family of lines of slopes $-M/S$ relating Y to X. It can be shown that these all pass through the point $X=X_o$, $Y=X_o$ on the diagonal $Y=X$ (Fig. 4). The lines cut the Y–X equilibrium curve at points which satisfy both equilibrium and materials balance requirements. The composition of the first

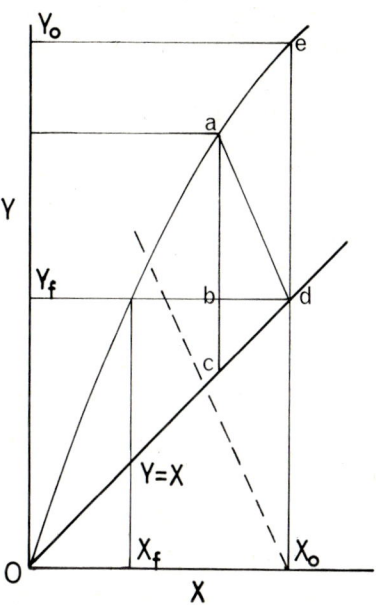

Fig. 4 Changes in composition of metal X and slag Y in batch oxidation of alloy initially of composition X_o. Slope of line ad is $-M/S=ab/bd$. $M_o/S=ac/bd$. Broken line is for oxidation with AO and is shown with same S/M ratio

trace of slag produced is Y_o. As oxidation proceeds, the line representing equation 10 rotates in an anti-clockwise direction, the slope becoming smaller (numerically) until, when oxidation is complete, the line is horizontal. The course of refining is thus represented by a point on the equilibrium line moving downward to the left from $(X_o Y_o)$ to Y_f, where $Y_f=X_o$. X_f is the composition of the last trace of metal (Fig. 4). One measure of the effectiveness of a refining operation is the ratio X_o/X, i.e. the ratio of the initial to the final concentration of the element being removed (here B).

From

$$X_o/X=(Y/X)(S/M_o)+M/M_o$$

if

$$S\ll M_o$$

so

$$M\approx M_o$$
$$X_o/X=(Y/X)(S/M)+1 \tag{11}$$

If Y/X is constant ($=K'$, say), equation 11 is identical in form with that given by Schenck and co-workers.[4,5] It should be noted that Schenck and co-workers' equation is based on weights of slag and metal, whereas equation 11 uses the weight of metal in both phases, and X and Y are the 'oxygen-free' fractions of B.

Equation 11 emphasizes the importance of the slag to metal ratio, and the selectivity of the oxidation as measured by the Y/X ratio. The quantity SK'/M is analogous to the extraction factor ε in solvent extraction with immiscible liquids.[10] The metal B is distributed between slag and metal in the proportion $SK'/M:1$, respectively.

Relations 7–11 are analogous to those for equilibrium flash distillation in which a two-component feed is partly converted into vapour in equilibrium with the remaining liquid.

Even if S/M_o is not small, but $Y=K'X$ empirically

$$X_o/X = \frac{SK' + M_o - S}{M_o}$$

$$= \frac{S(K'-1)}{M_o} + 1$$

or

$$\frac{(X_o - X)}{X} = \frac{S}{M_o}(K'-1) \tag{12}$$

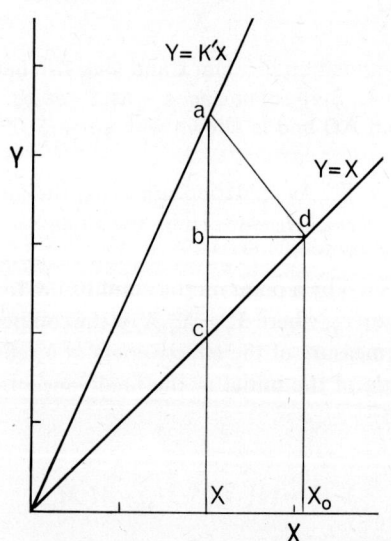

Fig. 5   Equilibrium line $Y=K'X$, and the diagonal $Y=X$

$$ac = (K'-1)X, \quad bd = X_o - X$$

Relations are those of equation 12

The graphical significance of this simple relation for batch refining can be seen from Fig. 5, where the line $Y = K'X$ and the diagonal $Y = X$ are shown.

Changes in composition during oxidation

The relations just given have the disadvantage that the variables metal and slag composition X and Y occur together with S/M_o, the fraction of the original metal oxidized. It would be helpful if X and Y were given as functions of the ratio S/M_o. This can be done graphically by using lines of differing values of (M/S) in equation 10. The method has the advantage that only an experimental relation between X and Y is required, but it is not very convenient, particularly for dilute solutions.

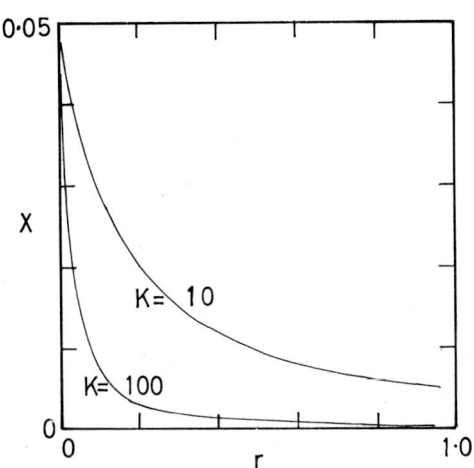

Fig. 6 Changes in metal composition on oxidation from equation 15; $X_o = 0.05$

A more general method is to combine the materials balance (equation 10) with the equilibrium relation between X and Y.

(*a*) If equation 6 holds, i.e.

$$Y = K'X$$

the results are particularly simple:

$$X = \frac{X_o}{1 + r(K' - 1)} \tag{13}$$

which is equation 12 with r written for the ratio S/M_o, the fraction of the original metal oxidized.

$$Y = \frac{K'X_o}{1 + r(K' - 1)} \tag{14}$$

(Equation 11 is limited to practically constant weight of metal, so $r \ll 1$, and equation 12 is more general.)

(b) If both solutions are ideal, equation 5 can be used:

$$Y = \frac{KX}{1 + X(K-1)}$$

which, on substituting in equation 10 and rearranging, gives

$$X^2(K-1)(1 - S/M_o) + X[1 + (K-1)((S/M_o) - X_o)] - X_o = 0$$

Putting $S/M_o = r$ gives

$$X = \frac{-[1 + (K-1)(r - X_o)] + \{[1 + (K-1)(r - X_o)]^2 + 4X_o(K-1)(1-r)\}^{\frac{1}{2}}}{2(K-1)(1-r)}$$

(15)

In principle, this method is the same as that used by Oeters,[3] but there are no approximations in the manipulation. Y can be obtained by substitution for X in equation 5, or directly from the relation

$$Y = \frac{K}{(K-1)}$$
$$\left[\frac{-[1 + (K-1)(1-r)] + \{[1 + (K-1)(r - X_o)]^2 + 4X_o(K-1)(1-r)\}^{\frac{1}{2}}}{2(1-r) + \{-[1 + (K-1)(1-r)]\} + \{[1 + (K-1)(r - X_o)]^2 + 4X_o(K-1)(1-r)\}^{\frac{1}{2}}} \right]$$

(16)

Both equations 15 and 16 are unwieldy to use, but they give an overall view of the refining reactions. Changes in X and Y as oxidation continues are shown for different initial concentrations X_o of B in Figs. 6 and 7. A computer program for equation 15 was kindly provided by Mr. P. Smith.

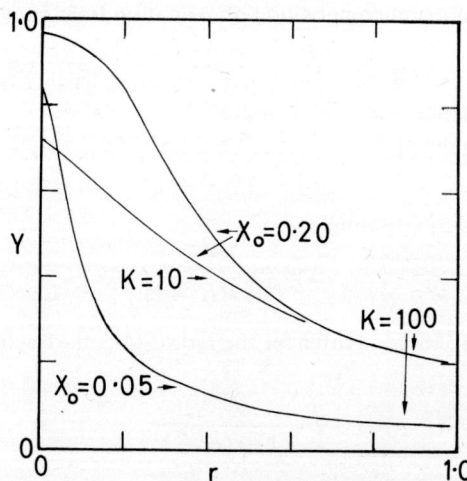

Fig. 7 Change in slag composition according to equation 16

(c) In many refining operations the concentration of B in the metal will be small and thus X is always $\ll 1$. Instead of equation 5, we have

$$Y = \frac{KX}{1+KX} \tag{17}$$

This approximation was also used by Schenck and co-workers.[4,5] Unfortunately, it does not simplify equation 15 very much.

Distribution of oxygen between metals during oxidation

For many purposes the total quantity of a metal slagged, or the amount still left in the metal, may be as important as the concentration.

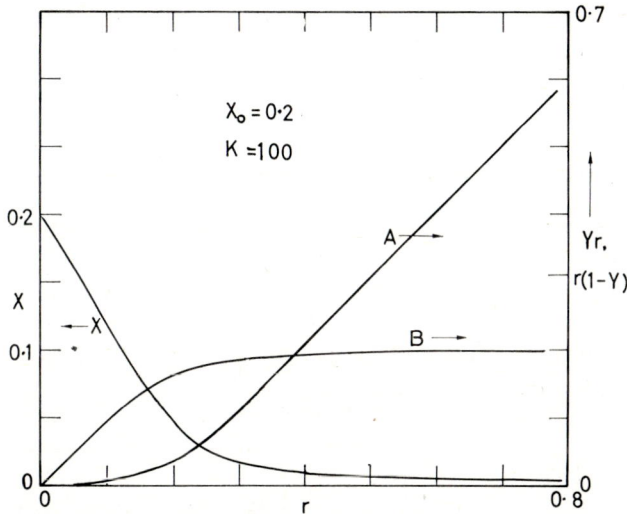

Fig. 8 Changes in metal composition X and in amount of A and B oxidized per mole of metal (Yr and r (1—Y), respectively)

Addition of a small amount of oxygen will oxidize some of each metal. There appears to be nothing in the literature to indicate just how much of each metal is actually oxidized, i.e. how the oxidation is distributed between the metals. Qualitatively, when the differences in stabilities of the oxides are substantial, most of the oxygen will be used in oxidizing the more reactive metal (here, B). For less favourable conditions, such as smaller differences in stability, and for lower concentrations of B, the course of the reaction is not so obvious. As refining proceeds there is a gradual change in favour of increasing oxidation of the nobler metal A. It seems useful to establish at least for some simple examples just how much of the oxygen is used by each metal at any stage.

It is tempting to assume that addition of a small amount of oxygen produces a small amount of the equilibrium slag, the composition of which gives the distribution of oxygen between the two metals. This is true only if the slag is continually removed as it is formed (see section *Continuous removal of slag*). For batch oxidation it could equally well be argued that a small amount of the equilibrium metal has been removed.

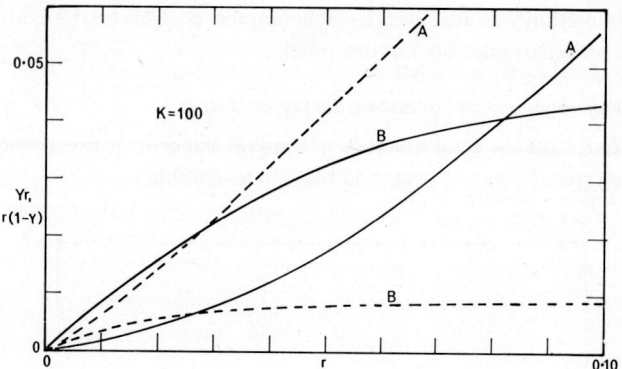

Fig. 9(a)   Oxidation of A and B: solid line $X_o=0\cdot05$; broken line $X_o=0\cdot01$

It is simpler to consider the total amount of metal oxidized rather than 'differential' quantities. If Y is the 'metal' fraction of B in the slag, the total quantity of B in the slag is YS, where S is the weight of metal in the slag. It is convenient to take $M_o=1$, then the amount of B originally present is X_o, and $S/M_o=S=r$.

Similarly for A, the amount slagged is $(1-Y)S=(1-Y)r$. Values of Yr and $(1-Y)r$ are plotted against r for various values of X_o in Figs. 8 and 9(a) and (b).

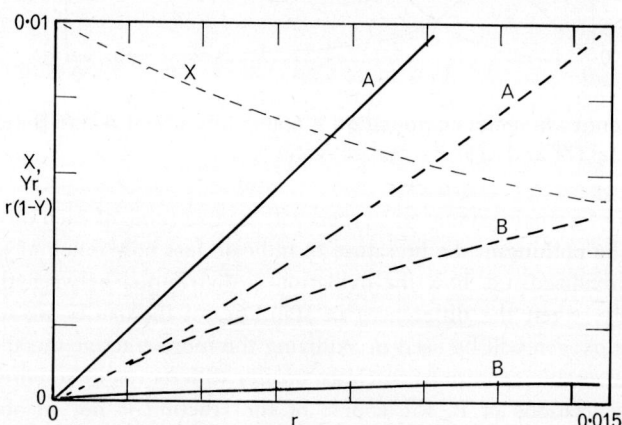

Fig. 9(b)   Oxidation of A and B: broken line $X_o=0\cdot01$; solid line $X_o=0\cdot001$. Change in concentration of metal is shown by X for $X_o=0\cdot01$

With reasonably high X_o values oxidation is initially confined almost exclusively to B. This is evident from the first trace of slag produced, which has the composition

$$Y_o = \frac{KX_o}{1 + X_o(K-1)}$$

which approaches unity if $KX_o \gg 1$.

As r increases, more A is oxidized and less B and, finally, practically all the oxygen is used in oxidizing A, and the line has a slope of unity, whereas the line for B is practically horizontal at X. This region may be characterized as one of inefficient refining, since the bulk of the oxygen is being used by the more noble metal A. It is efficient in the sense that the slag is dilute with respect to B, and low concentrations of B in the metal are only obtainable with a slag relatively rich in AO.

The difference between early and late stages of refining can also be seen from Fig. 2. Whether the two solutions are ideal or not, the equilibrium relations will be qualitatively similar to those shown in Fig. 2. In the flat part of the curve Y is not too far from unity over a range of X values; on the steep part X is small, and rapid changes in slag composition Y with X are found. This is the region where refining is inefficient in terms of oxygen utilization. There is no obvious sharp boundary between these regions. If K is large, the Y–X curve hugs the corner more closely, and the oxidation–r curves have sharper corners. From these the change takes place in the vicinity of $r = X_o$, and, the more closely, the larger the value of K.

If the original concentration X_o is small enough, the metal A combines with more of the oxygen than does B, even at the very beginning. The boundary between the regions is the condition at which they are equally oxidized at the beginning, i.e. $Y_o = \frac{1}{2}$, from equation 5, X_o is $1/(1+K)$. The slope of the Yr–r curve at the origin is

$$Y_o = \frac{KX_o}{1 + X_o(K-1)}$$

The product KX_o is a useful parameter; if $KX_o \gg 1$, $Y \to 1$; if $KX_o \ll 1$, $Y \to KX_o$. If $KX_o = 1$, the slope is $1/(2 - X_o) \approx \frac{1}{2}$ for $X_o \ll 1$.

It is necessary to distinguish between changes in concentration of B, and the quantities of A and B oxidized. If $KX_o \ll 1$, AO is formed to a much greater proportion than is BO, but the concentration of B is lowered steadily as oxidation proceeds. With comparatively little B present initially, the changes in its concentration are relatively high; although more A is oxidized, there is much more present originally, and so there is a much smaller percentage reduction in A. Thus, if $K = 10$ and $X_o = 0.01$, $Y_o = 0.092$, i.e. the first slag formed contains A and B in the ratio $0.908 : 0.092$. Thus, although about ten times as much A is oxidized as B, the metal has 99 times as much A as B.

Change in oxygen potential

For AO we have

E*

$$AO_{(l)} = A_{(l)} + \tfrac{1}{2}O_{2(g)}$$

$$K_A = \frac{a_A \cdot p_{O_2}^{\tfrac{1}{2}}}{a_{AO}}$$

and if both solutions are ideal

$$K_A = \left(\frac{1-X}{1-Y}\right) \cdot p_{O_2}^{\tfrac{1}{2}} \tag{18}$$

Similarly, for BO

$$K_B = \left(\frac{X}{Y}\right) \cdot p_{O_2}^{\tfrac{1}{2}} \tag{19}$$

Combining these with reaction 1 gives

$$K = K_A/K_B$$

Equations 19, 5 and 18 can be combined to give

$$Y/X = p_{O_2}^{\tfrac{1}{2}}/K_B =$$

$$\frac{2K(1-r)}{2(1-r) - [1+(K-1)(r-X_o)] + \{[1+(K-1)(r-X_o)]^2 + 4X_o(K-1)(1-r)\}^{\tfrac{1}{2}}} \tag{20}$$

Some typical curves have been plotted as $\log(p_{O_2}^{\tfrac{1}{2}}/K_B)$ in Fig. 10.

Each curve shows an end-point near $r = X_o$. For $r < X_o$, p_{O_2} is more or less buffered, as the slag is relatively rich in BO and changes in p_{O_2} are due to changes in the concentration of B in the metal. Similarly, for $r > X_o$ the metal is almost pure A, and oxidation is increasing the concentration of AO in the slag, and p_{O_2} changes comparatively slowly.

Use of oxide instead of oxygen

It is occasionally convenient to use oxide AO for the oxidation of the impurity B, rather than O_2. This may be done if a supply of the oxide is available from some other operation, e.g. litharge from cupellation can be used in softening lead. The equilibrium relations are, of course, unaffected, but the amount of slag formed and oxygen requirements are changed. If AO is used, *less* overall oxidation is required because the slag composition is always richer in AO, and, to a lesser extent, part of the reduction in the B concentration is due to dilution with reduced A. Conditions are shifted to the A-rich side for both metal and slag, as Fig. 3 shows.

If the metals have the same valency, then a reaction (e.g. reaction 1) leaves the total amount in moles of the metal phase unchanged and the moles of slag are the same as those of the oxide AO added. There is no need to distinguish between M_o (the initial quantity of metal) and M, which is now a constant.

If M moles of metal are refined by the addition of S moles of AO, from an initial mole fraction X_o to X, and if the metal fraction of B in the slag is Y, then

$$(X_o - X)M = Y \cdot S \tag{21}$$

and

$$X_0/X = 1 + (Y/X)(S/M)$$
$$= 1 + K'(S/M) \qquad (22)$$

if $Y = K'X$. This relation is true whether or not $S \ll M$, which is the assumption made for equation 11.

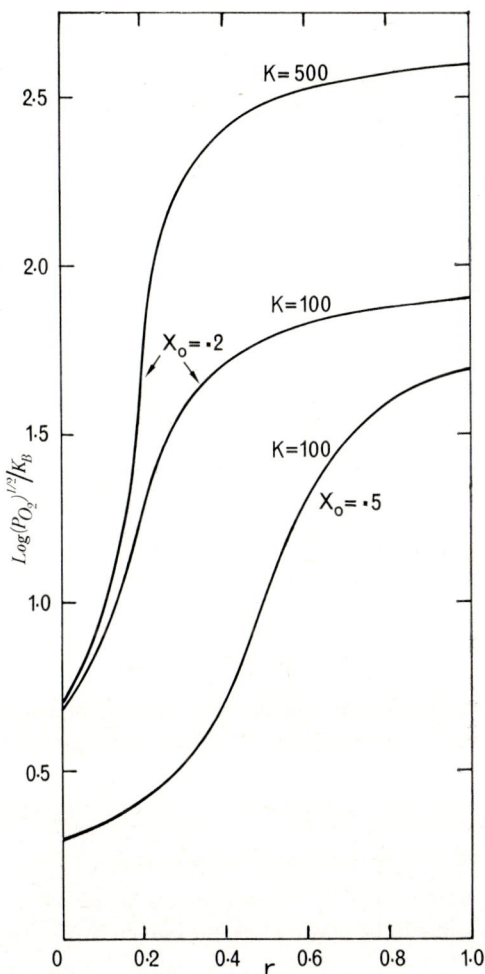

Fig. 10 Changes in oxygen partial pressure with oxidation from equation 20, as log $p_{O_2}{}^{\pm}/K_B$ versus r

Since

$$Y = (M/S)(X_0 - X)$$

the Y–X line has a slope of $-M/S$ as before. At $Y = 0$, $X = X_0$, so the slagging with AO can be represented by the anti-clockwise rotation of a line passing through the point $(X_o, 0)$ and of varying slope $-M/S$. The geometrical relations are shown in Fig. 4.

Combining equation 21 with equation 5 gives a quadratic relating X to r, for ideal solutions. The result is

$$X = \frac{-[1+Kr-X_o(K-1)] + \{[1+Kr-X_o(K-1)]^2 + 4X_o(K-1)\}^{\frac{1}{2}}}{2(K-1)} \quad (23)$$

Comparison with equation 15 shows slightly smaller X values for a given value of r. The important advantage of the oxide is that the quantity of metal is not reduced, as must happen if oxygen alone is used. From Figs. 3 and 4 it can be seen that for a given ratio of oxygen to metal the use of AO will give a lower concentration of B, or the slag/metal ratio for the same equilibrium concentrations is less with the oxide.

Use of equivalent fractions

Chiotti has shown that even if the metals are of different valencies, so that reaction 1 becomes

$$(p/q)[B] + (AR_p) = [A] + (p/q)(BR_q)$$

the distribution can be dealt with if *equivalents* and *equivalent fractions* are used instead of moles and mole fractions. The total number of equivalents in the metal phase, say, $= n_A + (q/p)n_B$, where n_A and n_B are the numbers of moles of A and B in the metal; the equivalent fraction of B is

$$\frac{(q/p)n_B}{(q/p)n_B + n_A}$$

Similarly, equivalent fractions for the metals in the slag phase (i.e. on an oxygen-free basis) are used. In the exchange of A and B the number of equivalents in each phase remains unchanged. With concentrations in equivalent fractions, and total quantities in equivalents, all the relations from the preceding section hold.

General graphical solution for slag–metal reaction

If it is not possible to represent the slag adequately by use of equivalent fractions, graphical methods can still be used. Thus, for a given S/M ratio the equilibrium tie-line can be found by trial and error. Alternatively, a number of lines can be drawn through the point representing the overall composition (a in Fig. 3) and values of Y and X read off from each, and Y plotted against X. The lines which cut the equilibrium line then give the required solutions.

Continuous refining

If there is a continuous flow of crude metal into, and of refined metal and slag out of, a furnace, the materials balances (equations 7–10) still apply, provided that quantities per unit time are used, instead of the quantities in one batch. The process is analogous to continuous flash distillation, or to continuous solvent extraction with one mixer–settler unit.

If contact of metal and slag is good enough to ensure that they leave in equilibrium with each other, then the equilibrium relations are also the same as for batch treatment.

It should be noted that the details of the flow of liquids *within* the furnace are not of importance. All that is necessary for this method is that the metal and slag leaving are in equilibrium with each other.

Refining with more than one slag

So far, it has been assumed that the slag remains in contact with the metal during the refining operation. If it is removed during the process, both the composition and quantity of slag are different from those obtained on oxidation without removal of the slag.

Perhaps the first indication that these differences existed was given by Williams,[11] who pointed out that in softening lead, if the dross is removed continuously, it is richer in Sb and less oxidation is required.

It can be shown that for the same initial and finishing compositions less metal is slagged if more than one slag is made and removed. In Fig. 11 metal of initial

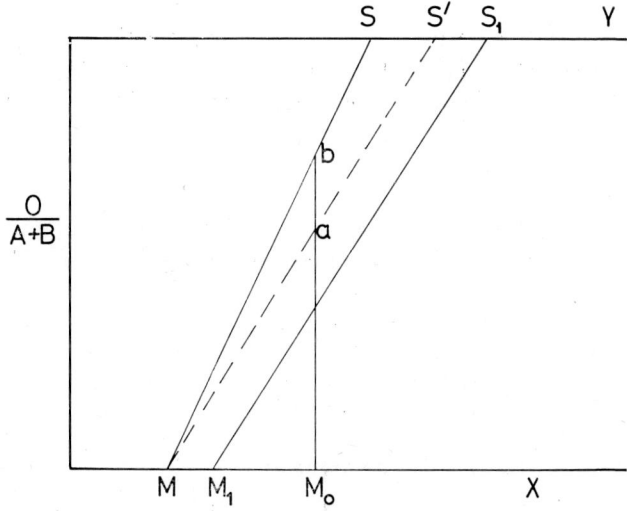

Fig. 11 Comparison of oxygen requirements with one ($M_o b$) and two slags ($M_o a$) for the same final composition M. MS' is not a tie-line

composition M_o is oxidized to slag S_1 and metal M_1. The slag S_1 is removed and metal M_1 is then oxidized to slag S and the final metal M. MS and $M_1 S_1$ are tie-lines joining the compositions of metals and slags at equilibrium. The same final composition of the metal M can also be obtained by oxidation in only one stage, along the path $M_o b$.

In the two-stage oxidation the composition of the combined slags must lie between S and S_1, at S' say. The line MS' is not a tie-line but is an operating line relating the overall slag and metal compositions to the amount of oxidation.

From Fig. 11 it is evident that less oxygen ($M_o a$) is needed for the two-stage process than for the single-stage oxidation ($M_o b$). Also the ratio Ma/aS' is less than Mb/bS; hence, a smaller proportion of metal is oxidized in the double slag method. Double slagging thus not only gives a richer slag but also retains a greater proportion of the more noble metal A in the metal phase.

If the miscibility gap between metal and slag phases closes with increasing concentration of B, it is possible for these relations to be reversed, as shown in the Appendix. Although this behaviour does not appear to occur in oxide systems, the possibility with, for example, sulphide, halide or arsenide systems should not be overlooked.

Refining with more than one slag, each of which is removed from the metal before the next is made, is in some ways analogous to solvent extraction with multiple contact. Schenck and co-workers gave equations and graphs showing the refining obtainable by repeated slagging with the weight of metal and of slag remaining constant in each of n steps

$$X/X_o = [1 + K'S/M]^n$$

This relation is identical with that for solvent extraction with immiscible solvent. However, Schenck *et al.* assumed that a previously formed slag was added in which the BO formed a dilute solution. Here it is assumed that the slag consists only of AO and BO.

Continuous removal of slag

The continuous removal of slag from contact with metal as fast as it is formed is analogous to batch distillation with continuous removal of vapour. The calculation is similar to that for the Rayleigh equation for distillation. It is assumed that the slag is removed in infinitesimal quantities dS, which are in equilibrium with the metal.

Since

$$S + M = M_o$$

$$dS + dM = 0$$

If the metal fraction of B in the slag is Y, in equilibrium with metal of composition X, then for the infinitesimal amount of B transferred from metal to slag

$$Y dS + d(M.X) = 0$$
$$Y dS + X dM + M.dX = 0$$
$$dM/M = dX/(Y - X)$$

Integrating from M_o to M, X_o to X, gives

$$\ln (M/M_o) = \int_{X_o}^{X} dX/(Y-X) \tag{24}$$

If the $Y-X$ equilibrium curve has been established, equation 24 can be integrated graphically.

There are a number of simplifications which can be used.

(a) The Nernst distribution: if B is distributed between metal and slag according to equation 6, $Y=K'X$,

$$\ln (M/M_o) = \frac{1}{K'-1} \ln (X/X_o)$$

or

$$\ln (X/X_o) = (K'-1) \ln (M/M_o) \tag{25}$$

(b) If the amount of slag produced is small, since

$$M/M_o = 1 - S/M_o$$

$\ln \{1-(S/M_o)\}$ can be approximated by

$$-S/M_o = \frac{1}{K'-1} \ln (X/X_o)$$

or

$$\ln (X_o/X) = (K'-1)(SM_o) \tag{26}$$

Schenck and co-workers[4,5] gave a similar but different formula for what they described as a 'transitory' slag:

$$\ln (X_o/X) = K'(S/M_o) \tag{27}$$

The difference between equations 26 and 27 comes from Schenck and co-workers' assumptions that the weight of metal is constant, and that the metal is treated with an infinitesimal amount of slag in which the oxide of B is dissolved. Their treatment is closer to that for differential solvent extraction, with constant amount of raffinate phase.

(c) If the quantity of metal remains constant, then

$$dM = 0$$

and

$$YdS + MdX = 0$$

and

$$\int YdS = -M\int_{X_o}^{X} K_o \, dX$$
$$= M(X_o - X)$$

If

$$Y = K'X, \quad K'XdS = -MdX$$
$$(K'/M)\int dS = \int dX/X = K'S/M = \ln(X_o/X)$$

This is identical with the formula of Schenck and co-workers (equation 27).

(d) If for reaction 1 both solutions are ideal and A and B have the same valencies, equation 5 gives

$$Y = \frac{KX}{1 + X(K-1)}$$

Integration of equation 24 leads to

$$\ln(M/M_o) = (1/(K-1))[\ln(X/X_o) - K \ln(1-X)/(1-X_o)] \tag{28}$$

Equation 25 is a special case of equation 28, where $X \ll 1$, $Y \ll 1$. Equation 28 is identical with that given by Treybal[8] for differential solvent extraction with pure solvent. In Fig. 12 continuous removal of slag is compared with batch treatments.

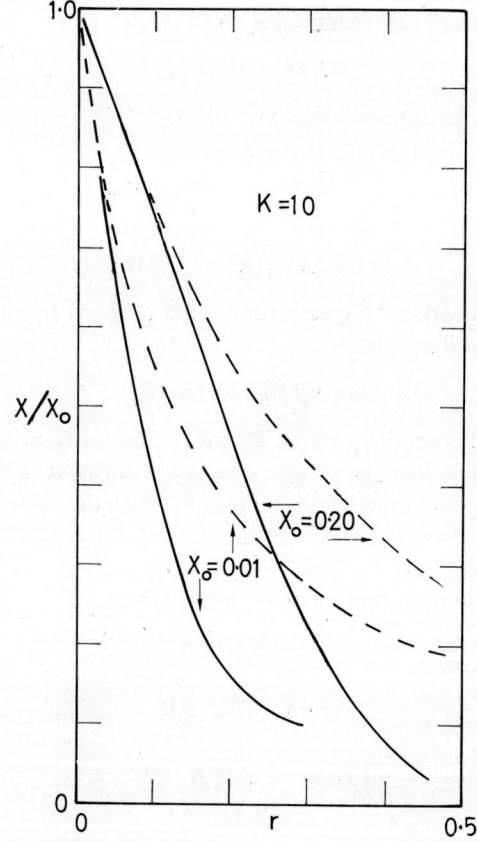

Fig. 12 Changes in composition with batch oxidation (broken lines) and with continuous removal of slag (equation 28)

Percentage removal of element B

Adding ln (M/M_o) to both sides of equation 25 and rearranging gives

$$\ln (XM/X_oM_o)=K'\ln (M/M_o)$$

or

$$\ln (B/B_o)=K'\ln M/M_o \tag{29}$$

where $B=XM$ and $B_o=X_oM_o$ are the amounts of metal B left and the initial amount B_o. This form is useful if the amount of metal removed, or present in slag, rather than the actual concentration, is of interest. Krupkowski and Fik[12] and Richter[13] have derived this equation by different methods for the distillation of metals with continuous removal of the vapour.

Similarly, if equation 28 is used

$$\ln (XM/X_oM_o)=K\ln (M(1-X)/M_o(1-X_o)) \tag{30}$$

Countercurrent refining: stagewise

Although repeated slagging can remove impurities to low levels, it still produces slags of low concentration of B. These could be enriched in B by reaction with fresh metal in a countercurrent operation.

Countercurrent methods have attracted little attention in pyrometallurgy, although their advantages are well known for hydrometallurgy. This is probably due to the difficulties associated with repeated handling of liquids at high temperatures.

Williams[11] pointed out the advantages to be expected in softening lead in a countercurrent process. Little attention has been given to the more quantitative aspects of such methods, but Davey and Floyd[14] have shown that in spite of not very favourable slag—metal equilibria in tin smelting, two countercurrent stages can be very effective. The same conclusion applies to the reverse path of oxidation.

A scheme for a two-stage preferential oxidation is shown in Fig. 13. It is

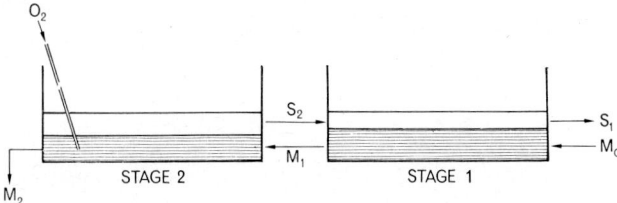

Fig. 13 Schematic two-stage countercurrent refining. M_o is refined to M_2 and slag S_1

assumed the process has reached a steady state, and that equilibrium is attained in each stage. The treatment can be extended to as many stages as desired, but will be limited here to two stages which can be handled, for example, by one rotary furnace. The process is in some ways analogous to countercurrent solvent extraction.

A batch of M_o moles of crude metal is treated with slag S_2 from the second stage, giving metal M_1 and slag S_1 which are in equilibrium with each other. In the second stage M_1 is refined by oxygen, giving the final metal M_2 and the equili-

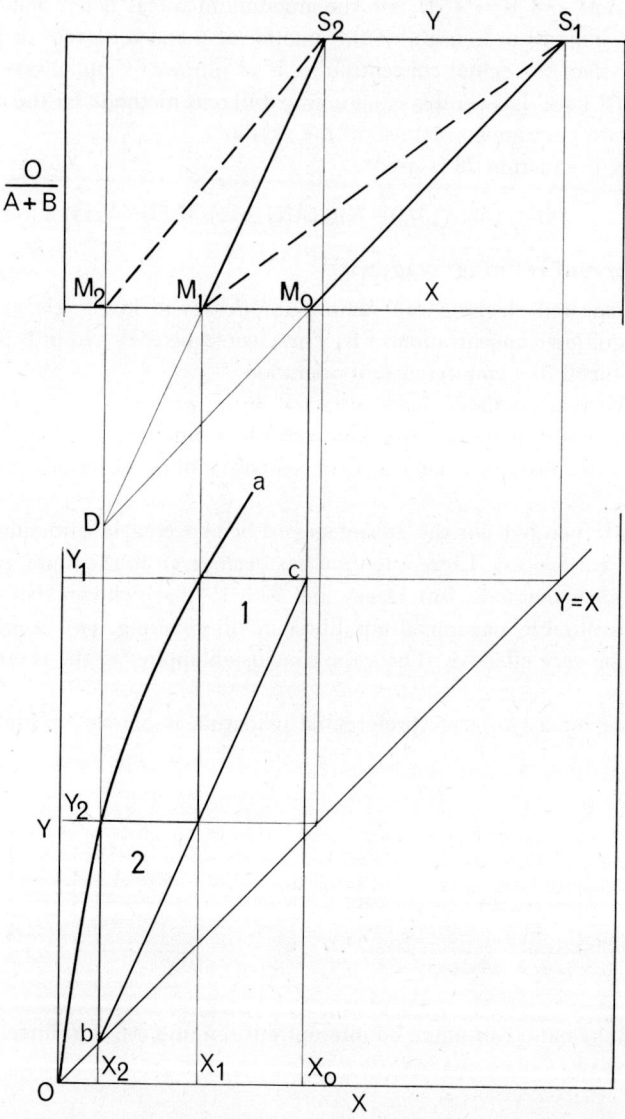

Fig. 14 Two-stage countercurrent refining on Jänecke coordinates (upper part of diagram) and on a Y–X diagram. Diagonal $Y=X$, the operating line bc and equilibrium line Oa are shown. Steps 1 and 2 represent the two stages in the McCabe–Thiele construction. M_1S_1 and M_2S_2 are tie-lines. Point D satisfies the relations $D=M_o-S_1=M_1-S_2$

brium slag S_2, which goes back to stage 1. Oxygen is supplied only to the second stage. Fig. 14 shows the relations plotted on Jänecke coordinates, and on a Y–X diagram, for metals of the same valency. As before, this leaves the number of moles of metal in each phase unchanged as a result of slag–metal reactions. Only in the second stage is there a change in the amount of metal as it reacts with the oxygen. Thus, $S_1 = S_2$ and $M_o = M_1 \neq M_2$.

Materials balances over the second stage give the total metal, in moles

$$M_1 = M_2 + S_2$$

and for B

$$X_2 M_2 = X_1 M_1 - Y_2 S_2$$

or

$$Y_2 = X_1 M_1 / S_2 - X_2 M_2 / S_2$$
$$= X_2 + (M_1/S_2)(X_1 - X_2) \tag{31}$$

Y_2 is a linear function of X_1, with a slope of $M_1/S_2 (= M_o/S_1)$.

Substituting $Y = X$ in equation 31 shows that it meets the diagonal at $X = X_2$. Y_1 and X_o lie on the same operating line. The quantity of slag made is determined by the oxygen supplied to stage 2. Fig. 14 shows the relation between Jänecke coordinates and the Y–X diagram. The standard 'step' construction of a McCabe–Thiele diagram is also shown. If X_2 is known, the slag in equilibrium with the metal leaving stage 2 is Y_2 on the equilibrium curve. Y_2 is related to X_1 by the operating line, so a horizontal line from Y_2 gives X_1. The quantities for the first stage can be found by proceeding vertically from X_1 to Y_1, the equilibrium slag from stage 1, and to the operating line for X_o. For given values of X_o and X_2, say, the correct slope of the operating line has to be found by trial and error.

If the equilibrium line is $Y = K'X$, compositions can be calculated by a modification of the method used—for example, for solvent extraction with immiscible liquids. The vertical distance from the end of the operating line on the diagonal to the equilibrium line is $(K'-1)X_2$. The horizontal 'step' is $X_2(S/M)(K'-1)$ and

$$X_1 = X_2[1 + (S/M)(K'-1)]$$
$$Y_1 = K'X_2[1 + (S/M)(K'-1)]$$

The vertical step in the first stage is

$$X_2 (S/M)(K'-1)$$

and the horizontal step is

$$X_2(S/M)^2 K'(K'-1)$$

Adding the horizontal steps gives

$$X_o = X_2 [1 + (S/M)(K'-1) + (S/M)^2 K'(K'-1)] \tag{32}$$

The reason for $(K'-1)$ appearing instead of K', as in the immiscible solvent case, is that in the second stage no slag is introduced—only oxygen to make the slag S_2. Values of X_2/X_o are shown in Fig. 15.

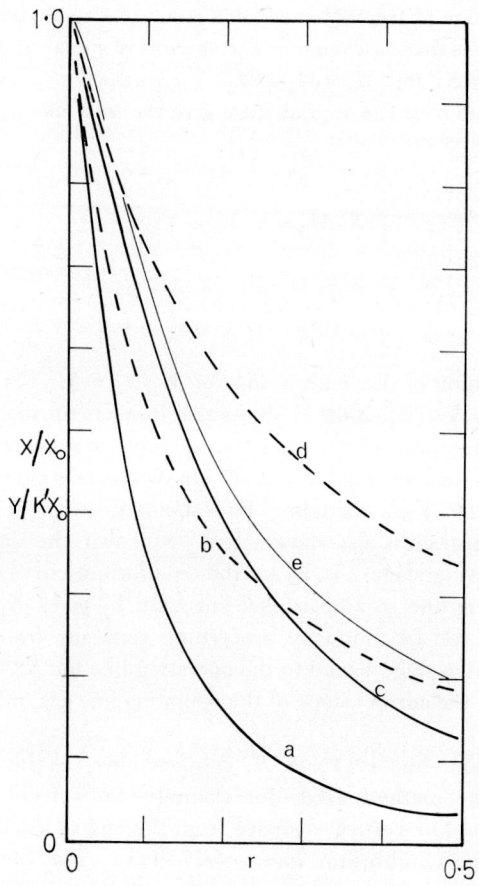

Fig. 15 Comparison of two-stage countercurrent (equation 32) and batch oxidation

	Two-stage countercurrent X refers to X_2 in equation 32	Batch
$K'=10$	a, e	b
$K'=5$	c	d

a and c are metal compositions, two-stage, as $X(=X_2)/X_o$
b and d give metal and slag compositions X/X_o and $Y/K'X_o$, respectively
e is $Y/K'X_o$ for $K'=10$ and should be compared with b for batch oxidation

For n stages the relation is

$$X_o = X_n[1 + (S/M)(K'-1) + \ldots (S/M)^n(K')^{n-1}(K'-1)] \qquad (33)$$

If the first stage is supplied with the oxide AO rather than oxygen, the moles of slag will remain constant throughout, and the analogy with solvent extraction with immiscible liquids is closer. In equations 32 and 33 the $(K'-1)$ is replaced by K', and the operating line finishes on the X axis at a point of coordinates $(X_2, 0)$. The slope is still

$$M_o/S_1 = M_1/S_2 = M_2/AO$$

Slag composition

Fig. 15 shows that for the same degree of oxidation a two-stage countercurrent process will give lower concentrations of B than does a batch process. The slag should be richer in B; its composition Y_1 can be calculated, e.g. for a two-stage countercurrent process. If

$$Y_1 = K'X_1$$
$$X_1 = X_2[1+(S/M)(K'-1)]$$

Substituting for X_2 from equation 32 gives

$$Y_1 = \frac{X_o K'\{1+(S/M)(K'-1)\}}{1+(S/M)(K'-1)+(S/M)^2 K'(K'-1)} \qquad (34)$$

Values of $Y/K'X_o$ are plotted in Fig. 15, and it will be seen from b and e that there is an intermediate region where the increase in concentration of B in the slag is most marked. For very small amounts of oxidation $Y \to K'X_o$ for both methods.

Continuous flow with multiple contact

The results just given also hold for continuous flow, in which metal and slag are equilibrated and separated in a stage, and then flow in opposite directions to neighbouring stages. Instead of the moles per batch, moles per unit time are used. The details of the flow *within* the stage are not important, so long as slag and metal are equilibrated before they are separated. Such a system is analogous to a set of mixer–settlers in solvent extraction.

Countercurrent refining with continuous contact

It is possible for slag and metal to flow countercurrent to each other while maintaining continuous contact. This is done, for example, in the WORCRA processes.[15]

Concentrations in metal and slag can be related to each other by a continuous operating line. The equilibrium line is unchanged. With continuous contact of the liquids it is not possible to combine equilibrium and operating lines to describe the operation as, for example, equilibrium stages which could be calculated have no physical significance.

Also, a vigorously agitated bath could behave as already described in the section *Continuous refining*, with metal and slag in equilibrium even though they leave at opposite ends of the furnace. At the other extreme is countercurrent 'plug' flow[16] in which the refining obtained depends on kinetic considerations. It may be negligible, as Williams found for unstirred countercurrent flow of lead and softener slag. Any type of flow and mixing between these extremes is possible, and, unless mixing characteristics and mass transfer rates are known, it is not possible to predict the behaviour of a countercurrent unit. Jenkins, Gray and Worner[17] have recently shown that a WORCRA continuous steelmaking pilot unit is equivalent to between 8 and 9 stirred tanks in series.

Limits in countercurrent processes

If the slag leaving the furnace is in equilibrium with the incoming metal, there is a lower limit to the concentration of B in the metal which can be reached by countercurrent refining. If the total B entering is MX_o, the amount in the slag leaving is $SY_o = SK'X_o$ if $Y = K'X$. The amount of B left in the metal is $X_o(M - SK')$ and if the quantity of metal is unchanged, the concentration of B in the metal leaving is

$$X_n = X_o(1 - K'S/M) \qquad (35)$$

This relation has been derived by Schenck et al. for continuous contact between metal and slag, but it is true for staged and continuous contact.[18] This equation, or its equivalent, has been derived for many countercurrent staged processes by a variety of methods—many of which tend to obscure the fact that it is basically a materials balance. As X_n cannot be negative, $K'S/M$ must be less than 1; this condition is required mathematically to give the above result.

On a Y–X diagram this means the operating line is steeper than the equilibrium line (assumed to be $Y = K'X$). They meet at $X = X_o$, $Y = K'X_o$, and an infinite number of equilibrium stages (or transfer units[18]) are required for this 'pinch'. Practically, the occurrence of a limit such as this means that K' is too small, or that too little slag is being made.

Equation 35 assumes constant S/M, which is true if AO is used, and the metals have the same valency. If O_2 is supplied at the outgoing end, the operating line finishes on the diagonal, and equation 35 becomes

$$X_n/X_o = \frac{1 - K'S/M_o}{1 - S/M_o} = 1 - (S/M_n)(K' - 1)$$

where M_o and M_n, respectively, are the moles of metal entering and leaving. The minimum slag rate is given by $(S/M_n)(K' - 1) < 1$.

The second composition limit occurs when $K'S/M > 1$ (for constant S/M). X_n can now be lowered indefinitely with enough stages. When $X_n = 0$, all the B is in the slag, which then has a maximum value of $Y = X_o M/S$, which is less than that for equilibrium with the incoming metal ($K'X_o$). The 'pinch' is now at the low concentration end. The condition $K'S/M > 1$ favours low final concentrations since, with large K', and adequate supply of slag, sufficient stages (or transfer units) make it possible to remove B to very low values.

If the refining is done with oxygen, the slag relations are unchanged for $X_n = 0$. If X_n is finite, since the operating line finishes on the diagonal $Y = X = X_n$, it does not actually meet the equilibrium line, although it may be very close to it, and the materials balance will be little affected.

Reflux in refining

The methods outlined so far cannot produce slags with a concentration of B greater than that in equilibrium with the incoming metal. In practice, it is often desirable to concentrate the slag as far as possible in B.

In distillation and solvent extraction reflux is used to give a better separation than would be otherwise obtained. In order to obtain higher concentrations of B in refining the slag S_1 (Fig. 13) can be partly reduced in a separate unit. It will give an enriched slag S_R and metal M_R, which can be returned to stage 1. M_R is richer in B than M_1, which is in equilibrium with S_1, and the reflux means that the level of B in stage 1 is higher than it would otherwise be.

Alternatively, the slag S_1 could be completely reduced to metal, which would have the same composition, part of this metal then being returned to the first stage. This resembles a total condenser in distillation, and the first method is analogous to a partial condenser. Chiotti[7] has described the use of reflux at the B-rich end of a metal–molten salt multi-stage process in which the bulk of the metal reduced from the salt phase is returned as reflux.

At the metal or A-rich end of stage 2 (Fig. 13) there is no comparable method of producing reflux, since oxygen is already being supplied there, and producing a new phase, the slag. Stage 2 is analogous to the re-boiler in distillation.

Detailed calculations of the possibilities of the use of reflux can be made by the methods described in standard texts on chemical engineering, and will therefore not be given here.

Conclusions

It will be evident that this work has drawn heavily on methods which are well established in chemical engineering. It is believed that the use of Jänecke coordinates helps to emphasize the analogies between slag–metal reactions and other separation processes. Many of the results are valid, however, if mole fractions, say, are used for concentrations in slag.

Although many drastic simplifications have been made in order to obtain quantitative results, many of these conclusions will be generally valid for real slag–metal systems. Even if graphical methods have to be used, it seems to be worth considering the possibilities of say, removing the slag, or countercurrent treatment, as alternatives to a batch process. Most of the results obtained here do not require ideal solutions, or equal valencies, to be at least qualitatively true.

Attention should be drawn to the differences between the results obtained here and those of Schenck and his colleagues. Where a slag is provided 'ready made', as it were, the behaviour resembles that in solvent extraction. Here, rather different results are obtained when the slag consists only of the oxides of the two metals.

It is perhaps worth pointing out that ternary A–B–O systems have been treated here by methods which, for the most part, were derived originally for the distillation of binary mixtures. It is hoped to extend these methods to more complex systems.

Acknowledgment

Discussions with Professor H. W. Worner and particularly with Dr. N. B. Gray have been most helpful. Mr. J. Balfour has assisted with calculations and the preparation of this paper.

References

1. KOOTZ T. Zur Theorie der Windfrischverfahren. *Stahl Eisen*, **61**, 1941, 1053–64.
2. BAUKLOH W. *Die physikalisch-chemischen Grundlagen der Metallurgie* (Berlin: Akademie Verlag, 1949), 304 p. (pp. 174–5)
3. OETERS F. Grundlagen der Frischreaktionen: Schlackenarbeit. In *Die physikalische Chemie der Eisen-und Stahlerzeugung* (Düsseldorf: Verlag Stahleisen, 1964), 380 p. (pp. 156–211)
4. SCHENCK H. STEINMETZ E. AND FROHBERG M. G. Ableitungen zum Ausmass chemischer Umsetzungen zwischen flüssigen Phasen in ruhendem und bewegtem Zustand. *Arch. Eisenhüttenw.*, **34**, 1963, 659–72.
5. SCHENCK H. Der Einfluss der Verfahrensweise auf den betriebstechnischen Wirkungsgrad der Reaktionen zwischen zwei Phasen, insbesondere Schlacke und Metall. *Stahl Eisen*, **84**, 1964, 311–26. (German and French text)
6. SCHENCK H. FROHBERG M. G. AND PAPAMANTELLOS D. Ergänzende Ableitungen zum Stoffaustausch zwischen Schlacke und Metall bei permanent und bei transitorisch wirksamen Phasen. *Arch. Eisenhüttenw.*, **37**, 1966, 13–9.
7. CHIOTTI P. Countercurrent extraction in salt–metal systems involving oxidation–reduction reactions. *I&EC Process Design Develop.*, **4**, 1965, 299–304.
8. TREYBAL R. E. *Liquid extraction, 2nd edn* (New York: McGraw-Hill, 1963), 640 p. (p. 197)
9. Reference 8, pp. 27 and 199.
10. Reference 8, pp. 214 and 250.
11. WILLIAMS G. K. The development and application of the continuous lead refining process. D. Eng. thesis, University of Melbourne, 1936.
12. KRUPKOWSKI A. AND FIK H. Proces rektyfikacji cynku. *Archwm Górn. Hutn.*, **2**, 1954, 243–352.
13. RICHTER S. Beiträge zur Theorie der distillativen Feinreinigung von Metallen. *Freiberger ForschHft.* B102, 1965, 35–53.
14. DAVEY T. R. A. AND FLOYD J. M. Slag–metal equilibria in tin smelting. *Proc. Australas. Inst. Min. Metall.* no. 219, 1966, 1–10.
15. WORNER H. K. Continuous smelting and refining by the WORCRA processes. In *Advances in extractive metallurgy* (London: Institution of Mining and Metallurgy, 1968), 245–63.
16. LEVENSPIEL O. *Chemical reaction engineering* (New York: Wiley, 1962), 501 p. (pp. 99 and 242)
17. JENKINS T. W. GRAY N. B. AND WORNER H. K. Application of the Levenspiel dispersion model to metal flow in pilot plant WORCRA continuous steelmaking furnace. *Metall. Trans.*, **2**, 1971, 1258–9.
18. TILLER F. M. Efficiencies in gas absorption, extraction, and washing. *Chem. Engng Prog.*, **45**, 1949, 391–401.

Appendix

Relations with closed miscibility gap

If there is no change in selectivity, the phase relations will be as shown in Fig. 1, where K is the critical point. If S' lies to the left of S, then

$$\frac{Ma}{aS'} > \frac{Mb}{bS}$$

This is, of course, the opposite of the more obvious result given above. It may possibly explain some of the conflicting observations in the metallurgy of mattes and speisses. Fig. 1 indicates that increased oxidation gives *lower* B contents in the metal phase, and *higher* B contents in the non-metallic phase.

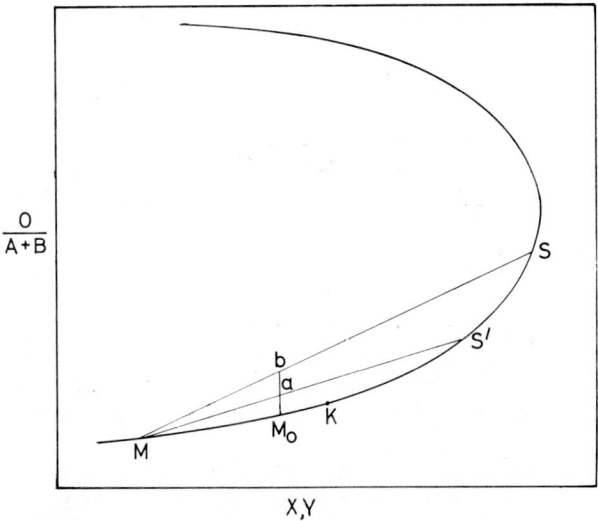

Fig. 1 Phase relations with a miscibility gap closing at *K*. *MS* is a tie-line, and *S'* is now to the left of S (cf. Fig. 11, p. 125). Oxidation of M_o gives *X* decreasing while *Y increases*

DISCUSSION

F. A. Garner, in introducing his joint paper, said that it surveyed some of the results concerning equilibria between copper metal, copper mattes and slags that had been obtained in the Department of Minerals Engineering at Birmingham University. The first section was an assessment of equilibrium relationships established between copper metal and iron silicate slags, the experimental techniques for which were refinements of those used by Ruddle and co-workers, i.e. the required metal and slag samples were brought to equilibrium with flowing gaseous mixtures of carbon monoxide and carbon dioxide in a vertical tube furnace. At the completion of the required heating time the samples were rapidly chilled to minimize the possibility of segregation of the copper dissolved in the slag. The metal and slag phases were then carefully separated prior to analysis.

Fig. 3 (p. 86) showed that the relationship between the equilibrium oxygen pressure of the system and the dissolved copper contents of silica-saturated iron silicate melts, first established by Ruddle and co-workers, was confirmed by Mihalop's work. Also, more recent work with an industrial slag had produced a curve of similar shape, but with copper tenors of a lower order.

By plotting the ratio Cu_2O/Fe in slag against oxygen pressure (Fig. 4, p. 87) it was shown that the results of all the workers could be represented by a single curve. That implied that a direct relationship existed between the dissolved copper and the iron content of iron silicate slags, and that the appreciable lime and alumina contents of the industrial slag tested acted only as inert diluents.

The workers cited had postulated relationships between the ferric iron content and the copper content of slags, but the present authors considered that although that might well be true, alternative explanations could be proposed, and until an accurate method for the determination of ferric iron in complex slags had been developed any proposed mechanism could only rely on tenuous evidence.

At the present time most of the data available were concerned with silica-saturated slags: further work on high-iron melts was therefore required.

The second section of the paper was concerned with equilibria between synthetic mattes of various compositions and silica-saturated iron silicate slags. Experimentally, that work had proved very difficult to develop owing to the mechanical problems that arose when an attempt was made to construct a closed furnace system in which the attendant gas could be recirculated over the melt. Additionally, it proved necessary to develop a method for the analysis of the gas phase for CO, CO_2 and SO_2 (or COS). Although the accurate determination of the relatively high CO and CO_2 contents was simple, the content of the sulphur-containing gases present in concentrations of less than one part per thousand proved difficult to measure on the available gas chromatograph.

Perhaps the most interesting information to arise from the work was that concerning the limits of oxygen pressure at which equilibrium could exist between the matte and slag phases. Those were from 3×10^{-12} atm (as defined by the slag phase) to $2 \cdot 3 \times 10^{-8}$ atm for copper-free mattes, the upper limit decreasing with increasing matte grade.

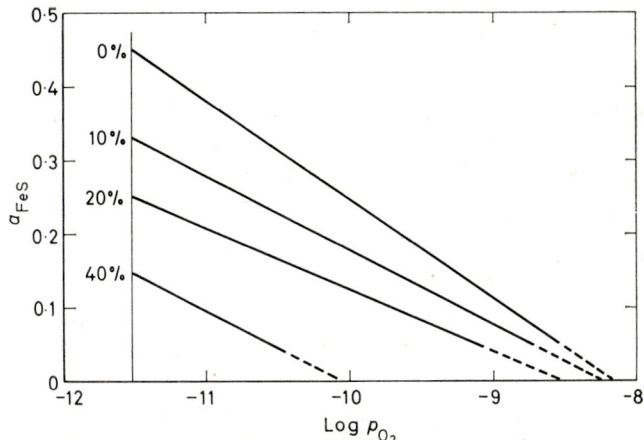

Fig. 1 Calculated a_{FeS} versus log p_{O_2} (for several matte grades)

Fig. 7 (p. 92) indicated that the maximum matte grade at which equilibrium could exist was of the order of 48% Cu. Recently obtained results for mattes containing 40% copper modified Figs. 6 and 7 (see Figs. 1 and 2). Thus, the maximum matte grade at 58% was higher than previously predicted and indicated the dangers of extrapolation in the interpretation of results.

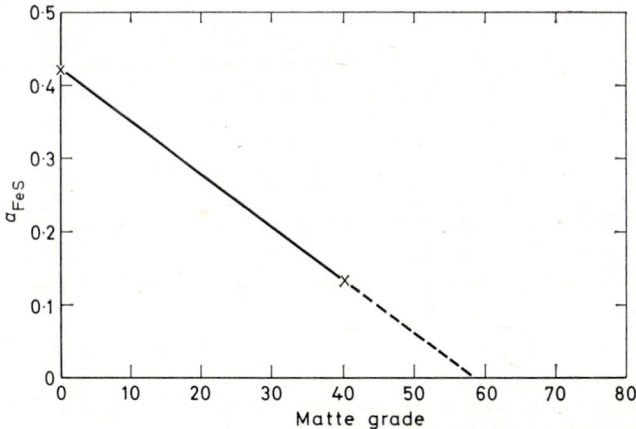

Fig. 2 a_{FeS} (when log p_{O_2} = $-11 \cdot 52$) versus matte grade

Requests had been made for data concerning the slag copper contents obtained in the work. Unfortunately, the necessary analyses were not yet completed, but it was hoped to submit them for publication in the near future.

Dr. D. J. Fray introduced his joint paper, summarizing its principal contents and conclusions.

Dr. D. G. C. Robertson* introduced the paper by G. M. Willis in the absence of the author.

P. V. Riboud† said that the very interesting treatment proposed by Willis on slag–metal reactions had not been used by IRSID since they were trying to approach the mechanisms of reactions rather than composition evolution of the bulk phases.

Recent advances in the theory of refining had shown that most reactions occurred between a phase dispersed into another one, with important oxygen activity gradients at the interface.

Historically, at the beginning of LD furnace development the tendency was to consider that, at variance with conventional open-hearth furnaces, oxygen transfer in BOF for the carbon reaction occurred without the intermediate oxygen passage through the slag. Then Meyer *et al.*‡ and Kozakevitch§ suggested that a substantial part of decarburization should occur in the slag transformed into an emulsion of liquid and solid oxides, metal and gas. Simultaneous reactions of iron carbon and phosphorus with oxygen had always been considered for a whole converter and not especially for a small droplet in a large quantity of slag.

To enable further progress to be made in the understanding of emulsion reactions, studies of the behaviour of single droplets in large quantities of slag had been undertaken by BISRA and IRSID. In their experiments 2-g droplets of molten iron–carbon–phosphorus alloy were introduced into an oxidized slag in which the oxygen activity had been adjusted to a given level at 1550°C. After various reaction times the whole system was water-quenched. Metal and slag were then analysed.

In Fig. 3 decarburization curves were presented schematically for the same slag containing 25% total iron oxides. The rates of reaction could be very different, depending on oxygen activity in the slag when it varied from $p_{O_2} = 10^{-8}$ atm, that was, close to the equilibrium value, to $p_{O_2} = 1$ atm.

For the very high decarburization rates the droplet exploded completely and only small fragments, without any definite shape, were recovered. For lower

* Department of Metallurgy, Imperial College, London.
† Institut de Recherches de la Sidérurgie (IRSID), Maizières-lès-Metz, France.
‡ MEYER H. W. *et al.* Slag–metal emulsions and their importance in BOF steelmaking. *J. Metals, N.Y.*, **20**, July 1968, 35–42.
§ KOZAKEVITCH P. Foams and emulsions in steelmaking. *J. Metals. N.Y.*, **21**, July 1969, 57–68.

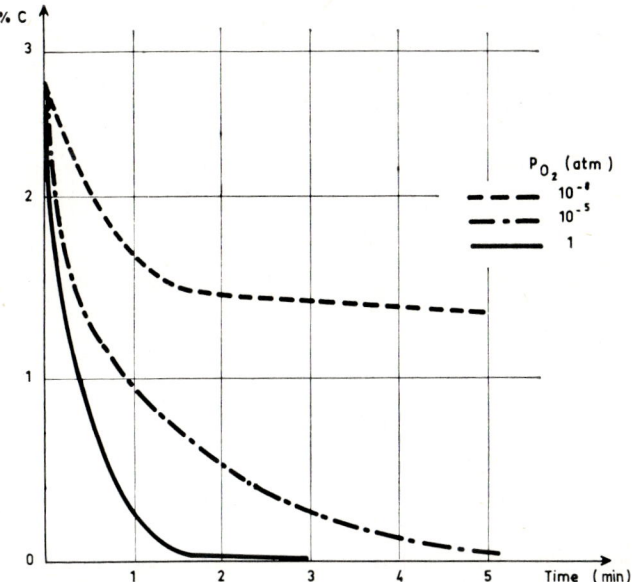

Fig. 3 Schematic representation of carbon content evolution for a droplet (2·8% C, 1·5% P) in a slag (FeO + Fe$_2$O$_3$ = 25%) at 1550°C for various initial oxygen activities in the oxide phase (different Fe^{3+}/Fe^{2+} ratios)

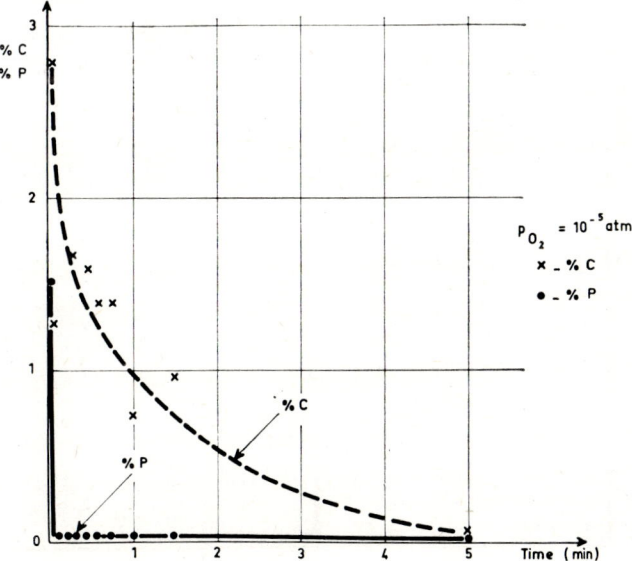

Fig. 4 Carbon and phosphorus evolution of a droplet in a basic slag (FeO + Fe$_2$O$_3$ = 25%)

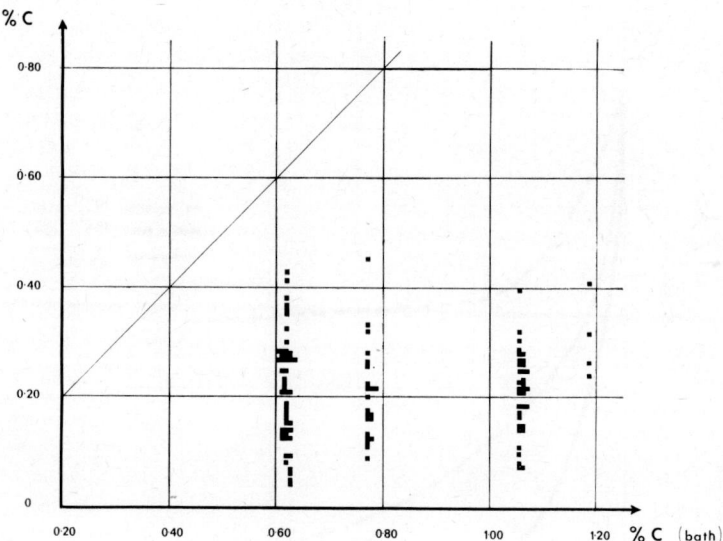

Fig. 5 Carbon content of droplets as a function of carbon content of bath from samples taken in an OLP converter

reaction rates the drop simply parted into two or several droplets. When decarburization slowed down even more, the drop recovered its shape and showed, after quenching, a smooth shining surface.

Simultaneous decarburization and dephosphorization curves were compared in Fig. 4. Dephosphorization was completed in less than 10 sec: the original sample, with 1·5% phosphorus, contained only 0·002–0·004% P after the shortest reaction time allowed.

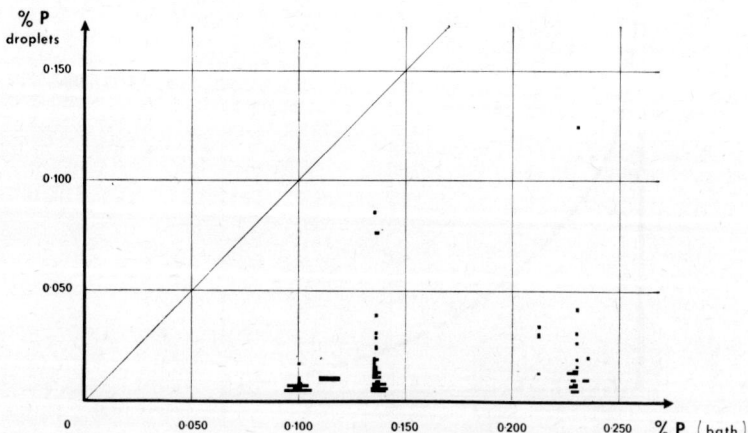

Fig. 6 As Fig. 3, but for phosphorus content

Those observations were in very good agreement with the analysis made on droplets sampled in an OLP converter. In Fig. 5 the carbon content of droplets was presented as a function of the percentage of carbon in the bath at the time of sampling. Although the carbon content of the droplets was always lower than that of the bath, significant scattering was observed.

As for the phosphorus analysis given in Fig. 6, the droplets' contents were in almost all cases very low and a large number contained less than 0.004% P in contact with a slag containing 23% P_2O_5.

Thus, for processes where a metallic phase was dispersed into a slag, the experiments drew attention to the fact that oxide phases should be overoxidized to decarburize fast enough. On the other hand, once basicity was high enough, dephosphorization was an extremely rapid process since a few seconds' contact was sufficient for every droplet.

Dr. C. F. Knights,[*] with reference to the paper by Bailey *et al.*, said that Dr. N. R. Large of AERE, Harwell, had explored the Mössbauer technique as a means of determining the individual concentrations of Fe^{2+} and Fe^{3+} and their ratio in a SiO_2–Al_2O_3–CaO–MgO slag $(53:15:28:4$ wt $\%)$. It was an accurate technique in the slag examined, but further work was required to establish whether the presence of various concentrations of transition metals had any effect on the Mössbauer spectra.

P. A. Wright,[†] with reference to the problem of determining the ferrous/ferric iron ratio in slags, suggested that the magnetic properties might offer a route. In his own company they used the size of slag particle which could be picked up by a magnet as the measure of the magnetite content. It should be possible to devise a scientific measurement on that basis.

Dr. Robertson, in his very able introduction of Mr. Willis' paper, had used the example of the iron–tin system as one to which selective oxidation might be applied to remove iron from the tin. He would like to remark that if they inverted the argument and examined the selective reduction of tin–iron oxide mixture, they arrived at the basis of tin smelting.

Professor T. R. A. Davey[‡] said that although there had been some signs of 'terror' as a result of the expressions developed in Willis' paper, he would, nonetheless, like to commend it to everyone's attention. The complications arose purely because Willis had made generalized expressions, which were actually very simple when applied to a particular case.

The speaker had applied those methods of calculation for the past 20 years to problems involving metal refining, and to the case of tin smelting, which had already been mentioned. No difficult mathematics were involved, and the tech-

[*] UKAEA, AERE, Harwell, Berkshire.
[†] Consolidated Tin Smelters, Ltd., London.
[‡] Colorado School of Mines, Golden, Colorado, U.S.A.

niques were relatively easy. Calculations of those kinds were quite familiar to chemical engineers dealing with separations of petrochemical substances, for example. There usually existed sufficient data nowadays for the metallurgist to be able to calculate what should be the results of refining operations, and, thence, to be able to optimize those.

He repeated that the mass of symbols in Mr. Willis' equations arose only because the expressions were general, and that in any particular case they were very simple indeed, and well within the competence of non-mathematicians such as himself.

Contributed remarks

Dr. T. W. Jenkins* For a single-stage batch process we have

$$\frac{X_0}{X} = K^1\left(\frac{S}{M}\right) + 1 \tag{11}$$

For a countercurrent process in which the slag is in equilibrium with the incoming metal we have

$$\frac{X}{X_0} = \left(1 - \frac{K^1 S}{M}\right) \tag{35}$$

If we start with the same quantity of metal M and compare the two processes

$$\left[\left(\frac{X_0}{X}\right)_B - 1\right] = K^1\left(\frac{S}{M}\right)_B$$

Therefore

$$(M)_B = \frac{K^1(S)_B}{\left[\left(\dfrac{X_0}{X}\right)_B - 1\right]}$$

for the batch process, where B = Batch.

Similarly

$$1 - \left(\frac{X}{X_0}\right)_c = K^1\left(\frac{S}{M}\right)_c$$

for the counterflow process, where c = counterflow.

Therefore

$$(M)_c = \frac{K^1(S)_c}{\left[1 - \left(\dfrac{X}{X_0}\right)_c\right]}$$

Now if $(M)_c = (M)_B$

$$\frac{K^1(S)_B}{\left[\left(\dfrac{X_0}{X}\right)_B - 1\right]} = \frac{K^1(S)_c}{\left[1 - \left(\dfrac{X}{X_0}\right)_c\right]}$$

* Conzinc Riotinto of Australia, Ltd., Melbourne, Australia.

Therefore

$$(S)_B \left[\frac{(X_0)_c - (X)_c}{(X_0)_c} \right] = (S)_c \left[\frac{(X_0)_B - (X)_B}{(X)_B} \right]$$

If we wish also to compare the two processes in terms of slag produced for the same degree of refining, then we put

$$(X_0)_c = (X_0)_B \text{ (initial concentration same)}$$
$$(X)_c = (X)_B \text{ (final concentration same)}$$

Thus, the two processes are refining the same quantity of metal of the same initial impurity to the same final impurity level: therefore

$$\frac{(S)_B}{(X_0)_c} = \frac{(S)_c}{(X)_B}$$

and

$$\frac{(S)_B}{(S)_c} = \frac{(X_0)_c}{(X)_B}$$

Now S is the amount of metal oxidized into the slag. $S = A+B$, or, for the system, say, Fe–Si, $S = Fe + Si$ oxidized. Thus, if each of the two processes refines the same quantity of metal to the same specification in, say, the Fe–B system, then

$$\frac{(S)_B}{(S)_c} = \frac{(Fe+B)_B^{oxidized}}{(Fe+B)_c^{oxidized}} = \frac{(X_0)_c}{(X)_B}$$

In both cases $B^{oxidized}$ will be the same, and therefore in the batch process much more iron will be oxidized, and hence lost, than in a counterflow process.

If we use the relationships

$$(Slag)_B (Y)_B = M(X_0 - X)_B$$

$$(Slag)_c (Y)_c = M(X_0 - X)_c$$

which, as Willis points out, are simply mass balances, with the limiting equilibrium relationships

$$\left(\frac{Y}{X} \right)_B = K' \text{ (i.e. metal and slag in equilibrium at end of a batch process)}$$

$$\left(\frac{Y}{X_0} \right)_c = K' \text{ (i.e. incoming metal in equilibrium with outgoing slag in a counterflow process)}$$

we may derive the relationship

$$\frac{(X_0)_c}{(X)_B} = \frac{(Slag)_B}{(Slag)_c}$$

which is similar to that derived by Willis, and has previously been derived by Thring[1] and Jenkins.[2] Thus, in the WORCRA steelmaking (WSM) process, where sequential oxygen lancing is used, we combine the speed of oxygen refining with a low level of iron units lost and oxygen units wasted.

F

Batch BOF	*Counterflow* WSM

Say, Slag $= 25\%$ FeO　　　　　　　Slag $= 8\%$ FeO

　　Slag $= 15\%$ of metal weight　　　Slag $= 10\%$ of metal weight

$0.25 \times 0.15 \times \dfrac{16}{72} \times \dfrac{2240}{0.089}$ (oxgyen in slag,　　$0.08 \times 0.1 \times \dfrac{16}{72} \times \dfrac{2240}{0.089}$
ft^3/ton Fe)

$= 210$ ft^3/ton metal　　　　　　　$= 47$ ft^3/ton metal

Therefore saving in oxygen $= 163$ ft^3/ton, which at \$0.50/1000 ft^3 is equivalent to a saving of $\$0.5 \times \dfrac{163}{1000} = \$0.08$. On an output of, say, 5 000 000 tons represents A\$407 500 or £190 300.

This assumes, of course, that all other oxygen, other than that lost as FeO, is used at 100% efficiency. This is not so, and the saving of the counterflow system is probably nearer 300–400 ft^3/ton steel.

There is also a substantial iron saving:

$0.25 \times 0.15 \times \dfrac{56}{72}$　　(tons of iron(Fe) lost as FeO/ton steel)　　$0.08 \times 0.1 \times \dfrac{56}{72}$

$= 0.0292$　　　　　　　　　　　　　　　　　　　　　　　　　　$= 0.0062$

which, at, say \$50/ton, represents a saving by use of the counterflow system of $\$50(0.0292-0.0062) = \$50 \times 0.0230 = \$1.15$/ton. On 5 000 000 tons that represents A\$5 750 000 or £2 685 000.

The difference in slag weights and the difference in operation (batch versus counterflow) also means that there is a lime saving by using the counterflow system of about 40–50 lb/ton. Thus, at \$25/ton for lime this represents a further saving of about $\dfrac{\$25 \times 45}{2240} = \$0.0502$. On 5 000 000 tons steel that approximates to A\$2 510 000 or £1 170 000.

Thus, a saving of at least £4 000 000 on 5 000 000 tons (£0.90 per ton steel) may be expected. There should be even further savings in WORCRA (low-level) continuous steelmaking integrated with continuous casting because of reduced capital charges resulting from the more compact plant, the lower building heights and the virtual elimination of most of the heavy crane transfer systems.[3]

References

1. THRING M.W. Mass transfer evaluation for continuous steelmaking. *J. Metals, N.Y.*, **21**, June 1969, 66–9.
2. JENKINS T.W. Contribution to discussion of reference 1. *J. Metals, N.Y.*, **22**, Jan. 1970, p. 2.
3. WORNER H.K. Continuous smelting and refining by the WORCRA Processes. In *Advances in extractive metallurgy* (London: Institution of Mining and Metallurgy, 1968), 245–63.
WORNER H.K. WORCRA (continuous) steelmaking. *J. Metals, N.Y.*, **21**, June 1969, 50–6.
WORNER H.K. AND BAKER F.H. WORCRA iron and steelmaking. In *Alternative routes to steel* (London: Iron and Steel Institute, 1972), 99–106.

I. Imriš*   Will Bailey *et al.* indicate the Cu, Fe, S and O contents in the matte in the matte–slag system (Table 3, p. 91)? If we assume that in the matte $a_{FeS} \simeq N_{FeS}$ and the matte contains mainly Cu_2S and FeS, i.e. $N_{FeS} + N_{Cu_2S} \simeq 1$, the copper content in matte must vary depending on the p_{O_2} value.

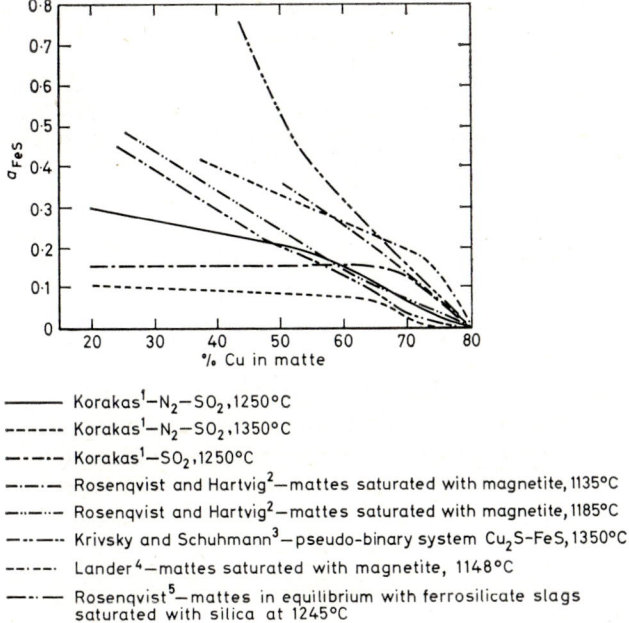

——— Korakas[1]–N_2–SO_2,1250°C
- - - - - Korakas[1]–N_2–SO_2,1350°C
—·—··— Korakas[1]–SO_2,1250°C
—·—·— Rosenqvist and Hartvig[2]—mattes saturated with magnetite, 1135°C
—··—··— Rosenqvist and Hartvig[2]—mattes saturated with magnetite, 1185°C
—···— Krivsky and Schuhmann[3]—pseudo-binary system Cu_2S–FeS,1350°C
—··—· Lander[4]—mattes saturated with magnetite, 1148°C
—··—· Rosenqvist[5]—mattes in equilibrium with ferrosilicate slags saturated with silica at 1245°C

Fig. 7

The activity of ferrous sulphide (Fig. 7, p. 92) differs from that given by Korakas[1] (see also Fig. 7).

References

1. KORAKAS N. Etude thermodynamique de l'équilibre entre scories ferro-siliceuses et mattes de cuivre. Thesis, University of Liège, 1964.
2. ROSENQVIST T. AND HARTVIG T. The thermodynamics of iron–copper mattes and their equilibrium with magnetite. *Meddelelse Metall, Komite*, Trondheim nr. 12. (Unpublished)
3. KRIVSKY W.A. AND SCHUHMANN R. JR. Thermodynamics of the Cu–Fe–S system at matte smelting temperatures. *Trans. Am. Inst. Min. Engrs*, **209**, 1957, 981–9.
4. LANDER H.N. The chemical behavior of oxygen in liquid mattes. S.B. thesis, Massachusetts Institute of Technology, 1954.
5. ROSENQVIST T. Some studies on the thermodynamics of iron–copper mattes and their equilibrium with iron-silicate slags. (Unpublished report)

G. J. Brittingham† It is now widely accepted that molten slags are ionic liquids. It is also firmly established that all copper smelting and converting

* Department of Chemical Principles of Metallurgy, Technical University, Košice, Czechoslovakia.
† Consulting Metallurgical Engineer, Broadbeach, Queensland, Australia.

slags carry an excess of oxygen above that which would satisfy stoichiometric relations for the existence of FeO, SiO_2, CaO, etc. Of the major constituents of the slag, iron is the only element present which exhibits more than one valency under the conditions of existence of the slags, and it is therefore not unreasonable in attempting to visualize the quantity of this extra oxygen to regard it as Fe_2O_3, the other possible stable form for iron oxide; this is also soluble in the slag under the ruling temperature conditions.

The partial pressure of oxygen in such a slag must be a reflection of the ratio of Fe_2O_3 to FeO. The authors also show that the copper solubility is proportional to the oxygen partial pressure, and for equivalent oxygen pressures to the iron content of the slag.

This is merely another way of saying that the copper tenor of a slag is proportional to its ferric iron content. This has a very simple and logical corollary: if the slag is reduced to its minimal Fe_2O_3 content—and this is consistent with the incipient appearance of metallic iron in the system—then the copper tenor will also be minimal. Judging by the work of Yazawa and Kameda,[1] this will be less than 0·1% copper.

It is worth noting that this minimal Fe_2O_3 concentration is a very much lower amount than occurs in the ternary eutectic $FeO-Fe_2O_3-SiO_2$. Consequently, when high copper tenor slags are solidified slowly, and then subjected to a mineral dressing operation, the copper recovered by flotation will be metal (for very high slags) or matte, which are the conjugates of the slag with decreasing oxygen potential due to the freezing out of magnetite. The ternary eutectic, according to Schuhmann and co-workers,[2] carries 9·5% Fe_2O_3, and, consequently, this last remaining liquid must still have an appreciable solubility for copper.

On solidification this liquid will have very finely distributed throughout it particles of matte so small that not only will they be unidentifiable but also irrecoverable.

This is the reason why high copper tenor slags which have been allowed to solidify slowly and are then subjected to mineral dressing techniques produce a metallic and or sulphidic concentrate and a tailing with an appreciable irrecoverable copper content.

References

1. YAZAWA A. AND KAMEDA M. Fundamental studies on copper smelting (II). *Technol. Rep. Tohoku Univ.*, **19**, 1954, 1–22.
2. SCHUHMANN R. JR. POWELL R. G. AND MICHAL E. J. Constitution of the $FeO-Fe_2O_3-SiO_2$ system at slagmaking temperatures. *Trans. Am. Inst. Min. Engrs*, **197**, 1953, 1097–104.

AUTHORS' REPLIES

J. B. W. Bailey, N. E. Brown, F. A. Garner and Professor S. G. Ward With reference to the comments of Dr. C. F. Knights and Mr. P. A. Wright

(p. 143), we would agree that, ultimately, some physical method for the determination of ferrous/ferric ratios in slags is likely to be the most accurate. Some work has been carried out on the Mössbauer technique at Birmingham University, but, unfortunately, the transition metals appear to affect the accuracy of the method adversely.

A method for measuring the magnetic susceptibilities of slags is now being investigated. This, at best, however, can only establish an empirical relationship in the absence of an alternative method for the determination of absolute values of the ferrous and ferric contents.

Mr. G. J. Brittingham (pp. 147–8) accepts that the copper tenor of a slag is proportional to its ferric iron content. This may well be true, but we are not convinced that ferric iron is the primary cause of dissolved copper losses. In a complex slag it is probable that a similar relationship can be demonstrated between 'available oxygen' associated with iron and the transition metals and the dissolved copper tenor. His comments concerning the attainment of minimal Fe_2O_3 contents in slags are most relevant, however, and demonstrate that minimum copper losses will be obtained by slag reduction techniques rather than mineral processing methods.

G. M. Willis I regret that I was unable to be present. I am grateful to Dr. D. G. C. Robertson for his presentation of the paper.

M. P. V. Riboud's comments (pp. 140–3) are more concerned with the detailed mechanism of slag–metal reactions. Even though equilibrium may not be attained, the materials balance relations would still hold throughout the course of the reaction.

In reply to Professor T. R. A. Davey (pp. 143–4), probably many metallurgists have used these methods in various forms, but the metallurgical literature contains very little on them. I deliberately chose to use the generalized expressions throughout in order to compare quantitatively the various methods of refining. If the comparison had been carried out by use of a specific system, such as Pb–Sb–O, the results would have been restricted to that system. It is unfortunate that simple relations give rise to such unwieldy solutions, but they can all be used in graphical methods. They are familiar to chemical engineers and I drew heavily on this literature.

In reply to Dr. T. W. Jenkins (pp. 144–6), the relations derived previously by Thring and by Jenkins were basically materials balances for countercurrent processes, but they were derived as limiting cases from kinetic considerations. The kinetic approach tends to give rather complicated derivations for the special case of equilibrium in countercurrent processes.

Dr. Jenkins' figures are an impressive indication of the advantages to be expected from the use of properly designed processes—particularly countercurrent processes.

Session 3

Hydrometallurgy

Chairman
Dr. F. A. Forward

Behaviour of manganese in the Peace River Mining and Smelting ferrous chloride reduction process

Tyson Rigg M.Sc., Ph.D., F.C.I.C.

Peace River Mining and Smelting, Ltd., Amherstburg, Ontario, Canada

669.094.1 :669.181 :546.711

Synopsis
The ferrous chloride reduction process developed by Peace River Mining and Smelting, Ltd., and presently being used in a plant capable of producing 150 tons of iron powder per day, represents a radical step away from conventional iron powder processes. This process depends heavily on chemical engineering techniques, as can be surmised from the following brief description. The iron source material (ore or scrap metal) is leached or dissolved in hydrochloric acid, converted to ferrous chloride dihydrate and reduced with hydrogen. The hydrogen chloride produced is absorbed in water to regenerate acid for use in the dissolving stage. Since manganese is almost always present in the source material, and since manganese chloride would not be expected to be reduced in this process, it is of interest to establish its behaviour. Investigations into the leaching, crystallization and high-temperature behaviour of manganese chloride are described.

In the iron process developed by Peace River Mining and Smelting, Ltd. (PRMS), ferrous chloride is produced by leaching a suitable ore,[1] or dissolving steel scrap, such as machine shop turnings,[2] in hydrochloric acid. The solution thus obtained is filtered and evaporated to yield crystals of ferrous chloride tetrahydrate, which are separated centrifugally and then partly dehydrated prior to briquetting and reduction by hydrogen at temperatures of up to 800°C. The hydrogen chloride produced during reduction is absorbed in water and recycled to the dissolver. The iron sponge is hammer-milled and screened to produce high-quality iron powder. Some of the powder is recycled to the briquetting stage to control the growth of the iron particles during reduction.

Since manganese tends to occur in practically all iron ores, and is present to some extent in almost all types of iron and steel, it is of interest to consider the fate of this element in the PRMS process.

Ore leaching and dissolution

The compounds of manganese occurring in iron ores are generally quite soluble in hydrochloric acid and, consequently, no favourable separation of manganese from iron can be expected in the leaching stage of the PRMS process in most cases. Defining the separation factor of a particular unit operation as follows:

$$S = \frac{(Mn/Fe)_i}{(Mn/Fe)_f} \tag{1}$$

where the subscripts i and f refer in this case to the initial Mn/Fe ratio in the ore and in the final leach liquor, respectively, it has been found that the leaching of Peace River ore can give rise to values of S as low as 0·87, indicating that the leach solution contains more manganese than the ore, relative to the iron content. This is because the manganese is largely present as carbonate, which is entirely soluble in the acid, whereas some of the iron remains behind in the form of relatively insoluble silicates. When scrap iron is used in the dissolution stage, there is no selectivity and $S = 1·00$.

Crystallization of ferrous chloride

Ferrous chloride separates from slightly acidified aqueous solutions as well defined blue-green monoclinic crystals. Because of the similarity of the Mn^{2+} and Fe^{2+} ions, however, it is very difficult to eliminate manganese during crystallization. The ionic radii of the Mn^{2+} and Fe^{2+} ions are 0·80 and 0·76 Å, respectively, and both chlorides form tetrahydrates. Two monoclinic crystal modifications of $MnCl_2 . 4H_2O$ exist,[3] one being metastable at room temperature but isomorphous with $FeCl_2 . 4H_2O$. The result is that appreciable amounts of manganese are found in solid solution in the ferrous chloride tetrahydrate phase. An investigation of this system has shown that the equilibrium factor

$$E = \frac{(Mn/Fe)_{cryst.}}{(Mn/Fe)_{liq.}} \tag{2}$$

has an average value of 0·50 at 15°C in the range 0–39·6% $MnCl_2 . 4H_2O$ in the crystals.[4] Crystals containing more than 39·6% $MnCl_2 . 4H_2O$ have a structure based on the stable manganese salt rather than the ferrous salt.

The separation factor S for the unit operation of crystallization can be defined as in equation 1, applying the subscripts i and f to the initial feed liquor and the final crystal product, respectively.

It can be shown for the steady state operation of a continuous crystallizer that

$$S = x + \frac{1-x}{E} \tag{3}$$

where x is the fraction of the iron in the feed liquor that eventually appears in the crystal product. For batchwise crystallization, under isothermal conditions, the following relationship is valid:

$$S = \frac{x}{1-(1-x)^E} \tag{4}$$

Preliminary experiments showed that crystallization carried out by the usual laboratory procedure of evaporation by boiling and then allowing the crystals to form on cooling frequently gave somewhat better manganese separation than would be expected on the basis of the equilibrium factor reported by Shchedrina and co-workers.[4] Consideration of the temperature coefficients of solubility for manganese chloride and ferrous chloride suggested that such an effect would be likely. For example, figures quoted for the solubilities of the chloride tetra-hydrates in 100 ml of water[5] are 151 g at 8°C and 160·1 g at 10°C for the manganese and iron salts, respectively. At 100°C the corresponding figures are 656 and 415 g.

Since technical considerations led to the conclusion that a temperature of 55°C would provide good operating conditions for a continuous vacuum crystallizer, a laboratory thermostat was set up in which batchwise crystallizations were performed at this temperature over a suitable range of Mn/Fe ratios. From the measured values of S and x the equilibrium factor E was determined by means of equation 4. The results obtained are shown in Table 1: they confirm the improved separation at the higher temperature.

Table 1   Separation of chlorides of manganese and iron by crystallization from aqueous solution at 55°C

Mn/Fe, % in crystal	S	x	E
4·31	2·35	0·225	0·395
2·15	2·40	0·226	0·386
2·10	2·45	0·190	0·384
0·477	2·41	0·240	0·383
0·296	2·20	0·267	0·417
0·282	2·30	0·282	0·395
0·092	2·38	0·130	0·402
			Mean 0·395

Subsequent results obtained by direct sampling of the mother liquor and crystal product under operational conditions substantiated these findings. In the PRMS Edmonton pilot plant E was found to be 0·410 when crystals with a manganese/iron ratio of 0·45% were being produced. Samples obtained from the centrifuge of the large installation at Amherstburg indicated an average E value of 0·398 when crystals with a manganese/iron ratio of 0·19% were being produced. No effect of free acid variation on E has been noted in the range up to 2·0 N—this is no doubt due to the very weak tendency toward hydrolysis exhibited by the ferrous and manganese ions. Chloride complexing is also very weak and would likewise be expected to give rise to no marked effect on the separation.

Although the manganese separation is improved at higher temperatures, the actual separation achieved when taking a deep cut of iron from the crystallizer is quite small. For example, the designed value of x for the Amherstburg plant is 0·93, and from equation 3 it follows that $S = 1·11$.

Dehydration of ferrous chloride tetrahydrate

No separation of manganese occurs during the flash-drying of ferrous chloride or the subsequent dehydration in the low-temperature end of the reduction reactor. Differential thermal analysis of the heating curves in a hydrogen atmosphere shows the following reactions to take place in the case of both ferrous and manganese chloride:

$$MCl_2.4H_2O \rightarrow MCl_2.2H_2O + 2H_2O \qquad (5)$$
$$MCl_2.2H_2O \rightarrow MCl_2.H_2O + H_2O \qquad (6)$$
$$MCl_2.H_2O \rightarrow MCl_2 + H_2O \qquad (7)$$

The temperatures at which peak rates occur for reactions 5, 6 and 7 in the case of ferrous chloride are 62, 117 and 161°C, respectively. The corresponding temperatures for manganese chloride are 58, 102 and 158°C.

Reduction of ferrous chloride

General behaviour of manganese chloride

The direct reduction of pure manganese chloride by hydrogen is thermodynamically extremely unfavourable at any temperatures considered feasible in the PRMS process. Nevertheless, the behaviour of manganese chloride has been investigated in both dry and moist hydrogen. In dry hydrogen the material merely dehydrates as described above; in moist hydrogen at 600°C some of the manganese chloride is hydrolysed to a light green crystalline oxide. This material displays a particularly well defined X-ray diffraction pattern identifiable as that of manganosite (MnO, cubic).

The reduction behaviour of mixtures of ferrous and manganese chloride is much more obscure. It has been claimed that metallic manganese can be obtained (together with iron) in some cases,[6] but this has not yet been unequivocally demonstrated in this laboratory; when only small amounts of manganese are present in a reduced iron sample, it is very difficult to determine whether it is present in metallic form or as the oxide.

As part of the programme to elucidate the behaviour of manganese chloride during the reduction of ferrous chloride, a sample of the latter that had been prepared by a single crystallization of a Peace River ore leach liquor was reduced in hydrogen at 600°C. The iron sponge obtained was compacted in a 25-mm diameter cylindrical die with a pressure of 980 kg cm^{-2}. The compact was then melted in an alundum crucible under an argon atmosphere in an induction furnace. The resultant small billet was found to consist of fairly clean massive iron with some dark brown glassy slag around the outside. Analysis of the slag showed the presence of more than 2% manganese, together with considerable amounts of alumina, silica and phosphate; minor amounts of chromium and vanadium were also present. The metallic iron was found to contain only 0·01% manganese, the only other detectable impurities being phosphorus and a trace of nickel. It was noted from the spherical nature of the few slag bubbles visible in the metal that the slag appears to have very good fluidity and high interfacial tension. Thus, relatively crude chloride process iron could possibly be quite interesting from the point of view of electroslag melting.

The above results support the view that manganese chloride is not co-reduced with ferrous chloride. It might be argued, however, that the manganese chloride merely enters into reactions with the slag-forming components alumina, silica and phosphate in preference to reduction to metal.

Vaporization of manganese chloride

Early attempts to follow the fate of manganese through the PRMS process were plagued by poor analytical mass balances from stage to stage. These difficulties were found to arise, first, from the presence of small amounts of organic matter in Peace River ore and, secondly, from the vaporization of manganese chloride in the laboratory reduction reactor. The organic matter interfered with the periodate oxidation during analysis of the manganese, but a preliminary treatment with perchloric acid was found to eliminate this trouble. The vaporization of manganese chloride has been studied in more detail and has led to a much better understanding of the processes occurring in the reactor.

The saturated vapour pressure of molten manganese chloride has been measured by Schäfer[7] by use of a continuous-flow carrier-gas method. For the temperature range 999–1216°K Schäfer deduced the following equation for the vapour pressure:

$$\log P \text{ (mm MnCl}_{2\text{liq.}}) = 8 \cdot 559 - 8 \cdot 448 \times 10^3 / T \tag{8}$$

Extrapolation of Schäfer's graphical data to the melting point (650°C) gives a vapour pressure of 0·24 mm, and use of the value of 8970 cal mole^{-1} for the latent heat of fusion given by Kelley[8] leads to the mean value of 49 800 cal mole^{-1} for the latent heat of vaporization of solid manganese chloride over the range 575–650°C.

Substitution of this value in the integrated form of the Clapeyron–Clausius equation enables the approximate vapour pressure of solid manganese chloride to be calculated for other temperatures in this range. On the assumption that the logarithm of the saturated vapour pressure is a linear function of the reciprocal absolute temperature, the following equation was deduced:

$$\log P \text{ (mm MnCl}_{2\text{solid}}) = 11 \cdot 13 - 10 \cdot 85 \times 10^3 / T \tag{9}$$

Equations 8 and 9 have been used to construct the manganese chloride vapour-pressure curve shown in Fig. 1, where the curve for ferrous chloride is shown for comparison. The vapour pressure of manganese chloride is much lower than that of ferrous chloride.

On the basis of these data and the relatively high Fe/Mn ratio in the usual grade of ferrous chloride employed in the PRMS process, some interesting consequences of the reduction mechanism previously suggested[9, 10] would be expected. The essential feature of this mechanism is that all the ferrous chloride must vaporize at the reaction interface before reduction.

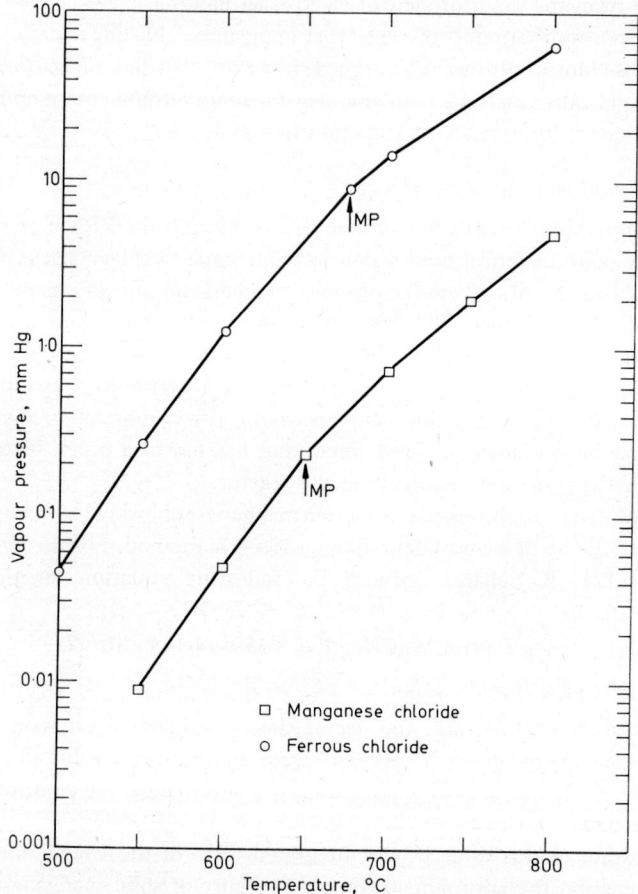

Fig. 1 Variation of vapour pressure with temperature for manganese chloride and ferrous chloride

Since the latent heat of vaporization of manganese chloride is close to that of ferrous chloride, it would be expected that small amounts of manganese chloride would also be completely volatilized at the reaction interface—especially if the manganese chloride were originally dispersed as a solid solution in the ferrous salt. It follows that a considerable amount of the manganese chloride might be swept out from the reaction zone by the hydrogen chloride arising from the reduction of the ferrous chloride.

To investigate this possibility a column of ferrous chloride was prepared and partially reduced in a continuously recirculated stream of hydrogen. The column consisted of six annular pressed blocks of ferrous chloride dihydrate (outer diameter, 76 mm; internal diameter, 22 mm; height, 29 mm; and weight 150 g each). The blocks were stacked vertically, care being taken that they were exactly in register, and loaded into a 100-mm internal diameter vertical downdraught reactor in such a manner that preheated hydrogen could flow over both the internal and external surfaces of the column. The reactor itself was heavily insulated, the whole of the reaction heat being provided by the hot hydrogen. Having left the reactor, the hydrogen passed through an 80-mm pyrex HCl absorption column before being recirculated to the heater by means of a fibre-glass centrifugal fan. The hydrogen therefore contained an appreciable amount of water vapour. Pure water was initially circulated through the HCl absorber and the reduction of the ferrous chloride was timed from the first appearance of an appreciable amount of acid. The hydrogen heater was turned off when it was estimated that about one-third of the ferrous chloride was reduced. The conditions used during the run are shown in Table 2.

Table 2 Heat conditions used during partial reduction of ferrous chloride column

Time, min	Heater temperature, °C	Reactor inlet temperature, °C
0	610	465
8	635	550
15	735	630
28	795	710
38	805	735

After cooling and purging with nitrogen, the partly reduced column was removed bodily from the reactor and sectioned for visual inspection. The sectioning was carried out by removing each segment of the column individually and cutting it through a diameter with a fine-toothed hacksaw, the same orientation being maintained for each segment. Sawing of the partly reduced blocks of ferrous chloride inevitably produced some smearing and cross-contamination of the reduced and non-reduced zones, but this was readily overcome by lightly shaving the sawn surfaces with a razor blade in a direction parallel to the reaction interface. Fig. 2 shows a section of the partly reduced column prepared in this way. It should be noted that the interface is very sharp, and there is little adhesion between the reduced iron sponge layer and the non-reduced core of ferrous chloride.

Samples were removed from the sectioned column in accordance with the scheme shown in Fig. 3. These samples, together with the original ferrous

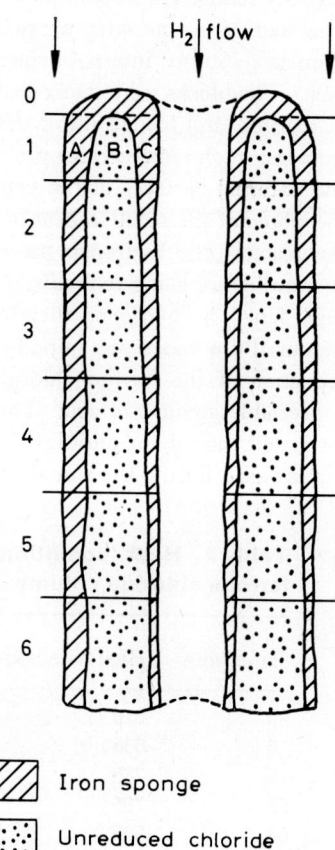

Fig. 2 Section of partly reduced column of ferrous chloride

Iron sponge

Unreduced chloride

Fig. 3 Sampling scheme for material from partly reduced column of ferrous chloride

chloride dihydrate, were analysed for iron and manganese, the results of these analyses being listed in Table 3.

From samples 0 and *A1–A6* it is evident that the reduced iron sponge is depleted in manganese. The mean Mn/Fe ratio of the *B* samples is 496×10^{-5}, showing clearly that no loss of manganese occurs from any particular point until the reaction front passes by. The Mn/Fe ratios in the *A* and *C* samples show a general increase towards the bottom of the column, where lower temperatures prevailed during the experiment. These results strongly support the view that all of the ferrous chloride, along with most of the manganese chloride, is volatilized at the reaction interface. The ferrous chloride is, of course, reduced, but the volatilized manganese chloride may be partly deposited in the cooler regions of the reactor, and some may be swept out with the off-gases.

Table 3 Manganese/iron ratios in samples from sectioned column

Sample	Mn/Fe ratio $\times 10^5$
0	215
A1	294
A2	316
A3	312
A4	312
A5	407
A6	438
B1	484
B2	513
B3	472
B4	513
B5	494
B6	498
C1	279
C2	339
C3	372
C4	351
C5	494
C6	498
Original $FeCl_2.2H_2O$	497

Hydrolysis of manganese chloride

The precise chemical form in which manganese is present in the iron sponge is of considerable importance. Some of the samples taken in the column experiment described above were therefore further examined. The samples (1·0 g) were leached first with water (10 ml) and then with 1% ammonium chloride solution (10 ml), the leach solutions being separately analysed for manganese. The results obtained show that, in this case, almost all of the manganese remained in the form of the water-soluble chloride. The ammonium chloride leach provided a measure of the amount of manganese oxide (MnO) present in the samples. The discovery that most of the manganese remained as chloride in this experiment was somewhat unexpected insofar as previous tests on iron sponge made in the same apparatus gave entirely different results. For example, an iron product analysing 0·16% Mn yielded only 0·01% of water-soluble manganese, whereas 0·11% Mn could be leached out with 1% ammonium chloride and 0·04% remained with the iron. This is attributed to the fact that in the column experiment the ferrous chloride was only partly reduced: hence, substantial amounts of HCl were present in the reactor throughout the experiment. During those runs carried out solely for the purpose of producing iron sponge, however, the hydrogen was recycled until no more HCl was evolved and considerably higher temperatures were attained. In such cases conditions are evidently much more favourable for hydrolysis of the manganese chloride. To verify this the equilibrium constant for the hydrolysis of manganese chloride was calculated for various temperatures in the range of interest, the relevant figures being listed in Table 4.

Table 4 Equilibrium data for hydrolysis of manganese chloride

Temperature, °K	ΔG, kcal mole^{-1}	$\Delta G/4\cdot575T$	Kp, atm
573	19·8	7·56	$2\cdot754 \times 10^{-8}$
673	16·6	5·38	$4\cdot169 \times 10^{-6}$
773	13·5	3·815	$1\cdot531 \times 10^{-4}$
873	10·2	2·554	$2\cdot793 \times 10^{-3}$
973	8·0	1·794	$1\cdot607 \times 10^{-2}$
1073	6·1	1·242	$5\cdot728 \times 10^{-2}$
1173	4·5	0·840	$1\cdot445 \times 10^{-1}$
1273	2·6	0·447	$3\cdot573 \times 10^{-1}$

From the figures for K_p (last column) the percentage HCl in equilibrium with manganese chloride and moist hydrogen of various moisture contents has been calculated. The results of these calculations are shown graphically in Fig. 4. The straight diagonal line is the 'operating line' on which the design of the PRMS reactors has been based.

In the column experiment described above, the dew-point of the hydrogen was approximately 20°C. Thus, on the basis of the thermal data given in Table 2, it can be seen from Fig. 4 that conditions would be favourable for manganese chloride hydrolysis only for the last few minutes of the run, and only at the extreme top of the column. This accounts for the finding that almost all of the manganese in the iron product from this experiment was water-soluble.

In any batchwise reduction of ferrous chloride it appears likely that some of the manganese originally present will be volatilized and carried out of the reactor as the heat front passes through the charge. The dust accumulating in a heat exchanger downstream from the reactor in the pilot plant was, in fact, found to be rich in manganese chloride, and provision has been made in the Amherstburg plant to clean out this material.

It is also possible for hydrolysed or sublimed manganese chloride to remain suspended in the reactor off-gas in the form of an aerosol. In this case it will be swept into the HCl absorber and dissolved in the regenerated acid. This behaviour was observed in laboratory and pilot-plant work, but the amount of manganese accumulating in the acid was not significant from the point of view of re-cycling to the dissolution stage. No manganese has been found in the acid pro-duced in the reduction circuit of the Amherstburg plant.

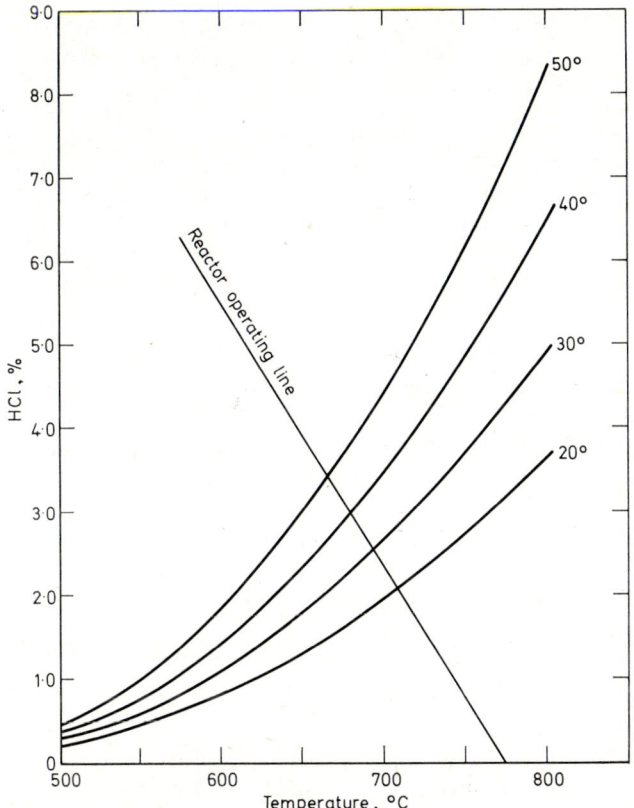

Fig. 4 Equilibrium lines for hydrolysis of manganese chloride in moist hydro-gen at a total pressure of 1 atm. Dew-point of hydrogen is shown against ap-propriate curve

Removal of manganese from PRMS sponge iron

From the above discussion it is apparent that most of the manganese originally present in the ferrous chloride liquor will appear in the sponge iron product. In the normal case of complete reduction of the ferrous chloride, the manganese chloride will be at least partly hydrolysed to manganese oxide (MnO). The removal of this oxide has been the object of a considerable amount of laboratory investigation.

Since the iron sponge displays a high degree of crystallinity (Fig. 5), it was thought that the manganese might be mostly associated with the fines after milling the sponge to powder. As is shown in Table 5, however, it was found that there is only a slight enrichment of manganese in the fines.

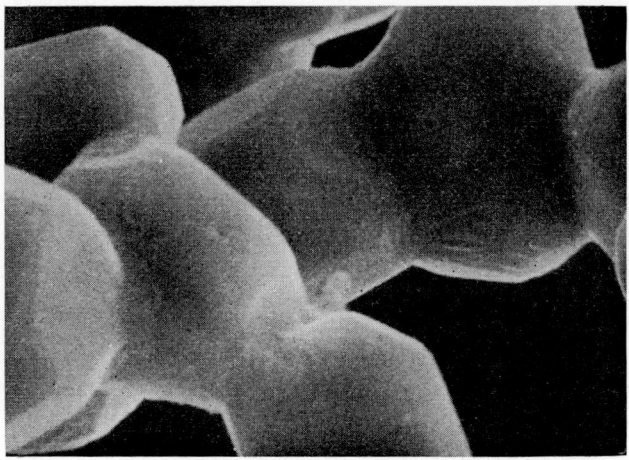

Fig. 5 Scanning electron microscope photograph of iron sponge made by reducing ferrous chloride at 600°C. Magnification, ×12 075

Table 5 Variation of manganese content with size fraction of PRMS iron powder (single cycle)

Mesh, cm^{-1}	Fraction	% Mn
+39	0·013	0·41
+59	0·035	0·41
+79	0·071	0·40
+98	0·035	0·45
+128	0·136	0·48
−128	0·70	0·48

On the basis of these results it was concluded that mechanical separation of the manganese compounds from PRMS iron powder is not feasible. On the other hand, a fairly obvious procedure for removal of manganese chloride would be water-washing of the iron powder. A less obvious possibility arises from the well defined basicity of manganous oxide: it will liberate ammonia from ammonium chloride solutions, the manganese going into solution as the chloride. This process can be represented by the equation

$$MnO + 2NH_4Cl \rightarrow MnCl_2 + H_2O + 2NH_3 \qquad (10)$$

Leaching trials on PRMS iron powder with hot dilute ammonium chloride solutions have been very successful. For instance, 1·0 g of a fully reduced iron powder (lab. batch no. *B13–26*) originally containing 0·16% Mn was leached with water. The leach solution was found to contain an amount of manganese equivalent to only 0·01% Mn in the original iron powder. Subsequent leaching with 10 ml of a 1% solution of ammonium chloride yielded an amount equivalent to 0·11%. Analysis of the washed iron product showed that the manganese content had been lowered to 0·04%.

In another example 100 g of a relatively high-manganese iron powder (lab. batch no. *MFe2*) was leached with 100 ml of 1% ammonium chloride solution at about 80°C for 15 min. The iron powder was vacuum filtered, washed with water, then dried and, finally, re-reduced in hydrogen at 600°C for 15 min. The results of chemical and spectrographic analyses carried out on the iron powder before and after this treatment are shown in Table 6. Other elements besides manganese

Table 6   Analysis of iron powder before (MFe2) and after (MFe3) leaching with ammonium chloride solution

Element	% MFe2	% MFe3
Mn (chem.)	0·57	0·065
C (chem.)	0·07	0·053
Al (spectr.)	0·1	0·001
Ca (spectr.)	0·05	Trace
Mg (spectr.)	0·1	0·004
Si (spectr.)	0·5	0·01

appear to be effectively removed by the ammonium chloride treatment. The removal of calcium and magnesium presumably occurs in a similar fashion to the manganese, but the processes whereby the others are removed most probably involve simple mechanical dispersion.

Other samples of the iron powder before and after the above treatment were subjected to metallographic examination: the samples were deoxidized in hydrogen at 400°C for 30 min, compacted at 6300 kg cm^{-2}, sintered at 980°C for 30 min, compressed at 100 tonnes, sintered again at 980°C for 1 h, mounted, polished and etched with 2% Nital. Photomicrographs of the prepared specimens are shown in Fig. 6(*a*) and (*b*): the ammonium chloride treatment practically eliminates the MnO inclusions.

During the ammonium chloride leaching the manganese tends to be oxidized by atmospheric oxygen to give a precipitate of hydrated manganese dioxide. Hindrance of the separation of the manganese from the iron can probably be overcome by purging the solution with nitrogen. Wet magnetic separation of the iron would, no doubt, give very good results, as it would enable the manganese dioxide precipitate to be washed away together with any extraneous insolubles that might be present.

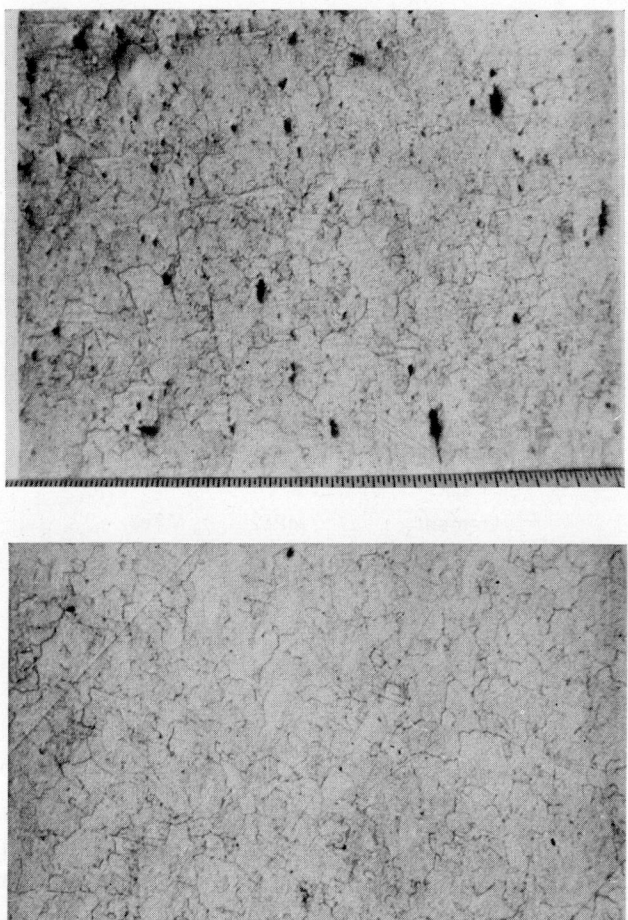

Fig. 6 Manganese oxide inclusions in compacted and sintered PRMS iron: *(a) (top)* before and *(b) (bottom)* after leaching iron powder with ammonium chloride solution. Magnification, ×85

Overall separation of manganese

If the separation factors for the individual operations involved in the process are obtained in a form analogous to that of equation 1, the overall separation achieved in the process is given by the product of the individual factors:

$$S_o = S_1 S_2 S_3 S_4 \tag{11}$$

where S_o is the overall separation factor and S_1, S_2, S_3 and S_4 refer, respectively, to the initial dissolution, crystallization, reduction and ammonium chloride leaching stages. S_1, S_2 and S_4 would be expected to be characteristic of the operation concerned rather than the actual technical system whereby the operation is carried out. The reverse situation holds in the case of S_3, and experience suggests that as the scale of operations increases, S_3 becomes closer to 1·0.

It is interesting to substitute values for the individual factors in equation 11 that have actually been observed in the laboratory: $S_1 = 0·87$, $S_2 = 1·35$, $S_3 = 1·1$ and $S_4 = 8·8$. These values give a product $S_o = 11·4$, showing clearly that the ammonium chloride leach is the only stage that contributes substantially to effective manganese separation. Applying this S_o value to a Peace River ore having typical iron and manganese contents of 35% and 0·085%, respectively, indicates that the final iron product should contain 0·021% Mn. If the final ammonium chloride leaching stage were omitted, however, this figure would rise to 0·19%. In the case of an iron powder process based on the dissolution of scrap iron containing an average of 0·5% Mn, S_1 will be 1·0, S_2 will be 1·1 for a 93% iron cut, and S_3 and S_4 remain the same as in the previous example. Hence, $S_o = 10·6$, so the product would be expected to contain 0·047% Mn. Omitting the ammonium chloride treatment would give a product containing 0·41% Mn.

Recovery of manganese as a by-product

The ammonium chloride leach solution, after separation from the iron powder, contains most of the manganese originally present in the iron. The solution will also contain small amounts of ammonium chloride, free ammonia and, most probably, some suspended manganese dioxide hydrate. The pH of such solutions is usually about 8·0.

The addition of hydrogen peroxide to ammonium chloride leach solutions causes the immediate precipitation of all the manganese in the form of hydrated dioxide. Presumably, oxidation by atmospheric oxygen could be employed to achieve the same result. The manganese precipitate can be readily filtered off.

In a laboratory experiment the manganese precipitate was ignited to convert it to Mn_3O_4 and subjected to wet-chemical and spectrographic analysis. The material was found to contain 69·5% Mn (compared with the theoretical 72·0% for pure Mn_3O_4). The spectrographic results shown in Table 7 illustrate the relatively high purity of this material.

Although the amount of manganese recovered from Peace River ore via the above process would not normally be significant from the economic point of view, it could probably be recovered in the form of battery-grade oxide, which is relatively valuable (approximately $500/ton). Alternatively, it could be stockpiled for later deliberate addition to the process stream for special purposes, such as the production of powder preforms for manganese steel forgings.

Table 7 Semi-quantitative spectrographic analysis of recovered manganese dioxide

Element	Percentage
Al	0·02
Ca	0·1
Cu	0·001
Mg	0·02
Mo	0·08
Ni	0·003
Si	0·1
Ti	0·007
V	0·02

Conclusions

Manganese poses the most difficult separation problem normally encountered in the PRMS process. Fractional crystallization of the ferrous chloride provides very little decontamination from manganese. The only worthwhile operation for the removal of manganese is leaching the crude iron powder with dilute ammonium chloride solution. This is not a difficult procedure *per se* and provides the opportunity for efficient recovery of high-grade manganese dioxide.

References

1. GRAVENOR C. P. GOVETT G. J. AND RIGG T. A hydrometallurgical process for the extraction of iron from low-grade ores. *Can. Min. Metall. Bull.*, **57**, 1964, 421–8.
2. GRAVENOR C. P. RIGG T. AND STONE J. N. A hydrometallurgical process to produce iron powder from scrap iron. *CIM Bull.*, **63**, 1970, 59–64.
3. ZALKIN A. FORRESTER J. D. AND TEMPLETON D. H. The crystal structure of manganese dichloride tetrahydrate. *Inorg. Chem.*, **3**, 1964, 529–33.
4. SHCHEDRINA A. P. OZEROVA M. I. AND KHOMYAKOV K. G. Study of solubility in the system $MnCl_2$–H_2O. *Vest. Mosk. Univ., Khim.*, **19**, no. 1, 1964, 51–2. (Russian text)
5. WEAST R. C. ed. *Handbook of chemistry and physics, a ready reference book of chemical and physical data, 45th edn* (Cleveland, Ohio: Chemical Rubber Publishing Co., 1964).
6. GRAHAM M. E. AND BEIDLER E. A. U.S. Patent 2 596 073, 1952.
7. SCHÄFER H. Sättigungsdrucke der Chloride $MnCl_2$, $FeCl_2$, $CoCl_2$ und $NiCl_2$. *Z. anorg. allg. Chem.*, **278**, 1955, 300–9.
8. KELLEY K. K. Contributions to the data on theoretical metallurgy. XIII. *Bull. U.S. Bur. Mines* 584, 1960, 232 p.
9. RIGG T. Kinetics of the reduction of ferrous chloride with hydrogen. *Can. J. chem. Engng*, **42**, 1964, 247–53.
10. RIGG T. Hydrogen reduction of the chlorides of bi-valent chromium and iron. *Can. J. chem. Engng*, **48**, 1970, 84–90.

Development of a process for the extraction of copper from tailings and low-grade materials at the Chingola Division of Nchanga Consolidated Copper Mines, Zambia

J. A. Holmes B.Sc., M.A.I.M.E., A.M.I.Chem.E., M.I.M.M.

J. F. C. Fisher B.A., M.I.M.M.

Both of Anglo American Corporation (Central Africa), Ltd., Lusaka, Zambia

669.337.123.002.68(689.4)

Synopsis

Owing to changing mineralogy and increased mining of ores from heavily oxidized areas the acid-soluble content of Chingola concentrator tailings has increased to approximately 0·5%. The experimental work that was carried out to evaluate a number of possible processes for recovering this copper is described. It led to a decision to employ solvent extraction for concentration and purification of low-grade leach liquor, followed by electrowinning of copper from the concentrated solution.

Various processes were examined on a laboratory scale, including leach–precipitation–flotation, with iron or H_2S gas as the precipitant; leach–cementation and leach–hydroxide precipitation. Consideration of the costs and copper recoveries obtainable from these various treatment routes led, eventually, to a decision to employ solvent extraction for treatment of solution containing 1–2 g/l copper; and to install a plant to produce approximately 4500 tons of copper per month from tailings and other low-grade materials available at Chingola.

The Nchanga concentrator currently treats approximately 700 000 tonnes per month of copper ore from seven different orebodies. This ore is of mixed oxide–sulphide mineralization, the most important minerals being chalcocite and malachite, with significant proportions of bornite, azurite, chrysocolla, pseudo-malachite and cupriferous vermiculite. The flotation process recovers the sulphide minerals satisfactorily, recoveries in excess of 90% being achieved. Of the oxidized copper mineral forms, malachite and azurite yield reasonably satisfactory recoveries—generally in the range 85–90%; but a significant proportion of these minerals, particularly in the fine-size ranges ($-20\,\mu$m), remains in the tailings. Recoveries of chrysocolla, pseudo-malachite and cupriferous vermiculite are low, and a large proportion of these minerals reports to the concentrator tailings. Since 1965 the ore mined has contained less sulphide and more oxide copper, and increasing proportions of the poorly floating minerals have been encountered such that the tailings currently produced contain an average of approximately 0·5% acid-soluble copper.* Early in 1968 a major research programme was started with the object of proving a method for recovering the acid-soluble proportion of the copper lost in tailings. Attempts to improve recoveries by flotation had not met with significant success, primarily because of the variable and complex mineralization of the tailings, and the decision was taken to examine hydrometallurgical methods of extraction.

In addition to tailings from current production, certain other materials were available for treatment.

(1) Tailings from previous operations; approximately 30 000 000 t of tailings, containing 0·5–0·7% acid-soluble copper, had been produced from operations prior to the introduction of satisfactory methods of oxide copper (malachite) flotation.

(2) 50 000 000 t of tailings from more recent operations, containing 0·3–0·6% acid-soluble copper.

(3) Residue from current operations at the Nchanga leach plant, amounting to some 50 000 t/month and containing 250–400 t/month of entrained copper in solution.

(4) 1 800 000 t of stockpiled low-grade oxide concentrates, surplus to current treatment capacity, containing 2–2·5% acid-soluble copper.

It should be noted that the test work reported in this paper occupied a period of no more than 18 months, from April, 1968, to November, 1969. The prime object of the test work was to define probable costs and recoveries, and to pinpoint areas where technical difficulties might be encountered. It was believed that, after a final decision had been taken on the process to be adopted, there would be ample time during planning and construction for such detailed work as might be required to determine optimum operating and plant design parameters. In consequence, much of the work, to a rigorous research mind, must appear somewhat disjointed and haphazard, and certainly lacking in detail. This approach was necessitated by the paramount urgency of installing a process to yield profits as soon as possible.

Leaching characteristics

Because of the low grade of the material to be treated, only leaching with sulphuric acid, which could be made available at relatively low cost from local smelters, was considered. Initial laboratory investigations showed that typical leaching characteristics of the current tailings, when leached with agitation at ambient temperature, at a pulp density of 10% solids, were as shown in Table 1. Leaching characteristics of the older dump tailings were similar. Further leaching tests at varying pulp densities up to 60% solids showed that this factor had a negligible effect on leaching efficiency.

* The amount of copper which dissolves in a standardized laboratory leach procedure, viz. agitation for 1 h in a 5% solution of sulphuric acid saturated with SO_2.

Table 1 Leaching characteristics of typical Nchanga current tailings (December, 1968)*

Acid tenor (constant), g/l	Leaching time, min	Copper extraction, % total Cu	Acid consumption, kg/t	
			Total	By gangue
5 (pH 1·2)	5	58	10	4
5 (pH 1·2)	30	72	12	4
5 (pH 1·2)	120	78	13	5
2 (pH 1·6)	5	49	8	3
2 (pH 1·6)	30	65	10	3
2 (pH 1·6)	120	74	12	4

* Assay: 0·69% total copper; 0·52% acid-soluble copper.

It was evident from these tests that no difficulty should be experienced in obtaining satisfactory extraction of the acid-soluble copper by sulphuric acid leaching at low acid tenors, and also that the acid consumption figures were low enough to form the basis for an economic process.

Examination of possible processes for recovery of copper from solution

Initial consideration of the problem led to the proposal of a number of alternative processes, the more important of which are listed below.

In the *leach–precipitation–flotation* process the tailings pulp is leached with sulphuric acid, and the copper in solution is precipitated either as the sulphide or with finely divided iron as metallic copper. This is followed by flotation to yield a concentrate for further treatment by smelting.

Leaching of the tailings pulp in the *leach–cementation* process is followed by solid–liquid separation, and the resultant solution is treated by cementation, either with scrap iron, or iron sponge, yielding a high-grade cement copper sludge for further treatment.

The *leach–hydroxide precipitation* process follows that of leach–cementation, but the solution would be neutralized with milk of lime and the resultant copper hydroxide treated by smelting or leaching and electrowinning.

The use of solvent extraction for the recovery of copper from solution was also considered at this time. Note was taken of the solvent extraction operations at Ranchers Exploration Co.'s 'Bluebird mine',[1] which had been reported to be experiencing some difficulties, and also of the pilot-scale work being carried out by the Bagdad Copper Corporation.[2] It was decided, however, to suspend judgment on this process until these operations had proved themselves. There were considerable doubts as to the scale of operating costs due to organic phase losses and also as to the effects of fungus growth and impurity build-up.

It was believed that, depending primarily on crud formation, losses of organic phase could be as great as 1–5 gal/1000 gal of aqueous solution—incurring a cost in the range K150–K600/t of copper produced. Fungus growth was also believed to be a major problem, which could lead to frequent stoppages and losses of organic inventory. If these problems were of the magnitude believed possible at this early stage, there is no doubt that a solvent extraction process would have been unable to compete with the more conventional precipitation processes. The major consideration, however, was time. It appeared that, owing to the largely unproved nature of the solvent extraction process, a long development programme would be required before any firm decision could be taken as to its feasibility. It was therefore believed that a decision to examine solvent extraction in detail would necessarily have involved a delay, perhaps of as much as two years, in the implementation of the project—with the consequent loss in potential profits.

Another factor was the development work being carried out at this time on the production of metallic iron by reduction of Rokana reverberatory furnace slag. This would have had the effect of making available substantial quantities of low-cost iron, since the bulk of the cost of this process would have been covered by the revenue from copper extracted from the slag together with the iron.

Investigation of the leach–precipitation–flotation (LPF) process

CEMENTATION WITH IRON

Initial investigations of the LPF process were directed towards the use of iron as the precipitant. The preferred source of iron was granulated iron ex smelter slag (see above).

Tests had shown that the size of the iron granules could be controlled anywhere in the size range 3–40 mesh by proper regulation of the water volumes and pressures used for granulation. There were, accordingly, two possible methods available for cementation: (a) use of coarse granules in a rotating drum, with a screen for removal of any granules entrained in the pulp, or (b) addition of fine (-30 mesh) granules to an agitator prior to flotation.

Cementation tests with a small rotating drum showed that the cementation reaction was reasonably fast, provided that there was a large excess of iron in the drum. Pulp residence time in the drum for 98–99% cementation from solution was no more than 2–3 min. No difficulty was experienced in the use of the coarsest ($-3 +10$ mesh) granules from water granulation, and, in this case, little iron would be carried over from the cementation drum to flotation. This method is similar to that used in the past by Miami Copper Corporation,[3] except that there scrap iron was used in the cementation drum.

Cementation in an agitator with fine iron granules was not so straightforward. In order to obtain reasonably fast cementation it was found necessary to use large excesses of iron (in the range 3–5 lb iron/lb of copper precipitated). A large proportion of this excess iron could, however, be recovered by magnetic separation of the tailings after flotation. This confirmed the results of operations at Ray Mines Hayden plant[4] and the earlier operations at Butte.[5] A further problem in the use of iron granules for cementation in an agitator was the formation of a dense, adherent coating of copper on the granules, which tended to inhibit further cementation.

Flotation after cementation posed few problems. Laboratory investigations showed that concentration by flotation could yield recoveries of approximately 90% of the copper dissolved in leaching, at concentrate grades in the range 60–70% copper. In order to maintain the recovery in this range it was necessary to maintain excess metallic iron in the pulp. This prevented air oxidation of the iron and resolution of the copper by ferric iron or by direct oxidation.

Owing to the lack of residual iron in the pulp with the use of coarse granules in a drum for cementation, recoveries to flotation concentrate were generally some 5–10% lower when this method was employed. Overall iron consumption was, however, somewhat lower. Table 2 summarizes the advantages and disadvantages of the two methods of cementation when applied to the LPF process.

Table 2   Recovery of copper by LPF process by use of iron cementation: comparison of methods of cementation

Method of cementation	Overall copper recovery from solution, %	Iron consumption, lb/lb copper recovered	Remarks
Coarse granules in rotating drums; iron granule size +3 –10 mesh	80–87	1·5–2·0	Possible explosion hazard in cementation drum
Fine iron in an agitated tank; iron size −30 +200 mesh	89–92	1·8–2·5	Large circulating load of iron necessary, which must be recovered by magnetic separation after flotation

PRECIPITATION OF COPPER AS THE SULPHIDE

Two possible methods for precipitation of copper from the pulp as copper sulphide were considered: (a) use of H_2S gas, which could be generated by the action of sulphuric acid on pyrrhotite or low-grade matte, and (b) use of a mixed calcium sulphide–iron reagent as used at Morenci.[6, 13]

It was realized that the use of H_2S gas would pose severe problems, due to its extreme toxicity, but it was believed that these could be overcome[14] if the process had any real advantage over iron cementation. A fairly extensive laboratory test programme was carried out by use of H_2S precipitation. Although acid would be required for the H_2S production, the overall acid consumption was not expected to be greater than that used for cementation. It was believed that if the precipitation could be carried out concurrently with the leaching, there would be considerable regeneration of sulphuric acid

$$H_2S + CuSO_4 \rightarrow CuS + H_2SO_4$$

which would then be available for further leaching. This, in fact, proved to be the case. It was found, however, that concentrate grades were adversely affected, and a slightly lower recovery to cleaner concentrates was obtained in comparison with leaching followed by precipitation. These effects were probably due to coating of unleached particles with copper sulphide, thereby preventing completion of the leaching reaction and downgrading the concentrate. This could be overcome by the use of much higher acid strengths in leaching—which, however, resulted in higher overall acid consumptions. Typical results with H_2S precipitation both concurrently with the leaching and after leaching are shown in Table 3. In order to prevent excess H_2S remaining in solution, the end-point was controlled to a redox potential of 150 mV, measured with a calomel reference electrode, at which point copper remaining in solution was less than 0·01 g/l. This control by redox potential was found to be simple and satisfactory, and would certainly have found application in a large-scale plant.

The low concentrate grades attained were somewhat disappointing; a further factor which gave concern was the poor settling and filtration characteristics of the concentrates produced. It proved impossible to filter these concentrates to moisture contents of less than approximately 40%.

Because of the extreme toxic hazard of H_2S gas, attention was directed towards other means of precipitating copper as the sulphide. The use of sodium hydrosulphide was considered, but was rejected owing to its high cost. It appeared, however, that a mixed calcium sulphide–iron reagent, patented by Phelps Dodge and used at Morenci,[6] might well be useful. This reagent is prepared by reaction of lime, coal and pyrites at temperatures in the region of 1000°C.

$$FeS_2 + 2CaO + 2C \rightarrow Fe + 2CaS + 2CO$$

The reagent would then precipitate copper from solution both as metallic copper

$$Fe + CuSO_4 \rightarrow FeSO_4 + Cu$$

and as the sulphide

$$CaS + CuSO_4 \rightarrow CuS + CaSO_4$$

Since all three starting materials (coal, pyrites and lime) were locally available, it appeared that such a reagent might be prepared at a cost comparable with that of H_2S gas, and, moreover, the toxic gas hazard would be avoided.

Laboratory investigations proved the feasibility of manufacturing such a reagent, and indicated that more than 90% of the iron and sulphur in the pyrites could be made available for precipitation of copper. Further tests were accord-

Table 3 LPF results with H_2S as precipitant

| Tailings feed | | | Consecutive (i.e. leaching followed by precipitation) or concurrent (leaching and precipitation simultaneously) | Rougher concentrate | | | Cleaner concentrate* | | | Flotation collector |
% Total copper	% Acid-soluble	Acid-soluble copper as % of total		Grade % total copper	% Recovery based on Total copper	% Recovery based on Acid-soluble copper	Grade % total copper	% Recovery based on Total copper	% Recovery based on Acid-soluble copper	
0·98	0·76	77·5	Consecutive	4·7	86·7	111·8	24·9	81·7	105·4	Aero 194
1·04	0·85	81·7	Concurrent	4·5	87·4	106·9	15·8	79·9	97·8	Aero 194
0·65	0·52	80·0	Consecutive	7·5	75·3	94·1	25·2	72·6	90·8	Cyanamid S3302
0·65	0·50	77·0	Concurrent	5·0	73·3	95·3	18·6	68·0	88·4	Cyanamid S3302

* Open-circuit, single-stage cleaning.

ingly carried out with this reagent as the precipitant in a LPF process. These tests were not particularly successful by comparison with the use of H_2S gas, since copper recoveries to concentrate were, in general, some 10% lower, at reduced concentrate grades. No satisfactory explanation for the poor flotation performance could be found. Flotation was carried out at pH 4·2–4·4, Cyanamid reagent S3302 being used as collector—conditions which had been found satisfactory for the flotation of both cement copper and copper sulphide from H_2S precipitation. It is possible that a more detailed examination of alternative flotation conditions and collectors would have yielded improved flotation performance, but considerable work would have been required and it was not believed that further investigation of this particular process route was justified at the time.

It should perhaps be noted that throughout the investigations on the various LPF processes relatively little work was done on optimizing flotation conditions. Had the investigations proceeded further, this aspect would have received more attention. In particular, investigation of flotation at higher pH ranges would have been carried out, if only for the purpose of saving on equipment costs.

Investigation of the leach–cementation process

The choice of a leach-cementation process necessitated the introduction of a solid–liquid separation stage. In view of the low grade and large tonnage of material to be treated, it was decided that a massive filtration plant would incur too great a capital cost, and attention was directed towards countercurrent decantation in thickeners for separation of the copper solution. Tests were therefore carried out to determine the settling characteristics of the materials under consideration, both before and after leaching. Settling rates and terminal pulp densities were found to be extremely high when a suitable polyacrylamide reagent was used for flocculation. It was shown that it would be possible to thicken the unleached tailings from approximately 35 to 65% solids at a rate of more than 1·0 t/ft²/day. Similar results were obtained for thickening the leached tailings from 17 to 65% solids. This meant that countercurrent decantation with four 250-ft diameter thickeners in series should achieve 98–99% recovery of the copper in solution for cementation from 1 000 000 t/month of tailings.

In view of the size of the proposed plant, and the form of the iron expected to be produced from smelter slag, cementation in conventional scrap launders was discounted in favour of a more sophisticated continuous cementation process. It appeared that the continuous cementation cones developed by the Kennecott Copper Corporation[7, 8] were the best alternative.

The advantages claimed for the Kennecott cones—low labour utilization, by comparison with scrap launders, lower iron consumption and relatively easy mechanization and automation—had already been proved by the operations at Bingham Canyon.

The work carried out at Rum Jungle[9] on a pilot pulsed column was also of interest, but this method was finally discarded as being insufficiently proved by comparison with the Kennecott method. The proposed plant would have been similar to the particulate iron cones developed by Kennecott. Some adaptation might have been necessary, since it was proposed that granulated iron produced from smelter slag should be used as the precipitant.

In view of the possibility that iron in this form would not be suitable for cementation in a cone precipitator, the use of a rotating drum precipitator similar to that used at Mangula[10] with scrap iron was considered. Pilot-scale tests were carried out with a small drum precipitator, and this was shown to yield satisfactory results with granules in the size range 2–5 mm. It was shown that a rotating drum with capacity for approximately 50 tons of granules would be required for production of 2000 ton/month of cement copper. Iron consumption in the pilot-scale drum was in the range 1·1–1·4 lb/lb of copper precipitated. A major disadvantage of the drum-type precipitator was the hazard of explosions in the drum caused by hydrogen evolved in the cementation reaction (as had been experienced at Mangula).

The leach–hydroxide precipitation process

A major cost in all the processes considered is the neutralization of any effluent or residue prior to disposal: this would be carried out by addition of lime to pH 7·5–8·0, thereby precipitating all iron and aluminium in solution, together with a proportion of the calcium and magnesium, and any remnants of copper. It became evident that lime precipitation of the copper from a clear solution, followed by thickening, filtration and subsequent smelting or leaching of the copper hydroxide precipitate, might have some merit. At first sight it appeared that no more lime would be required than was necessary in the LPF and leach–cementation processes, and the capital cost of the additional plant would not be high, unless capital were required to provide additional treatment capacity for the copper hydroxide–calcium sulphate precipitate. Tests showed, however, that this precipitate would be unlikely to contain more than approximately 17% copper, due to contamination with calcium sulphate, and iron and aluminium hydroxides; in addition, the filter cake would contain approximately 60% moisture. These facts would militate against reasonably cheap smelting of the precipitate. Capital costs would also be substantial if a leach process were to be considered.

In addition, problems of purification and solution balance would need to be solved, which would require the use of considerably more lime than that theoretically required for copper precipitation.

Evaluation of the various process routes

In mid-1969 an evaluation of the more promising processes was carried out. It had by then become clear that the recovery of iron from reverberatory furnace slag was rather more difficult than had previously been expected, and that a further lengthy and expensive test programme would be required to prove an economic process. The availability of iron from slag could not therefore be counted on, and attention was focussed on processes which did not involve the

G

use of granulated iron from the smelter. Four major variants were considered in detail.

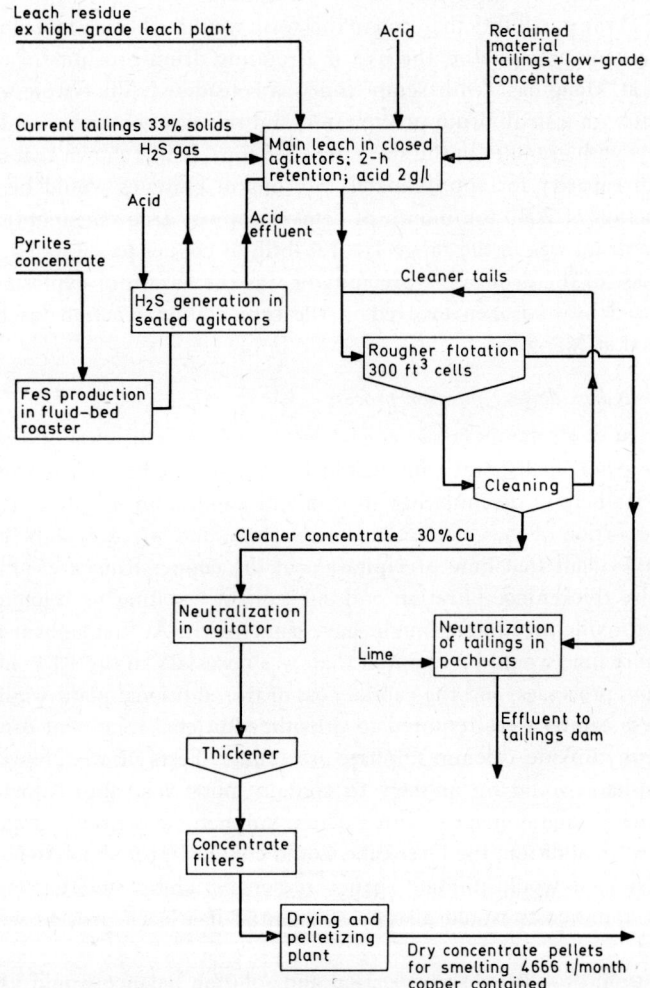

Fig. 1 Process 1: leach–precipitation–flotation by use of H$_2$S gas

(1) *Leach–precipitation–flotation* with H$_2$S gas generated by acid attack on a local pyrrhotite concentrate.

(2) *Leach–cementation* with imported shredded iron scrap in Kennecott-type cone precipitators.

(3) *Leach–cementation* with locally prepared particulate iron in a Kennecott-type particulate iron cone: the particulate iron would be prepared from imported pig iron, which would be melted, with additions of pyrites to improve grindability, and granulated.

(4) *Leach–hydroxide precipitation* with lime.

Flowsheets for these four processes are shown in Figs. 1–4. All other alter-

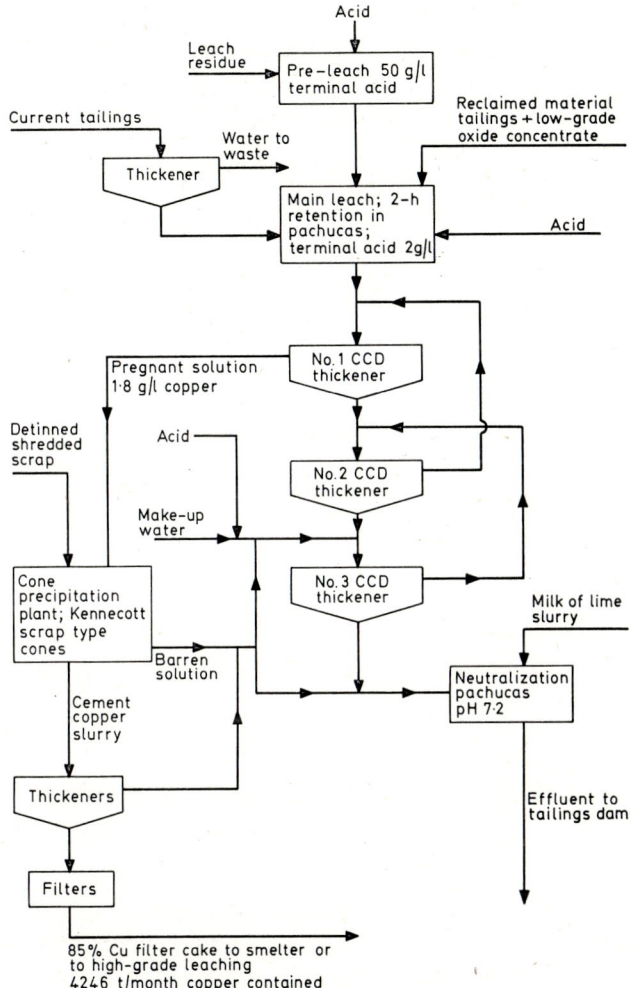

Fig. 2   Process 2: leach–cementation by use of imported shredded scrap

natives were discarded on grounds of higher capital or working costs, or of lower metallurgical recoveries. Preliminary estimates of the capital and working costs of the four processes are summarized in Table 4. It should be emphasized that the costs quoted refer to the specific product indicated in each case. Further costs, both capital and operating, would be incurred for processing through to finished copper. Where these differ between processes, appropriate notes are

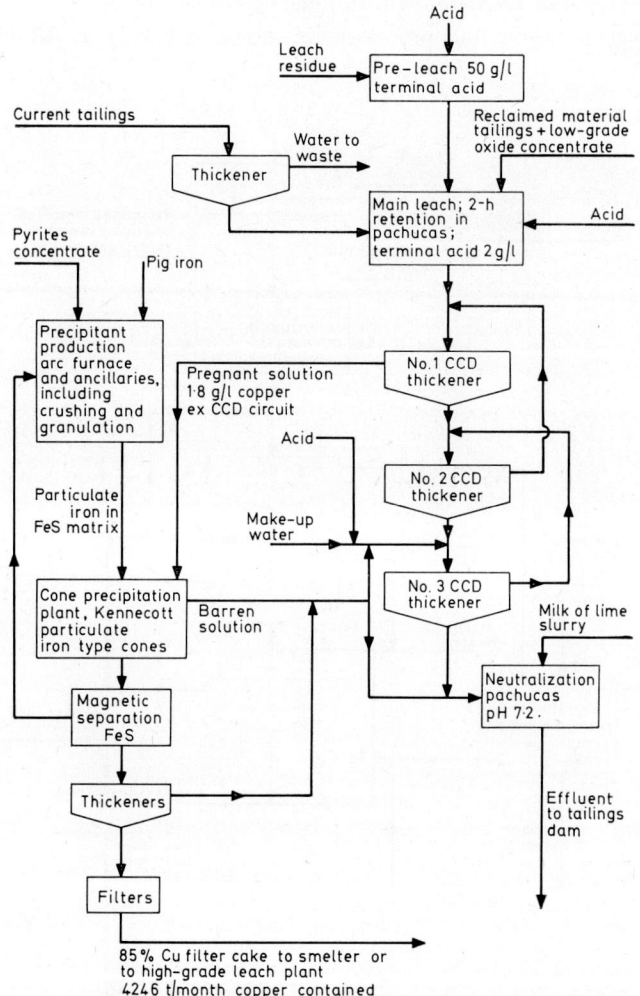

Fig. 3   Process 3: leach–cementation by use of granulated pig iron

given. In all cases the costs quoted refer to a total treatment rate of 463 000 t/month of current tailings, 136 000 t/month of high-grade dump tailings and 91 000 t/month of leach plant residue, making a total of 690 000 t/month of material.

Process 1, LPF with H_2S gas, was not particularly favoured, partly because of the high capital cost (to which must be added the cost of additional smelter capacity), but also because it could not easily be converted to cementation should cheap iron become available from slag reduction. It would, however, have had particular merit if a slag-cleaning process had been adopted at the Rokana smelter, which would have given rise to a low-grade matte suitable for H_2S production. It would also have been necessary to embark on a detailed pilot-scale study before the process could be adopted for full-scale use.

Processes 2 and 3 required little or no further investigational work, and treatment of the cement copper product did not appear to pose any major problems. Both processes could be adapted relatively easily to the use of cheap iron if it were made available from smelter slag, in which case the operating cost would drop by about K60–K90/ton of copper recovered, and the overall cost to finished copper would be less than for process 4. Kennecott cones were preferred to rotating drums for cementation, primarily on account of their lower capital cost; in addition, for scrap iron, they could be easily and quickly designed with

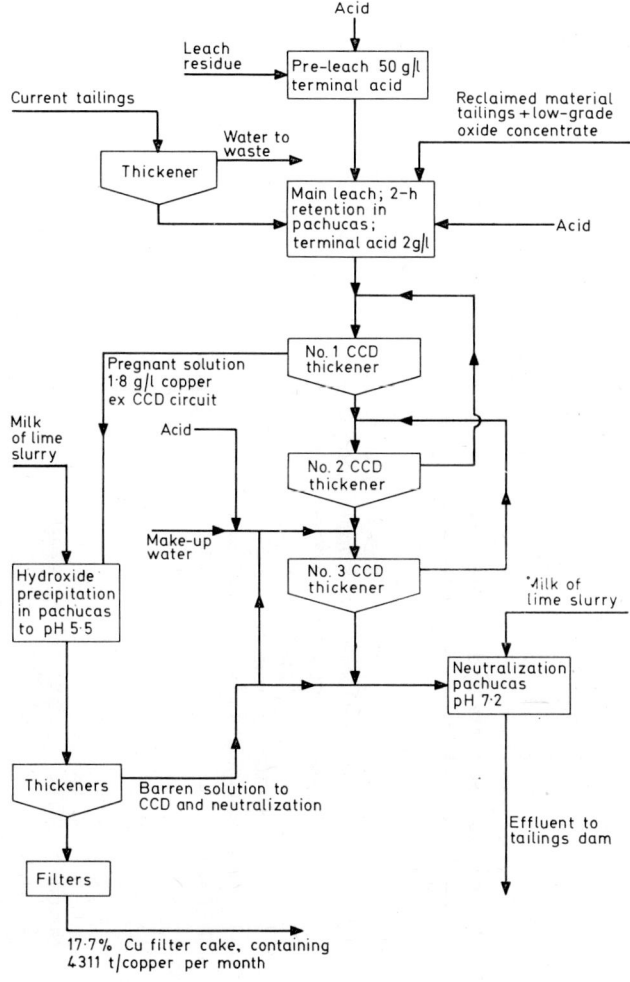

Fig. 4 Process 4: leach–hydroxide precipitation

Table 4 Comparison of costs and recoveries for the four processes

	Capital cost, $K \times 10^6$*	Operating cost, K/t copper in product*	Recovery of copper from leach solution, %	Product	Treatment route, product to finished copper	Overall recovery from solution to finished copper, %	Remarks
Process 1 (LPF with H_2S gas)	17·4	139	95–100	Sulphide concentrate containing 25% copper	Smelting via Rokana smelter	90–95	Further work required on H_2S production; disadvantage of toxic gas. No problem in smelting; difficulties in concentrate drying
Process 2 (leach–cementation with shredded scrap)	12·1	235	97–99	Filter cake containing 85% copper	(a) Smelting via Rokana smelter (b) Leach–electrowinning at Chingola	93–95 94–96	Recovery figure assumes reverberatory furnace smelting

Process							Remarks
Process 3 (leach–cementation with particulate iron)	13·9	195	97–99	Filter cake containing 85% copper	(a) Smelting via Rokana smelter	93–95	As for process 2, but development work required to prove manufacture of particulate iron
					(b) Leach–electrowinning at Chingola	94–96	
Process 4 (leach–hydroxide precipitation with lime)	13·6	93	97–99	Filter cake containing 17% copper	(a) Smelting via Rokana smelter	89–91	Low recovery and high smelting cost in smelter due to low grade of material and high moisture content
					(b) Leach–electrowinning at Chingola	94–96	Difficult water balance problems due to low grade of material. Solution purification problems require investigation. Both (a) and (b) would involve considerable extra capital for converting 17% copper filter cake into finished metal

*The costs obtained at this stage were not the subject of detailed estimates and must therefore be regarded as relative only. £1.00 = Kwacha 1.7.

guaranteed performance, whereas some further development work would have been necessary before rotating drum sizes could be specified exactly. The explosion hazard in rotating drums was also a factor which militated against their use. No major problems were foreseen in the adaptation of a Kennecott cone plant for use with granulated iron.

Process 4 required little further direct investigational work, but the further processing of the 17% copper product (also containing 60% moisture) posed a number of problems. The low smelter recovery and high drying and smelting cost made this route somewhat unattractive. Leaching, on the other hand, in the main Nchanga leach circuit, was not favoured, partly owing to the high moisture content and partly to solution balance and purification problems requiring additional lime and acid. Although the initial operating cost appeared low, the final cost from solution to finished copper would not have been much less than for processes 2 and 3, and the capital cost for leaching and washing the product and purifying the resulting solution for electrowinning would have been much higher.

Further economic calculations showed that all the processes considered were viable and would have given an acceptable return on capital.

Consideration of a solvent extraction process based on LIX 64N for recovery of copper from solution

During the course of these investigations operation of the solvent extraction process at Bluebird mine in Arizona[11] had been proceeding satisfactorily. It was realized that a process based on solvent extraction for recovery of copper from solution might well compete favourably with any of the processes so far considered. Visits were accordingly made to Bluebird mine and discussions were held with staff from General Mills, Inc., and with others interested in solvent extraction applied to copper recovery. It was apparent that there were indeed many advantages[12] to be gained from the use of a solvent extraction circuit, followed by electrowinning for copper recovery. Earlier misgivings as regards the scale of solvent loss and of fungus and crud formation were shown to be largely unfounded.

After some consideration, the circuit shown in Fig. 5 was proposed: this involved four major process steps: (1) leaching; (2) countercurrent washing in thickeners; (3) solvent extraction, yielding a high-grade solution for electrolysis, and a raffinate in which the copper has been replaced by acid—this raffinate is then returned to the countercurrent decantation thickeners and the acid is therefore partially reused; and (4) electrowinning. (It should be noted that all the processes which have been discussed would require an electrowinning or electrorefining stage for production of refined copper.)

The prime advantages of the solvent extraction process were seen as follows. (1) There is a large reduction in operating cost compared with any other process considered, which arises from three major sources: (a) the cost of the organic reagent at the expected loss of 0·1 gal/1000 gal raffinate is substantially less than

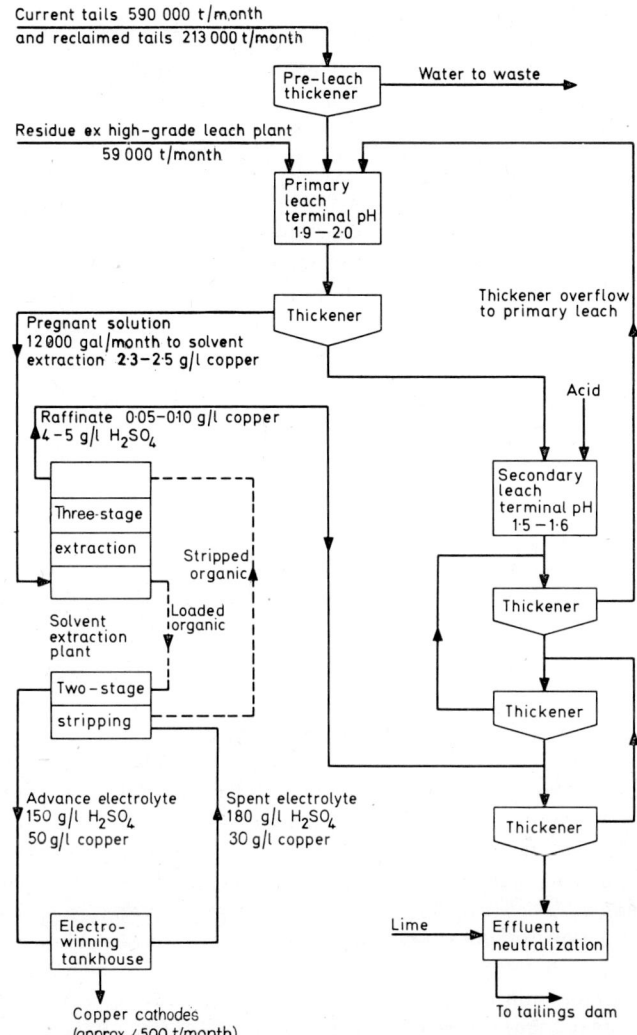

Fig. 5 Proposed leach–solvent extraction circuit

the cost of producing (or importing) any of the other precipitants considered (with the possible exception of iron produced from slag reduction, which was not a proved process at the time); (b) since the acid equivalent of the copper leached is regenerated, the total acid consumption is less by approximately 30%, and an equivalent reduction in lime consumption would also accrue; and (c) the capital and working costs of handling and treating any of the other products (see Table 4) to yield electrolytic copper are considerably greater than the cost of electrowinning copper from the electrolyte produced from solvent extraction.

G*

(2) The cathode copper produced from the solvent extraction and electrolytic process would be of good physical and chemical quality. The electrolyte produced from solvent extraction would contain very little iron, and negligible amounts of selenium, bismuth and other deleterious impurities. Selenium levels of less than 0·3 ppm could be expected (2–3 ppm in current electrowon cathodes at Nchanga).

In view of these factors a firm decision was taken in November, 1969, to proceed with the planning and implementation of a solvent extraction process in preference to any of the other processes which had hitherto been examined. It is currently envisaged that the full-scale process will come into operation late in 1973, and will produce approximately 4500 t of additional copper per month. Feed materials for this plant will be 590 000 t/month of current tailings, 213 000 t/month of high-grade dump tailings and 59 000 t/month of leach plant residue, making a total of 862 000 t/month of material.

Estimated capital and operating costs are given in Tables 5 and 6. A compari-

Table 5 Estimated capital costs (K × 10³) for plant for production of 4500 t/month of copper from low-grade materials via solvent extraction (LIX 64N) or cementation

	Solvent extraction	Cementation
Plant services	2381	1588
(water, air, steam, site clearing, drainage, roads, etc.)		
Housing	2166	1310
Tailings reclamation	889	889
Thickening, leaching, countercurrent washing	8290	7290
Neutralization and tailings disposal	919	1950
Lime storage, slaking and handling	1089	1634
Acid storage	455	733
Solvent extraction, including solvent inventory	9232	—
Cone cementation plant	—	900
Electrical installations	2079	2079
(excluding tankhouse)		
Electrowinning tankhouse	10 079	—
Miscellaneous offices, etc.	329	329
Cement copper filtration* drying, pelletization		1800*
Additional smelter casting facilities*		1300*
Additional electrorefining facilities		9200*
(including copper inventory)*		
Total, K × 10³	37 908	31 002

* These figures have not been subject to careful estimation and must therefore be regarded as approximate only.

son is also given with the costs of a similar-size plant with the use of cementation with scrap iron in Kennecott cones. These costs, by world standards, are relatively high: by way of comment, however, current estimating prices in Zambia for erected structural steel and for mass concrete are K450/t and K35/m^3, respectively.

In order to study the operating problems of this relatively new process, as far as copper is concerned, a small pilot circuit was set up in June, 1970, to treat approximately 1 gal/min of leach solution through the solvent extraction circuit. A larger-scale pilot circuit producing $\frac{1}{2}$ ton of copper per day will be commissioned in September, 1971.

The decision to adopt a solvent extraction route involved some delay in implementing the process, and, as an interim measure, it was also decided to

Table 6 Estimated operating costs (K/t copper) for extraction of copper from low-grade materials at Chingola by solvent extraction (LIX 64N) or cementation

	Solvent extraction	Cementation
Sulphuric acid (K25/t)	62	93
Lime (K15.56/t)	22	34
Flocculants	24	25
LIX 64N * ($2.44/lb)	20	—
Kerosene* (K0.75/gal)	8	—
Filter aid	3	—
Labour (operating)	8	5
Maintenance (labour and materials)	12	12‡
Power (including electrowinning)	21	6
Lead anodes	1	—
Furnacing	13	—
Iron† (K75.4/t)		113
Royalty (for use of cones)		8
Filtering, drying, pelletizing, railage to smelter‡		10
Cement copper smelting§		25
Refining		25
Total, K/t refined copper wirebar	194	356

* Figures based on loss of 0·1 gal of organic per 1000 gal raffinate.
† Iron consumption estimated at 1·5 lb/lb copper precipitated.
‡ Not examined in detail and cost figure must therefore be regarded as approximate only.
§ It is envisaged that this copper would be treated in the converters at Rokana smelter.

install as quickly as possible a limited-size cementation plant to treat the highest-grade materials available, i.e. stockpiled low-grade concentrates and residue from the high-grade leach plant, imported scrap iron being used in Kennecott cones for cementation. Apart from the cementation cones, much of the rest of this stage 1 plant (leaching tanks, thickeners, etc.) will form a part of the final solvent extraction process (stage 2). This intermediate stage will be commissioned shortly, and is expected to operate for about two and a half years, the main plant being commissioned in 1974. During this intermediate stage the plant is expected to produce 2000–2300 t of cement copper per month, which will be processed through the Rokana smelter.

The design and operation of both the stage 1 and stage 2 plants will be the subject of future publications.

Acknowledgment

The authors wish to thank the Managing Director of Nchanga Consolidated Copper Mines, Ltd., for granting permission for the publication of this paper. The investigation of the various processes was carried out by staff of the Research and Development Division of N.C.C.M. in Kitwe. These investigations involved a very considerable amount of work, only the barest details of which are included in this paper, but which, nevertheless, was necessary to enable a proper appraisal of the various processes to be made.

References

1. Ranchers' recovers Bluebird oxide copper by solvent extraction. *Wld Min.*, **22**, April 1969, 63; 79.
2. McGarr H. J. Solvent extraction stars in making Ultrapure copper. *Chem. Engng*, **77**, no. 17, Aug. 1970, 82–4.
3. Bean J. J. The leach–precipitation–flotation method of concentration at Miami Copper Company. *Colo. Sch. Mines Q.*, **56**, July 1961, 263–81.
4. Franz M. W. Leach–precipitation–flotation process. *J. Metals, N.Y.*, **11**, 1959, 383–5.
5. Huttl J. B. How new leach–float plant handles Greater Butte's ore. *Engng Min. J.*, **154**, June 1953, 90–3.
6. Barker L. M. U.S. Patent 3 168 396, 1965.
7. Spedden H. R. Malouf E. E. and Prater J. D. Cone-type precipitators for improved copper recovery. *J. Metals, N.Y.*, **18**, 1966, 1137–41.
8. Back A. E. Use of particulate iron in the precipitation of copper from dilute solutions. *Trans. Am. Inst. Min. Engrs*, **238**, 1967, 12–6.
9. Allman M. B. *et al.* Pilot-scale copper precipitation using particulate iron in a pulsed column. In *Mineral processing and extractive metallurgy* (London: Institution of Mining and Metallurgy, 1970), 95–106. (*Proc. 9th Commonw. Min. Metall. Congr. 1969, vol. 3*)
10. Mangula leach plant. *Chamb. Mines J.*, **7**, Sept. 1965, 54–8.
11. Rawling K. R. Commercial solvent extraction plant recovers copper from leach liquors. *Wld Min.*, **22**, Dec. 1969, 34–7.
12. McGarr H. J. Berlin N. H. and Stolk W. F. A. The cost of copper . . . Solvent extraction and electrowinning look great on paper. *Engng Min. J.*, **170**, Dec. 1969, 66–7.
13. Bolles J. L. The Morenci L.P.F. process. Paper presented at AIME Centennial meeting, New York, 1971.
14. Thornhill P. G. Wigstol E. and Van Weert G. The Falconbridge matte leach process. *J. Metals N.Y.*, **23**, July 1971, 13–8.

Unit operations of solid–liquid separation, product concentration and recovery in hydrometallurgical processing systems

P. J. D. Lloyd Ph.D.

Chamber of Mines Research Organisation, Johannesburg, South Africa

669.012.7:669.066:669.053.4

Synopsis

A comparison is made between three different systems for the recovery of metal values from leach slurries, and between ores ground to two different finenesses fed to each system. From this study it appears that, in general, countercurrent decantation should require somewhat greater capital expenditure than filtration, if no flocculants are employed, and that both should require more capital expenditure than a system involving desanding in cyclones, washing of the cyclone underflow on filters, and recovery by a system which can treat a slime-containing solution, such as resin-in-pulp. Moreover, it is shown that the capital requirement of the cyclone-desanding/filtration system is significantly less sensitive to the size distribution of the feed than that of the other two systems.

Arising from these conclusions a countercurrent cyclone cascade has been designed and tested. High efficiency for metal recovery with low overall water demand has been shown on the 120 t day^{-1} scale for feeds as fine as 50%—10 μm by weight. This has been integrated with a countercurrent resin-in-pulp contactor which utilizes a novel, high-density ion-exchanger. From the design parameters obtained from pilot-plant tests to date, an extrapolation is made to a full-scale plant. The results of this indicate that there is a possibility of a significant reduction in the capital requirement of plants to recover metal values from leach pulps containing a high proportion of fine slimes.

There are currently very few routes available to the hydrometallurgist to recover metal values from leach slurries. An ore must be ground to a certain size to permit the valuable constituents to be leached, and that size then sets the size of the equipment for separating the leach solution from the leached solids. For instance, filtration or settling rates are set by the fineness of the ore grind, and the sizes of filters or thickeners (in countercurrent decantation) are thereby determined.

Of course, in some cases, the size distribution of the ore particles in the leach slurry is set more by concentration considerations than by liberation. In a recent

study[1] an ore which could be concentrated by flotation only at a size of 80%
−37 μm could be leached readily at a size of 60% −150 μm, at which size it was
readily filtered or settled. This interaction between size distribution and process
parameters does not appear to have received much attention in the literature on
hydrometallurgy.

This problem became acute in a study of the recovery of uranium from the
Witwatersrand slimes dams, in which the gross worth of metal values in the
slimes was of the order of only R0.50/t.* An analysis of the problem showed
that the capital costs of filtration or countercurrent decantation (CCD) circuits
were excessive. Table 1 gives the order of magnitude of capital costs for typical
circuits to treat 5000 t day^{-1}. All circuits were designed to recover >99% of the
metal values and were costed on a similar basis.

**Table 1   Approximate capital costs of plants to recover metal values from
5000 t day^{-1} of leached solids**

Description of plant	Capital costs for grinds of	
	50% − 150 μm	50% − 44 μm
Two-stage filtration with solvent extraction	R900 000–1 300 000	R2 300 000–3 200 000
Countercurrent decantation with solvent extraction	R1 200 000–1 700 000	R3 100 000–4 100 000
Cyclone desanding, filtration of cyclone underflow, resin-in-pulp metal recovery	R1 200 000–1 700 000	R1 400 000–1 900 000

Analysis of these costs showed that (1) it was always more expensive to process
a fine slurry than to process a coarse one; (2) the cost of producing a dilute
slurry was far lower than the cost of producing a clear leach liquor; and (3)
the cost of metal recovery from a dilute slurry was far higher than that of recovery
from a clear solution.

Arising from this analysis, a circuit was designed which avoided total separation
of solids from liquids, but which recovered the soluble metal values in high yield
and at high concentration. Further analysis of systems for the recovery of metal
values from dilute pulps indicated that the costs of this step could also be reduced
very significantly. It is the purpose of this paper to describe the work on both
the partial separation of liquids from solids and on the recovery of metal values
from dilute slurries. The overall system shows promise of reducing both the
capital and operating costs for the recovery of metal values from leach slurries
very significantly in comparison with conventional systems.

* All costs in this paper are given in terms of Rand: R1.00 = $1.40, approximately.

Countercurrent cyclone washing circuit

Cyclones may be thought of as solid–liquid separating devices. Compared to filters or thickeners, the conventional solid–liquid separating units employed by the hydrometallurgist, they are remarkably efficient. For instance, a typical filter fed with a 50% by weight pulp may yield a liquor containing 0·5% solids and a cake containing 20% moisture. Then the efficiency as a solid–liquid separator may be defined as the product of the ratios of the solids in the cake to the solids fed and the liquid in the filtrate to the liquid fed, which for this example works out as 0·748. On the same basis, the solid–liquid separation efficiency of a cyclone can exceed 0·5.

Considerable effort went into the design of circuit to take advantage of this effect. The circuit which was eventually chosen is shown in Fig. 1. This circuit

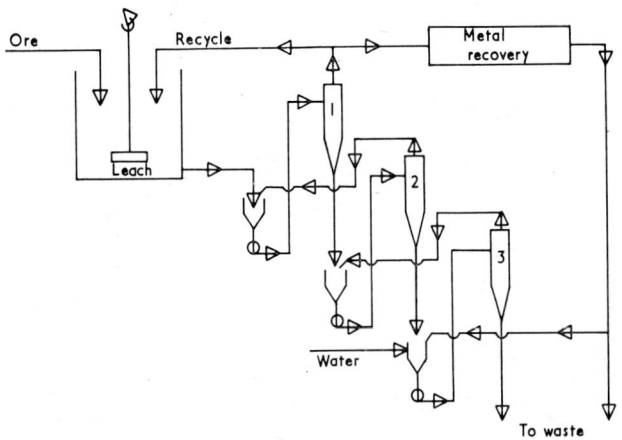

Fig. 1 Countercurrent cyclone cascade

has been employed in the starch industry,[2] but not previously in the metallurgical industry, except as a pilot plant.[3]* The circuit avoids filtration entirely, and, as such, permits the recycle of pulp about each cyclone in order to build up the concentration of metal values. Such recycle cannot be employed economically in conventional solid–liquid separation systems because there would be a drop in the efficiency of metal recovery of each stage in a countercurrent cascade, which, in turn, would require the addition of further stages to the cascade to maintain the overall efficiency. This is indicated in Fig. 2, in which the separating elements in the countercurrent cascade are assumed to give a clear 'overflow' and an 'underflow' containing 50% solids by weight, for a feed to the first stage of 25% solids by weight. The reflux ratio is here defined as the ratio of the amount recycled to the total overflow. Four stages with a reflux ratio of 0·4 at the first

* In this pilot plant water consumption was relatively high because gravity-fed cyclones were used, which did not permit recycle of slimes after metal recovery.

stage give a slightly higher efficiency than two stages with no reflux, and a metal concentration in the product solution nearly 70% higher than with two stages.

The technique of recycling in order to increase metal concentrations is economic in cyclone circuits because the cost of extra cyclone stages in a countercurrent cascade is small relative to that of extra thickener or filter stages.

A pilot plant to test these ideas has been operated continuously for the past 18 months on a South African gold mine. The design parameters for this plant

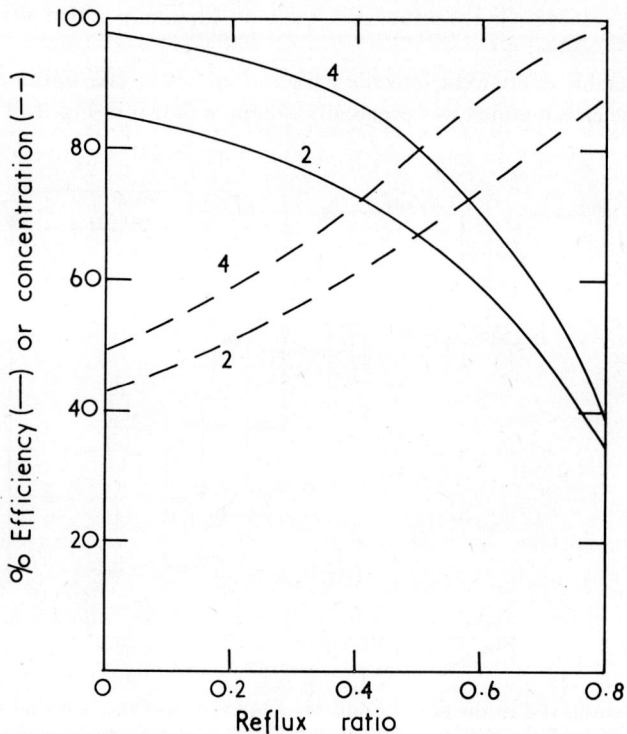

Fig. 2 Effect of reflux ratio on cascade efficiency and metal concentration for two and four countercurrent cascades

have been described previously.[4] The plant has operated with three countercurrent stages close to design expectations, although operability was reduced by sanding out in feed tanks, which made the feed to each stage finer than the 50% $-10\ \mu$m which was expected, and by excessive downtime on the cyclone feed pumps.

Nevertheless, an overall operability approaching 70% of the theoretical was achieved. During the period of optimum operation, a throughput of dry slime of nearly 120 t day^{-1} was attained for the entire cascade of three stages, each consisting of a single 150-mm cyclone (Krebs D6BB), and fed with a slurry containing approximately 25% solids by weight at 7·6 dm³ s⁻¹ (100 Imperial gal/min) and at a pressure of 330 kN m⁻². For a fresh feed in which the solids were effectively >50%−10 μm, more than 96% soluble uranium recovery was obtained in three stages for a total water demand of 1·1 t t⁻¹ feed slime, although this could be reduced to 0·8 t t⁻¹ feed slime by recycle from waste disposal. The resultant product slurry contained <17% solids by weight, the solids being >95%−20 μm, and the uranium concentration in the solution being >55% of the concentration in the feed slime.

To permit the extrapolation of the results of the plant to different feeds, a mathematical model of the plant was developed and tested. This model required the development of somewhat more sophisticated descriptions of the behaviour of the individual cyclones than had previously been available, and it is perhaps

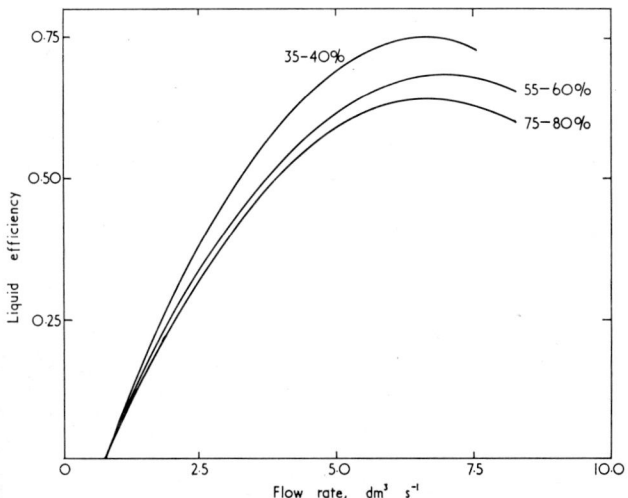

Fig. 3 Variation of liquid efficiency with flow rate for feeds of varying fineness (%−10 μm)

of interest to outline this description. For cyclones fed with slurries containing up to 28% siliceous solids, the split of liquid between the underflow and overflow was chiefly a function of the feed rate to the cyclone, and varied slowly with the fineness of the feed. The relationship is given in Fig. 3, in which the lines given are least squares polynomial fits to the experimental data.

The data from a number of runs at constant flow rate are shown in Fig. 4. From both Figs. 3 and 4 it is apparent that at feed rates of up to approximately 3·0 dm³ s⁻¹, feed rate alone determines the liquid efficiency. Above this, particle-size distribution plays an increasingly marked role for feeds finer than approximately 40%−10 μm.

Similar results were found for the size rejection function, defined as the ratio of the weight of solids in a given size fraction in the underflow to the weight in the same fraction in the feed. This is shown in Fig. 5. At feed rates above approximately 5·7 dm³ s⁻¹ the size rejection function becomes dependent only on the fineness of the feed. An increase in fineness from 35 to 55% − 10 μm has a marked effect on the size rejection function at flow rates above about 5·7 dm³ s⁻¹. A further increase to 75% − 10 μm has the same effect as a decrease in flow to about 4 dm³ s⁻¹ when the feed remains above 55% − 10 μm.

These results make it clear that there are significant simplifications in the descriptions of the behaviour of hydrocyclones published previously,[5−8] which neglect any possibility of interactions between feed flow rate and fineness, and liquid and solid separating efficiency. Nevertheless, the satisfactory modelling of

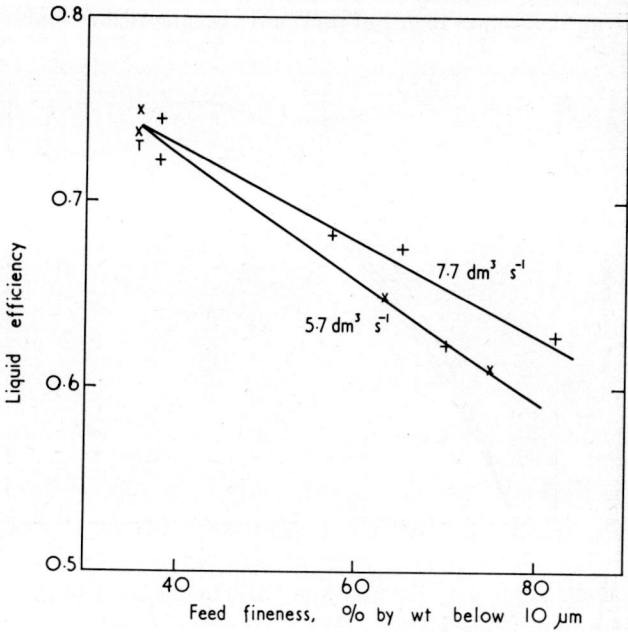

Fig. 4   Variation of liquid efficiency with feed fineness at constant flow rate

a countercurrent cyclone cascade has been found to depend rather critically on the development of models for the behaviour of the individual cyclones, such as has been presented here.

A comparison of the results of an experimental run and of the computed model is made in Table 2. The data for this model were merely the overall input streams to the plant, the descriptions of cyclone performance outlined above, the flow rate to the first cyclone and the description of any splits in streams within the plant to provide reflux, etc. These comparisons between experiment and model can thus be valuable in correcting experimental data on the plant and in finding the optimum conditions for operation.

The agreement between the measured and simulated values is thought to be

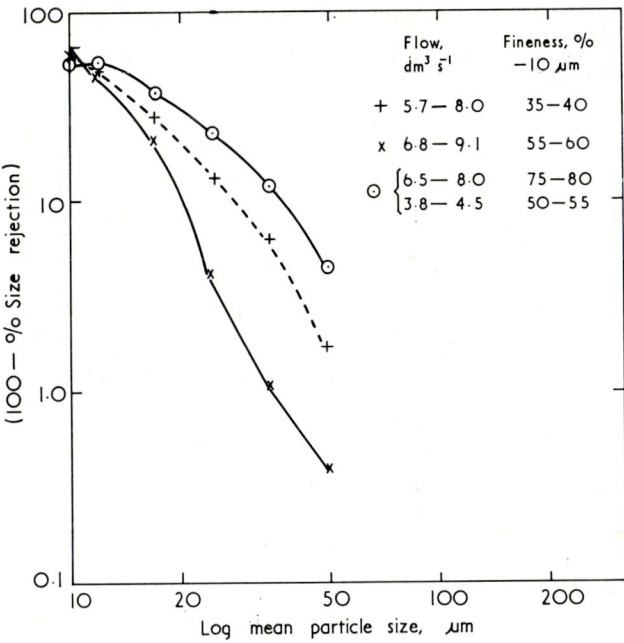

Fig. 5 Variation of size rejection function with feed rate and fineness

Table 2   Comparison of measured and simulated countercurrent cyclone cascade performance

Stream	Flow rate, dm³ s⁻¹		% −10 μm	
	Measured	Predicted	Measured	Predicted
Feed to No. 1 cyclone	8·62	8·62*	68·6	71·2
Overflow from No. 1 cyclone	5·17	5·25	81·7	90·2
Underflow from No. 1 cyclone	3·76	3·37	47·6	53·9
Feed to No. 2 cyclone	7·83	7·44	49·1	65·1
Overflow from No. 2 cyclone	4·79	4·53	84·0	88·2
Underflow from No. 2 cyclone	3·20	2·91	39·4	46·3
Feed to No. 3 cyclone	7·35	6·87	64·7	59·2
Overflow from No. 3 cyclone	5·02	4·32	81·5	86·5
Underflow from No. 3 cyclone	2·86	2·55	37·5	39·7

* Assumed identical to measured value.

very reasonable, particularly when the inherent experiment errors are considered. For instance, the measured flow rates to the cyclones have an estimated error (two standard deviations) of about 7%, the overflow rates an estimated error of about 4% and the underflow rates an estimated error of about 10%. Most of the computed values lie within these ranges and, although there is a tendency for the computed values to be less, this may well arise from a low value for the flow to the first cyclone. A more sensitive test of the model is the percentage by weight below $10\,\mu m$ in the solids fraction in a stream, which can be determined by direct measurement. The measurement is difficult and thus liable to higher absolute errors (probably of the order of 20%), but systematic errors are less likely. Comparison of the measured and computed values shows that there is no systematic difference between the values.

The model was used to predict the performance of the countercurrent cyclone cascade when operating on the coarse and fine slimes considered in the cost

Table 3 Comparison of performance of a four-stage countercurrent cyclone cascade for a feed of coarse or fine slime, using Krebs D6BB cyclones to treat 60% solids leach slurry

	Coarse slime	Fine slime
Feed to each cyclone, t solid day^{-1}	153·4	121·3
Number of cyclones for 5000 t day^{-1}	132	168
Feed to each cyclone, dm^3 s^{-1}	7·6	7·6
Product flow rate		
dm^3 s^{-1}	73	95
t day^{-1}	6360	8680
Relative metal concentration in product stream	0·83	0·65
Product stream, % solids	5·2	12·0
Water demand, t day^{-1}	2080	4170
Final waste slurry, % solids	48	40

study presented in Table 1. In each case four stages of cycloning were needed to obtain $>99.9\%$ soluble metal value recovery. A comparison of the performance of the circuit when treating the coarse and fine slimes is made in Table 3.

The total water demand is very low—this is partly because no bleed of fines from the system is necessary, the underflow of the last cyclone having a size distribution identical to that of the feed. If this final slurry were to be impounded in a slimes dam, some of the contained water would be expected to be recovered, reducing the water demand still further. Also of note is the relatively low flow rate of the product stream. Comparison with the flow rates for other circuits, such as those of Table 1, indicates that the product stream from this cascade is very significantly lower than that from either a CCD or a desanding/filtration circuit, and not much higher than that from a filter circuit.

Recovery of metal values from a product pulp

It was noted above that by currently known technology the recovery of metal values from the dilute pulps is more expensive than the recovery from clear solutions. The countercurrent cyclone cascade produces a pulp which is dilute in solids, and in which the solids are extremely fine.

The low concentration of solids reduces the viscosity of the pulp relative to that of more concentrated slimes, which means that higher rates of mass transfer can be obtained. The fine size of the solids reduces markedly the abrasive nature of the pulp, and also results in the ability to use moderate flow rates in processing equipment without there being danger of sanding-out. Thus, the pulp which is the product of a countercurrent cyclone cascade forms the ideal feed for a resin-in-pulp recovery system.

In a previous paper[4] the various types of resin-in-pulp equipment were compared and contrasted, and the conclusion was reached that use of a multi-stage fluidized-bed contactor offered the best means of developing an efficient and cheap form of equipment for this operation. Work on such a contactor has been progressing in several parts of the world,[4,9,10] with generally encouraging results. The form of contactor currently favoured is a sieve-plate type of column in which resin transfer down the column is by periodic reversal of flow. This type of contactor is satisfactory for very dilute pulps, but suffers from two drawbacks: (1) the throughput per unit area of column is severely limited by the relatively low difference in density between the resin and the solution or pulp and (2) the transfer of resin from stage to stage is rather uncontrolled because of uneven flow through the plates.

We have studied[11] a novel form of particulate ion-exchanger which has properties similar to those of the typical ion-exchanger resin, but which is of far higher density. This development has suggested a design of multi-stage fluidized bed contactor which is truly continuous.

The ion-exchanger is formed by the impregnation of a liquid ion-exchanger into a porous particle. The impregnate is stable provided that the liquid ion-exchanger preferentially wets the solid, i.e. the exchanger is retained within the pores, and its loss rate is determined solely by its solubility in the aqueous phase.

A range of such impregnates has been prepared by use of a variety of exchangers and porous particles. For the extraction of uranium from sulphate solution 0·6–1·0 mm fireclay particles having a free volume of approximately 15% and an average pore size of approximately 3 μm were treated with 0·1% by weight of a proprietary silicone (to make the surface oleophilic and hydrophobic) and then with 7% by weight of Alamine 336, a long-chain tertiary amine produced by General Mills, Inc. A gold exchanger for use in cyanide solutions was prepared by impregnating XAD-2, a macroreticular polystyrene adsorbent produced by Rohm and Haas, with Alamine 336. An exchanger for copper from acid sulphate solution was prepared by impregnating fireclay, pretreated with silicone, with LIX-64N, an exchanger also produced by General Mills, Inc.

The properties of the porous particle largely determine the physical and chemical behaviour of the exchanger. A high-density material can be produced in this way, the density of the impregnate being a function of the proportions of liquid ion-exchanger and porous substrate. A compromise is necessary between the use of a low proportion of liquid exchanger, which gives a high density, and a high proportion of liquid exchanger, which gives a high exchange capacity. Similarly, a high rate of exchange can be obtained by use of a large-pored particle, but this tends to increase the rate of loss of the liquid exchanger. For the treatment of the dilute slurries produced by a countercurrent cyclone cascade the best combination of porous substrate and liquid ion-exchanger yet found gives an exchanger of particle density 2·6 t m^{-3}, a capacity of 3·7 kg U m^{-3} wet-settled resin, and a relative rate of mass transfer of 70×10^{-6} s^{-1}. For comparison, an experimental batch of a high-density conventional resin had a particle density of 1·13 t m^{-3}, a capacity of 13·3 kg U m^{-3} and a relative rate of mass transfer of 12×10^{-6} s^{-1}. The selectivity of the impregnate type of exchanger, as determined by iron pick-up, was significantly higher than that of the conventional exchanger.

The importance of particle density in determining the allowable throughput may be judged from conventional terminal velocity equations, which indicate that the permissible velocity is proportional to the square root of the density difference between particles and fluid.

For particles of equal equivalent spherical diameter, in a slurry containing 5% siliceous solids (sp. gr., 1·033), the exchanger of sp. gr. 2·6 has a terminal velocity nearly four times higher than that of sp. gr. 1·13, and in a slurry of 15% solids it has a terminal velocity nearly nine times higher.

Thus, there are very strong incentives for increasing the particle density of exchangers when slurries are to be treated. The higher permissible flow rates mean that slurries containing relatively coarse particles may be treated without danger of sanding-out, and also means that smaller equipment may be employed, with a saving in capital.

A further advantage of the availability of a dense exchanger is that it enables a continuous fluidized-bed contactor to be designed. Fig. 6 is a diagram of two typical stages in the contactor. Basically, these each consist of a sieve plate and a weir/downcomer. A fluidized bed of the exchanger is maintained over each sieve plate (shown in light cross-hatching in Fig. 6), and the exchanger overflows each weir to form a packed bed (shown cross-hatched) at the bottom of each downcomer. By arranging that the angle at A in Fig. 6, which marks the limit of the blanked-off section of the sieve plate below the downcomer, is approximately equal to the angle of repose of the exchanger, the fixed bed can be maintained satisfactorily, and acts as a seal to prevent significant bypassing of liquid up the downcomer. The exchanger is picked up and drawn into the fluidized bed in the area of contact between the fixed and fluidized beds, which effectively increases the angle beyond the angle of repose and permits more exchanger to flow down the downcomer. Because pick-up rates are directly proportional to the difference in density between the solid and liquid,[12] it is relatively simple to operate this system satisfactorily when a dense exchanger is

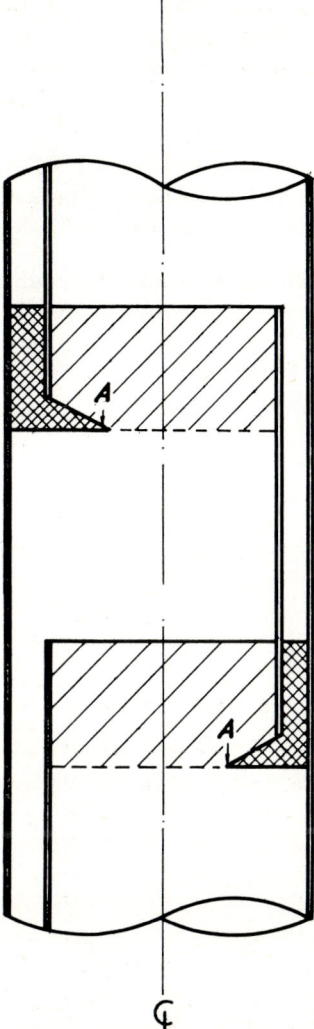

Fig. 6 Two stages of a continuous countercurrent resin-in-pulp column

being used, but nearly impossible with a conventional ion-exchanger, because pick-up rates are too high to permit a fixed bed to be formed.

The fixed bed can be maintained in a stable state quite satisfactorily. If there is a drop in the level of the bed, there is an increase in the flow up the downcomer, which reduces the net velocity at the pick-up surface and thus reduces the feed rate from the downcomer. The relatively small quantity of liquid which bypasses the stage by flowing up the downcomer reduces the efficiency of each stage slightly, even though some exchange does occur during passage through the fixed bed. By keeping the cross-sectional area of the downcomer small relative to that of the column, this loss of efficiency can be reduced to negligible levels.

This form of contactor has previously found wide application in the field of gas–solids reactions, but attempts to apply it in the field of liquid–solid reactions have not met with marked success previously—possibly because of a lack of understanding of the role played by the fixed bed in forming a seal between the stages.

Studies on extraction of uranium by fluidized beds of the dense exchanger have shown that a bed 400 mm deep can give the equivalent of a theoretical stage at

Table 4   Estimated capital costs of a countercurrent cyclone cascade–continuous resin-in-pulp system to treat 5000 t day^{-1} of ore

	Coarse slime	Fine slime
	R	R
Cyclones	61 000	84 000
Sumps	17 500	20 000
Pumps	40 800	46 000
Extraction columns	18 000	27 000
Eluting column	11 000	11 000
Precipitation	3 000	3 000
Filtration	10 000	10 000
Reagent make-up and storage	32 000	32 000
Equipment cost	193 300	233 000
Installation	38 700	46 600
Piping	58 000	69 900
Instrumentation	19 300	23 300
Electrical	48 000	56 000
Buildings	25 000	25 000
Physical plant cost	382 300	453 800
Engineering and construction	76 500	90 800
Resin inventory	4 400	5 200
	R463 200	R549 800

superficial velocities of 25 mm s^{-1}. For treatment of the product of the countercurrent cyclone cascade considered previously, eight theoretical stages would be sufficient to give >99% recovery from a solution containing 320 or 255 ppm U (from the coarse and fine slimes, respectively, see Table 3), and the resin flow rates would be 5·91 and 6·14 dm^3 s^{-1}, respectively, in order to attain an 80% loading. To treat the whole of the flow from the cascades treating the coarse and fine slimes in single columns would require columns of 2·16- and 2·64-m diameter, respectively. These parameters are used in Table 4 to estimate the capital costs of the complete system on the assumption that the resin is eluted by use of ammonium sulphate, with added ammonia for pH control, and precipitated directly.

Of importance is the low cost of the recovery circuit, brought about by the small size of the extraction and elution columns. This enables the complete plant, including the countercurrent cyclone cascade, to be installed in a single building about 16 m × 33 m in plan. Further, the low inventory of resin (about 12 m^3) and its low cost (about R350/m^3) reduces the cost of the extraction reagent inventory markedly. In contrast, the inventory or organic phase in the typical solvent extraction plant can easily be worth more than R100 000.

Although it is apparent that the continuous resin-in-pulp system which utilizes a dense, impregnation-type resin offers a means of substantially reducing the cost of resin-in-pulp recovery or soluble metal values, it must be stressed that this conclusion is based on only short-term tests of the resin-in-pulp system in 0·3-m columns at flows of up to 1·5 dm^3 s^{-1}. Nevertheless, such encouraging performance has been obtained that it is felt valid to make the extrapolation presented here with reasonable confidence.

Discussion and conclusions

Comparison of the costs of the solid–liquid separation section for countercurrent cyclones with those for desanding/filtration suggests that countercurrent cycloning will be slightly more expensive than desanding/filtration for coarse slime, but slightly less expensive for fine slime. Preference must lie with the countercurrent cyclone system, however, in view of the lower volumes of product pulp, and the far lower water demand, for this system and for the same tonnage treated.

It may be noted that the capital cost of both CCD and filtration increases by a factor of about three when fine rather than coarse slime is being treated. Similarly, the capital cost of both countercurrent cycloning and desanding/filtration increases by a factor of only about 1·2. The reduced sensitivity to the fineness of the feed solids is largely brought about by the ability to treat a pulp containing fine solids for metal recovery. By correct selection of cyclones, the size distribution of the solids in this pulp can be maintained in the very fine range for a significant change in the size distribution of the feed. Moreover, the density of this pulp need change only slowly with change in feed size distribution, when running a countercurrent cyclone cascade near optimum operating conditions. This occurs because to attain these optimum conditions it is necessary to increase the water feed to the circuit. Even for the finest solids feeds, however, the water demand can remain significantly below that of a CCD or desanding/filtration circuit performing the same duty.

The availability of a low capital cost method for recovering at high efficiency metal values at high concentrations in dilute pulps containing only very fine solids places accent on the need to develop low-cost methods for the recovery of metal values from such pulps. The design of a continuous countercurrent resin-in-pulp contactor using a dense resin has indicated that such a low-cost method is available. The combination of countercurrent cycloning and resin-in-pulp recovery offers a system which could reduce significantly the capital cost for the recovery of metal values from leach pulps in comparison with conventional systems.

Acknowledgment

The author wishes to express his thanks to the Chamber of Mines of South Africa for permission to publish this paper, and to his many co-workers who have assisted with the experimental work on which the paper is based.

Particular mention should be made of Mr. D. Sheppard, who was in charge of the operation of the countercurrent cyclone pilot plant for nearly two years.

References

1. LLOYD P. J. D. Unpublished work.
2. BRADLEY D. *The hydrocyclone* (Oxford, etc: Pergamon, 1965), p. 237 *et seq.*
3. ARDEN T. V. *et al.* Extraction of uranium from acid leach pulps by jigged-bed ion exchange. In *Proc. 2nd U.N. intn. Conf. peaceful Uses Atomic Energy* (Geneva: U.N., 1958), vol. 3, 396–414.
4. LLOYD P. J. [D.] Economic recovery of low-grade uranium values from Witwatersrand ores. In *The recovery of uranium* (*Proc. Symp., São Paulo, 1970*) (Vienna: I.A.E.A., 1971), 437–54.
5. YOSHIOKA N. AND HOTTA Y. Liquid cyclone as a hydraulic classifier. *Chem. Eng.* (*Japan*), **19**, 1955, 632–41; *Chem. Abstr.*, **50**, 1956, 1381.
6. DAHLSTROM D. A. Fundamentals and applications of the liquid cyclone. *Chem. Engng Prog., Symp. Ser.*, **50**, no. 15, 1954, 41–61.
7. MODER J. J. AND DAHLSTROM A. D. Fine-size, close-specific-gravity solid separation with the liquid–solid cyclone. *Chem. Engng Prog.*, **48**, 1952, 75–88.
8. MULAR A. L. AND BATES M. W. Modelling of parallel cyclones in the absence of flow measurement. *CIM Bull.*, **64**, 1971, 51–6.
9. ROSENBAUM J. B. AND GEORGE D. R. Cost reductions in ion exchange processing of uranium ores. In *The recovery of uranium* (*Proc. Symp., São Paulo, 1970*) (Vienna: I.A.E.A., 1971), 297–309.
10. STEVENSON D. G. Development of a continuous ion-exchange process. In *Ion exchange in the process industries* (London: Society of Chemical Industry, 1970), 114–20.
11. LLOYD P. J. D. South African Patent 70/4209, 1971.
12. ZWIETERING T. N. Suspending of solid particles in liquid by agitators. *Chem. Engng Sci.*, **8**, 1958, 244–53.

DISCUSSION

Dr. T. Rigg introduced his paper, summarizing its principal contents.

J. A. Holmes, in opening the introduction of his joint paper, said that the Chingola Division of Nchanga Consolidated Copper Mines, previously known as Nchanga Consolidated Copper Mines, Ltd., had experienced a massive increase in opencast mining rates in recent years. The additional ore had contained greater proportions of oxidized copper minerals, some of which responded relatively poorly to flotation (e.g. cupriferous mica, pseudo-malachite and chrysocolla). In consequence, the grade of the final flotation tailing had increased to a level of about 0·7% copper, of which about 0·5% was in the form of oxidized minerals, the copper in which was acid-soluble.

The paper described the preliminary R and D studies conducted to establish a process for the successful treatment of tailings for copper recovery. There was some urgency involved and, in consequence, the study was confined to an examination of processes based on sulphuric acid leaching, since it was known that acid could be made available from local smelters at low cost. Insofar as recovery of copper from solution in the leached pulp was concerned, attention was limited to techniques which had already been developed elsewhere, the main purpose being to establish their suitability in local circumstances as quickly as possible.

An added spur to the project was the existence on surface of tailings from earlier treatment of relatively high-grade ores, amounting in all to some 70 000 000 tonnes of material containing economic amounts of acid-soluble copper. There was also the possibility of recovering simultaneously a small additional amount of copper entrained in residue from the existing leach plant at Chingola.

The test programme was initially influenced by a concurrent study on the feasibility of treating Rokana reverberatory furnace slag by a reduction process to recover copper and cobalt, and at the same time produce metallic iron in a form suitable for copper cementation. That study, which was subsequently overtaken by other events, indicated that to prove such a process would take some time and, in consequence, the development of a tailings treatment process had to proceed on an assumption that iron from slag would not necessarily be available.

A brief description of the test work conducted would be given by Mr. Fisher. As a result of the test programme and discussions with others, a decision was taken to install as rapidly as possible a cementation plant, using the Kennecott cone principle and scrap iron to treat liquors arising from the leaching of certain relatively high-grade materials available (stage I) and to proceed with the planning and design of a large-scale plant featuring recovery of copper from leach solutions by solvent extraction and electrowinning (stage II). The stage I plant was in the process of commissioning and stage II was expected to come into operation in 1974 and to produce approximately 4500 ton/month of additional copper from tailings and residues.

J. F. C. Fisher, in continuing the introduction, said that he would first like to make a few points on the organization of the R and D work covered in the paper.

The main point concerned the speed of the work. The initial calculations carried out in 1968 indicated the particularly high profitability of the project and the desirability of implementing a process as soon as possible to maximize the present value of the project. No real progress was possible, however, until a decision had been taken on the process flowsheet. That meant that during the initial stage maximum effort was called for from the R and D department. They would, he believed, have preferred to spend some time developing an expertise in the cementation reaction, which appeared at the time to be the most promising route (three to four months viewing other operations). That was not really possible and they had to learn as they went along. They gave some consideration to buying in the required expertise, but that too would have involved unacceptable delays. Looking back, he believed that it was far easier and quicker to develop expertise in a new field than was frequently realized, and he was sure that they were right to rely on the staff available rather than buy in specialized knowledge, even if that had not involved delay.

The paramount need for speed also affected the character of the work. It was believed that any detailed work to provide plant design parameters could be carried out after the flowsheet was finalized. Thus, the work carried out on any process step was limited to answering four basic questions: (1) 'what is roughly the capital cost?'; (2) 'what is roughly the operating cost?'; (3) 'is the process technically feasible?'; and (4) 'what is the expected copper recovery?'

Once those questions were answered, they moved on to another stage in the investigation. Frequently, those questions could be answered by reference to the literature, or examination of other operating plants. Frequently, also, an alternative process stage would be abandoned if it became evident that too much time would be taken up in studying it sufficiently to answer the basic questions.

The result was an extremely patchy piece of development work, with many obvious gaps that would only have been filled in eventually if a decision had been taken to use that particular process.

Of the four process flowsheets finally considered, all were, he believed, feasible. The LPF route with H_2S gas for precipitation was possibly the least well proven and would have required a considerable amount of further work before implementation. The cementation routes, with Kennecott cones, were well proven technically, the major areas of doubt being the cost and consumption of iron in the cones, with the low-iron tenor in solution when compared with any of the Kennecott operations.

The lime precipitation route, although superficially simple, posed many problems in treatment of the product which at the time were not completely understood and which, eventually, would probably have caused that process route to be abandoned.

The final 'about-turn' decision to opt for a solvent extraction route was taken primarily on the operating costs. It was significant that, even had they been able to obtain iron for cementation at zero cost, cementation would still have incurred a higher operating cost than the solvent extraction route.

Dr. P. J. D. Lloyd introduced his paper, summarizing its principal contents.

M. J. Cahalan,* speaking, first, on the Rigg paper, said that he was not certain about the way in which ferrous chloride was charged to the reduction reactor. Were the special forms which divided the reactor into compartments manually filled and loaded? What efforts had been made to develop a continuous reactor and what were the problems associated with continuous operation?

Holmes and Fisher stated that development of a reduction process to obtain iron for cementation from reverberatory slag had encountered difficulties and, presumably, was abandoned. In view of the development and operation of a reduction process by Phelps Dodge, admittedly with converter slag, it would be interesting to know the kind of difficulties encountered with Rokana slags and whether the decision to abandon was related to technical difficulties or economic factors.

A. W. Fletcher,† speaking on the Rigg paper, asked if the author could give some information on the mechanism of the reduction reaction of ferrous chloride in order to indicate the problems which had to be overcome in the design of equipment. For example, was that a gas–solid, gas–liquid or gas-phase reaction?

It would also be of interest to know just how serious the manganese separation problem was in the commercial application of the process.

A. G. Moncrieff‡ said that many people must be wondering how it was that Nchanga had allowed nearly 100 000 000 tons of tailings, containing about 500 000 tons of copper, to accumulate on their tailings dam over the last 20 years or so without doing something about it earlier. Having been both leach plant super-intendent and concentrator superintendent at Nchanga for periods at the end of the 1950s, he supposed that he had a share of the responsibility! He would, therefore, like to suggest some reasons for that, but would welcome the authors' own comments.

First, it must be realized that during that period Nchanga must have produced about 4 000 000 tons of copper, so the percentage loss was not so great. He suggested, however, that the main reason was that Nchanga always had very high reserves of high-grade ore, and it was more economical to increase production by

---

* R.T.Z. Services, Ltd., Bristol.
† Warren Spring Laboratory, Department of Trade and Industry, Stevenage, Hertford-shire.
‡ Consolidated Gold Fields, Ltd., London.

exploitation of new deposits rather than by squeezing the last drop out of the lemon.

It was disappointing to learn that it had not been possible to operate the low-grade leach circuit to capacity owing to acid shortage. Considering that there were three major copper smelters in the area treating sulphide ores, that might sound surprising, and he was sure that copper smelters in other parts of the world would welcome such an opportunity to dispose of acid.

Although the authors said that their test work had to be carried out with some urgency (and he could appreciate that with the rising amount of oxidized ores treated), he thought that he would be right in saying that all the processes investigated in the paper were considered for various problems at Nchanga since before 1960, and some since before 1954. One of those problems was the treatment of the cupriferous mica—to which the authors had referred—of which he believed many million tons at about 1% copper to be available. He would like to ask the authors if the solvent extraction process now being developed by them might be suitably applied to those cupriferous mica 'ores'. When that material was being considered years ago the major problems were high acid consumption and thickening problems, which made it difficult to obtain a high recovery into a solution of sufficient strength for direct electrolysis. Dr. Lloyd might be interested to know that they even considered electrolysis in pulp with rotating electrodes.

The hydroxide precipitation process considered in the paper had, of course, been used for a long time by Nchanga for treatment of dilute wash solutions from their leach plant. He recalled that they always ran into thickening problems when the strength of solution treated fell below about 5 g/l copper. He wondered if the authors expected any difficulty in that respect when treating solutions containing only 1·8 g/l copper.

In Table 4 (pp. 182–3) the authors quoted an overall recovery of 94–96% by use of the leach hydroxide method followed by treatment of the copper hydroxide in the leach electrowinning circuit. Did that recovery allow for the lower volume of wash solution that would be used in the present leach circuit as a result of entrained water in the hydroxide filter cake and the water required to wash the calcium sulphate residue (both of which would enter the closed circuit of leach electrolysis)? Of course, that could be overcome by taking more solution from the leach electrolysis circuit to hydroxide precipitation, but, as the hydroxide cake (17% Cu, 60% water) was equivalent to a solution of only about 110 g/l copper (which was only two or three times the strength of the most dilute wash solution entering the leach electrolysis circuit), that method could lead to the need to precipitate nearly twice as much copper as would be recovered from the old tailings to be treated.

Unfortunately, the Lloyd paper only became available yesterday, so he hoped that the author would forgive him if, as a result of his brief study of it, he had not fully appreciated the concepts proposed.

The author wrote of cyclones as solid–liquid separating devices that 'Compared to filters or thickeners . . . are remarkably efficient' (p. 191). He then went on to say that the efficiency of cyclones might be 0·5, compared with an example of 0·748 for a filter. When it was realized that, on the scale of efficiency used by him, a simple division of a pulp into two equal parts gave an efficiency of 0·25, he suggested that the conclusion he should have drawn was that, in spite of the remarkable inefficiency of cyclones, they could be a very economical tool for solid–liquid separation.

Then, on page 197, Lloyd wrote that a pulp which was dilute in solids, and in which the solids were extremely fine, was an ideal feed for a metal recovery process. It might be better than one with a high concentration of coarse particles, but, personally, he would prefer one with no solids at all. Perhaps the author recognized that at the end of his paper in indicating (p. 201) the '*need to develop* low-cost methods for the recovery of metal values from such pulps' (speaker's italics).

Of course, he accepted the economic advantages of cyclones rather than thickeners or filters in a washing circuit, provided that the solid content of the solution was no trouble to further processing. What he could not understand was why the author believed that treatment of solutions containing fine solids was better than the use of a single stage of clarification (thickening or filtering) after CCD washing in cyclones, followed by simpler means of metal recovery from a clear solution.

The author mentioned the advantages of recycle to increase solution strength. Of course, that was only possible where a water leach was used or where a concentrated lixiviant was added to the leach, as in the processing of uranium ores. When a spent electrolyte was used for leaching, as for copper or zinc, it would be difficult to obtain that advantage.

Dr. N. M. Rice,* speaking on the Holmes and Fisher paper, asked how much iron was present in the feed to the solvent extraction plant. What effect would recycled iron have on the leaching operation and would it be necessary to operate a bleed? He enquired if there had been any problems with crud formation at the settler interface in the small pilot plant.

He would like to know whether any contactors other than mixer–settlers had been considered, particularly as the solvent inventory appeared to form a considerable part of the capital costs given in the breakdown in Table 5 (p. 186). Finally, he asked if any allowance had been made for 'solvent obsolescence' in the consideration of the operating costs.

M. J. Redman† said that in his company they were beginning to pay more attention to the effect of the host rock when leaching oxidized copper. Information on the nature of the host rock in the Nchanga operation would be very welcome—as would a fuller analysis of the leach liquor, particularly ferrous, ferric and aluminium contents.

* Department of Mining and Mineral Sciences, University of Leeds.
† Kennecott Copper Corporation, Lexington, Massachusetts, U.S.A.

What were the copper recoveries in the leaching stage in the 1 gal/min plant and what had been predicted for the $\frac{1}{2}$ ton/day plant?

G. C. I. Warwick* said that for anyone who was considering the installation of solvent extraction systems for copper recovery it would be of interest to mention that a new range of reagents was being developed by General Mills and others. Those reagents would enable copper contents as high as 50 g/l to be recovered economically and selectively from solutions of low pH. That was in contrast to the practical systems at Ranchers Bluebird mine and at Bagdad Copper, where the copper content of the leach liquors was in the range 1–3 g/l and was therefore ideal for treatment by Lix-64N. The same would apply at Chingola.

Power Gas had been carrying out work on the long-term stability of those new reagents for several months. Results to date had been extremely promising and within a year the reagents should be fully proven.

Dr. K. J. Reid,† speaking on the Lloyd paper, said that the author referred to the use of a countercurrent cyclone cascade system in the starch industry, and he would like to draw attention to a similar operating system in the metallurgical industry, namely that at the Rio Algom plant at Elliot Lake, Ontario, Canada, in which a final waste solid stream was produced and the primary cyclone overflow provided feed to a countercurrent decantation system.

While he was on the staff of the Department of Mining Engineering and Applied Geophysics at McGill University, Montreal, Canada, some preliminary studies of the behaviour of countercurrent cyclone operations were carried out, including simulation studies, which gave a reasonable fit to the limited information provided from operating data. Those studies indicated the range of expected soluble losses associated with the waste solid stream and showed a practical limit to the extent to which those losses could be minimized.

In order to overcome those inherent losses the proposal was made to use Cyclowash units in a countercurrent cascade, and modelling studies were carried out to evaluate that proposal. The Cyclowash unit provided for water addition to the apex of the cyclone and was originally designed‡ to improve classification performance by removing the fines normally present in cyclone underflows. In the present case the improved classification was of secondary importance, the basic concept for its application in hydrometallurgical processes being its potential as an effective countercurrent solid–liquid contactor, i.e. the interest was not in the washing out of fine solids but the liquid phase itself.

Operating data on the classification performance of the Cyclowash unit were scarce and there appeared to have been no work done to investigate the operating characteristics from the liquid displacement point of view, as now proposed.

---

* Power Gas, Ltd., London.
† Nchanga Consolidated Copper Mines, Ltd., Zambia.
‡ KELSALL D.F. AND HOLMES J.A. Improvement of classification efficiency in hydraulic cyclones by water injection. In (*5th*) *Int. Miner. Process. Congr., London, 1960* (London: Institution of Mining and Metallurgy, 1960), 159–70.

For the simulation studies two extreme mechanisms for the water behaviour in the apex regime were used: (1) assumed perfect mixing between the *cyclone* underflow stream and the injected water and (2) assumed replacement of the *cyclone* underflow water by the injected water without mixing. In the latter case water injection at the same rate as the normal cyclone underflow water rate resulted in a zero solute loss.

The results of that study showed that, even under the unfavourable assumption of perfect mixing, significant reduction of the solute losses could be detained. As a result of that preliminary study he was convinced that the Cyclowash unit would find increasing application in hydrometallurgical processing. To anyone considering the use of countercurrent wash systems he would urge the consideration of water-injected cyclones, and to those with pilot-plant facilities he would recommend studies of water behaviour in Cyclowash units to permit more detailed simulations and design calculations.

He would like to ask the author the extent to which those aspects had been examined in Johannesburg.

AUTHORS' REPLIES

Dr. T. Rigg In reply to Mr. M. J. Cahalan (p. 205), the reduction system employs a series of trays stacked inside a cylindrical cartridge, which is transferred bodily into the reactor. After being placed in the cartridge, each tray is filled with ferrous chloride dihydrate briquettes by use of a conveyor and chute. Each tray is raked level before the next one is lowered into position. The loaded cartridge is then picked up by means of a gantry crane and placed in the reactor. After reduction, the reactor is unloaded in the reverse sequence, the sponge iron product on the trays being tipped into a 'sponge chopper' and the trays returned for reloading. The handling system is extensively mechanized, but presently requires two men, one of whom drives the crane, to operate it. Loading and unloading occupy less time than the reduction reaction and are therefore not limiting factors so far as production rate is concerned.

Considerable attention has been paid to the problem of a continuous reactor. Fluidized-bed systems suffer from a number of difficulties. For example, at temperatures where the reaction rate would be adequate ($> 600°C$) the particles have a strong tendency to stick together; also, the back-reaction appears to be very rapid. To obtain reasonable thermal efficiency hydrogen should be supplied at about $800°C$, which is considerably above the melting point of ferrous chloride. In a fixed-bed operation with constant gas flow the endothermic heat of reaction is sufficient to prevent melting of the chloride. If, however, something happens which interrupts or diverts the gas flow, it is possible to get local melting. This is disastrous in fluidized-bed and moving-grate systems, but in the fixed-bed system, even in the unlikely event of such an incident, the only effect is to extend the reduction time as a result of the impaired gas–solid contact. The

H

very poor load-bearing properties of ferrous chloride briquettes *while actually undergoing reduction* and the problems encountered with conventional fluidized beds suggest that a continuous reactor employing the spouted-bed principle or some alternative 'dispersed-solids' system is the only type likely to succeed.

In reply to Mr. A. W. Fletcher (p. 205), the mechanism of the gas–solid reaction was discussed at some length in earlier papers.*

Manganese was found to pose no problems in the commercial application of the process: in fact, PRMS iron powder generally gives rise to cleaner sintered products with better mechanical properties than that produced by other processes. It should be noted that the samples shown in Fig. 6 (p. 166) were prepared without any graphite or lubricant addition and were sintered in pure hydrogen. When similar iron powders are treated according to normal industrial practice, i.e. with graphite and lubricant addition, and sintering in atmospheres of controlled carbon potential, a completely homogeneous product results.

It is only necessary to adopt special processing techniques if it is desired to produce powder suitable for hot-forging preforms of, for example, a 1·5% manganese steel where the end-use demands optimum mechanical properties.

J. A. Holmes and J. F. C. Fisher Mr. M. J. Cahalan (p. 205) queried the difficulties encountered in the reverberatory slag reduction process. It should be explained that the slag in question is highly siliceous, and contains no more than 18–24% Fe—a very poor starting material compared with the Phelps Dodge converter slag. Because of its low grade, it could not stand the costs of casting and granulating, reducing in the solid state, and then remelting, so reduction of molten slag only was considered. Test work showed this to be feasible, with addition of limerock flux. The prime economic object of the reduction, however, was to recover copper and cobalt in a relatively rich alloy with iron for further treatment, and then iron as a separate product from a second reduction stage.

It became obvious that the development of an economic process for iron production in this way would take some time, and, in consequence, the development of a tailings treatment process had to proceed on the assumption that cheap iron might not be available.

Mr. A. G. Moncrieff (pp. 205–6) asked, first, about the treatment of the cupriferous micas. The use of solvent extraction for treatment of low-grade solutions certainly makes recovery of copper from these ores more attractive. Acid consumption is still, however, a major drawback. The leaching of these materials is now being re-examined in some detail, and dump or heap leaching is being considered, as well as agitation leaching. We believe that a process can be developed which will be economic if sufficient additional sulphuric acid can be made available at low cost.

Thickening of copper hydroxide precipitate from solutions containing 1·8 g/l copper did not pose any real problem, as long as the thickener was big enough.

* See references 9 and 10 on page 168.

The difficulty mentioned by Mr. Moncrieff was perhaps due to the fact that copper tenors of less than 5 g/l in the precipitation section of the present leach plant were associated with the use of larger quantities of water for repulping in the filter plant than the thickeners were designed to handle.

Further investigation of the hydroxide precipitation process, subsequent to the evaluation quoted in the paper, did show that the recovery of 94–96% was rather optimistic, due to the reasons Mr. Moncrieff has quoted. Actual recovery would probably have been some 2–3% lower.

Dr. N. M. Rice (p. 207) put a number of questions on the solvent extraction plant and process.

The iron content of the solvent extraction plant feed is, as yet, somewhat uncertain. Initial leaching tests showed that a value of 1–2 g/l Fe, with about half this figure as ferric, might be expected to build up in the closed circuit. However, in operation of the small-scale pilot unit with some recycling of the raffinate, iron concentrations were very much lower, in the range 0·1–0·3 g/l total iron, with less than 0·2 g/l ferric iron. These results were rather surprising, but may be partly due to some precipitation of iron as ferric phosphate. As far as the leaching operation is concerned, the recycled iron is not expected to have any important effect on copper extraction, due to the low proportion of copper sulphides in the feed. It will be necessary, however, to operate a bleed in the electrolyte circuit for control of iron content in electrolyte. The size of this bleed will be dependent on the amount of iron pick-up and will be designed to limit iron content of the electrolyte to less than 2 g/l.

Crud formation was one of the problems examined in the pilot plant. It appeared to be a function of the suspended solids in the aqueous feed to the plant. When the suspended solids level was maintained in the range 10–15 ppm, a small, stable crud band was formed 2–4 cm thick. At suspended solids contents in the range 50–60 ppm crud grew rapidly and would have shut the pilot plant down in 2–3 weeks. In all cases some organic fungus was present in the crud, but, although it frequently appeared voluminous, removal of the inorganic suspended solids from the aqueous feed always resulted in rapid decrease in the thickness of the crud layer.

The use of multi-stage contactors was considered as an alternative to mixer–settlers right at the outset, and tests were carried out with a rotating disc column contactor, but the kinetics of the Lix-64N reaction were found to be too slow for such contactors to be an economic alternative to mixer–settlers. There is, however, little doubt that multi-stage contactors would be more economic for other solvent extraction systems, with faster reaction kinetics.

Dr. Rice's last question concerned solvent obsolescence. This is not believed to be an important factor in the operating cost of the plant. Certainly, improved reagents may be expected to come on the market in time, but, unless these reagents are compatible and miscible with Lix-64N, it is doubtful whether they will replace it, except possibly on grounds of cost. It should be pointed out that the manufacturers of Lix-64N are currently installing additional plant.

In reply to Mr. M. J. Redman (pp. 207–8), the ore at Nchanga is derived from a large number of ore sources, with varying types of host rock, including quartzites, sandstones and siltstones, some of which are dolomitic. The tailings feed to the leach plant represents a variable mixture of these ore types. A single-pass leach gave the following typical solution analysis (with 1·8 g/l Cu).

	Total Fe	Fe^{+++}	Mg	Ca	Al	Mn
g/l	0·17	0·10	0·30	0·59	0·13	0·13

With maximum raffinate recycle, as proposed for the new process, these elements are expected to build up to 4–5 times these values, subject to some precipitation taking place (e.g. ferric phosphate and calcium sulphate).

Leaching conditions in the 1 gal/min pilot plant were far from optimum, but a leach efficiency of approximately 70% of total copper content was frequently obtained. This figure is predicted for the $\frac{1}{2}$ ton/day plant. Leaching efficiency, as a percentage of acid-soluble copper content, is generally greater than 97%, but it should be pointed out that the acid-insoluble proportion will vary from time to time from 20 to 40% of the total copper content, depending on mineralization of the ore and efficiency of the flotation process. This factor will have the greatest effect on leach efficiency and overall copper recovery.

Mr. G. C. I. Warwick's remarks (p. 208) on the new reagents for solvent extraction are interesting. One of the prime advantages of solvent extraction is the treatment of the stripping solution by direct electrolysis. With Lix-64N the stripping solution, containing no more than 160 g/l acid, is a suitable feed for an electrowinning tankhouse. The new reagents, however, being able to extract copper from solutions of high-copper tenor and low pH, require very much stronger acid for stripping—in the range 300–500 g/l. This solution would pose problems in electrolysis due to the enhanced corrosion effects.

Dr. P. J. D. Lloyd In reply to Mr. A. G. Moncrieff (pp. 206–7), I would like to stress that far from having difficulty with the concepts proposed, he appears to be one of the few metallurgists who has understood them fully. Many appear to feel that a cyclone cannot act as a solid–liquid separating device, and for those who do feel this it is thus probably correct to speak of the relative *efficiency* of cyclones. However, the highest efficiency we have determined is only of the order of 0·65, whereas a filter can exceed efficiencies of 0·75, and thus, in absolute terms, the cyclone is inefficient.

As regards the idea of clarifying a metal-containing pulp completely, as is conventionally done, I would like to refer to Table 1 (p. 190), which indicates quite clearly that a very significant capital investment is necessary to clarify solutions containing fine solids. We have estimated that, for an ore ground nominally to 50% – 74 μm, every 1% increase in the fraction – 44 μm increases the capital expenditure for a typical Witwatersrand gold circuit by 2% if the same metallurgical performance is to be obtained. By accepting fines in the 'liquid' stream of a solid–liquid separating circuit, drastic reductions in the capital expenditure necessary for that circuit can be obtained for relatively small increases in the capital expenditure on the metal recovery circuit, and a very considerable overall saving.

It is also rather costly to attempt to clarify the pulps resulting from CCD washing in cyclones, because these pulps contain that fine fraction of solids which increases the capital cost in the manner indicated above.

Table 1 Typical test results for Krebs D6BB cyclones fed with slurry of milled Rand ore (25-mm diameter underflow nozzle; Cyclowash mechanism fitted)

	Without Cyclowash	With Cyclowash
Feed rate, gal/min	102	124
Feed % solids	27·7	27·0
Feed % +40 μm	31·8	26·0
% –10 μm	38·2	43·7
Cyclowash rate, gal/min	0	6
Overflow, gal/min	65	112
% solids	10·6	19·3
% +40 μm	0·6	5·4
% –10 μm	78·0	54·9
Underflow, gal/min	32	18
% solids	47·3	52·9
% +40 μm	45·6	9·8
Solid–liquid separation efficiency	0·52	0·31

As regards the use of recycle to increase solution strength when spent electrolyte is used for leaching, it may still be possible to operate the circuit suggested in the paper by using the spent electrolyte in the washing circuit and balancing the inevitable bleed of electrolyte from the circuit with the liquid in the flow of the final stage.

I would most heartily subscribe to Dr. K. J. Reid's enthusiasm (pp. 208–9) for the Cyclowash system *for improving classification*. It is, however, useless for solid–liquid separation in the finer size ranges. We tested Cyclowash on our cyclones with the rather dramatic effects noted in Table 1. The introduction of a mere 6 gal/min of water through the Cyclowash changes the volumetric split (the ratio of the overflow to underflow rate) from 2:1 to 6:1, and thus improves the efficiency of soluble metal recovery in the overflow very significantly; however, the solids rejection is markedly impaired. The underflow to overflow

Production and trials of Bergbau-Forschung formed coke

E. Ahland Dr.-Ing.
B. Bock Dr.-Ing.
H. J. Jagnow Dr.-Ing.
J. Lehmann Dr.-Ing.
W. Peters Prof., Dr. rer. nat.

All of Bergbau-Forschung GmbH, Essen-Kray, Germany

662.749.2

Synopsis
One of the processes developed by Bergbau-Forschung GmbH for the *continuous* production of formed coke consists of the cold-briquetting or pelletizing of coal followed by heat-treatment in the BF sand carbonizer. An alternative process employs hot-briquetting to produce coke, for a variety of metallurgical uses, with or without subsequent treatment in the carbonizer.

The application of these processes will increase the range of coals suitable for coke-making—an important factor in view of the worldwide shortage of coke. Additional benefits of the processes are the avoidance of noxious emissions and the ability to stop and restart the plant at will. Products of these processes have been used for various metallurgical purposes—for example, more than 10 000 t for the blast-furnace production of pig iron.

Approximately 70% of the cost price of metallurgical coke is accounted for by coal, the remaining 30% being due to the carbonization process. The application of new coke-making methods could lead to a reduction in both these cost factors, but, clearly, the major effect would be obtained by lowering the costs due to coal requirements. Processes for the production of formed coke,[1,2,3] permitting the carbonization of coals which, formerly, had been looked on as unsuitable for coke-making, could lead to savings by the use of low-volatile coals, such as semi-anthracite or anthracite. As the present market situation is characterized by the decreasing value of the by-products of carbonization and, correspondingly, a higher coke value, a higher coke yield is economically advantageous.

On the other hand, world reserves of easily accessible low-volatile coals are insufficient to serve as a basis for a substantial production of metallurgical coke. High-volatile coals, in contrast, are available in abundance and in suitable geological conditions; hence, their use for the production of metallurgical coke would seem attractive, provided that they were so much cheaper than conventional coking coals that losses resulting from the higher proportion of tar and gas in the total output of the carbonization process were more than offset by the lower coal price.

Careful calculations have shown that the cost inherent in the carbonization process is reduced by continuous operation, even if the same type of coal is used. These calculations include, at the present time, many uncertain factors, being based, necessarily, on a number of assumptions in the absence of commercial-scale production units. Formed-coke processes will facilitate the suppression of emissions to a level compatible with government regulations, because, in contrast to the conventional carbonization technique, the entire process is performed in completely closed apparatus—a factor which, in the long term, will contribute to cost reductions.

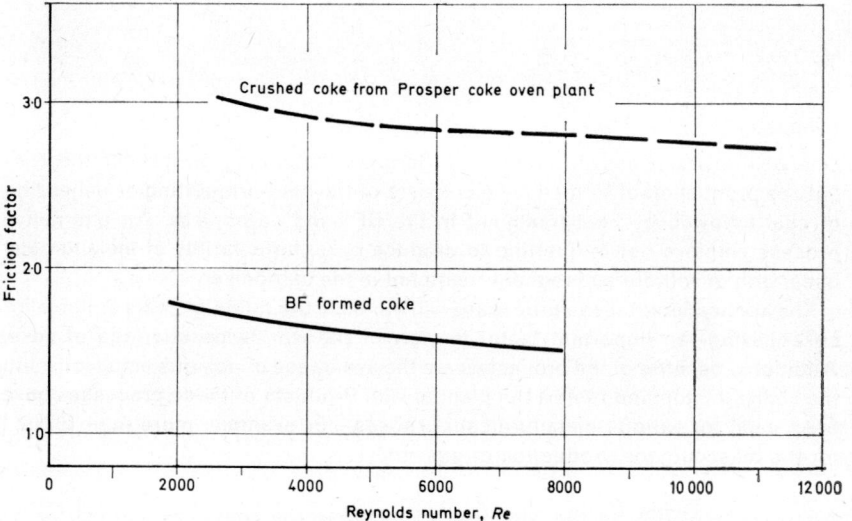

Fig. 1 Friction factor against Reynolds number

The production of by-products can be governed to some extent in continuous processes by recycling the tar to avoid the formation of high-boiling tar fractions and to increase the yield of coke, oil and gas.

Besides costs, the properties of the products are clearly of great importance; again, a distinction must be drawn between properties that depend on the nature of the coal and properties that depend on the carbonization process. Ash and sulphur contents of the coke, for example, are closely related to the nature of the coal and, to a high degree, independent of the process, whereas strength, volatile matter, shape, size and density are governed by the carbonization process.

Ledent and co-workers[1] stated that blast-furnace coke should meet the following requirements: (1) great strength, in particular resistance to abrasion, as characterized by the Micum indices; (2) sufficient voidage between the pieces of coke for the gas and the hot metal to find their way through the coke bed at the level of the boshes (size and density of the coke, free space between the pieces); and (3) sufficient specific surface area for the gas–solid reactions and the heat exchange to take place with the required velocity within the fusion zone (size and density of the coke, shape factor).

These requirements are to some extent contradictory. As a rule, high strength is attained first of all by high density, which, however, has a detrimental effect from the viewpoint of the third requirement, because high density is accompanied by small specific surface area. The second requirement, high voidage, is less well satisfied by uniform coke than by coke of irregular shape. This leads to a higher pressure drop in the coke layer, but, as Fig. 1 shows, this effect is compensated, in part at least, by the fact that formed coke has a lower friction factor.

The oven coke used at the present time represents a reasonable compromise between the above requirements. Processes for the production of formed coke developed so far, or which are still at the development stage, offer so many possibilities of variation that it seems quite possible that an even better compromise will be found, i.e. there is a good chance of producing a formed coke better suited to the blast-furnace process than the conventional oven coke. Other metallurgical processes, of course, will call for other properties, but the flexibility of the processes for making formed coke justifies the expectation that here, too, it will be possible to find a better compromise than that which exists at present and to adapt the character of the coke to specific requirements.[4]

Processes for formed-coke manufacture

The methods for the manufacture of formed coke developed by Bergbau-Forschung[2] differ in the sequence of the successive stages: in the hot-briquetting process heat-treatment precedes shaping, whereas in the other processes it follows shaping.

Hot-briquetting process

In the hot-briquetting process (Fig. 2) 70% of hot, fine-grained char, carbonized at temperatures between 600 and 800°C, is mixed with 30% of caking coal. It is not imperative to use a prime caking coal as the second component, but it must meet certain basic process requirements. The caking coal is dried and crushed to <1 mm in size.

The hot char and the caking coal are rapidly and intimately mixed in a specially designed double-screw mixer. The blend is then fed through a distributing box to a double-roll press and briquetted at temperatures between 400 and 500°C, corresponding to the softening range of the coal. Presses of this type can attain a capacity of 50 t/h. The product can be used as an excellent smokeless fuel for domestic purposes, but tests described below have shown that it is also suitable for the blast-furnace, in spite of the fact that the hot briquettes still contain about 7% of volatile matter.

For certain metallurgical processes the remaining volatile matter has to be expelled by heat-treatment, which can be done in the hot-sand BF carbonizer. In such cases the hot briquettes are passed immediately, without cooling, to the

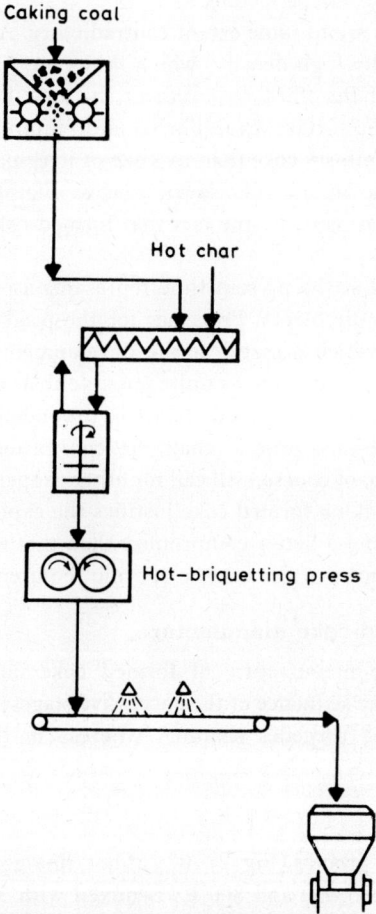

Fig. 2 Hot-briquetting process

secondary treatment stage. A summary of the characteristic properties of both green and coked hot briquettes is given in Table 1.

Preparation of char

ENTRAINED-BED PROCESS

For the preparation of the hot char different processes are available (Fig. 3). With poorly caking coals the entrained-bed process can be applied. The coal is crushed to −3 mm and introduced into the lower part of a pneumatic lift. The

Table 1 Properties of formed coke

	Hot briquettes Green	Carbonized	Pitch-bound briquettes, carbonized	Carbonized pellets
Dimensions, mm	48·61·35	47·60·35	33·43·24	30
Weight, g	48	44	19·5	13·0
Ash content (dry basis) %	6·7	7·8	7·8	7·4
Volatile matter (d.m.m.f.), %	6·5	1·0	6·4	6·4
Sulphur (dry basis), %	0·85	0·80	1·08	0·87
Porosity, %	49·0	58·6	23·0	38·0
Upper calorific value, H_o, kcal/kg	7461	7154	8070	7320
Breaking strength, kp	185	260	205	210
Resistance to abrasion (<10 mm), %	7·8	7·1	10·0	9·2
Bulk density, t/m^3	0·508	0·495	0·656	0·490

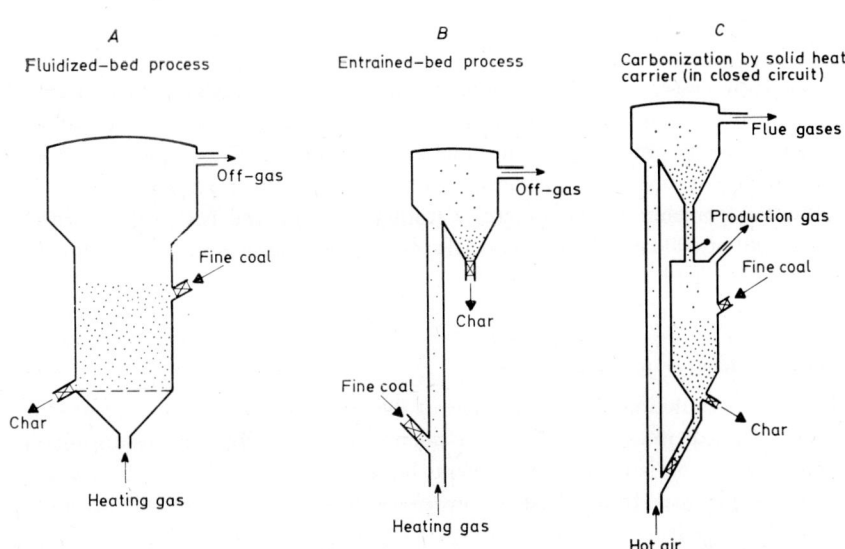

A Fluidized–bed process   B Entrained–bed process   C Carbonization by solid heat carrier (in closed circuit)

Fig. 3 Various processes for preparation of fine-grained char

heat required for the semi-carbonization of the coal is generated by partial combustion. The hot char is collected in a settling chamber and directed to the hot-briquetting plant. By installing a combustion chamber before the airlift the burn-off of solid carbon can be reduced, in part at least, by combustion of tar or gas. A disadvantage of this process arises from the mixture of the carrier gas with the emitted volatile matter, a gas of low calorific value being produced.

FLUIDIZED-BED PROCESS

Another means of preparing the hot char is by fluidized-bed carbonization, which permits medium-caking coals to be used. Again, the burn-off of the char can be restricted to some extent by the installation of a gas-fired combustion chamber. The fluidized-bed process also yields a lean gas; but, often, it is desirable to obtain a rich gas as by-product; in such cases the application of the Lurgi–Ruhrgas (LR) process is appropriate.[5]

LR PROCESS

In the LR process hot char flows in a closed circuit. Fresh coal is added in a double-screw mixer and heated to the carbonization temperature. The mix is passed into a bin, in which the degasification of the nascent char is completed. The mix of the recirculated and the fresh char is directed to an ascending pipeline, in which it is heated to about 100°C. The hot char is collected in a bunker, and part of it is re-fed to the screw mixer. A side-stream is withdrawn and directed to the hot-briquetting plant. This process also enables caking coals to be used. The maximum throughput per unit lies between 200 and 250 t/h.

Tests

All these processes have been tested in smaller or larger pilot plants. A 5 t/h hot-briquetting plant is run by Bergbau-Forschung at the 'Königin Elisabeth' test site; char is produced by the fluidized-bed process. Tests have also been made on an entrained-bed carbonizer with a throughput of 300 kg/h.

Bergbau-Forschung also operates a testing plant for the LR process, with a throughput of 100 kg/h. The largest LR plant built so far has a capacity of 67 t/h in two units; it is used to convert Creka lignite into a char required as diluent matter.[6]

Cold-briquetting or pelletizing process

Clearly, it is sometimes a disadvantage of the hot-briquetting process that 30% of the feed coal must exhibit special caking properties. In some countries no suitable caking coal is available and it has to be imported over considerable distances at high freight costs. In such cases the processes developed by Bergbau-Forschung in which briquetting is the first step and carbonization the second are advantageous. Under the most favourable conditions the coal can be briquetted with no preliminary treatment, pitch or some other binder being used, and carbonized in the hot-sand coker. If, however, the coal tends to dilatation, its swelling power must be reduced, e.g. by addition of anthracite, if available, or of iron ore. Pre-oxidation of the coal can be taken into account.

Another way of reducing the swelling power of the briquetting mix is to semi-carbonize part of the coal and to briquette a mixture of char and coal. Certain coals, in particular anthracite and semi-anthracite, call for the addition of a higher volatile caking coal for the necessary strength values to be obtained after carbonization of the briquettes. This method is applied, for example, in Belgium[1] and France.[3]

The most common method of shaping the coal is briquetting, with pitch as a binder, because the pitch originating from the coal can be recirculated into the process. Other shaping methods than briquetting can, however, be applied.

Pelletization is practised by Bergbau-Forschung (Fig. 4). The agglomerates,

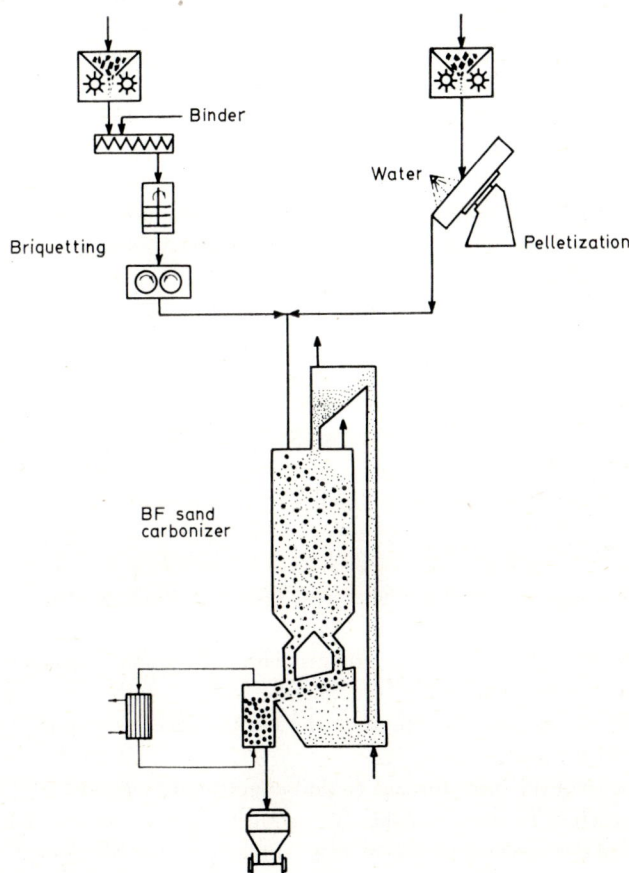

Fig. 4 Production of formed coke by briquetting or pelletization

briquettes or pellets, are fed to the BF sand carbonizer, where they are heated by hot sand travelling in a closed circuit. The agglomerates and the sand enter the reactor at the upper end, are mixed and move downwards. *En route* the sensible heat of the sand is transferred to the briquettes to degasify and carbonize them. At the discharge end the formed coke and the sand are separated, the sand being fed to an airlift, which has the double task of returning it to a bin above the reactor and to reheat it as it does so. The formed coke travels through a cooler, where it is cooled by inert gases running in closed circuit. The waste heat can be recovered, e.g. for steam raising. The cooled coke is ready for immediate shipment.

In the hot-sand carbonizer the green briquettes or pellets are treated by single-stage shock heating. This, on the one hand, enables a very simple arrangement of the apparatus to be accepted, but, on the other hand, the thermal stresses to which the agglomerates are exposed in the carbonizer have to be taken into account in the preparation of the briquetting mix. As a rule, the temperature in the carbonizer should range from 600 to 700°C. It is not expected that the volatile matter still present in the formed coke will cause problems in the blast-furnace, none having been caused by the hot briquettes already tested.

In comparison with the carbonization of the briquettes in a stream of sweep gas, the method frequently applied for the second stage of the process, the hot-sand carbonizer has two advantages. First, it gives a support to the briquettes in the temperature range where their strength is restricted, owing to the softening of the pitch and the coal. Secondly, the absence of sweep gas makes it possible for the BF sand coker to yield a gas which, in many cases, can be turned to better use than lean gas. A hot-sand carbonizer with a capacity of 5 t/h is operating in the Königin Elisabeth pilot plant. The maximum throughput per unit is likely to amount to about 80 t/h.

Blast-furnace trials

Fig. 5 shows the blast-furnaces in which BF products have been tested to date.

Airbo

The first test was run in September and October, 1967, in the experimental blast-furnace of Airbo at Ougrée in Belgium, consisting of 500 t of formed coke produced by the hot-briquetting process with subsequent carbonization in a hot-sand carbonizer.[7] Normally, the furnace was fed with oven coke ranging from 5 to 20 mm in size. For the tests the normal coke was replaced by 100% pillow-shaped briquettes (21 g).

The capacity of the blast-furnace could be increased by almost 70%, the limit not being reached for lack of coke. Subsequent experiments carried out with closely graded oven coke gave almost as good results as the BF formed coke.

In the autumn of the same year (1967) another test was made in the same blast-furnace on a formed coke produced by the Carmonoix process (briquetting of coal with pitch as a binder, followed by carbonization in Koppers retorts[8]). The main difference between the BF formed coke and the Carmonoix coke was the much lower porosity of the latter. The findings of the comparative tests can be summarized as follows.

Both cokes retained their shape down to the tuyères. With the Carmonoix coke the extent of the combustion zone was much larger than with BF coke or normal oven coke. With BF coke the throughput of the furnace was raised without notable difficulties, whereas with Carmonoix coke efforts to improve the output of the furnace led to irregular operation, and it was not possible to equal the performance of the BF coke. Probably, the outer surface of Carmonoix coke was insufficient, on account of its lower porosity and, hence, the reactions in front of the blast tuyères did not reach the required intensity.

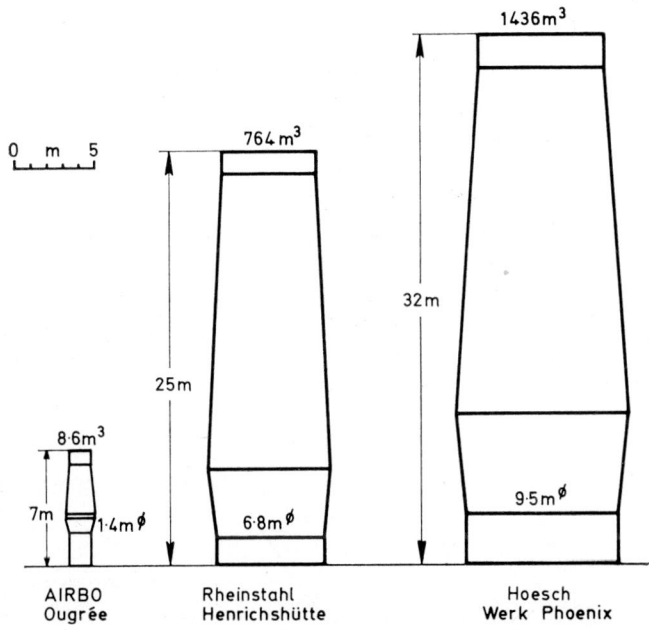

Fig. 5 Blast-furnaces used to test BF formed coke

Hoesch

By virtue of the good results obtained with BF formed coke in the experimental furnace at Ougrée, the first test was run in a 9·5-m works blast-furnace belonging to Hoesch AG Hüttenwerke in April, 1969. 1400 t of formed coke was tested.

Insofar as this 24-h preliminary experiment can be regarded as a guide, it was found that the formed coke withstood well the mechanical stresses during delivery, unloading on to the stockpile and charging of the blast-furnace. During unloading into a bunker drop heights of up to 10 m occurred. The abrasion (M_{10}) measured was only 1% greater than that of oven coke. The first formed coke was visible in front of all blast tuyères about eight hours after charging. The samples taken at this point still showed clearly the original form of the briquettes. They had become lighter and smaller due to gasification or partial combustion, but they were in no way disintegrated. The air blast to the furnace remained practically unchanged, and it is noteworthy that the amount of flue dust had not increased to any appreciable extent. The smoothness or unevenness of furnace operation corresponded with the previous working period. Because of the short duration of the experiment, the consumption of coke per ton of pig iron could not be calculated, and, with regard to the quality of the pig iron, there was no difference compared with normal operation. When all the formed coke was used up, reversion to normal blast-furnace coke was carried out without difficulty.

Rheinstahl

The most important tests so far have been run in a blast-furnace of the Henrichshütte Steel Works at Hattingen operated by the Rheinstahl Company.[9] The hearth diameter of the furnace was 6·8 m, its height 25 m, and the useful volume 764 m³. The blast is enriched with oxygen, the humidity of the blast is controlled and fuel oil is injected into the furnace. The normal daily output of the furnace varies from 1250 to 1350 t of pig iron. In this furnace green hot briquettes were tested as well as carbonized hot briquettes.

Before the large-scale test on green briquettes were started, three preliminary trial runs were made of gradually increasing duration: first, the blast-furnace

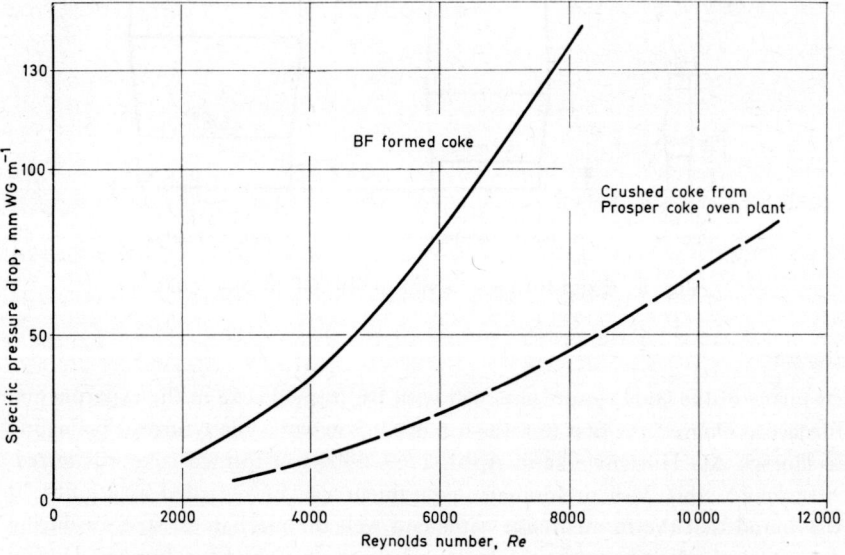

Fig. 6 Specific pressure drop against Reynolds number

was fed 100% with green hot briquettes for one hour, then for 4 h and finally, for 12 h.

The results of these trials having come up to expectations, the furnace was fed for three days with hot briquettes in February, 1970, on the whole 2700 t, and it became clear that uncoked hot briquettes are also able to sustain the stresses of blast-furnace operation, although they are inferior in strength to carbonized formed coke. In fact, the hot briquettes are, as it were, post-carbonized in the blast-furnace, reaching their maximum strength in front of the tuyères, where they are exposed to the highest stresses. The volatile matter still present in the hot briquettes caused no difficulties; the calorific value of the top gas was improved, which is desirable in most steelworks.

Subsequently, 7000 t of carbonized hot briquettes was used as metallurgical fuel in the same blast-furnace, this test lasting seven days. Again, the result was that this product, like the green hot briquettes, compared favourably with conventional blast-furnace coke. No increase in productivity was observed, but the duration of the test was clearly too short.

It is questionable, however, that it will be possible to obtain the optimum performance of an industrial furnace with the size of hot briquettes used for this test (50 g). A comparison of the pressure drop per unit of length measured with usual oven coke and formed coke (Fig. 6) seems to lead to the conclusion that the formed coke was too small: it is therefore intended to run further tests with larger-size coke.

Summary

For various reasons the production of formed coke can be a useful alternative to the conventional process of coke-making in coke-oven plants. The range of coals suitable for carbonization can be enlarged in this way, the by-products can be turned to good account, the quality of the product can be adapted to the end use and the emission of pollutants is reduced.

Bergbau-Forschung has developed several processes for the production of formed coke which differ in the sequence of the successive stages, i.e. shaping and heat-treatment. In the hot-briquetting process hot char is mixed with cold coal and immediately briquetted on a roller press; with the BF sand carbonizer process the coal is first pelletized or briquetted in the conventional manner and then the pellets or briquettes are continuously carbonized by contact with hot sand.

In the pilot-scale hot-briquetting plant (production capacity, 5 t/h) several consignments of hot briquettes and formed coke, ranging from 500 to 7000 t, have been produced for tests in different size blast-furnaces run by Airbo, Hoesch and by the Rheinstahl Company. The operation of the furnaces fed with BF formed coke was normal, and, with the Airbo test furnace, a substantial increase in throughput was achieved.

References

1. LEDENT P. BURTON G. AND MARCOURT M. Le développement du procédé INIEX pour la fabrication du coke moulé. In *Technique et évolution dans le domaine de la cokefaction* (Luxemburg: Centre d'Information et de Documentation de la Communauté Européenne, 1979), 187–205. (French edition)

2. PETERS W. AHLAND E. and LANGHOFF J. Verfahrensentwicklung der Bergbau-Forschung auf dem Gebiet der kontinuierlichen Formkoksherstellung. In *Technique et évolution dans le domaine de la cokefaction* (Luxemburg: Centre d'Information et de Documentation de la Communauté Européenne, 1970), 207–30. (French edition)
3. SOUBRIER L. Recherches et essais effectués par les houillères du Bassin du Nord et du Pas-de-Calais (H.B.N.P.C.) et la Société Fusion et Volatilisation (FUVO). In *Technique et évolution dans le domaine de la cokefaction* (Luxemburg: Centre d'Information et de Documentation de la Communauté Européenne, 1970), 231–61. (French edition)
4. AHLAND E. AND LEHMANN J. Kohleforschung—Anwendung in der Bergtechnik— Grundlage für neue Erzeugnisse. Paper presented at Coal Research symposium, Luxemburg, 1970.
5. AHLAND E. Kreislaufverfahren mit festen Wärmeträgern. *Erdöl Kohle*, **24**, 1971, 149–52.
6. RAMMLER R. Betriebserfahrungen mit dem Lurgi-Ruhrgas-Verfahren zur Entgasung feinkörniger Brennstoffe. *Erdöl Kohle*, **19**, 1966, 117–21.
7. DECKER A. AND POOS A. Neue Ergebnisse des Versuchshochofens in Ougrée. *Stahl Eisen*, **88**, 1968, 1407–14.
8. POOS A. LIMPACH R. AND BALON R. Résultats obtenus au fourneau expérimental de Liège avec des cokes moulés. *Circ. Centr. Docum. Sidér.* no. 5 1969, 1217–33.
9. DÄRMANN O. HENKEL S. AND HAVERKAMP K. D. Die Verwendung von Heissbriketts und Formkoks im Hochofen. *Stahl Eisen*, **90**, 1970, 1009–12.

Metallic iron–carbon composites as a source of iron and energy for the steel industry

D. A. Reeve B.Sc., Ph.D., A.M.I.M.M.
R. P. Charbonnier D.Sc.
J. H. Walsh M.Eng., Sc.D.

All of Metals Reduction and Energy Centre, Mines Branch, Department of Energy, Mines and Resources, Ottawa, Canada

669.181 : 661.666

Synopsis

Non-blast-furnace processes for the reduction of iron ore have been devised that are sufficiently attractive to be considered for installation at mine sites or shipping points remote from normal steelmaking centres. A major difficulty is that, although energy costs may be acceptable at the sites chosen for the reduction processes, when the metallic iron pellet or briquette is delivered to the steelmaking centres, electric furnace steelmaking is usually contemplated. This method of steelmaking has a low capital cost, but is often high in both energy and electrode costs. If the metallic iron product is directed to conventional steelmaking—for example, as a coolant in the basic oxygen process—the low capital cost of the direct reduction route is not realized. Basic oxygen steelmaking is not capital-intensive in itself, even including the attendant oxygen plant, but the preceding coke-oven and blast-furnace stages of the combination represent most of the investment. Although it is true that the cupola process has been considered as an intermediate stage for melting directly reduced iron into hot metal, it has the disadvantage of needing an expensive coke and is, after all, another stage that has its attendant air pollution problems.

The possibility is considered of preparing briquettes of carbon and metallic iron—representing a 'pre-packaged' form of energy. It is envisaged that these briquettes would be preheated by the off-gases from the steelmaking stage and then reacted with oxygen to produce steel. Thermochemical calculations are presented with the results of laboratory-scale studies of the behaviour of this type of composite in the presence of oxygen. Attention is drawn to the need for a low-sulphur carbon, for which possible sources are noted together with considerations of energy supply and transportation factors.

Economically, among the different items included in the manufacturing cost of steel, raw material costs are of major importance. The charging of pre-reduced pellets to the blast-furnace continues to be a topic of interest, and direct reduc-

229

tion processes producing metallized pellets for steelmaking feeds are just now beginning to usurp the established position of the blast-furnace in many areas of the world;[1] the intensity of interest in these sources of iron tends to fluctuate with the scrap market.

Pre-reduced burdens for blast-furnace feed and metallized pellets suitable for addition to all types of steelmaking vessels offer the economic advantages of handling metallized rather than oxide (normally non-magnetic) pellets and the reduced shipping costs of a commodity higher in iron content, although the impending introduction of 'slurry' tankers must be taken into account. Nevertheless, non-blast-furnace processes for the reduction of iron ore are sufficiently attractive to be considered for installation at mine sites or shipping points remote from normal steelmaking centres. Geographical considerations and the availability of inexpensive energy supplies at remote locations in some cases may make it more economical to reduce iron ore before it is shipped to the steelmaking facility.

Unfortunately, when the metallic iron pellet or briquette is delivered to the steelmaking centres, electric furnace steelmaking is usually contemplated. This method of steelmaking is low in capital cost, but often high in both energy and electrode costs. If the metallic iron product is directed to conventional steelmaking—for example, as a coolant in the basic oxygen process—low capital cost, a feature of the direct reduction route, is not realized. Basic oxygen steelmaking is not capital-intensive in itself, even taking into account the attendant oxygen plant, but the preceding coke-oven and blast-furnace stage of the combination represents most of the investment. Although oxygen is generally produced by electrical means, direct steam operation is possible. The cupola process may be considered to be an intermediate stage for melting directly reduced iron into hot metal, but it has the disadvantage of needing an expensive coke and is, after all, another stage that has its attendant air pollution problems. Mains-frequency, large-scale induction furnaces have also been considered for the conversion step.

An answer to this dilemma may lie in producing a briquette of iron and carbon at a location remote from the steelmaking facility; the carbon would be the contained-energy source. It is envisaged that these briquettes would be preheated by the off-gases from the steelmaking stage and then reacted with oxygen to produce steel. The addition of carbon would also produce an increase in gas volume, which would be beneficial for preheating but would require more oxygen.

Such a product with a 'pre-packaged' form of energy would provide not only a scrap substitute for steelmaking but, perhaps more important, a hot-metal substitute. With the development of the basic oxygen process metallic charge requirements have shifted to an average of 30% scrap and 70% hot metal. These requirements are more restrictive than the open-hearth process metallic charge requirements, which vary from 70% hot metal to 100% cold charge. The basic oxygen process is therefore indeed dependent on a continuing hot-metal supply to maintain production, and methods of increasing the scrap:hot metal ratio may be economically attractive.

It should be pointed out at this stage that substitutes for hot metal in the basic oxygen process other than those discussed in this paper have been proposed. Notable among these has been calcium carbide as an additional heat source. Gregory et al.[2] have described trials in Australia of the use of calcium carbide instead of limestone as flux in a miniature basic oxygen steelmaking vessel. The calcium carbide was oxidized to lime and carbon, and the additional heat was generated by the oxidation of carbon to carbon monoxide and carbon dioxide. Pittsburgh Steel[3, 4] further developed the use of calcium carbide as a solid fuel in a production unit (limited to low-carbon steels) and succeeded in increasing scrap consumption to between 51 and 62%. Another suggestion for a hot-metal substitute for basic oxygen steelmaking has been to use preheated low-sulphur iron carbide containing controllable and high contents of carbon.[5] Oxidation of the hot iron carbide to iron and carbon monoxide and the subsequent exothermic oxidation of carbon monoxide to carbon dioxide should, theoretically, produce ample heat to allow the reaction to continue.

Iron–carbon composites as a hot-metal substitute for basic oxygen steelmaking

References to the use of carbon as a solid oxidizable fuel to make possible a greater scrap:hot metal ratio in basic oxygen steelmaking have appeared already in the patent literature.[6, 7]

D'Entremont and Taylor[6] have obtained a patent on the limiting case when 100% solid charge is used in the basic oxygen steelmaking furnace. In their invention solid oxidizable fuels, such as coal, coke, petroleum coke, ferrosilicon, silicon carbide and calcide carbide, were deposited at the bottom of the steel-making vessel. In the case of coke 90–180 lb/ton of charge was necessary to effect the conversion. Scrap, heated by the combustion of coke with natural gas and air in a preheating vessel, was added to the solid fuel in the steelmaking furnace. The surface temperature of the scrap was then raised to the oxygen ignition temperature ($\sim 840°C$) and, as soon as ignition was achieved, the oxygen lance was burned down through the scrap to a position just above the solid fuels. The direct oxidation of these solid fuels provided sufficient thermal energy to melt the scrap.

Rouanet[7] has described the addition of pre-reduced iron pellets, containing 10–25% carbon, to a continuous steelmaking bath being refined with oxygen to generate additional heat with the result that more low-carbon pellets can be melted and production rates can be increased.

In the present paper the case is considered in which the solid feed to the steelmaking vessel contains iron and an energy source and is preheated to 1100°C by utilizing the waste gases from the steelmaking furnace. In basic oxygen steelmaking a gas rich in carbon monoxide is exhausted from the process at about 1600°C, and it is reasonable to assume that methods of preheating the iron–carbon feed to approximately 1100°C could be developed.

Thermochemical calculations have been made to determine the percentage by weight of carbon which, theoretically, must be included in a metallic iron agglo-merate, preheated to 1100°C before charging to a basic oxygen steelmaking furnace, in order to effect melting of the iron without the use of any additional energy source. Also, bench-scale experiments were done to observe the behaviour in oxygen of preheated iron–carbon composites.

Thermochemical calculations

Constant pressure conditions were assumed in these calculations, and it was also assumed that the metallic iron contained no carbon in solution, i.e. its melting point was 1536°C. Thermochemical data were taken from Kubaschewski, Evans and Alcock[8] and three cases were considered: (1) the carbon reacted with oxygen at 1100°C to produce carbon monoxide only; (2) 20% of this carbon monoxide reacted with more oxygen to produce carbon dioxide, as happens in basic oxygen furnaces; and (3) 50% of the carbon monoxide reacted with more oxygen to produce carbon dioxide.

Details of these calculations have been given elsewhere,[9] but the results for the three cases are summarized in Table 1. Also included are the maximum

Table 1

	Case 1	Case 2	Case 3
Amount of carbon monoxide burned to carbon dioxide, %	Nil	20	50
Heat required to convert solid iron at 1100°C to liquid iron at 1536°C, kcal/mole	7·61	7·61	7·61
Heat available from combustion of carbon with oxygen at 1100°C, kcal/mole	−18·25	−31·85	−52·25
Theoretical percentage of carbon required for a self-sustaining iron feed	8·2	4·87	3·02
Allowable sulphur content in the carbon, %	0·24	0·42	0·66

allowable sulphur contents of the carbon used to make the composite pellets calculated on an average steel specification demanding 0·025% sulphur by weight. It is assumed here that all the sulphur in the carbon will ultimately report in the steel from the basic oxygen furnace, although, in practice, some sulphur will report in both slag and gases.

Bench-scale observations

Following these favourable indications from the thermochemical calculations, the effect of exposing to oxygen agglomerates of iron and carbon which had been preheated in an inert atmosphere was investigated.

A schematic diagram of the apparatus used is shown in Fig. 1. A gas train (not shown in Fig. 1) allowed an accurately controlled mixture of helium and oxygen to be supplied to the heated sample. Helium and oxygen, controlled with needle

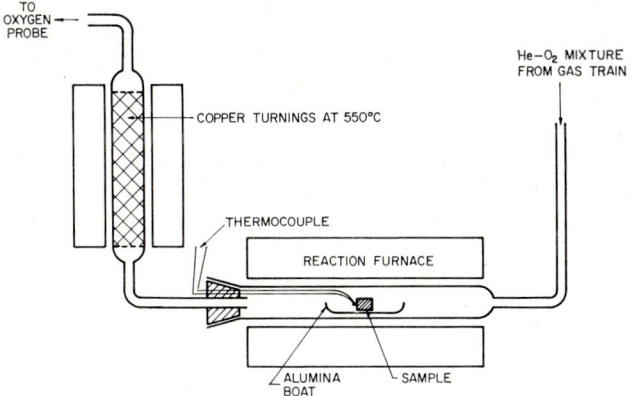

Fig. 1 Schematic diagram of apparatus

valves, were metered with calibrated capillary flow meters; bleed-off tubes dipping into vacuum-pump oil reservoirs controlled pressure fluctuations in the system. The gases were mixed in a tower packed with glass balls before being passed to the reaction furnace. The iron–carbon sample, in an alumina boat, was placed in a silica tube in the reaction furnace; a Pt/Pt–13% Rh thermocouple was introduced close to the sample. Exit gases from the reaction furnace passed over fine copper turnings at 550°C to remove any oxygen which had not reacted with the sample. It was assumed that carbon dioxide or carbon monoxide would pass through this reactor unaffected, and this was borne out by the results shown in Fig. 3. Finally, the exit gases passed into an oxygen probe (Fig. 2), based on a

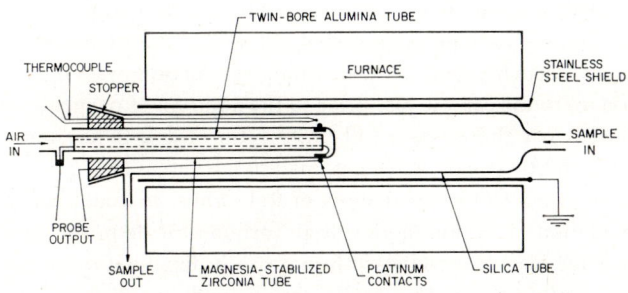

Fig. 2 Schematic diagram of oxygen probe

design by Whiteway *et al.*[9] The oxygen probe measured partial pressures of oxygen by an electrochemical cell of magnesia-stabilized zirconia. The cell operated in the region of 900°C, and compressed air from a cylinder was used as the reference half-cell. The partial pressure of oxygen in the gas entering the probe was given by the relationship

$$p_{O_2} = 0.2095 \exp\left(-46.425\, E/T\right) \tag{1}$$

where E is the emf, mV, and T is the absolute temperature of the cell.

The procedure adopted was to preheat the sample to 1100°C (and, in some cases, to 1200°C) in a stream of helium (215 cm^3/min). Oxygen was then introduced into the helium stream, usually for 1 min, at such a flow rate that slightly more than the stoichiometric amount theoretically required to oxidize the carbon in the sample to carbon dioxide was added. In all cases the oxygen partial pressure in the helium-containing exit gases from the reaction furnace, as measured by the oxygen probe, was approximately 3×10^{-4} atm. The ratio of carbon dioxide to carbon monoxide in the exit gases may be calculated from the oxygen partial pressure, assuming the following relationships for the reaction between carbon monoxide, oxygen and carbon dioxide:

$$CO + \tfrac{1}{2}O_2 \rightleftarrows CO_2 \tag{2}$$

$$K = \frac{p_{CO_2} \cdot p_{O_2}^{-\frac{1}{2}}}{p_{CO}} \tag{3}$$

$$\log K = \frac{14\ 754}{T} - 4 \cdot 536 \text{ (reference 8)} \tag{4}$$

where K is the equilibrium constant for reaction 2 and p represents partial pressures, atm.

Assuming equilibrium conditions in the gases passing in the vicinity of the probe, an oxygen partial pressure of 3×10^{-4} atm corresponds to a $CO_2 : CO$ ratio of 10^6. A typical oxygen probe result is shown in Fig. 3, the theoretically calculated probe output for pure carbon dioxide being given for comparison. The oxygen partial pressure in equilibrium with copper and copper oxide at 550°C is also shown.

The very small amount of carbon monoxide in the exit gases was confirmed by conventional gas analysis, although carbon monoxide must have been a reaction product. A gas-quench experiment, in which a cold tube was inserted into the reaction tube up to the sample just prior to the addition of oxygen to the helium stream, showed that there was a $CO_2 : CO$ ratio of $3:2$ in the initial reaction products (as found by conventional gas analysis), whereas after a 15-sec reaction time a sample gave a $CO_2 : CO$ analysis of $9:1$. Thus, it would appear that the degree of oxidation of carbon monoxide to carbon dioxide in the vicinity of the sample may have been increasing with increase in temperature of the sample.

The agreement between the probe results and conventional gas analysis results from samples taken directly from the reaction furnace exit indicated that the very small amount of carbon monoxide in the exit gases could not, in general, be ascribed to the carbon-deposition reaction:

$$2CO \rightleftarrows CO_2 + C \tag{5}$$

although, in a few experiments, some carbon was deposited on the walls of the reaction tube.

The first series of experiments was done by use of 325- to 400-mesh electrolytic iron powder and 40-mesh willow charcoal as starting materials. Composites

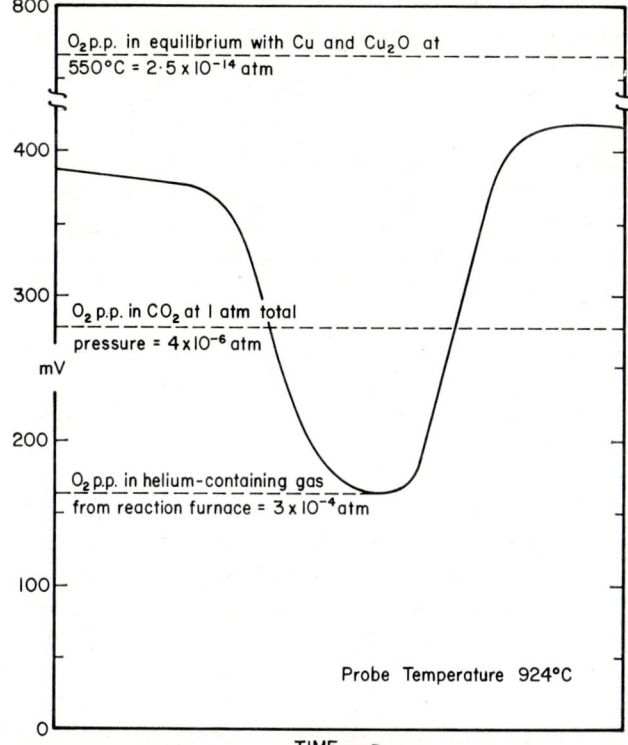

Fig. 3 Typical oxygen probe result

weighing 0·25 g were made with carbon contents varying from 3 to 15% by weight. Pellets were not pressed but, rather, the iron and carbon were intimately mixed and heaped in the alumina boat and preheated to 1100°C in helium. In each case the introduction of oxygen into the system caused the samples to melt, as evidenced by round balls formed because of surface tension effects while the iron was in the molten state. A melt made from a composite containing 3% carbon contained 0·68% dissolved carbon, and a melt made from an iron–10% carbon composite contained 2·5% dissolved carbon. It would seem likely that the iron was raised to its melting point before carbon dissolution occurred because composites containing 10% carbon, but preheated to only 1040°C, did not yield good melts; iron containing 2·5% dissolved carbon melts at 1340°C. Little or no sintering of the samples occurred at 1100°C in helium before oxygen was introduced—carburizing prior to reaction was therefore probably insignificant.

In the next series of experiments the same starting materials and compositions were used, but the composites were lightly pressed into 6-mm × 2-mm pellets. Melting in the same way as obtained in the first series of experiments was not achieved in this series. The pellets retained their shape, except for some rounding of the edges, although it was evident that a layer on the surface of the pellets had melted. Microscopic examination revealed that the thickness of this molten layer increased with increasing content of the carbon in the pellets. Better melting was obtained from pellets, again with the same compositions, prepared so that the carbon completely surrounded the iron. Pellets prepared in this manner with more than 10% carbon were estimated to be half-melted.

X-ray powder diffraction analysis revealed that the melted surfaces of these pellets were comprised of magnetite as the major phase, together with some wustite; no iron was detected. (In one case, small octahedral crystals of magnetite were observed under the microscope.)

It would appear that, for the pellets, the oxygen, which was limited by the calculated stoichiometric requirements of the carbon, reacted first with the accessible carbon near the pellet surface and then oxidized the liquid iron rather than diffusing into the interior of the pellets to react with more carbon. For the heaps of carbon and iron the porosity was sufficient to allow good oxygen access and, hence, good reaction and complete melting of the composite.

Some experiments were also done with a western Canadian coal (low-volatile, containing about 78% carbon, dry basis, and about 0·4% sulphur) in place of the charcoal used previously. In these experiments temperatures of 1200°C were employed, as well as 1100°C, and composites were made containing 5 and 10% by weight of the coal. Similar results were obtained as for the previous series, i.e. partial melting was observed for pressed pellets and complete melting was obtained when heaps of the two components were used.

These sets of experiments revealed that, under the conditions used in these tests, it was indeed possible to melt a very loose heap of iron–carbon composite preheated to 1100°C and containing as little as 3% by weight of carbon, as predicted by thermochemical calculations, but only partial melting of pressed pellets was achieved. To obtain a more porous pellet other tests were made with a coarser (40 mesh) iron. Although microscopic examination of the reacted pellets indicated a greater degree of melting for all pellets than had been obtained by use of the iron powder, a pellet containing 10% carbon needed to be preheated to 1200°C to cause it to melt completely.

During these experiments a significant observation was that no iron oxide fume deposited on the cooler parts of the silica reaction tube (Fig. 1). This lack of fume was consistent with D'Entremont and Taylor's[6] observation that in their basic oxygen processing of a solid charge fuming loss associated with the oxygen blow was less than from a modified open-hearth with oxygen lances and far less than from the conventional molten-metal basic oxygen process.

Besides mesh size of iron and carbon and porosity of pellets, other factors which would affect the melting characteristics of composite pellets would be the reactivity of the carbon, the rate of heat transfer into the composites and the general opportunity for gas–solids energy exchange. With respect to the latter factor, the only true test for the usage of iron–carbon composite pellets would be a pilot-plant type experiment in which heat-transfer conditions would be more favourable than with single pellets. Laboratory simulation of actual-scale conditions is virtually impossible. Single pellets containing 25% carbon (maximum amount of carbon used by Rouanet[7]) and preheated to 1100°C did melt completely in the test apparatus.

Manufacture of iron–carbon composites

From an industrial point of view various possibilities are available for the manufacture of iron–carbon composites, but the main problem would inevitably be a supply of low-sulphur carbon, although new techniques for obtaining such low-sulphur carbon from the cracking of petroleum products are thought to be under development.

The contact-cracking of methane and other hydrocarbons at 1100–1200°C in fixed-bed reactors packed with granulated coke produces a coating of pyrolytic carbon on the coke granules.[10] A scheme could be envisaged in which hydrocarbons, such as natural gas or vaporized fuel oil, are thermally cracked on metallized pellets heated to 1100–1200°C with off-gases from a steelmaking furnace. Carbon could be deposited on the surface of the pellets, which would then become the self-sustaining feed for the steelmaking furnace. The major disadvantage of this scheme would be expected to be the low chemical reactivity of the deposited carbon. Nevertheless, this principle of decomposing hydrocarbons on hot surfaces has been described in a U.S. patent[11] for protecting from oxidation during cooling compacted iron powders made from the product of the gaseous reduction of iron ores in fluidized beds. It is claimed that the carbon coating is advantageous when such briquettes are used as an iron source in steel production.

The most accessible form of carbon for this application may be a low-sulphur coal, but the availability of this commodity is a serious problem at the present time. Certain western Canadian coals do, however, have sufficiently low sulphur levels (about 0·4%) for the production of iron–coal composites. A hot-pelletizing technique in the temperature range 350–450°C, taking advantage of both partial carbonization of the coal and the binding properties when the coal is in the plastic stage, may hold several advantages over the conventional briquetting and pelletizing techniques.

One of the previously considered disadvantages of the new direct reduction processes may be turned to advantage for the production of a self-sustaining feed material for steelmaking. During the course of reduction of iron oxide to the metallic state, carbon may be produced by the carbon-deposition reaction (reaction 5). In fact, the presence of iron or iron oxide is known to have a catalytic effect on this reaction. Carbon deposition occurs especially in iron reduction processes employing gaseous reductants, and may be controlled. In the HyL process (fixed-bed reactor) hot sponge iron is cooled by contact with fresh reducing gas. This cooling completes the reduction and allows the controlled deposition of carbon, which can be varied between 1·50 and 2·25%.[12] Residual carbon may also be expected in metallized pellets from rotary-kiln direct reduction processes, e.g. the SL/RN process, especially when reactive reductants are used.

Future of self-sustaining feeds for steelmaking

For many years it has been confidently predicted that the next generation of steelmaking processes will be, to a certain degree, continuous, and characterized by the use of less expensive forms of energy than those employed at present. If continuous steelmaking is considered interlinked with direct reduction processes for the purpose of fuel economy, the economic advantages of self-sustaining feed materials of the type discussed in this paper can be appreciated.

From another point of view the production of a pre-packaged reduced-iron product may aid in bridging the two divergent pressures which usually bear on the decision as to where to locate a steel plant. On the one hand, marketing imperatives require that the finishing facilities be in the large consuming areas, whereas, on the other hand, ore and energy supply factors and air pollution restrictions are tending to force the relocation of the industry to remote locations.

Transportation

Relocation to remote areas introduces the problem of transportation and the behaviour of the composite pellets during transportation. Internationally, the rapidly expanding annual demand for iron ores—predicted to be 1000 000 000 tons in 1980[13]—is introducing major changes in the ocean-going transport capability of the iron ore industry. With respect to the ocean shipment of sponge iron, deterioration of cargoes is an unknown factor, but a press announcement[14] on the arrival in Japan after a 48-day voyage from Hamilton, Ontario, of a 650-ton consignment of metallized pellets from a SL/RN direct reduction kiln has indicated that no unusual shipping precautions are necessary other than to ensure that the cargo be kept dry at all times.

In order to achieve the lowest transportation rates possible with the 500 000-ton vessels (now under construction) or the 100 000- to 300 000-ton vessels (now in operation) and, at the same time, avoid the great costs of super-ports and huge handling facilities, it is likely that loading and unloading of the super-carriers will be done offshore by hydraulic pipelines, which also would then be used in many cases between the mines and tidewater and at the delivery end, if the consumer is located inland. In such cases it is probable that both the iron ore and the coal would have to be of rather fine sizes for economical pipeline transportation, possibly remaining in a dewatered condition aboard the ship, as in the 'Marcona' slurry tankers. With this new direction in shipping, the advantage of reduction installations at favourable assembly points for raw materials may be lost, because the production of the iron–carbon composites would have to be done at the delivery end. Further studies are required to determine if composite metallic iron–carbon pellets could be produced at a size sufficiently small to allow hydraulic handling in a form where oxidation of the iron would be inhibited.

As an indication of the very important effect of transportation costs on basic process decision, some information is presented here on the current situation. Some operations based on long-term commitment between producers, transporters and consumers seem all the more desirable because of the widely fluctuating charter freight rates[15] recently observed: for instance, the average rate per long ton for iron ore increased from U.S. $6.25 in the fourth quarter of 1969 to U.S. $12.00 (in 1970) from the St. Lawrence to Japan, and from U.S. $2.57 (in 1969) to U.S. $4.31 (in 1970) from the St. Lawrence to Belgium. For coal shipments between Hampton Roads (northeastern U.S.A.) to Japan the average rate per long ton in the fourth quarter of the year went from U.S. $6.62 to U.S. $9.72, but in early October, 1970, the rate was U.S. $12.40, declining to U.S. $8.25 at the end of 1970. For agglomeration the very fine sizes required by pipeline transportation factors should be advantageous and, in any case, coarser sizes would have to be reduced. Even on the Great Lakes, where distances are relatively short and ship sizes limited by canal lock dimensions, the trend is definitely towards larger self-unloading vessels—for example, the new 1000-ft long Bethlehem Steel vessel of 67 000-ton capacity. Such ships will accept 10 000 ton/h and self-unload 10 000–20 000 ton/h of iron ore, and should help prolong the stability of Great Lakes iron ore transportation rates, which have remained at around $2.00/ton since 1957. However, the pelletization is done at mine site; for Minnesota the present rate of 34 000 000 tons per year is almost as much as the 1959 total ore shipments from that state. It was estimated[16] that suitable low-sulphur coals could be supplied from some U.S. sources and also in large quantities from western Canada at acceptable transportation cost to eastern Canadian steelmaking centres.

Summary

The advent of non-blast-furnace processes for the reduction of iron ore has led to the suggestion of manufacturing an iron-bearing product with a contained-energy source, such as carbon. Preheating of this product to about 1100°C with waste gases from the steelmaking process, and subsequent exposure to oxygen, should cause the product to melt without the need for additional energy inputs. Such a product could be made at a site remote from the steelmaking facility, where energy sources are relatively cheap, although certain transportation factors should be considered. For example, only fine material can be transported in a slurry pipeline; if sufficient economies of transport can be achieved by integrated hydraulic methods, then the production of the iron–carbon composites would be moved back to the delivery or steel plant end. This product could act as a hot-metal substitute and as a scrap substitute in steelmaking and, indeed, blast-furnace hot metal may not be required at all.

Thermochemical calculations have shown that, theoretically, with a preheat temperature of 1100°C, carbon contents of the iron–carbon composites can be as low as 3% by weight, but laboratory tests indicate that considerably higher carbon contents may be required unless a higher preheat temperature can be used. The surprising result from these bench-scale investigations was that simple heaps of metallic iron and carbon were the most satisfactory. These findings suggest that, without small-scale studies of this kind, premature 'works-type' trials might have had discouraging results that might have caused premature abandonment of this proposal. What is required is a strong agglomerate sufficiently porous for oxygen to have good access to the carbon—otherwise the metallic iron will oxidize. It is not possible, however, to duplicate practical heat-transfer conditions around the agglomerates in a small apparatus, and the next stage of this study should be undertaken in pilot-plant facilities, if it proves to be economically attractive.

Possibilities for the manufacture of iron–carbon composites that might be investigated include (1) hot-pelletizing with a low-sulphur coal, (2) contact-cracking of hydrocarbons on to metallized iron ore pellets and (3) the deliberate encouragement of carbon deposition in direct-reduction processes. Self-sustaining feeds containing 'pre-packaged' energy would undoubtedly have a future in continuous steelmaking processes. It is thought that no deterioration of cargoes would occur while this type of material was being transported over long distances, at least under dry conditions.

Acknowledgment

The authors thank Mr. N. J. Ramey for doing the bench-scale tests, Mr. R. G. Sabourin for carbon analysis, Mr. R. G. Draper for gas analysis and Mr. E. J. Murray for X-ray analysis.

References

1. McManus G. J. Gun goes off for direction reduction. *Iron Age*, **206**, Aug. 27 1970, 69–76.
2. Gregory J. A. *et al.* Calcium carbide as an additional heat source in basic oxygen steelmaking. *Iron Steel*, **38**, 1965, 87–9.
3. Calcium carbide increases scrap usage at Pittsburgh Steel. *Steel Times*, **193**, 1966, p. 313.
4. Bailey D. R. and Onuscheck J. W. High scrap charge in the BOF utilizing solid fuel. *Iron Steel Engr*, **44**, Jan. 1967, 119–23.
5. Walsh J. H. Developments in iron- and steelmaking processes and their effect on energy balances. In *Advances in extractive metallurgy* (London: Institution of Mining and Metallurgy, 1968), 26–48.
6. D'Entremont J. C. and Taylor C. R. U.S. Patent 3 535 106, 1970.
7. Rouanet J. South African Patent 67/5348, 1968.
8. Kubaschewski O. Evans E. Ll. and Alcock C. B. *Metallurgical thermochemistry*, 4th edn (Oxford, etc.: Pergamon, 1967), 495 p.
9. Whiteway S. G. *et al.* Decarburization of iron–carbon alloys by argon–oxygen mixtures. *Can. metall. Q.*, **7**, 1968, 211–5.
10. Electrode carbon from thermal cracking of hydrocarbons. *Coal Res. C.S.I.R.O.* no. 40, 1970, 9–12.
11. Wald E. W. U.S. Patent 3 392 008, 1968.
12. Gearhart H. E. and Jackson K. A. Production of metallized pellets by the HyL process. *Iron Steel Engr*, **48**, March 1971, 53–8.
13. Iron ore in 1980—a billion tons per year. *Engng Min. J.*, **171**, Oct. 1970, p. 10.
14. *Japan Echo*, **10**, Jan. 13 1970.
15. The ocean freight market. *Foreign Trade, Ottawa*, Feb. 13 1971, 36–7.
16. Charbonnier R. P. and Walsh J. H. Improving the preparation transportation and transformation of coal for better utilization of this energy in Canada. Paper presented at World Energy Conference, Bucharest, 1971.

Plasma processes in extractive metallurgy

I. G. Sayce Ph.D.

Division of Inorganic and Metallic Structure, National Physical Laboratory, Teddington, Middlesex

533.9:669.053

Synopsis

The more important developments in plasma techniques which affect or could influence progress in the field of extractive metallurgy are reviewed. The various types of apparatus available for generating plasma temperatures in the laboratory and on a larger scale are discussed, and applications of these devices to ore beneficiation, chlorination, reduction and metal melting and refining are described. The available data on process costing are considered, and some of the more promising techniques are summarized.

The recent demands of the aerospace industry for methods of testing materials at high temperature, coupled with the growing requirements of high-temperature materials processing, have, over the last 15 years, resulted in the development of a variety of devices for producing the flows of hot partially ionized gas we know as plasma. Some of these devices have proved very convenient for laboratory studies of high-temperature chemistry, for it has been possible to achieve gas temperatures well above those of chemical flames without contamination by any products of combustion. The systems studied have ranged widely over the fields of inorganic and organic chemistry, and much of the published data is included in recent reviews.[1-10] These publications survey the field as a whole, but describe few new commercially viable processes and do not pay special emphasis to the promising area of extractive metallurgy. It therefore appears appropriate at this time to survey the scattered developments in the field of plasma technology from this point of view.

Because of the wide range of studies which could be included, and the commercial secrecy which surrounds the more promising developments, this survey will be somewhat selective and, inevitably, incomplete. It is hoped, however, that it will prove of use to those not yet actively involved in the field. No attempt will be made to cover the better known chemical processes of acetylene production, nitrogen fixation, or the production of oxides, carbides, nitrides, etc., except where these processes illustrate a development of apparatus or technique

I   241

of potential importance in extractive metallurgy. Nor will research in low-pressure plasmas form part of this review. These processes have all received adequate coverage in the surveys mentioned above. Finally, the techniques of plasma spraying, welding and cutting and conventional electric arc melting are now well tried commercial techniques and will also be excluded from the present work.

Techniques available for generating plasmas in the laboratory are considered first, and some of the large-scale developments are described. The various reactions and processes which have been studied are then discussed, before some consideration is given to costs and the promise of these methods in commercial extractive metallurgy.

Laboratory-scale plasma devices

Because of its convenience for welding, cutting and spraying, one of the best

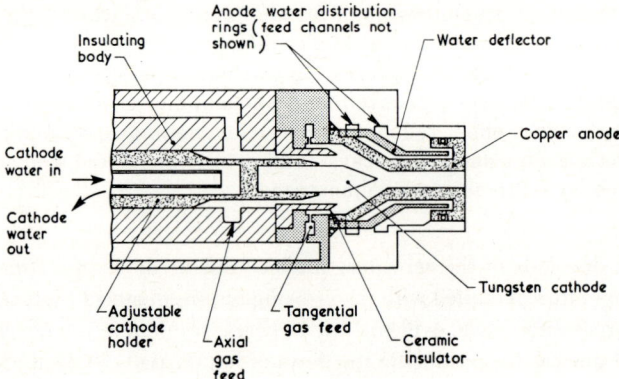

Fig. 1   Cross-section of typical dc plasma jet in use at NPL

known methods of heating gases to plasma temperatures is the dc plasma torch. A cross-section of a typical torch in use at the National Physical Laboratory (NPL) is shown in Fig. 1. In this device an arc is struck between axial water-cooled cathode (typically thoriated tungsten) and an annular water-cooled copper anode. A gas stream, fed axially or tangentially into the arc chamber, sweeps the anodic arc root into the constricted section of the anode nozzle and the combined constriction and lengthening of the arc raises the voltage and enables much higher temperatures to be attained than in the unconstricted arc. Typical axial temperatures lie in the range 8000–30 000°K, although high temperature gradients exist between the plasma core and the cooler outer zone.[11] Powers of up to 100 kW are typical for this simple type of torch, and thermal efficiencies usually lie in the region 60–85%. The common operating gases are argon (also used as starting gas because of its relative ease of ionization), helium, nitrogen, hydrogen and ammonia, or their mixtures. Corrosive gases and hydrocarbons are not usually passed through the arc because of erosion of the electrodes, or deposition of carbon, but these gases may, of course, be introduced into the plasma downstream of the arc zone. Methods have been proposed for permitting use with oxygen-containing gases in which the cathode is fabricated from zirconium,[12] or is protected in other ways,[13] but these approaches do not appear to be in common use. Another type of cathode suitable for air operation is the hollow water-cooled 'cold-cathode' type, but this is normally only used in high-power applications and is therefore dealt with in the next section.

The arc in the simple dc plasma jet may be rotated magnetically about its axis by surrounding the anode with a solenoid. Magnetic rotation, however, is usually unnecessary because the anodic arc root is normally in rapid oscillation at some 25–35 kHz,[14] and with tangential gas feed is also in rapid rotation. This movement spreads the thermal load and permits electrode lives of 50–100 h or more, and contamination levels in the plasma of only a few parts per million. Reliable dc plasma jets are now marketed by a number of manufacturers, but the commercial units are quite expensive and many workers still find it convenient to use their own designs.[15–19]

In the above designs the anode serves both as electrode and as arc constrictor, but in other designs the two may be separate, in which case the constricting section may be an insulator. This principle forms the basis of the Gerdien arc,[20] in which the dc arc between two electrodes is constricted by a vortex of water, and, more recently, the method has been used in a range of torches for cutting and other applications.[4] An ingenious extension of this principle has been the subject of two recent patents, which disclose the use not of water as a coolant and stabilizing agent but of liquid compounds of metals, metalloids or hydrocarbons (or their mixtures), which, on evaporation, form the plasma gas.[21,22] In this way the compounds are heated to high temperature with high efficiency without the need for any 'work' gas as a heat-transfer agent.

Constriction by a layer of fluid coolant is again used in certain transpiration-cooled torches, in which the plasma-forming gas is passed radially inward through the walls of the constrictor.[23] Such devices (Fig. 2) have been shown to have higher efficiencies and higher peak plasma temperatures than conventional torch designs.

It is also possible to pass the plasma-forming gas directly through the anode walls, and this has been done in a torch of conventional configuration by use of a porous carbon anode.[1] The electrical properties of transpiration-cooled anodes have been extensively studied by Sheer and co-workers,[24] and have also been exploited in the unusual design shown in Fig. 3. A tungsten cathode is positioned in the centre of an annular porous carbon anode, the two being separated by an insulating section. Gas is passed through the anode and the anodic arc root is diffused over the entire surface of the electrode. The device is both an efficient gas heater and a powerful source of illumination.[25] An instrument of this type has been developed for experimental purposes at NPL (Fig. 4).

Another laboratory device developed at NPL is the expanded arc furnace

(Fig. 5), in which a vertical dc arc is expanded to fill a large volume.[26,27,28] The apparatus employs a principle, first observed by von Engel and Steenbeck,[29] that the main cause of constriction of an arc is thermal convection of the sur-

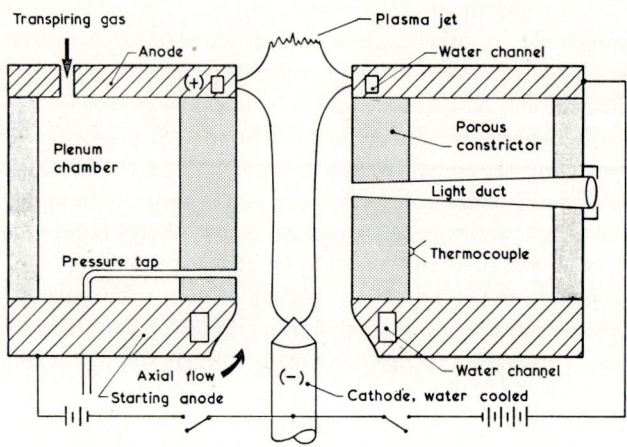

Fig. 2 Transpiration-cooled plasma jet used for spectroscopic studies[23]

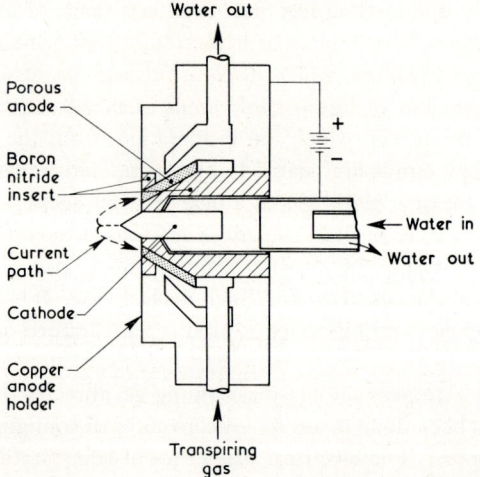

Fig. 3 Co-conical transpiration-cooled torch used as illumination source and gas heater[25]

rounding gas; but, by rotating the walls of the containing vessel, convection effects are minimized and the arc expands to fill the cylindrical rotor tube. This type of device has been described by several authors,[30-33] and has been used to evaporate refractory materials,[28] where the long retention time which results from the large volume plasma is an advantage. The electrical and other characteristics have also been studied analytically.[34]

Two ac devices deserve mention as small-scale gas heaters. The first is a 100-kW torch intended for operation at 50 Hz.[35] By use of coaxial water-cooled copper electrodes and magnetic rotation of the arc, a variety of gases may be heated, including air. In order to re-establish the arc after each current zero a 1-MHz ignition unit is employed. Efficiencies of more than 60% are claimed.[36] Much higher efficiencies are reported for a very simple three-phase 100-kW heater recently described by Bonet and co-workers (Fig. 6).[37] This consists of

Fig. 4 Co-conical transpiration torch developed at NPL

three movable electrodes arranged about a central axis, each electrode consisting of a simple water-cooled copper rod surrounded by a flow of sheath gas. The electrodes are brought together in the plasma issuing from a dc torch, and the three-phase arc is ignited. The electrodes may then be withdrawn, increasing the arc voltage to its normal operating level, and the dc pilot arc may then be extinguished. Efficiencies of more than 90% and low electrode cost make this device attractive if electrode losses can be minimized.

The above plasma generators all employ electrodes of some form, but there is another important class of device widely used in the laboratory for heating gases. This is the induced plasma torch, which employs no electrodes, and thus enables even corrosive gases to be raised to plasma temperatures with negligible contamination. A typical laboratory unit is shown in Fig. 7. This is made from quartz tubing and may be air- or water-cooled. The plasma is generated by induction from the radio-frequency current circulating in the water-cooled

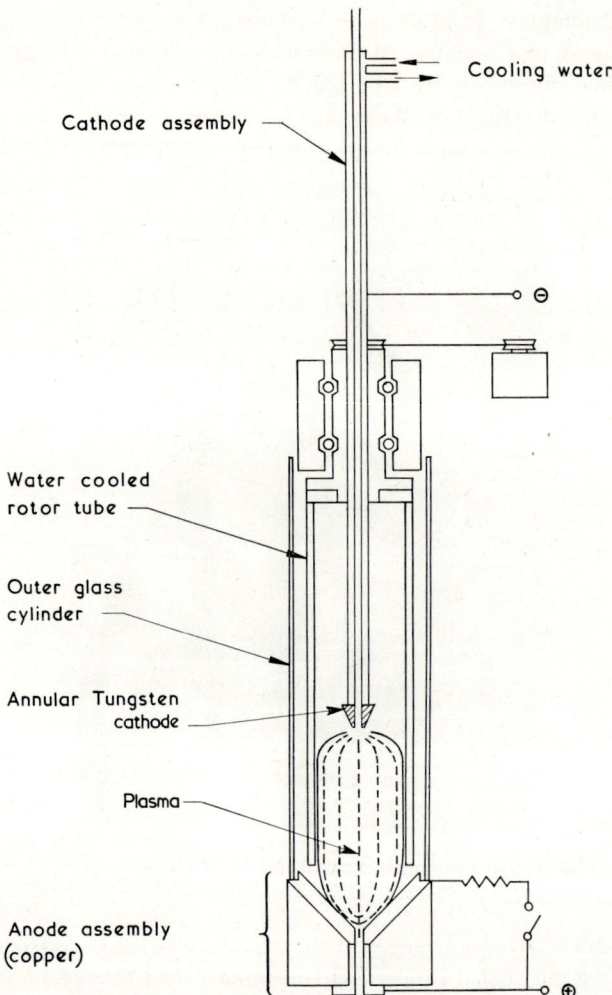

Fig. 5   Expanded arc furnace[26,27,28]

copper coil. The plasma is initiated, usually with argon as plasma gas, by excitation with a Tesla coil or by a variety of less convenient techniques (including a pilot arc discharge, heated conductor, or by breakdown of the gas at reduced pressure). Once the plasma is operating, the argon flow may be replaced with other gases and, if sufficient power is available, any gas may be heated in this way.

The development of these torches, operating principles and their application to chemical processes have been discussed in several papers,[1,38-42] and most laboratory torches embody the design principles described therein. Commercial units are also available. Laboratory devices typically operate at frequencies of 1–10 MHz, but, as described below, there are advantages in operating at lower frequencies, where possible.

Induced plasmas have proved useful gas heaters, although a large proportion of the gas feed bypasses the hottest plasma region. Again, when heating a powder stream, bypassing causes difficulties, and special measures are necessary to ensure that particles pass through the plasma zone. This is because magneto-hydrodynamic pumping causes the high-temperature viscous plasma to stream

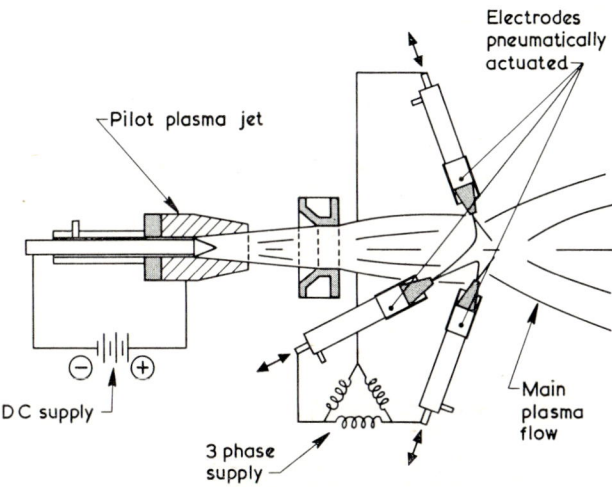

Fig. 6 Three-phase ac arc heater[37]

away from the fireball in both directions and, unless the powder is projected into the plasma with sufficient momentum, or, alternatively, fed through a cooled probe into the centre of the fireball, the particles tend to bounce off the plasma and pass through the cooler, outer layers of gas.[43] In many applications of the induced plasma, however, the required reaction may be effected in the tailflame region, when these considerations are not important.

The devices described above are moderately efficient for heating gases, but often it is more important to heat a condensed phase in order to bring about fusion, vaporization or chemical reaction. For fusion of powders simple passage of the powders through a dc plasma (as in ceramic spraying) or induced plasma (as in spheroidizing or Verneuil crystal growth) is usually sufficient, although thermal efficiencies on a laboratory scale are low; but for economic vaporization this elementary approach is quite inadequate. For greater efficiencies it is necessary to improve heat transfer, to increase the retention time, or both.

One means of increasing the rate of heat transfer, applicable to conductors, is to make the material the anode of a dc arc device. This technique is exemplified for the melting of metals by the Linde Plasmarc furnace,[44] shown in Fig. 8. The furnace is made from conventional materials, and the roof–side wall joint is made with a labyrinth sand seal, permitting escape of gases. A modified dc plasma jet is mounted in the roof, and the metal charge makes contact with an electrode set in the floor of the furnace. With argon as feed gas the torch is started in the usual way with the pilot arc switch closed. Once electrical contact is

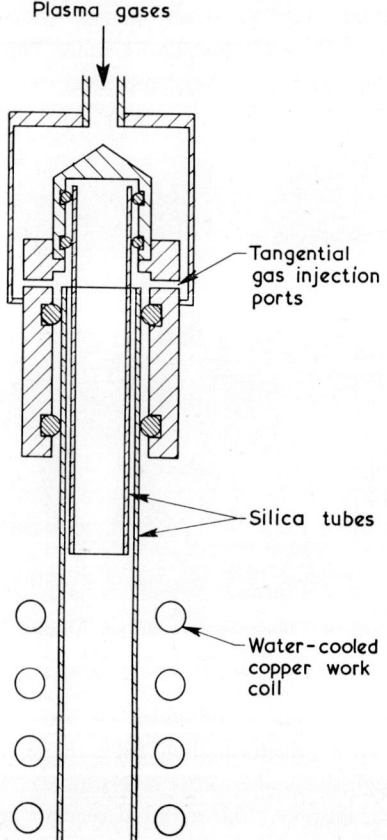

Plasma gases

Tangential gas injection ports

Silica tubes

Water-cooled copper work coil

Fig. 7 Typical induced plasma torch as used at NPL

established between the plasma and the bottom electrode, the pilot arc switch is opened and the full plasma power is then transferred to the metal bath. The greater part of the heat generated in the arc occurs at this anodic arc root, and radiation and conduction from the plasma are relatively unimportant. The metal bath is gently stirred by passing the arc current through electromagnetic stirring coils set in the side wall. The electrical stability of the system can be seen from the current and voltage traces (Fig. 9) taken during a melting operation. The long reach of the plasma makes it possible to place the torch in the furnace roof, avoiding the possibility of short circuits resulting from charge collapse. The low voltage gradient in the inert gas plasma also means that

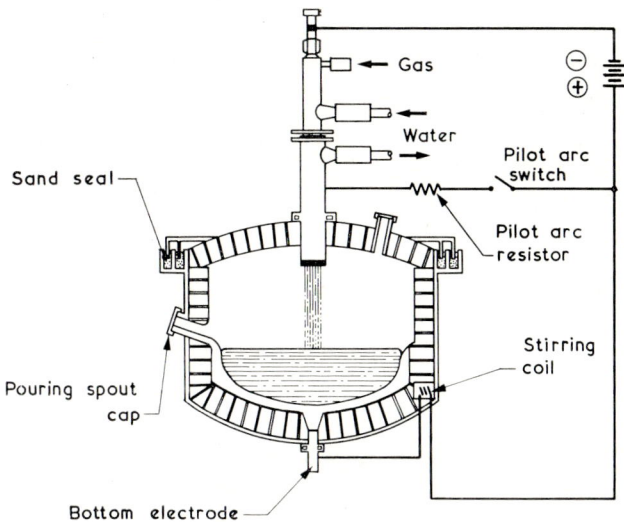

Fig. 8 Schematic diagram of Linde Plasmarc furnace[44]

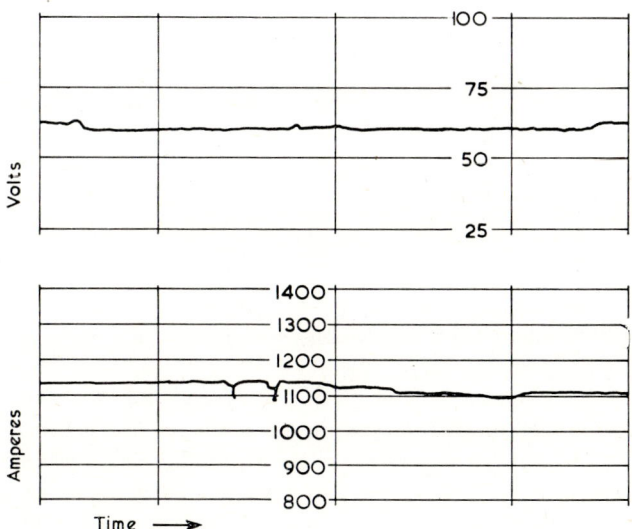

Fig. 9 Current and voltage plots for Linde Plasmarc furnace

changes in arc length cause smaller fluctuations in current than occur with carbon arcs operating in diatomic gases. Finally, the absence of consumable electrodes means that low contamination levels can be achieved. As is discussed

I*

in the next section, the principle of the Plasmarc furnace is also applied on a large scale in a three-phase version which employs three plasma jets.

The centrifugal furnace offers a second approach for improving heat transfer from the gas to the melt, and also permits containment of liquid materials at much higher temperatures than is possible in conventional furnaces. The advantages of a centrifugal furnace for the treatment of molten refractories with high thermal efficiencies were first pointed out by Zotos,[45] who proposed the use of a chemical flame as heat source. The principle appears to have been re-discovered independently by Grosse *et al.*[46] and Foëx and Delmas,[47,48] who have employed plasma-jet heated centrifugal furnaces to fuse refractory oxides.

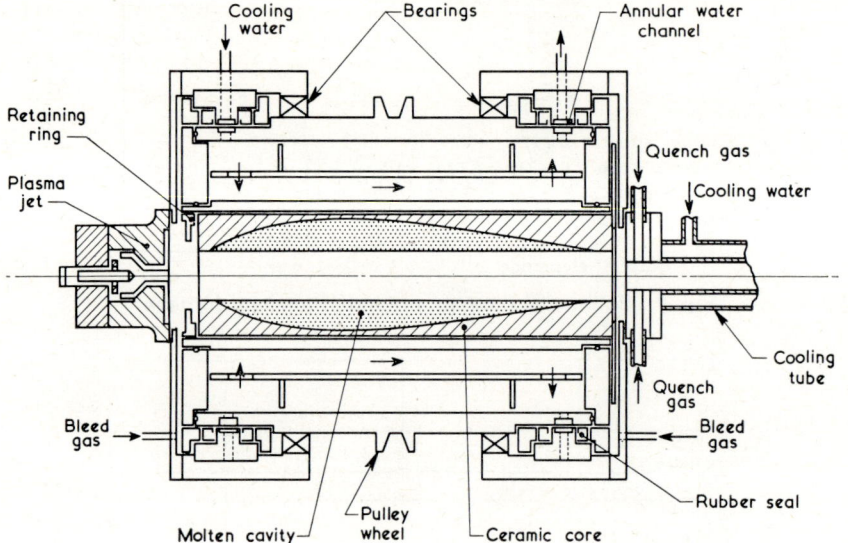

Fig. 10   Schematic diagram of centrifugal furnace

A version of the method has also been developed at NPL for both fusion and vaporization studies.[49] The device (Fig. 10) consists of a water-cooled cylindrical vessel lined on the inside with refractory, and rotated about a horizontal axis. The furnace is heated by means of a plasma jet and, as the contents melt, they are retained by centrifugal force as a stable layer on the inner wall of the furnace. The maximum temperature of the contents is thus limited only by the boiling point of the material, and by maintaining a thermal gradient through the refractory wall, attack of the container may be completely avoided. The assembled furnace and ancillary equipment are shown in Fig. 11.

Recently, two developments of the technique have been described. For refractory fusion it has been shown that high efficiencies may be achieved by use of not one but two plasma jets, one at each end of the furnace, and transferring a high-power dc or ac arc between the two (Fig. 12).[50] The length of the plasma

Fig. 11 NPL centrifugal furnace assembled: plasma torch is shown in foreground; quench and collection system in background

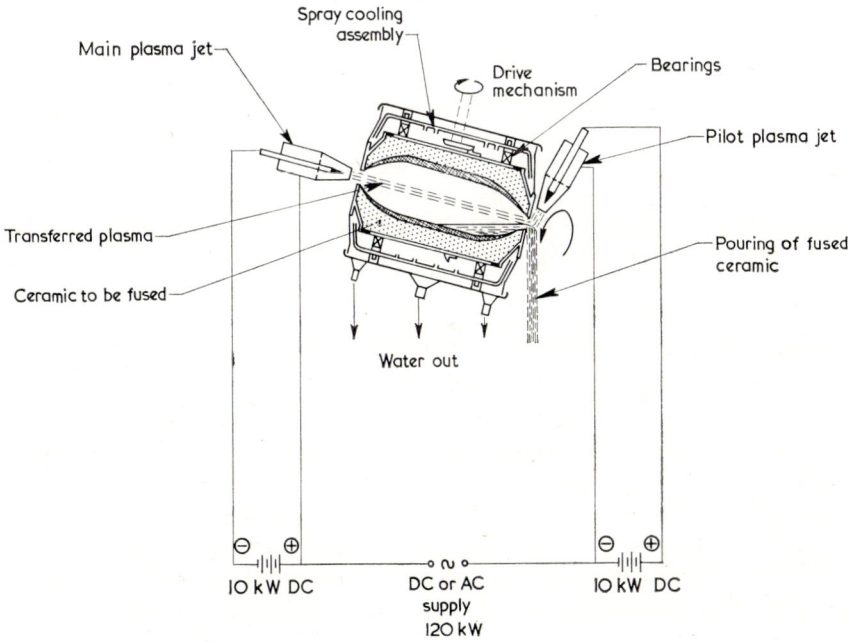

Fig. 12 Transferred arc centrifugal furnace: two plasma jets are employed for efficient fusion of ceramics[50]

column is about 500 mm and, with a transferred power of about 100 kW (power to each of the pilot plasmas about 10 kW), zirconia has been fused with a power consumption of only 3–4 kWh/kg. By tilting the furnace the fused contents may be poured into moulds or quenched with water to yield powdered ceramic.

The second development employs only one plasma jet and, by using powers of up to 30 kW, has demonstrated not only efficient fusion of ceramics but also vaporization of such refractories as alumina,[51,52] silica,[53] etc., at high rates (about 1·9 kg/h at 25 kW) and low power consumptions (down to 13 kWh/kg for alumina). A reducing environment aids vaporization, and rapid oxidation and cooling of the vapours yield sub-micron powders with novel properties.[53] The main reasons for the efficiency of this device are that although only one torch is employed, maximum use is made of the thermal energy in the plasma flow. Efficient heat transfer occurs in the highly turbulent interior of the furnace and gas emerges from the exit port at the effective boiling point of the material in question, having transferred as much heat to the ceramic as possible. Radiant losses from the end ports and conduction through the ceramic to the cooling water are kept to low levels even in this prototype furnace.

A very different method of vaporizing refractories has been developed by Sheer and Korman,[54] and was at one time used commercially to produce a variety of sub-micron powders.[55] The method is based on the fact, first described by Beck[56] and later by Finkelnburg,[57] that as the current density in an unconstricted arc is increased, a growing proportion of the input energy is released in the region of the anode (Fig. 13), until the point is reached when the heat input is too great to be dissipated by conduction and radiation and the anode either sublimes or, if molten (and suitably contained), boils. The transition from normal arc to high-intensity arc is accompanied by a change in the usual falling voltage versus current plot to a rising curve and the appearance of a brilliant plume of vapour streaming away from the anode. In order to ease collection or treatment of this plume the two electrodes are normally held at an angle of less than 180°, and provision must be made to feed the anode rapidly, preferably with continuous rotation to maintain a uniform surface. A small high-intensity arc unit has been used at NPL for evaporation purposes (Fig. 14). The method has proved to be amenable to scale-up, but an underlying disadvantage of the technique is the need to fabricate the material to be treated, mixed with carbon if required for electrical conductivity, into the form of electrodes capable of withstanding the high thermal shock and the mechanical handling of the anode feed system. Despite these reservations it has proved a very efficient and convenient vaporization method. Typical data for the vaporization of manganese silicate in pilot-scale operation (40–60 kW) are in the region 1–6 kWh/lb at erosion rates of 5–25 lb/h.[58]

In the interests of completeness a survey of laboratory plasma generators ought to include one further class, that of electrically augmented flame devices, which, although yet to find widespread application, do provide a source of heat intermediate between conventional chemical flames and the higher temperatures available with the plasma techniques described above. Whether or not they are to be employed in any commercial process will depend on the development of reliable units and on the detailed costing of the operation.

Various designs exist, most of which require the flame to be seeded with alkali-metal vapour to maintain electrical conductivity. Some designs have the appearance of a burner nozzle in which electrodes have been placed,[59] whereas

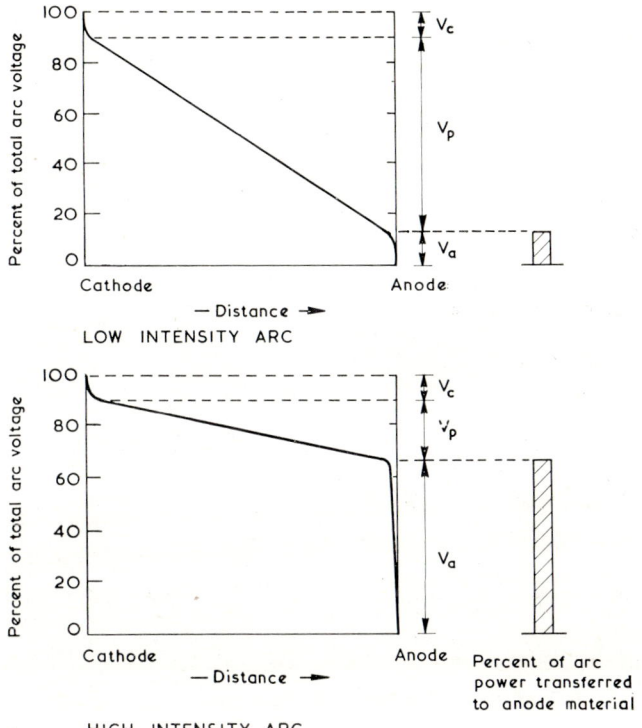

Fig. 13 Voltage distribution between electrodes in open arcs: V_a = voltage drop across anode sheath, V_c = voltage drop across cathode sheath, V_p = voltage drop across remainder of plasma[55]

others appear more like plasma jets which are fed with combustible gas,[60] and, finally, the radio-frequency augmentation of combustion-heated gas has also been demonstrated.[61] The various devices and their potential applications have recently been reviewed,[62,63] and an experimental study by use of an electrically augmented flame for production of acetylene has been published.[64]

Large-scale plasma devices

Relatively few of the devices described above have been developed for large-scale use. The first, and probably best known, are the units developed for acetylene production, and, in that they demonstrate the feasibility of plasma techniques on a large scale and are potentially useful for certain metallurgical techniques, they will be briefly described.

The most successful arc acetylene process has been that operated by Chemische Werke Hüls AG in West Germany. The arc unit has been described by Gladisch and is depicted in Fig. 15.[65] The gases are fed tangentially into the heater, creating a vortex within the hollow water-cooled electrodes. With the aid of the ignition device a dc arc is struck between the electrodes, and the motion of the gas ensures that the arc roots rotate rapidly, spreading the thermal load. The electrodes are made from iron with a wall thickness of 10–20 mm. Anodes are

Fig. 14 High-intensity arc apparatus in use at NPL

replaced after about 150 h, but cathodes last some 800 h. The arc units are not expensive and each plant has two arc units to reduce downtime on replacing electrodes. Typical operating conditions are 7000 V at 1150 A, giving some 8 MW of energy input.

A very similar series of high-voltage arc heaters has been developed by Eschenbach and co-workers at the Linde Division of Union Carbide, and developed in particular to yield high-temperature flows of oxygen and air for chemical and aerodynamic studies.[66,67,68] In these devices it was shown that a higher enthalpy could be achieved by operating the nozzle electrode at cathode polarity (the reverse of the Hüls case). Magnetic rotation of the anode arc root is employed and in one of its modifications a silver–copper alloy anode and copper cathode combination was found to give minimal electrode losses. The design is convenient in that it is subject to scaling laws, permitting extrapolation from laboratory models to large-scale units, and when heating gases to average temperatures of 7000–8000°C efficiencies of 70–80% are possible. The torch is being used for the vapour-phase oxidation of titanium tetrachloride to manufacture pigment titania.[2]

Another approach to large-scale dc plasma generation with a power consumption of 10 MW is that developed by Du Pont, and operated commercially for several years.[69] The Du Pont unit is of relatively simple design. Operating at 3100 A and 3500 V, a continuously fed carbon cathode is employed together

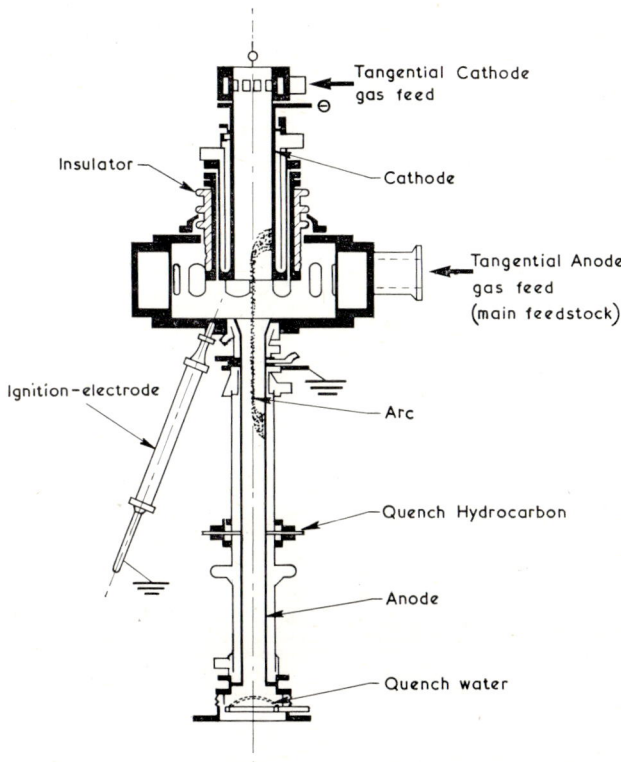

Fig. 15 Simplified diagram of Hüls arc acetylene reactor[65]

with an annular copper anode. Carbon build-up on the cathode is unimportant, and a mechanical scraper removes any carbon deposit from the anode. The arc is rotated magnetically and spreads until it almost fills the reaction chamber. Fairly homogeneous gas temperatures in the region 1500–2000°C are thus obtained at the operating pressure (400 mm Hg). The relatively low enthalpy means that a high thermal efficiency and long anode life are possible. The electrical power requirement for the reactor (including magnetic field generation) was 3·0 kWh/lb acetylene. The process appears to have been commercially viable for some five years, even at a relatively high electricity cost, but reduced demand for acetylene and access to inexpensive supplies of calcium carbide have rendered the process uneconomic and it was closed down in 1968.[70]

Although a version of the Linde torch has been operated on ac,[67] the above gas heaters are basically dc devices, which require facilities for rectification which may be expensive, but a three-phase ac heater with no such requirement had been described by workers from Knapsack-Griesheim AG.[71] This device, with

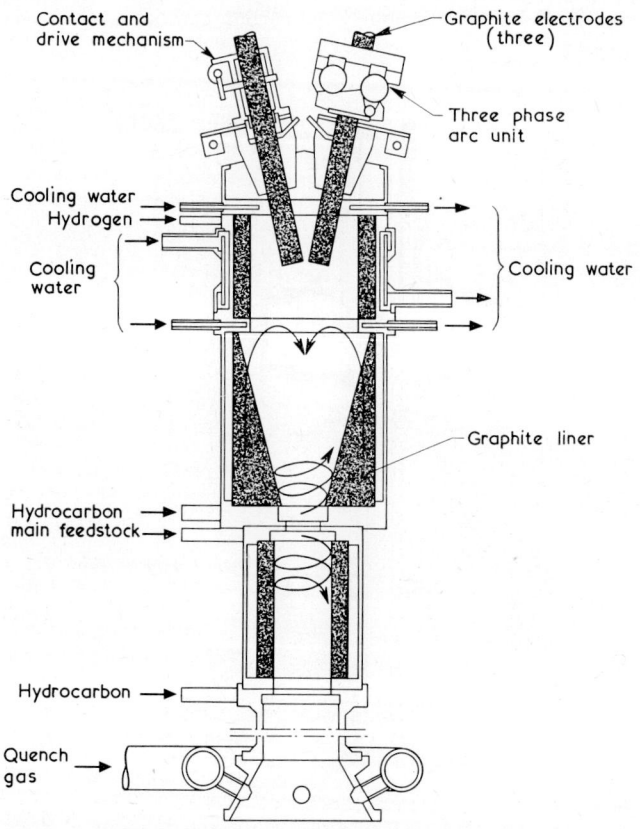

Fig. 16 Simplified diagram of Knapsack-Griesheim three-phase arc acetylene reactor[71]

power up to 4 MW, heats a hydrogen gas stream by means of an arc between three continuously fed carbon electrodes (Fig. 16). Petroleum vapour is fed into the hot hydrogen stream and a mixture of acetylene and ethylene is obtained with an energy requirement of 4·5 kWh/kg of acetylene–ethylene mixture. A high efficiency is obtained because there is no need directly to water-cool the electrodes in the region of the arc root—as there is when metal electrodes are used.

Development of a three-phase carbon electrode heater has also been described by Iwasyk.[72] The device was being studied as a potential tool for the Du Pont acetylene synthesis, and although economic assessment of arc heaters for this purpose led the firm to choose the dc arc heater described above, the paper provides a useful description of the design of an efficient three-phase unit for powers of up to 65 kW, operating in argon, nitrogen and hydrocarbon mixtures.

The efficiency and reliability of the carbon arc approach has also been recognized by workers at the Ionarc/TAFA organization, who have developed the units employed in the Ionarc process.[73,74] Although described elsewhere,[74a]

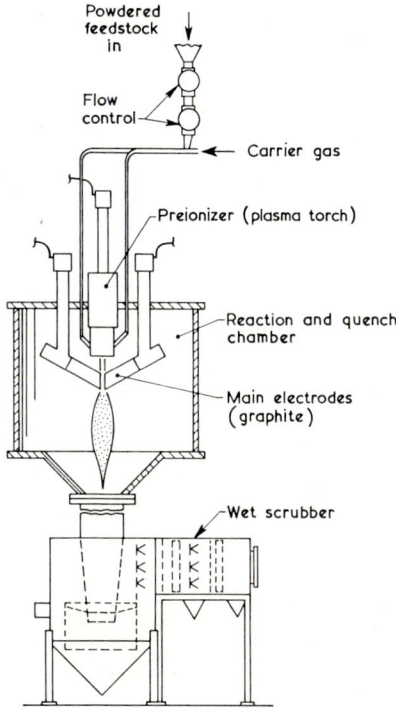

Powdered feedstock in

Flow control

Carrier gas

Preionizer (plasma torch)

Reaction and quench chamber

Main electrodes (graphite)

Wet scrubber

Fig. 17 Ionarc apparatus for plasma treatment of ores and concentrates[74]

brief mention will be made here. The units again employ three continuously fed carbon electrodes, to which an arc is struck (Fig. 17) with powers of up to 1 MW. The arc operates in the high-intensity mode to produce a large plasma flame (10-in diameter, 4 ft long) of carbon vapour, which streams downward through the vertical reactor. A small dc or induced plasma may be used to provide a flow of pre-ionized gas to enable re-ignition of the arc when ac is used. The apparatus is particularly suitable for processing particulate feeds to produce spheroidized material or to obtain reactions in the molten droplet.[73] The arc can be operated in a variety of gaseous environments, and, where the presence of carbon is not deleterious, such a carbon arc device is said to be the most economical heat source for this type of process. Where a carbon-free environment is required, it is possible to employ induction heating and, here again, Ionarc/TAFA have developed large-scale equipment.

Arising out of government contract work for the simulation of a gas-cored nuclear reactor, induction plasma torches of 1-MW capability are now available. The frequency of the power unit may be decreased as the power is increased and a typical frequency for 1-MW operation is 450 kHz (compared with about 4 MHz for the small laboratory units). The plasma produced is some 3–6 in in diameter and is contained in a segmented wall water-cooled torch which enables diatomic gases to be heated to enthalpies of up to 40 000 Btu/lb.[75] The device has been proposed for titanium dioxide pigment production, and typical costings for this process have been published.[76] More recent developments in induced plasma generators include operation with transpired gas entering the plasma region through permeable walls (raising the torch efficiency to about 60–70%), operation at pressures of up to 1000 lb/in² and reduction of the frequency to 10 kHz. It was hoped that operation at 60 Hz could be demonstrated during 1971.[77] This latter innovation would radically alter the present position where induced plasmas are the most expensive form of plasma. Reduction of frequency from the megahertz range means that the power source, which originally had to be an electron-tube device, may now be a motor generator or solid state device.

Operation at mains frequency is one of the advantages claimed for another high-power plasma unit, the Marc 31 generator made by Westinghouse, and described recently by Fey and Hirayama.[78] This device lacks the basic simplicity of the induction unit, but operation at 3·5 MW (single-phase ac) is claimed, with efficiencies of up to 90%. Air may be heated to 8000 Btu/lb, and methane to 25 000 Btu/lb (the latter figure with corresponding thermal efficiency of about 70%). The heater, shown schematically in Fig. 18, consists of two annular water-cooled copper electrodes, each of 5-in internal diameter and 10 in long, separated by a narrow gap (about 0·04 in). When a voltage (up to 4500 V) is applied across this gap, electrical breakdown occurs and the arc is immediately blown into the arc chamber by the flow of feedstock, part of which enters at high velocity through the inter-electrode gap. Electrode erosion is minimized by rotating the arc magnetically at about 60 000 rev/min by use of dc coils located in each electrode. The dc power used in this way amounts to about 10 kW. Operating on air at 1 MW gives an electrode erosion rate of about 1 g/h, or a feedstock contamination of a few parts per million. Electrode lifetime under these conditions is more than 100 h and, by virtue of a simple electrode design and short downtime for electrode replacement, it is claimed that low-cost operation may be achieved for such processes as acetylene synthesis and ore beneficiation.

One final development in the field of large-scale plasma devices employs the principle, patented by Foëx and Delmas,[79] of transferring electrical power between the jets of plasma issuing from dc torches. Thus, Arcos make a 250-kW three-phase arc heater, depicted in Fig. 19, in which three dc plasma jets provide

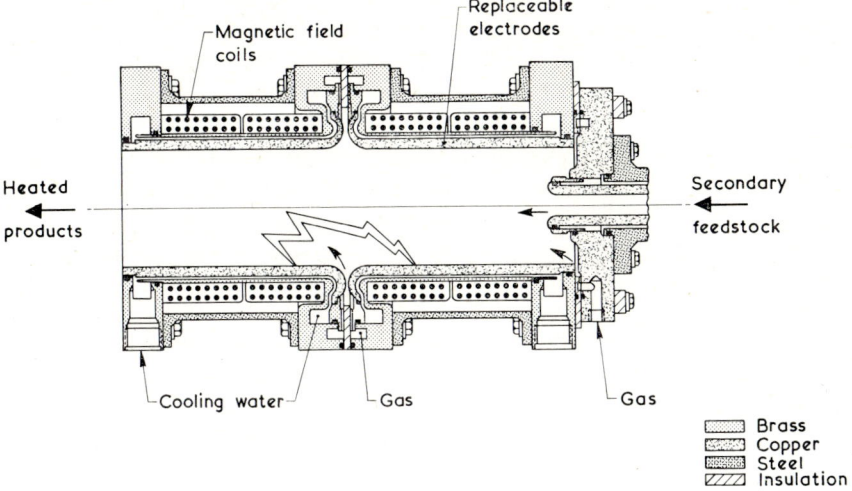

Fig. 18 Westinghouse single-phase ac arc heater

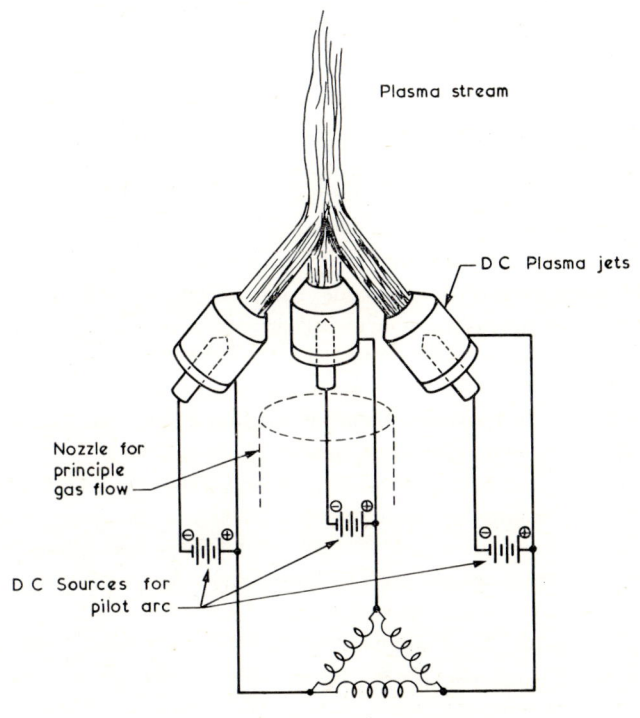

Fig. 19 Schematic diagram of Arcos three-phase gas heater

a pilot plasma and three-phase power is transferred between these, the bulk of the gas to be heated being fed axially into the plasma formed.[80] The device has been used for the oxidation of titanium tetrachloride and in another version can be used for heating a pool of metal in a furnace when the metal pool itself forms part of the current path. This principle closely resembles the proposals of Lunau and Paine,[81] who pointed out the advantages of replacing the electrodes of a three-phase arc metallurgical furnace with plasma jets. The use of dc torches to supply pilot arcs permits ready re-ignition of the arc at each current zero, enables the transfer of a long arc to the metal surface and minimizes contamination and electrical fluctuations.

Metallurgical extraction processes which employ plasmas

The more important devices available for generating plasmas having been briefly outlined, some of the metallurgical applications of such equipment are now considered under the headings *Ore chlorination,, Ore beneficiation, Oxide reduction, Other reductions, Plasma electrolysis* and *Plasma remelting and refining*.

Ore beneficiation

The first, and still the most quoted, example of the use of a plasma for ore beneficiation was the use of the high-intensity arc for the vaporization of rhodonite, a refractory manganese silicate which may contain more than 33% manganese, but which without high-temperature treatment cannot be employed as a source of this metal.[58] The ore (80–85%) was combined with carbon and compacted into electrodes of some 2-in diameter. These were evaporated, at up to 25 lb/h, and the fume was treated with a quantity of air sufficient to oxidize the vaporized manganese species only to manganous oxide. The fume product was cooled and collected with bag filters. It was found to consist of a fine-particle mixture of silica and manganous oxide, from which the latter could readily be extracted by leaching with sulphuric acid or ammonium carbamate solution.

In their patent Sheer and Korman also cited the vaporization of ilmenite to yield, on quenching in air, titanium and iron oxides, beryl yielding beryllia, alumina and silica, and euxenite yielding uranium dioxide and titania.[82] Zircon is one of a number of other complex oxides also mentioned.

These studies have been followed by other workers, who have heated these ores in induced plasmas, when some degree of separation occurs at sufficiently high powers and low feed rates.[83,84] Wilks and Thorpe have obtained extensive dissociation of a zircon sand (<150 μm) by passing through a 1-MW plasma in an Ionarc furnace with a power consumption of 1 kWh/lb.[77] Although it has been proposed that dissociation of zircon occurs by total dissociation of the oxides into atomic species, it is not possible to vaporize the ore with this apparatus or with this low power consumption, and it appears likely that dissociation occurs in the molten droplet to yield, on quenching, a material from which the desired components may be leached.

This is an example of the so-called 'fuse-quench' process—a method which has been studied extensively and recently surveyed.[85] Comparable processes have been investigated for extracting beryllium from beryl, a complex beryllium aluminium silicate. Thus, beryl concentrates may be fused (in a crucible, or as particles fed through a flame) and quenched to produce a glass. Under certain circumstances this glass may be leached with acid to extract beryllium, or, alternatively, the glass may first be devitrified before leaching, as in the commercially operated process.[86,87]

The ability to effect reaction in the molten droplet as it passes through the plasma is the subject of the Ionarc patent application recently published.[74] The Ionarc apparatus has been described above, and provides a large volume plasma through which a powdered ore is fed. The method is exemplified by the treatment of a complex waste product resulting from pressure-leaching of a nickel–cobalt concentrate. The nickel–cobalt values (0·85 and 0·19%, respectively) were hitherto considered unrecoverable. The powdered material was fed through a 60-kW plasma at 454 g/min, in an atmosphere of natural gas. The solid products were collected in a bag filter and submitted to a simple ammonia-leaching process, and it was shown that 67% of the available nickel was removed in this way without application of pressure. This may be compared with 24% removal of nickel by use of the best laboratory leaching conditions on a test sample, even with the application of pressure. Other examples included in the patent employ an ore feed to which small amounts of sodium chloride have been added, and by passage through the arc it has been shown possible to solubilize low values of gold, platinum and nickel which could not otherwise have been economically recovered. The use of chlorine itself and other reactive gases could obviously extend the applications further.

This novel process appears to be an important development in extractive metallurgy, especially as supplies of ores capable of treatment by conventional techniques become increasingly scarce, and the use of low-frequency induction heating of the plasma gas could well make the method even more economical.

Another study depending principally on reaction in the molten droplet is that of Brown, who fed ground ilmenite ore, suspended in hydrogen or ammonia, into an argon plasma issuing from a dc plasma spray torch.[88] Considerable reduction of iron was achieved and two types of product were obtained. Part occurred as a fused titanium-rich slag, containing particles of metallic iron, and part occurred as a powdered material less highly reduced. Development of the process to yield a reduced powder from which the iron could be leached was not possible, but might well be attractive in view of the importance of ilmenite as a source of titanium dioxide. Patents do exist, however, describing comparable processes occurring at considerably lower temperature, when a plasma is not necessary.[89]

Ore chlorination

An extension of the above work to chlorination in a chlorine gas environment is clearly potentially useful, and is included in the Ionarc patent application.[74]

Again, the high-intensity arc was one of the first techniques to be employed for the purpose. Sheer and Korman evaporated carbon–metal oxide mixtures in an atmosphere of chlorine, thereby producing chlorides of all the metal constituents of the arc.[90] In the case of a complex silicate it was claimed to be unnecessary to chlorinate the whole of the ore, but partial chlorination was possible,[91] yielding silica, which was readily collected, and the halides of other metals originally present in the ore.

A more recent patent describes the use of a dc plasma jet (55–60 kW) of nitrogen to heat a stream of chlorine containing finely ground beryllium oxide concentrate, or beryl ore.[92] More than 60% conversion to $BeCl_2$ was obtained, with an energy consumption (in the case of oxide concentrate) of 52·5 kWh/lb.

Oxide reduction

Carbothermic reduction of oxides is the oldest and still the most widely used method of extracting metals from their ores, and it is not surprising to find that the high-intensity arc method has been applied to the process.[93] Vaporization of magnesia in a carbon arc, followed by rapid quenching, resulted in more than 60% reduction with an equivalent power consumption of 8·2 kWh/lb of metal.[94] Rapid quenching, essential to prevent back-reaction of the metal vapour with carbon monoxide, means that the metal is obtained as a very fine powder, which must be subsequently purified and compacted. These difficulties were also associated with the Hansgirg process for carbothermic reduction of magnesia,[95] and account for the failure of that process. The high-intensity arc technique does not appear to offer any outstanding advantages when used in this way, but an alternative method of use does have much to offer.

In this process the metal oxide and carbon are again compacted into the form of an anode, but the current is much lower: thus, the arc is not uniformly distributed over the face of the anode and the electrode does not evaporate rapidly.[96] The arc is operated at reduced pressure, and the anode is rotated so that it burns uniformly. With an anode of niobium pentoxide and carbon in stoichiometric proportions, reduction occurs under the influence of the arc and carbon monoxide is evolved. Molten niobium collects on the surface of the electrode, and impurities in the metal are vaporized. The metal collects as spherical drops, which fall from the anode as $\frac{1}{4}$-in diameter spheres of 99·8% purity. The method has also been applied to the production of high-purity uranium carbide spheres,[96] and the process is understood to be under development for molybdenum production by the Molybdenum Corporation of America.[5]

There are several reports of the use of plasma processes in other oxide reductions. Total reduction of iron oxide occurred when the oxide suspended in hydrogen was fed into a helium plasma.[97] Tungstic oxide was reduced with up to 95% yield in the same apparatus. Both products were pyrophoric powders. A CIBA patent claimed the preparation of tungsten and other refractory metals in very good yields from their oxides or salts by plasma reduction.[98] Tungstic oxide, ammonium paratungstate and the oxides of molybdenum and rhenium were each fed into a dc hydrogen plasma at powers of up to 24 kW, and the metals were produced in yields of 95–98%. The products were treated for some hours in a vacuum or in hydrogen at 550–750°C, during which time the bulk density increased considerably, although the surface area of the product remained high (5·5–19·4 m^2/g). The final powders oxidized slowly on exposure to air, but were non-pyrophoric.

The reduction of iron oxide has been extensively studied. Gilles and Clump obtained 69% reduction of ore in small scale (9–32 kW) experiments with a dc hydrogen plasma,[99] and patents have been issued which describe large-scale processes. An arc transferred to the metal pool in the floor of the furnace has been used to heat an ore in the presence of a hydrocarbon gas, and iron has been made in this way.[100] Chromium oxide was also reduced in the apparatus to make an iron–chromium alloy. A similar process is also described in an East German patent,[101] and development of the principle into a large-scale three-phase apparatus operating with a methane plasma supplemented by fuel oil has

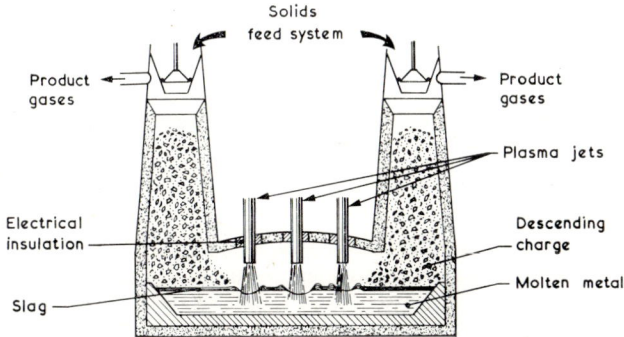

Fig. 20 Furnace for three-phase plasma smelting of ores[102]

also been covered by patent.[102] The latter describes an apparatus (Fig. 20) in which the hot exhaust gases leaving the furnace are used as in a conventional blast-furnace to heat and partially reduce the descending charge of ore.

Studies of alumina reduction on passing the powder through an induced plasma of argon or argon with hydrogen, carbon monoxide and methane have been reported by Rains and Kadlec,[103] and conversions of up to 30% have been achieved. It was shown, however, that vaporization of the oxide was the controlling factor, and high conversions were only obtained when very low feed rates of fine powder were used. The heat-transfer rates to alumina particles in induced plasmas have been studied by other workers,[104,105] and it is evident that this method, at least on the laboratory scale, does not give sufficient retention time for extensive reaction to occur.

The centrifugal furnace, on the other hand, permits efficient use of the thermal energy of the plasma and enables a long retention time and good heat transfer to be achieved. The device has been used for the carbothermic reduction of stoichiometric mixtures of carbon and such oxides as alumina or magnesia.[51,52] Under reducing conditions alumina vaporizes as a mixture of Al and Al_2O ($+CO$), and magnesia evaporates as the metal. Rapid quenching of the vapour leaving the furnace with jets of argon yields a pyrophoric product containing much free metal, but the vapour species have generally been oxidized to produce sub-micron powders, which are valuable as additives to ceramics, as fillers and as catalysts. It is clear, however, that this method could form the basis of a carbo-thermic reduction process, if suitable quench and purification methods could be achieved.

Other reductions

As has been pointed out above, one of the difficulties observed in the reduction of many oxides in plasmas is that of vaporizing the refractory oxide itself. This difficulty does not arise in the case of halides, and hydrogen reduction of metal halides (mainly chlorides) has received extensive study.

Case claimed the reduction of boron trichloride with a yield of 91·6% and a power requirement of 79 kWh/lb boron with a small dc plasma jet with a power of 11·5 kW to heat hydrogen.[106] The same reaction has also been carried out in an induced plasma.[107]

Another patent disclosed the production of niobium, in 93% yield, by passing the pentachloride in argon into a 24-kW hydrogen plasma.[108] Fine powder niobium was produced at 32 g/min and this was heated for a time first in hydrogen and later in vacuum. This process removed unchanged halides and yielded non-pyrophoric niobium with surface area 6·5 m^2/g (75% particles <0.05 μm). It was reported that tantalum, molybdenum, tungsten, zirconium and hafnium could be obtained in the same way with yields of 96%, 90%, 94%, 65% and 70%, respectively.[108,109]

Hydrogen reduction of titanium tetrachloride has been studied by a number of workers. Reduction in dc[110,111] and induced[112] plasmas has produced titanium trichloride in yields of more than 60%, and, in the presence of gross excess of hydrogen, some titanium dichloride. Free titanium, however, appears as a significant component in the equilibrium mixture only above 4000°K[112] and no metal appears in the product, even when rapidly quenched. Titanium trichloride has also been prepared by use of the liquid vortex stabilized torch with titanium tetrachloride as the liquid stabilizing agent.[22] When this device was fed with silicon tetrachloride, reduction to silicon was achieved.

Although reduction of titanium tetrachloride to the metal may be impossible with hydrogen, reduction with sodium or magnesium is well known, and a recent patent claimed the use of these metals in a plasma process.[113] A dc plasma is transferred on to the face of a movable ingot of titanium, which slides in a vertical water-cooled mould (Fig. 21). The upper surface of the ingot melts and on to this hot surface are projected streams of titanium tetrachloride and sodium. Pure titanium is said to form as a molten pool with yields of up to 90%. Yields are greatest when the process is run under pressure. As the ingot builds up it is withdrawn through the bottom of the apparatus. The process is, of course, attractive in that it produces not sponge but bulk titanium metal. The other metals included in the claims of the patent include zirconium, niobium and molybdenum.

By the use of the same apparatus titanium tetraiodide could be decomposed to the metal in the absence of reducing agent (an example of the van Arkel process). Other examples of the use of plasmas simply to dissociate compounds to yield metals are the decomposition of molybdenum disulphide in an induced

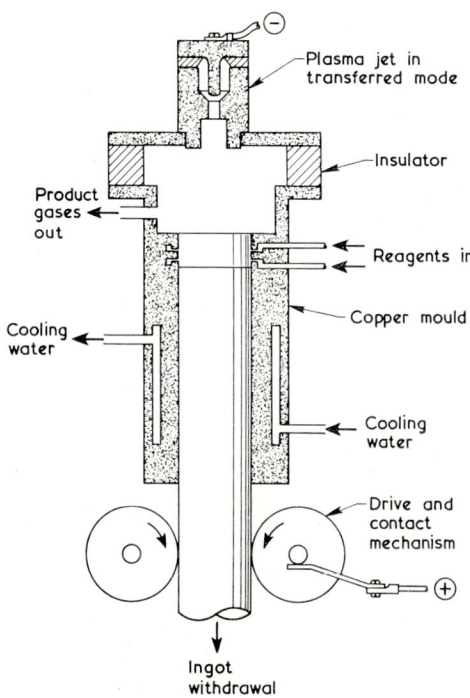

Fig. 21 Apparatus for plasma reduction of titanium compounds[113]

plasma, yielding the metal and sulphur,[114] and the decomposition of nickel carbonyl in a dc plasma to give a fine powder containing free nickel.[115]

Plasma electrolysis

In metal cutting, welding and melting applications it is common to transfer the arc to the metal surface, but it is also possible in suitable apparatus to transfer the arc to the surface of a molten electrolyte, when the plasma can act as a gaseous electrode for the electrolytic process. Examples mentioned in the literature include the electrolytic separation of manganese from a melt of $MnO-CaO-SiO_2$.[116] With a cathode pool of manganese and a conventional anode of carbon a high yield of manganese was obtained with up to 0·1% carbon as contaminant, but by raising the anode from the melt and striking an arc to the melt surface the carbon content of the manganese obtained was reduced by half.

Another application of the principle has been the use of arc electrolysis to remove iron from a bauxite melt.[117] An impure bauxite (26·7% Fe) was fused in a specially designed cold skull induction heater. The electrodes were a molten nickel pool, acting as cathode, and a water-cooled tungsten anode, held just above the surface of the melt and protected from oxidation by an inert gas flow. Once the arc had been struck, the electrolytic current (50–70 V, 100 A) was sufficient to maintain the melt temperature. During the electrolysis iron was liberated at the cathode, and it was reported that silica and titania impurities were fumed off at the anode.

A development of this technique, also involving arc fuming, is the arc electrolysis of lead silicate melts, described by Shelley and Charles.[118] A dc arc between two carbon electrodes was maintained over the fused silicate in such a way that the plasma was projected down on to the surface of the melt. This plasma was then used as one electrode for electrolysis, the other being a molten lead or tin electrode at the base of the crucible. It is found that with the arc as either anode or cathode to the cell lead oxide fume was evolved at the arc root, and with the arc anodic and lead pool cathodic the latter increased in weight owing to liberation of metal. The authors interpreted their results as indicating the presence of positive and negative lead-containing ions, but no allowance was made for thermal fuming, which may well have been important. Whatever the mechanism, however, transferring the arc to the electrolyte is a useful method of heating the melt to obtain fuming, and the method may well have application in extractive metallurgy. The technique has since been applied to tin-containing melts.[119]

At NPL fuming experiments have also been carried out as a means of recovering metal values from low-grade slags, transferred arcs being employed from both solid electrodes and from a dc plasma jet. Our experiments indicate that in the systems studied to date electrolysis may occur, but only with low efficiency. High fume rates have been obtained, however, again with either polarity of arc: thus, we conclude that in the systems studied thermal fuming was the most important process to occur.

Plasma remelting and refining

A number of recent papers have described the use of plasmas in metal remelting or refining processes. The majority of these refer to the treatment of steels, and have described the production of steels with reduced levels of sulphur, phosphorus, gaseous impurities and non-metallic inclusions. The processes fall into two categories—simple remelting and plasma electroslag refining processes.

Rykalin and co-workers have demonstrated plasma remelting of steels in the absence of slag. By this means it was possible to reduce dissolved oxygen and nitrogen contents by 15 and 23%, respectively, and the inclusion content was markedly reduced, and losses of volatile alloying ingredients (aluminium and carbon) were relatively small.[120] In further experiments the plasma remelting of a ball-bearing steel was compared with vacuum remelting, and it was concluded that the plasma method was more convenient, and yielded a better product.[121] Similar control over the composition of steels has been reported for the Plasmarc furnace,[94] and a comparable steel remelting process has been developed by the British Steel Corporation, giving a stable arc with rapid remelting and low losses of fume or metal.[122]

By the use of a plasma gas containing a known partial pressure of nitrogen it was claimed that the nitrogen level in a plasma heated melt may be controlled,[123] and the use of plasmas containing oxygen to remove carbon, or hydrogen to remove oxygen, has also been described.[124]

Plasmas have been used as the heat source of electroslag remelting baths. Just as a plasma may be used as a gaseous electrode for electrolysis, so it may also be used to supply power to the electroslag bath. The principle appears to have been first mentioned by Russian workers as a simple extension of plasma jet remelting,[125] but was first described in detail in a patent claiming the use of one or more plasma jets for single- or multiphase heating of the slag, for remelting metal rod, wire, powder, etc.[126] A system employing transfer of three-phase power between three dc torches is now being marketed for remelting and, presumably, for electroslag refining. Powers of up to 250 kW are available and higher-power versions are envisaged.[80]

Costing data

Relatively little has been published on costings for plasma processes, but what few data have appeared demonstrate that these techniques are not as expensive as might at first appear. Dundas and Thorpe have published estimated hourly operating costs for a variety of plasma systems and further figures have also appeared in the trade literature.[127,128] These figures are shown in columns 1–6 of Table 1, and they refer to operation at such powers that approximately 650 kW leave the apparatus as useful heat imparted to the feedstock. For certain of their processes Dundas and Thorpe quoted energy inputs of about 1 kWh/lb for treating a particulate feed. Thus, although the penultimate row of Table 1 shows hourly operating cost, the final row, showing cost/kWh, represents the total cost of treating 1 lb of material at this power level, costs of handling and collection of products being neglected.

Columns 1 and 2 are for the induction heating of argon and air, respectively, the differing totals reflecting the cost of the inert gas. The relatively high capital amortization figure is apparent, and results from the high cost of the power supply. Columns 3 and 4 show comparable figures for dc heating of argon and nitrogen. The capital cost is much lower, but now maintenance costs are increased, because the authors have assumed electrode lives of only 100 and 25 h for argon and nitrogen operation, respectively, and changing of electrodes requires the inclusion of both electrode and downtime costs. It is felt that these

Table 1 Cost per hour of operating various plasma systems and cost per pound of powder treated at 1 kWh/lb (For more complete data see references 127 and 128)

	Induction		DC		Carbon arc		Induction (O$_2$ or air)	
	Ar	Air	Ar	N$_2$	Air/Ar	Powder	4 MHz	10 kHz
Enthalpy, Btu/lb	8000	10 000	8000					
Assumed efficiency, %	55	55	45	65	65	90	50	50
kW input	1180	1180	1445	1000	1000	725	1000	1000
Costs, $ U.S. per hour								
Amortization	12·50*	12·50*	3·30*	2·75*	3·73*	3·40*	10·00†	4·29†
Maintenance	14·57	14·57	16·97	21·96	6·72	6·72	7·30	2·60
Gas	30·00‡	—	30·00‡	10·00§	1·20**	1·20**	—	—
Electricity, $0.006/kWh	7·07	7·07	8·68	6·00	6·00	4·35	6·00	6·00
Downtime	—	—	2·00	8·00	—	—	—	—
Total hourly cost, $	64·14	34·14	50·95	48·72	17·65	15·67	23·30	12·89
Cost/lb ore treated at 1 kW/lb, $	0·10	0·052	0·078	0·075	0·027	0·024	0·047	0·026

* Amortized over 5 years or 40 000 h. † Amortized over 5 years or 30 000 h. ‡ 1000 Sft³/h Ar at $0.003/ft³.
§ 1000 Sft³/h N$_2$ at $0.001/ft³. ** 40 Sft³/h Ar at $0.003/ft³.

figures may be based on pessimistic estimates of electrode life and cost, and could well be reduced somewhat, but by how much will depend on the choice of design and specific enthalpy and gas requirement under consideration. Columns 5 and 6 present costings for the use of a carbon arc based system, presumably of the type employed in the Ionarc furnace, column 5 referring to the simple heating of the gas stream and column 6 to the heating of a powder stream. The difference arises because it is claimed that for heating a particulate stream the carbon arc is more efficient than other devices, and, thus, a lower power level may be used. The capital costs of a carbon arc heater are comparable with the dc plasma unit, but the running costs are substantially reduced, the main item being the replacement of the consumable carbon electrodes. The final two columns of Table 1 represent a more recent assessment of costs,[120] and also enable comparison of the conventional induction plasma (4 MHz) with solid state circuitry except for oscillator tubes, with projected costs for operation at much lower frequency (10 kHz) when a motor generator may be used. The figures refer to slightly different power levels, etc., than the remaining figures for Table 1, but suffice to show a reduction in operating cost of the conventional torch, and a very much reduced cost for the low-frequency device, whose economy of operation now rivals the carbon arc unit. The advantages of the low-frequency torch lie in the lower initial cost and in the lack of oscillator tubes, which have only a finite life. Clearly, if the authors can substantiate their claim that 60-cycle operation will soon be possible, this type of plasma heating device will be even more economical.

It is of interest to compare these figures with some of the estimates which have been calculated by Fey and Hirayama[78] for a possible ilmenite beneficiation process. The calculation was based on the treatment of 87 600 ton/annum (or 10·95 ton/h) at 1·45 kWh/lb, i.e. three times the theoretical requirement. The process was thus assumed to require 35·4 MW, for which the capital cost of heaters and power supplies was estimated at \$2 800 000. Modifying these authors' figures to omit the cost of ore material and costs of handling ore and products, and replacing their electricity cost with the value \$0.006/kWh, the figures should be brought into line with those of Dundas and Thorpe given above. By use of natural gas at $\$0.50 \times 10^3/ft^3$, and assuming an electrode cost of \$0.001/kWh, the net cost of treating the ore is \$33.23/ton, including labour, amortization, depreciation, etc. This corresponds to \$0.015/lb, comparing favourably with the lowest of the values in Table 1. The approximations involved are considerable, and the latter calculation is based on a different system and a much larger operation, but the similarity in figures is significant.

More detailed analysis is not possible without access to real data on both reliability and costings for any given application, but it is clear that the low-frequency induction plasma, the carbon arc heater, the Westinghouse and, presumably, the Linde arc heaters may all provide economical plasma heating at high powers, and no doubt each will find its application in chemical processing in the years to come.

Conclusions

This survey has demonstrated that plasma temperatures can now be achieved reliably and economically both in the laboratory and on a large scale. It is apparent that many applications have already been investigated and, in conclusion, it may be useful to summarize some of the more promising developments.

Ore beneficiation is clearly one technique which will be developed to treat a range of ores and residues. The simple approach of the Ionarc and related methods can use any of a variety of plasma heat sources to enable the extraction of valuable ingredients and, although clearly of utility for the fuse-quench processes outlined above, their importance in precious metal recovery should not be overlooked. The extraction of gold and platinum from low-grade ores by use of an Ionarc-type process would appear to be a development in which such a convenient high-throughput technique could have much to offer.

Although limited vaporization can be achieved by such processes, it appears that for extensive vaporization to be attained with economical input powers it may be necessary to adopt the more thermally efficient approach offered by the centrifugal-furnace technique, and developments of this method are also to be expected.

Plasma electrolysis is an interesting technique, which may find application in certain specific cases, but where the same results can be achieved by a purely thermal process, as appears to be the case in some fuming reactions, the thermal approach offers greater likelihood of success—particularly if high efficiencies can be obtained.

Plasma smelting and refining both appear to be useful developments, although relatively little has been published on plasma reduction processes. Again, it is likely that improvements in heat transfer and thermal efficiency will be necessary before some of these reduction processes become commercially viable; but, meanwhile, the methods are clearly useful at least for the preparation of the less reactive metals, and especially where fine powder products are required.

It thus appears that although plasma technology offers no panacea for the problems of the extractive metallurgist, the various techniques which the term covers do offer a very useful extension to those already available. They are likely to find increasing application in the years to come as the drive to find increasingly efficient and economical processes becomes more severe and as it becomes ever more important to recover metal values from ores and residues hitherto considered intractable.

References

1. Warren I. H. and Shimizu H. Applications of plasma technology in extractive metallurgy. *Trans. Can. Inst. Min. Metall.*, **58**, 1965, 169–78.
2. Reed T. B. Plasmas for high temperature chemistry. *Adv. high Temp. Chem.*, **1**, 1967, 259–316.
3. Kubanek G. R. and Gauvin W. H. Recent developments in plasma jet technology. *Can. J. chem. Engng*, **45**, 1967, 251–7
4. Gross B. Grycz B. and Miklóssy K. *Plasma technology* (London: Iliffe 1968), 475 p.

5. FREEMAN M. P. Chemical research in streaming thermal plasmas. *Adv. high Temp. Chem.*, **2**, 1969, 151–202.

6. BADDOUR R. F. AND TIMMINS R. S. eds. *The application of plasmas to chemical processing* (Oxford, etc.: Pergamon, 1967), 223 p.

7. IBBERSON V. J. Plasma chemical reactions. *High Temp. high Press.*, **1**, 1969, 243–68.

8. VURZEL F. B. AND POLAK L. S. Plasma chemical technology—the future of the chemical industry. *Ind. Engng Chem.*, **62**, June 1970, 8–22.

9. LANDT U. Developments in inorganic arc plasma chemistry. *Angew. Chem. intn. Edn*, **9**, 1970, 780–92.

10. HANUSCH K. AND WINTERHAGER H. Die Anwendung des Lichtbogenplasmas für metallurgische Aufgaben. *Metall.*, **24**, 1970, 1061–8.

11. JAHN R. E. Temperature distribution and thermal efficiency of low power arc-heated plasma jets. *Br. J. appl. Phys.*, **14**, 1963, 585–8.

12. WEATHERLY M. H. AND ANDERSON J. E. A new high-current cathode for operation in reactive gases. *Electrochem. Technol.*, **3**, 1965, 80–4.

13. GEJO T. *et al.* U.S. Patent 3 515 839, 1970.

14. JORDAN G. R. AND KING L. A. The nature of fluctuations present in d.c. plasma jets in argon and nitrogen. *Br. J. appl. Phys.*, **16**, 1965, 431–6.

15. BRZOZOWSKI W. S. AND CELIŃSKI Z. Plasma generators (plasmotrons, arc plasma torches, arc heaters). *Bull. Acad. polon. Sci., Ser. Sci. Techn.*, **10**, no 5 1962, 7–13. (English text)

16. BOSCH F. M. AND DE VYNCK I. A. Essai de synthèse du carbure et du nitrure de bore. *Silicates Ind.*, **27**, 1962, 587–90.

17. LEUTNER H. W. Production of hydrogen cyanide using a plasma jet. *I&EC Process Design Develop.*, **2**, 1963, 315–8.

18. SHEWARD J. A. The design and testing of a plasma jet. *Rep. NPL IMU* EX 1, 1966, 25 p.

19. FAUCHAIS P. Etude expérimentale d'un générateur à plasma. *Revue int. hautes Temp. Réfract.*, **5**, 1968, 71–8.

20. GERDIEN H. AND LOTZ A. Uber eine Lichtquelle von sehr hoher Flächenhelligkeit. *Wiss. Veröff. Siemens-Konz.*, **2**, 1922, 489–96.

21. KUGLER T. AND SILBIGER J. DBR Patent application 1 961 339, 1970.

22. KUGLER T. AND SILBIGER J. DBR Patent application 1 962 989, 1970.

23. PFENDER E. GRUBER G. AND ECKERT E. R. G. Experimental investigation of a transpiration-cooled, constricted arc. In *High temperature technology* (Proc. 3rd intn Symp., 1967) (London: Butterworths, 1969), 593–602.

24. SHEER C. COONEY J. A. AND ROTHACKER D. L. Fluid transpiration through anodic boundary of an electric arc. *AIAAJ.*, **2**, 1964, 483–9.

25. JAATINEN W. A. CHAPPEL R. M. AND COOK W. R. U.S. Patent 3 136 915, 1964.

26. WHYMAN D. A rotating-wall, d.c.-arc plasma furnace. *J. scient. Instrum.*, **44**, 1967, 525–30.

27. BRYANT J. W. COX J. M. AND WHYMAN D. A cathode assembly for feeding powders into the plasma of expanded d.c. arcs. *J. Phys. E, scient. Instrum.*, **2**, 1969, 779–81.

28. BRYANT J. W. AND WHYMAN D. Rotor tube allowing observation of expanded arc columns. *J. Phys. E, scient. Instrum.*, **3**, 1970, 917–9.

29. VON ENGEL A. AND STEENBECK M. Uber die Temperatur in der Gassäule eines Lichtbogens. *Wiss. Veröff. Siemens-Konz.*, **10**, 1931, 155–71.

30. FOITZIK R. Untersuchungen am stabilisierten elektrischen Lichtbogen (Wälzbogen) in Stickstoff und Kohlensäure bei Drücken von 1 bis 40 at. *Wiss. Veröff. Siemens-Konz.*, **19**, 1940, 28–58.

31. KING L. H. A. DBR Patent 1 230 938, 1966.

32. PULLEN J. Rotating plasma furnace. *The Engineer*, **222**, 1966, 589–91.

33. GRYCZ B. Estimate of radial temperature distribution in the rotating plasma furnace. Paper presented at 8th international conference on phenomena in ionized gases, Vienna, 1967.

34. YEH H.-C. AND YANG W.-J. Characteristics of rotationally stabilized long plasma arcs in a chamber. *J. appl. Phys.*, **40**, 1969, 3687–93.

35. HARRY J. E. Factors affecting the design and performance of a mains frequency

plasma torch for industrial process heating. In *6th intn. Congr. Electro-heat, Brighton, 1968* (Paris: Union Internationale d'Electrothermie, 1968), 4 p.

36. ROOTS W. K. AND KADHIM M. A. H. Efficiency of a 50-Hz 100 kW plasma torch. *Proc. IEEE*, **57**, 1969, 1673–4.

37. BONET C. LAMOS J. AND FOËX M. Ecoulements permanents de plasma de grande puissance. *Entropie*, 34–35, 1970, 36–48.

38. REED T. B. Induction-coupled plasma torch. *J. appl. Phys.*, **32**, 1961, 821–4; 2534–5.

39. MARYNOWSKI C. W. AND MONROE A. G. R-F generation of thermal plasmas. In *High temperature technology* (*Proc. intn. Symp.*, *1963*) (London: Butterworths, 1964), 67–84.

40. BEGUIN C. P. *et al.* Chemical syntheses in radio-frequency plasma torches. Reference 6, 35–53.

41. FREEMAN M. P. AND CHASE J. D. Energy-transfer mechanism and typical operating characteristics for the thermal rf plasma generator. *J. appl. Phys.*, **39**, 1968, 180–90.

42. AUDSLEY A. AND BAYLISS R. K. The induced plasma torch as a high-temperature chemical reactor. I. Oxidation of silicon tetrachloride. *J. appl. Chem.*, **19**, 1969, 33–8.

43. CHASE J. D. Magnetic pinch effect in the thermal rf induction plasma. *J. appl. Phys.*, **40**, 1969, 318–25.

44. MAGNOLO G. The plasmarc furnace. *Can. Min. Metall. Bull.*, **57**, 1964, 57–62.

45. ZOTOS G. A. A new method of melting glass and silicates. *J. Soc. Glass. Technol.*, **16**, 1932, 284–92.

46. GROSSE A. V. *et al.* The centrifugal plasma jet furnace. *Mater. Res. Stand.*, **5**, 1965, 173–7.

47. FOËX M. AND DELMAS R. Four à plasma pour l'étude des produits réfractaires. *C.R. Séanc. Acad. Sci., Paris*, **265C**, 1967, 9–12.

48. FOËX M. U.S. Patent 3 257 196, 1966.

49. SELTON B. AND SHEWARD J. A. The centrifugal liquid wall furnace. *J. Mater. Sci.*, **4**, 1969, 302–9.

50. FOËX M. YEROUCHALMI D. AND DELMAS R. Four centrifuge à plasma d'une centaine de kilowatts pour la fusion et la coulée de produits réfractaires. *C.R. Séanc. Acad. Sci., Paris*, **270C**, 1970, 1082–4.

51. EVEREST D. A. SAYCE I. G. AND SELTON B. Preparation of ultrafine alumina powders by plasma evaporation. *J. Mater. Sci.*, **6**, 1971, 218–24.

52. SAYCE I. G. AND SELTON B. Preparation of ultrafine refractory powders using the liquid wall furnace. In *Special ceramics 5* (Stoke on Trent: British Ceramics Research Association), in press.

53. EVEREST D. A. SAYCE I. G. AND SELTON B. Preparation of ultrafine silica powders by evaporation using a thermal plasma. In *Electrochemical engineering* J. D. THORNTON ed. (London: Institution of Chemical Engineers, 1972), in press.

54. SHEER C. AND KORMAN S. The high intensity arc in process chemistry. In *Arcs in inert atmospheres and vacuum* (New York: Wiley, 1956), 169–83.

55. HOLMGREN J. D. GIBSON J. O. AND SHEER C. Some characteristics of arc vaporized submicron particulates. *J. electrochem. Soc.*, **111**, 1964, 362–9.

56. BECK H. Die Theorie des Beck-Lichtbogens. *Elektrotech. Z.*, **42**, 1921, 993–9.

57. FINKELNBURG W. The high current carbon arc and its mechanism. *J. appl. Phys.*, **20**, 1949, 468–74.

58. HARRIS V. *et al.* Arc decomposition of rhodonite. *J. electrochem. Soc.*, **106**, 1959, 874–6.

59. MARYNOWSKI C. W. KARLOVITZ B. AND HIRT T. J. Electrical augmentation of natural gas flames. *I&EC Process Design Dev.*, **6**, 1967, 375–9.

60. LAWTON J. PAYNE K. G. AND WEINBERG F. J. Flame-arc combination. *Nature, Lond.*, **193**, 1962, 736–8.

61. JOHNSTON P. D. AND LAWTON J. Flames augmented by inductive coupling of electrical energy. *Nature, Lond.*, **230**, 1971, 320–1.

62. LAWTON J. AND WEINBERG F. J. *Electrical aspects of combustion* (Oxford: Oxford University Press, 1969), 355 p.

63. FLETCHER F. J. HARKER J. H. AND FELLS I. Electrically augmented flames: the characteristics and applications of D.C. systems. In *Electrochemical engineering*, J. D. THORNTON ed. (London: Institute of Chemical Engineers, 1972), in press.

64. MARYNOWSKI C. W. AND HIRT T. J. Acetylene synthesis by partial combustion combined with a diffuse electrical discharge. In *High temperature technology (Proc. 3rd intn. Symp., 1967)* (London: Butterworths, 1969), 465–78.

65. GLADISCH H. How Huels makes acetylene by DC arc. *Hydrocarb. Process. Petrol. Refin.*, **41**, June 1962, 159–64.

66. ESCHENBACH R. C. Development of stable high power high pressure arc air heater for a hypersonic wind tunnel. *WADD-TR*-61-100, 1961, 30 p.

67. SARLITTO R. J. Development of high enthalpy, high power arc air heaters. *U.S. RTD-RDR*-63-4055, 1964, 85 p. (AD 433212) (*Star* N64-18011)

68. BRYSON D. A. AND ESCHENBACH R. C. Arc plasma heating. Paper presented at 7th biennial electric heat conference, IEEE, Cleveland, 1965.

69. SCHULZE R. A. Du Pont arc acetylene process. *Chem. Ind.*, 1968, 1539–40.

70. Du Pont is closing down its electric-arc acetylene plant at Montague. *Chem. Week*, **102**, 18 May 1968, p. 69.

71. SENNEWALD K. SCHALLUS E. AND POHL F. Erzeugung von Acetylen durch thermische Spaltung von Kohlenwasserstoffen mittels hocherhitzten Wasserstoffes. *Chemie-Ingr-Tech.*, **35**, 1963, 1–6

72. IWASYK J. M. The three-phase alternating-current arc reactor. In *High temperature technology (Proc. 3rd intn. Symp., 1967)* (London: Butterworths, 1969), 453–63.

73. Plasma: the lab toy that grew up. *Business Week*, 22 Aug. 1970, 74; 78.

74. BAINBRIDGE R. South African Patent application 68/7766, 1968.

74a. THORPE M. C. High-temperature technology and its relationship to mineral exploitation. In *Advances in extractive metallurgy and refining* (London: Institution of Mining and Metallurgy, 1972), 275–88.

75. THORPE M. L. AND SCAMMON L. W. Induction plasma heating; high power, low frequency operation and pure hydrogen heating. *U.S. NASA CR*-1343, 1969, 56 p.

76. DUNDAS P. H. AND THORPE M. L. Titanium dioxide production by plasma processing. *Chem. Engng Progr.*, **66**, Oct. 1970, 66–71.

77. WILKS P. H. AND THORPE M. L. The heating of solids in high temperature plasma. Paper presented at American Chemical Society Symposium on high temperature, Chicago, 1970, 13 p.

78. FEY M. G. AND HIRAYAMA C. Large A.C. arc heater design: performance and economics. Paper presented at American Chemical Society Symposium on high temperature, Chicago, 1970, 1 p.

79. FOËX M. AND DELMAS R. British Patent 1 178 771, 1970.

80. ARCOS S. A., Brussels, Belgium. Technical literature.

81. LUNAU F. W. AND PAINE E. W. The plasma jet theory of metal transfer in welding arc. In *Colloquium on plasma jets* (London: Institution of Electrical Engineers, 1964), 5–7.

82. SHEER C. AND KORMAN S. U.S. Patent 3 099 614, 1963.

83. CHARLES J. A. *et al.* Processing of minerals in an induction-coupled plasma torch. *Trans. Instn Min. Metall. (Sect. C: Mineral Process. Extr. Metall.)*, **79**, 1970, C54–9.

84. DAVIES G. J. JERVIS R. M. AND THURSFIELD G. Processing New Zealand titaniferous sands in an induction-coupled plasma torch. *NZ J. Sci.*, **13**, 1970, 468–81.

85. Thermal treatment of minerals as an aid to metal extraction—a survey. *Warren Spring Lab. Miner. Process. Inf. Note* no. 4, 1970, 120 p.

86. BAYLISS R. K. AND DERRY R. High-temperature studies in the extraction of beryllium. *J. appl. Chem.*, **16**, 1966, 114–21.

87. EVEREST D. A. NAPIER E. AND WELLS R. A. Processes for the extraction of beryllium from flotation concentrates of beryl. In *High temperature refactory metals* KRIVSKY W. A. ed. (New York: Gordon and Breach, 1968), 113–28. (*Metall. Soc. Conf.* vol. 34, pt 1)

88. BROWN R. A. S. Treatment of ilmenite in a plasma jet reactor. *Can. metall. Q.*, **10**, 1971, 47–55.

89. British Titan Products. French Patent application 2 015 642, 1970.

90. SHEER C. AND KORMAN S. U.S. Patent 2 616 843, 1952.

91. SHEER C. AND KORMAN S. U.S. Patent 2 617 761, 1952.

92. ORBACH H. K. BEDJAI J. G. AND MARTINDILL R. E. U.S. Patent 3 390 980, 1968.

93. SHEER C. AND KORMAN S. U.S. Patent 2 979 449, 1961.

94. KORMAN S. DINIAK A. AND SHEER C. Vapour phase carbothermic reduction of

K

magnesium oxide in the high intensity arc. *Contract no. AF* 18 (603)-3, KLX-10116, 1958, 18 p.

95. KIRKPATRICK S. D. Magnesium by the Hansgirg Process. *Chem. metall. Engng*, Sept. 1941, 91–4.

96. SHEER C. KORMAN S. AND GIBSON J. O. U.S. Patent 3 101 308, 1963.

97. STOKES C. S. *et al.* Plasma jet chemistry. *AFOSR*-62-196, 1964 (final Rep.), 32 p.

98. CIBA LTD. British Patent 1 141 776, 1969.

99. GILLES H. L. AND CLUMP C. W. Reduction of iron ore with hydrogen in a direct current plasma jet. *I&EC Process Design Dev.*, **9**, 1970, 194–207.

100. DEATH F. S. AND MORCIO J. A. U.S. Patent 3 347 766, 1967.

101. TISCHENDORF J. DDR Patent 33 152, 1964.

102. IRSID. French Patent 1 452 850, 1966.

103. RAINS R. K. AND KADLEC R. H. The reduction of Al_2O_3 to aluminium in a plasma. *Metall. Trans.*, **1**, 1970, 1501–6.

104. BORGIANNI C. *et al.* The behaviour of metal oxides injected into an argon induction plasma. *Comb. Flame*, **13**, 1969, 181–94.

105. CAPITELLI M. *et al.* Decomposition of Al_2O_3 particles injected into argon–nitrogen induction plasmas of 1 atmosphere. *Comb. Flame*, **15**, 1970, 23–31.

106. CASE L. E. U.S. Patent 3 320 145, 1967.

107. MURDOCH H. D. AND HAMBLYN S. M. L. French Patent 1 582 154, 1969.

108. CIBA LTD. British Patent 1 141 775, 1969.

109. NEUENSCHWANDER E. Herstellung und Charakterisierung von ultrafeinen Karbiden, Nitriden und Metallen. *J. less common Met.*, **11**, 1966, 365–75.

110. HARNISH H. HEYMER G. AND SCHALLUS E. Inorganic reactions with arc-heated gases. *Angew. Chem., intn Edn.*, **2**, 1963, 238–42.

111. HARNISCH H. MEHNE A. AND RODIS F. U.S. Patent 3 211 520, 1965.

112. MILLER R. C. AND AYEN R. J. Reactions of titanium tetrachloride in a radio-frequency plasma torch. *I&EC Process. Design Dev.*, **8**, 1969, 370–7.

113. RIO ALGOM MINES, Ltd. British Patent 1 054 162, 1967.

114. HUSKA P. A. AND CLUMP C. W. Decomposition of molybdenum disulfide in an induction-coupled argon plasma. *I&EC Process Design Dev.*, **6**, 1967, 238–44.

115. SELOVER T. B. Jr. Properties of nickel fume generated in a plasma jet. *AIChEJ.*, **10**, 1964, 79–82.

116. DEMOUSTIEZ A. HANON J. AND WINAND R. Production of manganese by electrolysis of fused oxide mixtures. *Industrie chim. belge*, **32**, special no., 144–55. (French text)

117. RECASENS J. BORTAUD P. AND BONNIER E. Fusion et électrolyse d'oxydes métalliques réfractaires. *Revue intn. hautes Temp. Réfract.*, **4**, 1967, 281–8.

118. SHELLEY T. R. AND CHARLES J. A. Arc electrolysis of lead silicate melts. *Trans. Instn Min. Metall. (Sect. C: Mineral Process. Extr. Metall.)*, **78**, 1969, C177–80.

119. SHELLEY T. R. AND CHARLES J. A. Arc electrolysis of complex tin-containing oxide melts. *Trans. Instn Min. Metall. (Sect. C: Mineral Process. Extr. Metall)*, **79**, 1970, C259–68.

120. RYKALIN N. N. *et al.* Plasma remelting of ball-bearing steel and nickel alloy. *Stal*, **22**, 1967, 806–8; *Stal Engl.*, 1967, 752–4.

121. FARNASOV G. A. AND FILLIPOV A. F. Research into the special features of remelting grade ShKh15 steel in a plasma arc furnace. *Stal*, **22**, 1967, 809–10; *Stal Engl.*, 1967, 754–5.

122. English Steel Corporation's new steel-process. *Met. Treat. Drop Forg.*, **32**, 1965, p. 101.

123. EBELING F. JACOBS W. AND SPIEGELBERG K. DDR Patent 51 439, 1966.

125. SPERNER F. DBR Patent 1 217 986, 1966.

125. PATON B. E. *et al.* The transferred plasma arc jet remelting of metals and alloys. *Avtom. Svarka*, **19**, no. 8 1966, 1–5; *Automatic Weld.*, **19**, no. 8 1966, 1–5.

126. BRITISH IRON AND STEEL RESEARCH ASSOCIATION. French Patent 1 572 667, 1969.

127. DUNDAS P. H. AND THORPE M. L. Economics and technology of chemical processing with electric-field plasmas. *Chem. Engng*, **76**, 30 June 1969, 123–8.

128. TAFA Division, Humphreys Corporation, Bow, New Hampshire, USA. Technical literature.

High-temperature technology and its relationship to mineral exploitation

M. L. Thorpe

Ionarc Smelters, Ltd., Bow, Concord, New Hampshire, U.S.A.

533.9:669–978:669.053

Synopsis

Developments in ultra-high-temperature technology are outlined. Actual and potential applications of plasma technology are considered with reference to chemical breakdown, physical heat affection, direct reduction, chlorination, gasification, oxidation, reduction, and carburization and nitriding.

One of the major characteristics of the mining industry is that it processes huge quantities of materials—quantities which most other industries regard as awe-some. One of the characteristics of ultra-high-temperature technology, on the other hand, is that most developments have been confined to relatively small, often laboratory-scale, equipment. Consequently, one would not expect either industry to have much practical knowledge of or interest in the other. Recently—within the past two or three years—however, techniques have been developed to yield quite large-scale ultra-high-temperature generators, and there is now a heightened interest within the mining industry in plasma technologies on account of the new range of possibilities that exist for the exploitation of both metallic and non-metallic minerals.

Ultra-high temperatures can be produced in specially designed furnaces by use of superheated gases produced with electric arcs. Whenever an arc discharges, intensely hot gas is produced: this gas, which has a temperature two to three times that of the surface of the sun (5000°C) produces some unusual results when it is applied to solids and gases. (1) Materials are heated much more rapidly than by conventional techniques: this means shorter contact times, higher throughputs and reduced heat losses. (2) Unusually high cooling rates occur as material leaves the plasma—in some cases in excess of 20 000 000°C/sec. Such an unusual environment freezes many materials in an unusual state, which would not occur if the material were allowed to cool at more conventional rates. (3) The latest plasma heaters permit heating of gases such as chlorine and oxygen to these very high temperatures. Both these elements are chemically active at moderate temperatures, but at elevated temperatures they become extremely reactive. This again permits chemical reactions to occur at much higher speeds, in some cases reducing the time involved from hours to fractions of a second.

All the characteristics of plasma reactors tend to increase reaction speed and reduce apparatus size, thus leading to the generalization that most proposed plasma processes offer high throughputs, continuous operation and low capital investment per unit of production.

Small-scale plasma equipment has been in existence for some years, being used primarily in such applications as coating, welding and flame spraying. Ionarc Smelters, Ltd., with more than 14 years' experience in the field, decided several years ago that this high-temperature plasma technology could be applied in the ore reduction field, and a large-scale development programme was initiated. A number of multi-purpose pilot plants have been constructed for evaluation of a variety of processes. As an indication of size, one is powered with 1000 kW, and another is capable of producing 20 tons per month of product.

A typical plasma furnace is shown in Fig. 1; the reduction of iron ore is depicted, but, the feedstock can be a solid, liquid or gas, the particular form of

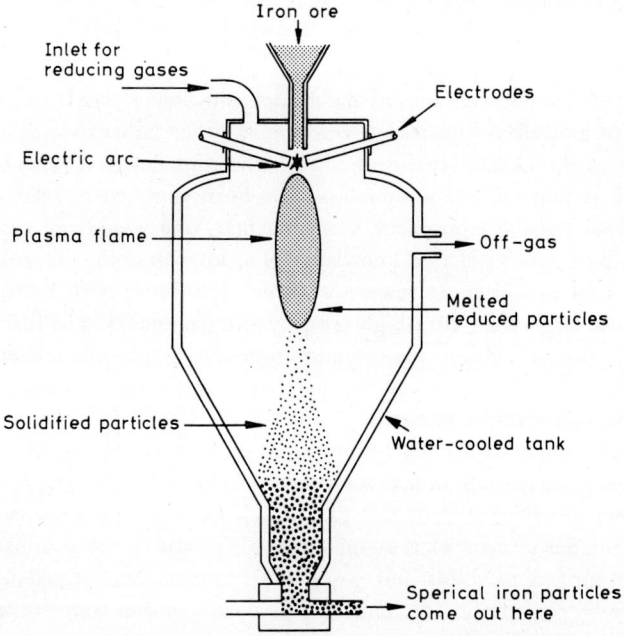

Fig. 1 Sketch of plasma breakdown of ores

feed being dictated by overall process economics. Because of the rapidity of changes within the furnace, design parameters are critical, and the injection of raw materials must be very uniform and symmetrical to take advantage of the high temperatures available and to ensure uniform heating in cases where rapid quenching is necessary to achieve 'freeze-out' of a particular high-temperature chemical species, material form or crystal structure. The point and uniformity of quench gas injection is measured in fractions of an inch.

Applications

Fig. 2 indicates the various forms taken by plasma metallurgy and the typical products which might be produced. Clearly, it cannot be implied that all ores are amenable to plasma processing or that, even if they are, the economics of the

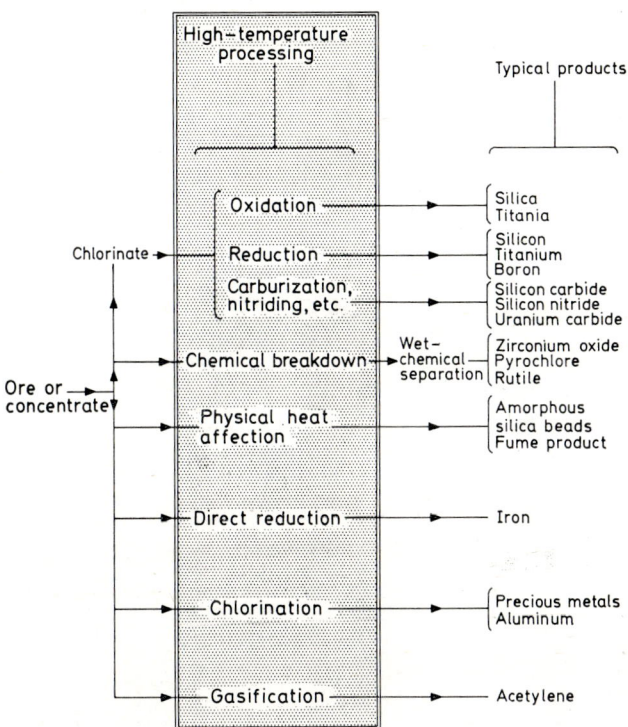

Fig. 2 Forms of plasma technology

process are competitive with those of conventional techniques: most of the typical products listed, however, do show promise and are in various stages of development—ranging from preliminary feasibility analysis to actual production and evaluation by customers. Since the technology is so new the main point to be made is that these materials should be considered as examples, and, hopefully, they may suggest other likely candidates. Each of the high-temperature processes presented in Fig. 2 is now discussed.

Chemical breakdown

Zirconium oxide is a good example of a typical product of chemical breakdown. The raw material is available as a fine granular sand—zircon. Some conventional processes arc-melt the zircon ($ZrO_2.SiO_2$), fuming off the silica and leaving a nugget of zirconium oxide. Approximately 35 lb of silica must be removed for every 100 lb of zircon. In conventional processing the fine fume must be collected to control pollution. The purity and crystal structure of the nugget formed varies, depending on the distance from its centre.

Zircon sand is quite difficult to digest directly, but this difficulty is overcome by an intermediate plasma processing step. When the zircon sand is passed through the plasma furnace (Fig. 3), its complex structure of zirconium silicate is

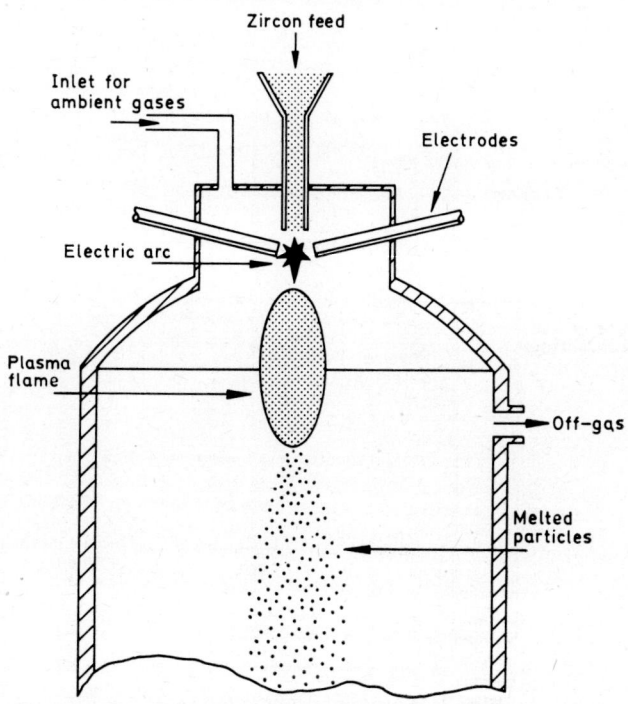

Fig. 3 Schematic drawing of Ionarc plasma furnace arc head

immediately broken down into zirconium oxide and silica. Because of the rapid quench the particles are under tremendous microscopic stresses and, because of the high surface area of the silica produced by its uniform distribution through the zirconia, very rapid leaching by proprietary techniques occurs at low temperatures with inexpensive leach materials (Fig. 4). A high-purity zirconium oxide and complete elimination of the fume pollution problem result. The product is shown in a series of scanning electron micrographs (Fig. 5). The dried mud flat appearance of the leached particles is indicative of the uniformity of the product and the extremely small crystallite size. The leached product, before it is crushed, typically appears as a 100-μm diameter sphere with a surface area of about 40 000 ft^2/lb of product.

Zirconium oxide is used as a high-temperature refractory (melting point, 2500°C), as a colouring agent in ceramic tile, in some chemicals, and as a polishing agent. Some tons of this material have been furnaced and lesser amounts leached. An intensive market survey is now being undertaken and the material is being tested by end users, and commercial production facilities are being installed.

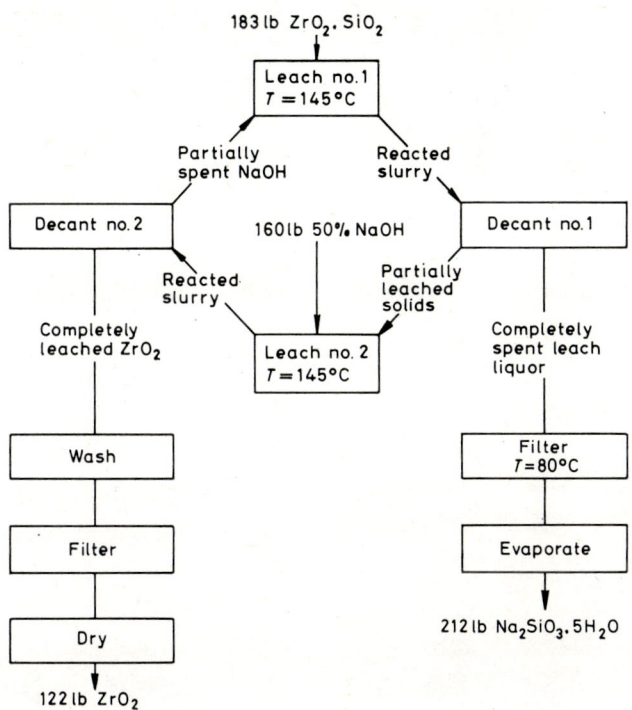

Fig. 4 Flowsheet for production of zirconium dioxide and sodium silicate from dissociated zircon (basis: 1 lb mole of feedstock)

This product demonstrates very well the advantages of an entirely new technique. The continuous nature of the process yields a more consistent, uniform product compared with that from the conventional batch process (inconsistency of product from carload to carload and from supplier to supplier appears to be one of the major complaints by end users to date). With this shortcoming removed, high-yield, high-speed pressing and sintering of refractory shapes may replace slower melting and pouring. In addition, the small crystallite size permits crushing to a finer product and may give more uniform distribution of colouring within ceramics, and, hopefully, more square feet of colour per pound of product. There has also been some interest on the part of the catalyst industry to use the

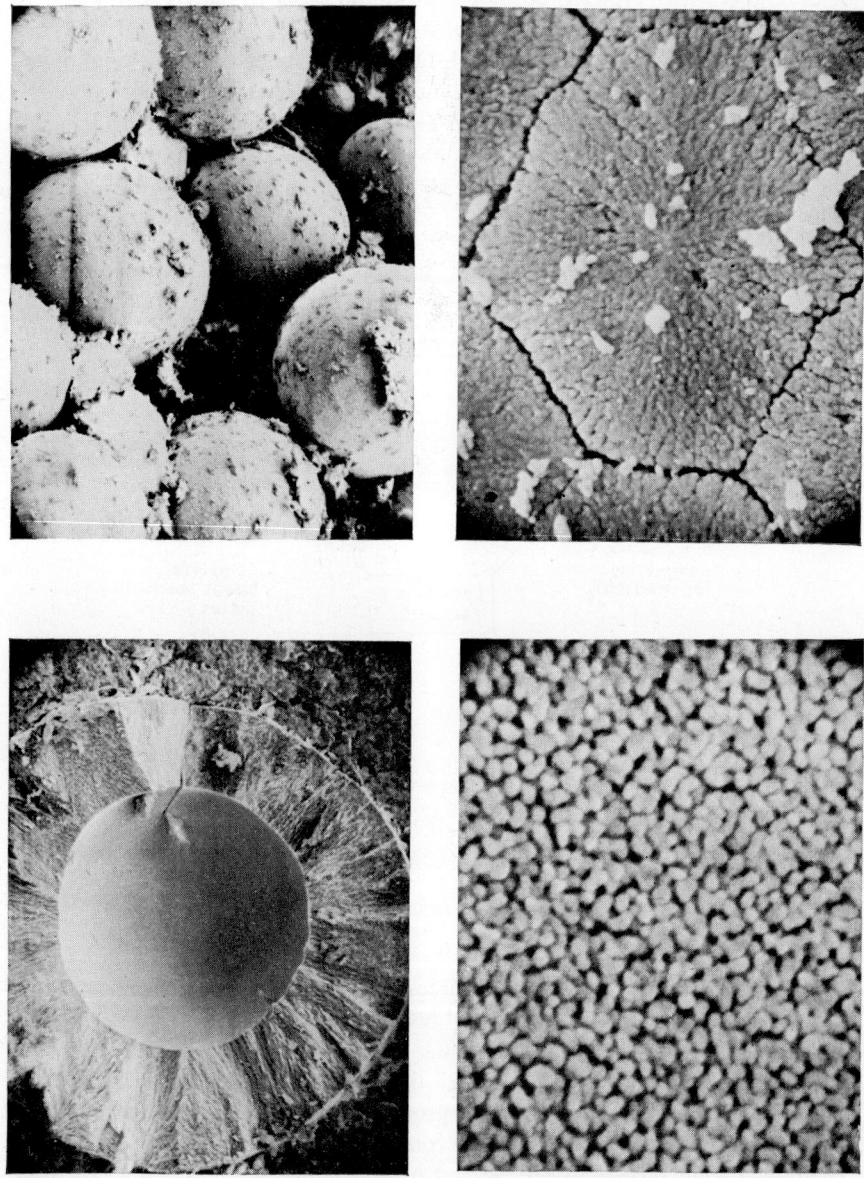

Fig. 5 Scanning electron micrographs of Ionarc 99+% zirconium oxide: *top left*, zirconia spheres after leaching (magnification, ×250); *top right*, typical surface of porous sphere showing pattern of large cracks and smaller crystallites (magnification, ×6800); *bottom left*, fractured sphere showing centre void (magnification, ×600); *bottom right*, typical uniformity of individual crystallites 0·1–0·2 μm in diameter (magnification, ×26 000)

large surface area of the beads as a catalyst substrate. The economics of this process—which involves energy input levels of 0·5–1·0 kWh/lb—appear quite favourable at this stage, cost being, of course, dependent on volume.

In another application the as-produced furnace output (unleached) is being tested directly as a mould sand. After the part is cast, the plasma-solubilized silica can be leached away to leave a friable, porous zirconia matrix which can be removed without damage to the part.

Stated in different terms, what has been developed is a method of processing a silica-bearing ore and making the silica much more leachable. The question then arises as to other zircon-like materials to which the process could be applied. Minerals such as thorite, rhodonite, sillimanite, garnierite, chrysocolla, braunite, calamine and beryl may be candidates: calamine $(ZnOH)_2SiO_3$, chrysocolla $CuSiO_3.2H_2O$ and beryl $(BeO)_3.Al_2O_3(SiO_2)_6$ appear to be particularly interesting, but they have not been plasma-processed at the present time.

Pyrochlore, another complex mineral, contains approximately 55% columbium oxide, bound up with calcium, sodium and other oxides. The columbium oxide is now complexed with iron and aluminium in a thermite reaction and the products are sold directly to steel producers as an additive to improve the weldability of steels. When one sample of pyrochlore was processed by means of plasma, most of the oxides could be dissolved in dilute hydrochloric acid and the resultant product upgraded to approximately 95% columbium oxide. In a different sample containing rare earths, the complexing which resulted from plasma processing and leaching was not effective. These results show that one cannot generalize on the applicability of a process without actual furnace and leaching tests on materials from a number of different sources. For this reason, among others, versatile pilot-plant facilities have been installed.

Zirconium oxide and pyrochlore were selected as initial candidates because of their high value ($2000/ton), which, in turn, permits economical processing with the existing 1000-kW furnaces. Upgrading of rutile, on the other hand, requires much larger equipment (300 000 ton/year) and it has a considerably lower value—of the order of $125/ton. With rutile, ilmenite is plasma-furnaced in the presence of a reducing gas to render the iron oxide content to iron, which, it is contemplated, would be removed by mechanical separation followed by a hydrochloric leach of the remaining iron. Preliminary furnacing tests have been made, but separation and leaching have not yet been attempted.

The typical economics of such a process are shown in Table 1. Rutile is presently quoted at $125/ton, but there is considerable speculation that the price will rise to the $160–$180 per ton range. More conventional processes are also under development on the North American continent and in Australia. During the next year Ionarc hopes to locate a partner or licensee to explore the commercial potential of ilmenite processing more fully.

Physical heat affection

Silica sand in its natural state exists as a crystalline material. Upon plasma

K*

Table 1   Preliminary analysis—ilmenite separation costs by Ionarc furnace

Assumptions

Plant size, 145 000 tons/year ilmenite or 100 000 tons/year of 94% rutile (100% yield assumed)
Ilmenite ore, $20/ton
Electricity, $0.006/kWh; 18 000-kW system
Rutile, $125/ton
Natural gas, H_2 content only used (35·9 lb FeO requires 1 lb H_2)
Operation, 8000 h/year
Power consumption, 0·5 kWh/lb ilmenite
Total plant investment, $10 000 000

Direct costs	Unit cost	Annual quantity	Annual cost
Ilmenite ore	$20/ton	145 000 tons	$2 900 000
Natural gas	0·05/10^3 Sft^3	272×10^6 Sft^3	136 000
Electricity	0·006/kWh	145×10^6 kWh	870 000
Other consumables	$167/h	8000 h	1 336 000
Labour	$10/h	96×10^3 h	960 000
Additional processing	$13.80/ton	145 000	2 000 000
Total direct			$8 202 000

Indirect costs	
Overhead (150% labour)	$1 440 000
Plant maintenance (3% of investment)	300 000
Depreciation (10% of investment)	1 000 000
Total indirect	$2 740 000
Net manufacturing cost	$10 942 000
Cost per ton 94% rutile	$109.00
Iron credit 39 600 tons @ $9/ton or $3.56/ton rutile	(4.00)
Net cost of 94% rutile/ton	$105.00

processing each individual sand particle becomes molten and freezes rapidly in an amorphous (non-crystalline) state. These tiny glassy marbles hold some promise of being a superior reflective bead in signs and road markings.

Proper furnace design and regulation of power input and ore feed rate permit almost all the silica to be vaporized. Under these conditions an extremely fine particle (200 Å) with a surface area of 100–200 m^2/g is produced (see Fig. 4). Such products have values in the range $500–$4500/ton. Fine silica, for example, is priced in the range of $0.60/lb, and is used in paints, plastics and cosmetics.

Direct reduction

One of the minerals processed in the greatest tonnage is, of course, iron ore. Tests with iron ore have demonstrated that iron oxide can be reduced in one pass through the furnace at a power consumption of less than 2 kWh/lb—seemingly, the maximum tolerable by such a process. No attempts have been made at optimization, but the high yields were achieved so simply that it is felt that this application merits further consideration. Also, iron chloride, which presently presents a disposal problem for many processes being developed, including ilmenite, has been processed directly in the furnace, producing small iron spheres.

Chlorination

The chlorination route to many metals holds promise because the metal chloride can be gasified and, therefore, purified by means of simple distillation techniques. One of the limitations in some chlorine processes is the maintenance of the containment vessel. Zircon, for example, chlorinates directly at about 1150°C. One of the most practical containment vessels appears to be quartz, but it passes through a phase change at 1200°C and, hence, fractures. Operation of a chlorinator so close to the failure point obviously presents problems. Preliminary results have indicated that after plasma processing some ores chlorinate more readily at temperatures well below those of the raw ore. If the material under consideration can stand the plasma furnacing costs—which are about $0.06/lb at 1000 kW and significantly lower at higher powers—the availability of such a raw material may not only reduce containment vessel failures but corrosion problems as well. Preliminary, basic investigations are being carried out.

There is also some technical speculation that precious metal ores which contain complexed platinum, gold and silver can be unlocked by plasma processing, the concept being direct chlorination of the ore in a chlorine plasma. The hot ore particles and gas are collected in a dilute solution of acid and water as they leave the plasma. The precious metal chlorides are readily dissolved and later extracted by hydrometallurgy. More work must be done in this area before the worth of the process can be demonstrated. The major problem to date has been the location of an ore for testing, with satisfactory values, which is of a complex nature not amenable to conventional processing techniques.

Considerable sums of money have been spent by the aluminium industry in the investigation of direct reduction techniques: one such scheme involves the use of heated monochloride in contact with a bed of bauxite. Through proper temperature control at various stages in the process pure aluminium metal can be deposited at a controlled location. Apparently, one of the limitations of this process is the heating of the chloride—an extremely corrosive material. One device[1] permits indirect heating of almost any gas without electrodes or hot heat-exchange surfaces—this is accomplished by an induction technique which couples electric power by transformer-like action into a hot gas stream, thereby permitting water-cooled or ceramic walls to surround the gas stream.

Gasification

The U.S. Bureau of Mines has sponsored a large programme in gasification.[2] Coal was passed through the plasma generator in the presence of hydrogen, a chemical reaction occurring between them to form acetylene (C_2H_2), which is a raw material for several industries, including the chemicals and plastics industries.

Oxidation

At the present time chlorides manufactured by conventional techniques are flamed with oxygen and fuel gas to produce an ultra-pure, extremely fine oxide. Titanium dioxide is produced in large quantities as a pigment for the paint industry. Titanium tetrachloride is oxidized at elevated temperatures by the reaction

$$TiCl_4 + O_2 \rightarrow TiO_2 + 2Cl_2$$

Since the quality of the resulting pigment depends on the level of contamination, the utmost care must be exercised in handling the reactants and products. In addition, the carbon monoxide used as fuel gas in conventional processes complicates chlorine repurification and recycling—in some cases it changes the character of the pigment. In an alternate process oxygen is heated with a plasma device and the energy in this hot gas replaces the burning energy produced by the carbon monoxide, thereby eliminating it. The flowsheet of such a process is shown in Fig. 6 and the associated energy economics are given in Table 2. This material sells for approximately \$0.26/lb.

The electrical energy consumption is relatively low. Assuming a power cost of \$0.01/kW, the electrical cost is an insignificant factor in the selling price. In this case the chloride is one of the major components in the production of pigment.

Other oxides could also be produced, but no large markets for them exist (other than silica) at present.

Reduction

The refractory metals offer another promising application for plasmas. The contamination levels tolerable in refractory metals to obtain the maximum benefit of their properties are extremely low. With silicon, electronic requirements reduce the contamination level to parts per billion. Small quantities of silicon and titanium and larger quantities of boron have been produced by passing a mixture of chloride and hydrogen through a plasma device. Thermodynamic calculations indicate that the metal is formed along with HCl at temperatures in the range 2000–5000°C, depending on the particular chloride.

Taking titanium as a model, one can make the following comments about the potential advantages of such a process. Titanium is conventionally produced in the Kroll process, which reacts titanium tetrachloride with an alkaline-earth metal such as magnesium or sodium. The resultant sponge contains residual chlorides and active metal. The level of contamination is reduced by further processing, which involves extensive heating and vacuum operation.

The plasma process adds none of these contaminants and produces a powder directly (Fig. 7). This powder should be as pure as the feedstocks, which are available at the ppm impurity level. The powdered material can be used directly in powder metallurgy operations, which should eliminate the high loss factors (50%) associated with the fabrication of parts from billets. The availability of a powder in the price range of $1–$2/lb (see Table 3)—present powder costs are $5–$10/lb—should lead to an expansion of the market for titanium.

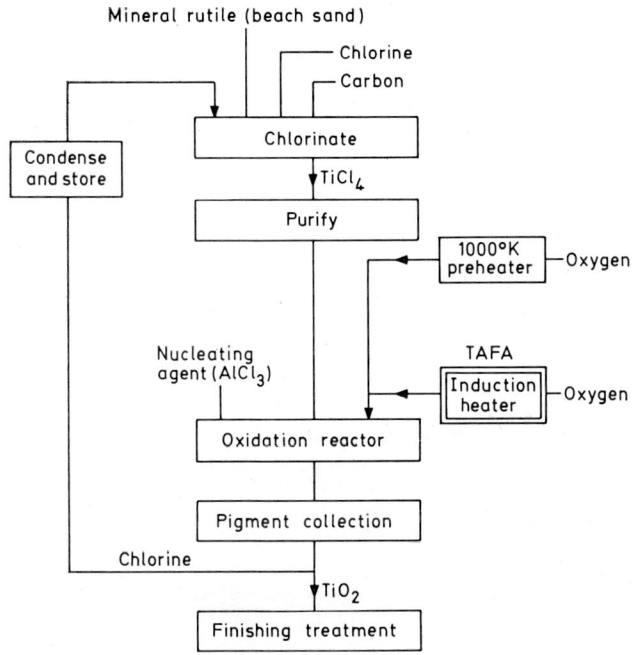

Fig. 6 TiO$_2$ manufacture by use of induction heating

Pure boron has already been made in significant quantities by this technique,[3] but this material was apparently a poor choice at this stage because of the limited market.

Carburization and nitriding

In flowsheets quite similar to that discussed for titanium, nitrogen can be substituted for hydrogen and the nitride produced. Carbon vapour can also be used to produce various carbides. Fine particles of such rather advanced materials are now beginning to find uses in such exotic applications as dispersion-hardening of metals, gas turbine blade fabrication and various electronic devices. These materials can also be produced in a larger particle size range—for example, by

Table 2 Analysis of plasma-heating schemes for TiO₂ production

	Induction heater			Conventional resistance heater					
Case	Energy in O_2 leaving torch, kW	Required exit enthalpy, kcal/mole	Oxygen flow rate, lb/h	O_2 leaving heater, kW	Required exit enthalpy, kcal/mole	Oxygen flow rate, lb/h	Total power input, kW	TiO_2 production rate, ton/day	Energy to produce TiO_2, kWh/lb
1	500	13·2	1665	—	—	—	1000	46·0	0·26
2	500	23·4	1299	177	5·5	3240	1177	64·8	0·22
3	500	176	174	300	5·5	3300	1300	69·6	0·20

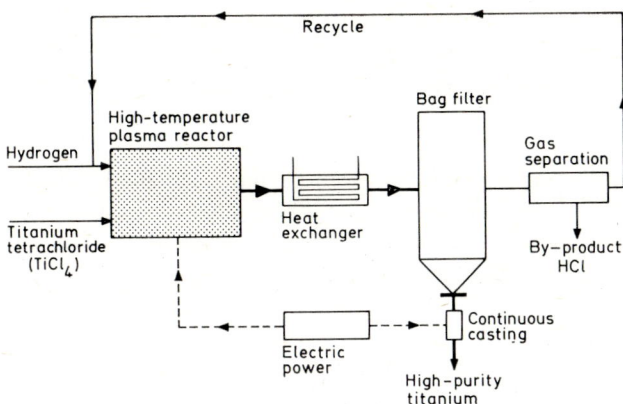

Fig. 7 Proposed plasma process titanium flowsheet

passing silicon metal powder through a nitrogen plasma to form silicon nitride directly.

Summary

Ultra-high-temperature processing can yield a variety of unique results, which promise to produce materials more economically than by conventional processing. The author's company is optimistic with regard to the potential of plasma processing in the mining and metallurgy industries, and currently has several operations on a tons per day level.

A start has been made with the more expensive, lower-tonnage materials, which provide adequate price latitude to make any commercial development

Table 3 Estimate of capital costs—10 000 ton/year Ti plant

(1) Power supplies and torches	$13 300 000
(2) Metal handling and fabrication	10 000 000
(3) Contingency	5 000 000
	$28 300 000

Estimate of costs/lb Ti

(1) Equipment depreciated in 10 years	$0.14
(2) Labour (100 men averaging $9000/year)	0.05
(3) Overhead (200% of labour)	0.10
(4) $TiCl_4$ purchased on site	0.60
(5) Hydrogen (17 ft³ at 4 mills/ft³)	0.07
(6) Electricity (6 mills/kWh)	0.06
	$1·02

economically sound; however, this is regarded as a 'stepping stone' to yield experience and promote confidence. The objective, of course, is to demonstrate sound process economics and the feasibility of round-the-clock operations with controlled consistency of product. Appropriate steps are being taken to achieve this objective.

Tonnages, by mining standards, are still quite small, but by plasma technology standards they are many times those of even a few years ago. It is confidently predicted that both the range of applications of plasma technology to mineral processing and the size will increase at a substantial rate in the years ahead.

References

1. THORPE M. L. AND SCAMMON L. W. Induction plasma heating: high power, low frequency operation and pure hydrogen heating. *NASA CR*-1343, 1969, 56 p.
2. AVCO SPACE SYSTEMS DIVISION. Phase I feasibility report on AVCO arc-coal process. *U.S. Dep. Inter. R & D Rep.* **34,** 1968.
3. BIDDULPH R. H. AND McCLOSKEY A. Personal communication. (Borax Consolidated, Ltd., Chessington, Surrey, England.)

DISCUSSION

Dr. E. Ahland, in introducing his joint paper, said that he would like to review briefly the advantages and disadvantages of processes for the production of formed coke.

Processes for the production of formed coke permitted one to choose the appropriate shape and size of the pieces: thus, the optimum operational conditions could be obtained by adapting the shape and the size of the coke to the burden of the furnace. In addition, the range of coals suitable for carbonization was enlarged considerably. In other words, coke could be made from coal which it would be impossible to use in conventional coke ovens. If one bore in mind that the cost of the coal accounted for approximately 70% of the coke price, it was clear that the use of cheaper coal for carbonization would result in a substantial reduction of the price of the coke, because the coke price depended much more on the price of the coking blend than on the cost of the carbonization process, which was to say that greater profit could be derived from a reduction of the coal cost.

Whereas in coke ovens the walls of refractory bricks served for heat transfer, the refractory lining of the reactors used for production of formed coke was only needed for heat insulation. Thus, plants for production of formed coke could be started and stopped without major difficulties and without any detriment to the brickwork. That was of particular importance if the gas released from the coal was to be used in a power station, because in such a case the running hours of the formed-coke plant could be adapted, entirely or partly, to the running hours of the power station.

In plants for the production of formed coke automation could be achieved more easily, and that could lead to savings by reduction of the manpower required.

A study carried out recently by the Ruhrkohle Company in collaboration with Lurgi had led to the conclusion that plants for the production of formed coke were likely to require a lower capital expenditure than conventional coke-oven plants. Air pollution problems could be solved more easily in such plants because the processes were operated in closed reactors, which permitted the use of conventional means for dedusting the waste gas released from the reactor.

On the other side, there were some disadvantages. Many processes required high rates of heating, and that entailed a higher yield of tar and a lower yield of coke than in conventional coke-oven plants. In addition, it was unavoidable, in several processes, that part of the fixed carbon was burnt to cover the heat demand, but such a fuel was very expensive. Under certain conditions the tar obtained had other properties than the usual tar, and that might restrict the prospect of selling it. An attempt was made to overcome those disadvantages by recycling the tar, or at least its highest fraction, into the process. Thus, the yield of coke was increased and no tar at all was recovered—only oil and gas. Tests with that end in view were being carried out by Bergbau-Forschung.

Dr. D. A. Reeve introduced his joint paper briefly, summarizing its principal contents. He pointed out that the proposal in the paper was the use of a metallic iron–carbon composite pellet which would melt when preheated to only 1100°C, thus providing a new source of energy and, possibly, becoming a hot-metal substitute in steelmaking. New emphasis was being placed on low-sulphur western Canadian coals, and he discussed the use of such coals at remote locations for the production of those iron–carbon composites.

Dr. I. G. Sayce introduced his paper briefly, summarizing its principal contents.

M. L. Thorpe introduced his paper briefly, summarizing its principal contents.

R. Healey[*] said that the object of the development of formed-coke production was to obtain a substitute for metallurgical coke which would be less subject to price increases due to the current world shortage of coking coal. Moreover, because of its uniform size and shape, formed coke might even turn out to be a better fuel for the blast-furnace than conventional oven coke, when there was adequate experience of its use. Those considerations applied just as much to the Imperial Smelting zinc–lead blast-furnace as to the iron blast-furnace.

The requirements for good blast-furnace coke were quoted by Ahland *et al.* as (1) strength and abrasion resistance, (2) adequate voidage for gas and liquid flow and (3) adequate surface for mass and heat transfer. Those requirements were equally important in the ISF, but in that case emphasis must, in addition, be put on the reactivity of the coke to carbon dioxide. Due to the nature of the reactions zinc reduction in the blast-furnace could take place only in the vicinity of the tuyères. The carbon solution reaction, which continued farther up the shaft, was deleterious since it absorbed heat, causing zinc reoxidation and re-cycling, and the enriched reducing gas could not be fully utilized in the upper part of the charge for preliminary reduction as it could in the iron blast-furnace.

The Bergbau-Forschung process was capable of producing formed coke of fairly low reactivity to carbon dioxide, equivalent to that of the more reactive cokes already in use by some ISF operators. In addition Bergbau-Forschung had shown that the reactivity of formed coke could be further reduced by treat-ment with boric acid, and that the reactivity of conventional oven coke could also be reduced in that way.

Test work with formed coke for the ISF had been encouraging, though it must be admitted that they had not yet completely proved the case in furnace trials. Three trials had been carried out so far.

The first trial was run at the Swansea Vale furnace in November, 1968, when 100 tons of formed coke was charged in about 11 h. That trial was not successful. The reactivity of the formed coke used at the time was high (more than twice that of the oven coke) and that produced cold conditions in the lower shaft. The

[*] Imperial Smelting Processes, Ltd., Avonmouth.

smaller size of the formed coke (1·25 in against 2·0 in for the oven coke) was also a probable contributory factor.

The second trial was held in March, 1970, at the Peñarroya furnace at Noyelles-Godault in northern France. The formed coke had been treated with boric acid solution and its reactivity was similar to that of the oven coke in normal use (about 70% higher than the oven coke at Swansea). The formed and oven cokes were also similar in size (1·25 in). About 180 tons of formed coke was used in that trial, which covered a total time of 36 h. The trial was successful, and the furnace did not appear to distinguish between the two types of coke.

The third trial took place in February, 197 , at the Metallgesellschaft furnace at Duisburg. About 600 tons of formed coke was fed to the furnace over a period of seven operating days. Although the reactivity of the formed coke after boric acid treatment was similar to that in the second trial, that was still about 40% greater than the reactivity of the oven coke in use at Duisburg. The oven coke was also larger, with a mean size of 2·25 in. The change in reactivity was sufficient to cause some deterioration of conditions in the lower furnace shaft, though nothing like so great as in the first trial at Swansea, but the level of zinc output was completely unaffected by the trial.

To sum up, test work to date had indicated that it would be possible to operate the ISF on formed coke, but that it was necessary to adapt furnace practice to suit the properties of the fuel, whether oven or formed coke, which was to be used. As with the iron blast-furnace, the case for formed coke would only be finally proved in extensive furnace operation.

Dr. J. T. Fitton* said that the authors indicated (p. 218) that continuous carbonization reduced inherent costs. Perhaps they would say how the processes described compared in capital and operating costs with a modern coke-oven battery operating in an integrated ironworks, say, at 3000 ton/day.

The analyses of the products given in Table 1 (p. 221) were very interesting. It would be helpful to have some more information on the analyses of the starting coals—in particular, the agglutinating values, swelling indices and ranges of volatility. Were the Micum indices extended Micum figures? From his own experience he would expect the hot briquettes to show higher abrasion once the hard high energy outer surface was breached by extended abrasion.

In his company's own studies they had noted fundamental differences between the carbonizing techniques which could be applied to briquettes and to pellets. Those differences extended to coke properties—in particular, to reactivity. He would welcome the authors' comments on those differences.

Dr. Howard K. Worner† said that work such as that carried out by Bergbau-Forschung and Lurgi was of considerable importance at present with escalating prices of conventional metallurgical coke and the problems of controlling

---

* Simon Engineering, Ltd., Stockport, Cheshire.
† Conzinc Riotinto of Australia, Ltd., Melbourne, Australia.

emissions from battery and beehive oven coking plants. Many would wish those companies success in that timely development.

On page 224 the authors referred to two advantages of the sand carbonizer—support to the briquettes in the temperature range where their strength was restricted and the possibility of using the off-gas from the carbonization stage. There were, of course, other carbonization processes for which those claims could also be made. Perhaps the authors would comment further on the advantages and disadvantages of sand carbonization versus other methods, such as moving-grate or hearth processes. The results of the Rheinstahl blast-furnace trials on semi-carbonized briquettes were of considerable significance to ironmakers and indicated that a shaft furnace could act as its own carbonizer–coker. For some years he had been interested in exploiting that possibility: a development along those lines—known as the WSF (WORCRA Shaft Furnace) was briefly described in a recent paper.[1] It used uncoked composite pellets.

In the light of the Rheinstahl results with lightly carbonized hot briquettes and the work which his colleagues and he had been doing, one might query the view that it was absolutely essential to charge a blast-furnace with low-reactivity coke. He would concede, however, that when semi-carbonized briquettes or pellets formed the fuel reductant, it might be advisable to employ lower shaft heights to reduce both the load on the formed fuel in the bosh region and the somewhat increased resistance to the blast.

Since 1963 he had been keenly interested in the principle enunciated in the paper by Reeve and his colleagues. It was the basis of one of the patented WORCRA approaches to Combined IronMaking And Steelmaking—CIMAS.[2]

In the work on electric WORCRA steelmaking at Luleå, Sweden,[1] they were able to demonstrate that composite briquettes made from sponge iron fines and coke breeze could be continuously melted in the 'bowl' of the furnace to a semi-steel. That could then be continuously refined to steel by sequential lancing with oxygen with counterflow slag in the associated launder section of the furnace. Unfortunately, they did not have facilities at Luleå to utilize the furnace CO-rich off-gases to preheat the ingoing composite briquettes. That, as the authors pointed out, would achieve a much improved overall energy balance.

It was relevant to point out that some of the gas reduction processes, particularly Midrex, could produce sponge iron pellets or lumps with up to 3·5% carbon. Such agglomerates, with, e.g. 1·5% carbon, could, with advantage, be charged hot to *truly continuous* steelmaking furnaces.

There were several low-sulphur coals in Australia, as well as in western Canada, which should be suitable for incorporation in 'self-sustaining feeds' for continuous steelmaking.

References

1. BAKER F. H. AND WORNER H. K. WORCRA iron- and steelmaking. In *Alternative routes to steel* (London: Iron and Steel Institute, 1972), 99–106.
2. WORNER H. K. Continuous smelting and refining by the WORCRA Processes. In

Advances in extractive metallurgy (London: Institution of Mining and Metallurgy, 1968), 245–63.

Dr. M. W. Davies,* commenting on the Thorpe paper, said that he would welcome further information on the most important factors influencing the processing costs. In particular, perhaps the author would comment on the figure of \$0.06/lb quoted for the processing of zircon (p. 283): that contrasted with a figure of \$0.003–0.007 given by the author on an earlier occasion for the conversion of $TiCl_4$ to TiO_2. Why did it cost more to process zircon?

He would also like to ask the author how far the endothermicity of the process affected the efficiency. One suspected that a highly endothermic reaction such as an oxide reduction process might tend to extinguish the plasma. Did that mean that that type of process was going to be inherently less efficient than, say, an exothermic process or one where the chemical heat change was very small?

A. W. Fletcher,† with reference to the Thorpe and Sayce papers, asked if any information were available on the residence time of solids in the plasma, since that would appear to be the main problem in applying the technique to mineral processing. Work at the University of New South Wales‡ indicated that even when a gas was injected into a torch very little of it actually went through the plasma—the majority passed around the sides.

Dr. B. Waldie§ said that the important problem of achieving adequate residence times for particles on plasmas had been noted by Sayce and had been raised in the discussion. Considerable increases in mean effective particle residence time had been achieved by operating an induction plasma in a countercurrent mode rather than in the 'conventional' cocurrent mode. Mean residence times of several hundred milliseconds had been obtained. Those were several times those possible in a cocurrent induction plasma, and orders of magnitude higher than those in some plasma jets. Initial results had already been reported.¶

Research on that topic was continuing, as was work to ensure that all feed particles were adequately exposed to the plasma.

Dr. T. R. Shelley,‖ speaking on the Sayce paper, asked the author to answer a few questions concerning comparisons between plasma jet electrodes as used in the 'Plasmarc' furnace and conventional carbon arc furnace electrodes. (1)

---

* BISRA, London.
† Warren Spring Laboratory, Department of Trade and Industry, Stevenage, Hertfordshire.
‡ LITTLE T.M. AND WALSH B.N. Induction heated plasmas for chemical synthesis. Paper presented at 'Chemeca 70', a conference organized by the Australian Academy of Sciences, Aug. 1970.
§ Department of Chemical Engineering, Heriott-Watt University, Edinburgh.
¶ WALDIE B. Heating of powders in counter-current and co-current induction plasmas. *Trans. Instn chem. Engrs*, **49**, 1971, 114–6.
‖ Department of Metallurgy, University of Cambridge.

What would be the voltage drop per unit distance down the length of the plasma jet electrode column? (2) How would the voltage drop of an inert gas plasma jet electrode compare with that of a hollow carbon electrode with inert gas flowing down it into the arc? (3) How did the tendency to wander (to find the best conducting path) shown by conventional carbon arcs compare with any similar tendency in a plasma jet electrode on to a melt?

He queried the remark (p. 266) concerning his own joint published work on arc electrolysis: 'no allowance was made for thermal fuming'. The speaker and his colleagues had shown that the rate of fume evolution from melts studied in their experiments depended on the electrolytic current passed through the melt in the case of ion-conducting melts, and not in the case of electronically conducting melts, where fume evolution was always at a lower level. The conduction mechanisms in both cases were experimentally determined by separate experiments.

Their arc electrolysis work, which was based on the use of the conventional electric arc furnace, differed in many ways from the work performed at the National Physical Laboratory, e.g. surface area/bulk ratio, degree of mixing in the slag bath, and it was reasonable, therefore, that there could be divergence in the results obtained.

He would, however, like the author to explain his view in the light of their published observations.

Contributed remarks

Dr. R. Thompson* Thorpe refers in his paper to pure boron being made by Borax Consolidated, Ltd., by use of a plasma technique. A pilot plant was, in fact, constructed in 1968 on the basis of research reported subsequently.† It was designed around a single water-cooled silica torch in which a plasma is induced (in argon) at 5 MHz, and with a power input of 30 kW. The unit operates continuously under automatic control and produces boron in good overall yield at the rate of 250 g/h from boron trichloride and hydrogen; 30% of the BCl_3 is reduced per pass, the remainder being recycled. The product is obtained as a high-purity micron-size powder which is non-pyrophoric.

This work demonstrated the suitability of induction plasma devices for the hydrogen reduction of a metal halide. A particular advantage of the technique is product cleanliness: reactants can be purified by distillation or similar methods and pick-up of impurities from equipment is entirely absent. The method is ideally suited to the direct preparation of fine powders for use in powder metallurgy, avoiding mechanical comminution, which can be a source of contamination, especially with refractory hard metals. Elements other than boron have been obtained from their chlorides in the same equipment. Throughput on a weight

---

* Borax Consolidated, Ltd., Chessington, Surrey.

† HAMBLYN S. M. L. RUEBEN B. G. AND THOMPSON R. Hydrogen reduction of boron trichloride to boron in an R.F. plasma. In *Symposium on special ceramics*, 5 (Stoke-on-Trent: British Ceramic Research Association, 1972), in press.

basis and power efficiency improve as the atomic weight and specific gravity of the element increase (boron being at a disadvantage on both counts). Experience suggests that a battery of relatively small torches might in some ways be preferable to scaling up to a single torch of high power.

AUTHORS' REPLIES

Dr. E. Ahland, Dr. B. Bock, Dr. H. J. Jagnow, Dr. J. Lehmann and Professor W. Peters In reply to Mr. R. Healey (pp. 290–1), the reactivity of the coke, which is of importance in the Imperial Smelting process, must be measured on the whole piece, because the reactivity depends to a high degree on the overall size, as has been confirmed by tests in our laboratories. The formed coke tested at Duisburg was much smaller than the usual oven coke. Thus, the formed coke was *a priori* in a worse position, because its reactivity was too high. Recently, we have succeeded in producing formed coke of larger size, and there is no doubt that this coke, when used in the furnace of the Duisburg Berzelius smelting plant, will show a much better result.

In reply to Dr. J. T. Fitton (p. 289), in collaboration with the Ruhrkohle Company Bergbau-Forschung has made a comparative calculation of the capital expenditure and the operational costs of the hot-briquetting process, on the one hand, and the modern coke oven plant on the other. The hot-briquetting process was chosen because its evolution is more advanced.

The basis of the comparison was a coke oven plant with a production capacity of 3 500 000 tons per year. It was assumed that the same feed coal would be used, which is to say that the great advantage of the hot-briquetting process— the possibility of using cheap weakly or non-caking coal—was not taken into account. The result of the calculation was that the hot-briquetting process would require lower capital expenditure costs (by about 20%) and that the price per ton of hot briquettes would be 5–10 DM lower than the price of oven coke.

In the evaluation of the hot briquettes a loss of returns was assumed on account of their volatile matter content and, correspondingly, in the evaluation of the oven coke a loss of returns due to coke breeze and small coke was taken into account.

As to the starting coals used for the production of the formed coke (Table 1, p. 221), the char coal used for the hot-briquetting process was a semi-anthracite, volatile matter content: 13·5% (d.a.f.), swelling index: 1/2. The caking coal was a rich coal, volatile matter content: 22%, swelling index: 9, dilatation: 61%. A mixture of these two coals at a ratio 1:1 was also used for production of the pellets. The coal in the pitch-bound briquettes was an anthracite with a volatile matter content of 10%, swelling index: 0.

The Micum indices given in the paper were determined according to the ISO standard, that is to say after 100 revolutions. In other words, they are not extended Micum figures.

We cannot confirm Dr. Fitton's assumption with regard to the behaviour of hot briquettes in the case of extended drum tests. We have always found that the abrasion was higher at the beginning of the drum test than at the end. This invalidates the assumption that the hot briquettes have a hard outer surface and a soft core.

In principle, we do not see differences in the carbonization of briquettes and pellets. We have shock-carbonized pellets as well as briquettes in our hot-sand carbonizer and obtained good products. We should like to add, however, that it is recommended that the pellets be dried prior to shock-carbonization in order to expel the enormous quantities of water—up to 20%. It goes without saying that the composition of the blends used for pelletization—either different types of coal or coal and char—must meet the requirements of the carbonization process.

The reactivity of formed coke depends to a high degree on the nature of the char component produced by shock heating, e.g. by the fluidized-bed process. This is true for pellets as well as for briquettes. In principle, we could not find a difference in reactivity when comparing pieces of the same size.

In reply to Dr. Howard K. Worner (pp. 291–3), in our opinion the hot-sand carbonizer offers the following advantages over the moving-grate or hearth processes: (1) there are no mechanically movable components in a sand carbonizer; (2) low-temperature or high-temperature carbonization of briquettes yields, in contrast to the two other processes, a rich gas, which can be turned to better account than the lean gas normally obtained; and (3) during the carbonization process no carbon is consumed by combustion, inert heat carriers being used—therefore, the yield is higher.

It is a disadvantage that the breeze which forms in the reactor of the sand carbonizer is discharged together with the sand into the airlift, where it is burnt. This handicap, however, is not decisive in our opinion, because the breeze contributes in this way to covering the heat demand of the process.

Dr. D. A. Reeve, Dr. R. P. Charbonnier and Dr. J. H. Walsh We are grateful to Dr. H. K. Worner (pp. 291–3) for his very kind remarks on our paper and for underlining the economic advantages of such self-sustaining feed materials.

A continuous steelmaking process developed by Polaris International Metals Corporation, Arizona, also utilizes a similar type of composite pellet, but, this time, with flux also added to the composite.*

With respect to the production of sponge iron pellets containing carbon by direct reduction methods, it is perhaps of interest to note that HyL sponge iron containing controlled amounts of carbon between 1·50 and 2·25%† has been used as a coolant in BOF steelmaking.‡

* McManus G. J. That 'blue sky' on steelmaking's horizon. *Iron Age*, **208**, no. 23, Dec. 2 1971, 65–71.
† See reference 12 on page 240.
‡ Peña I. N. and Radke D. HyL sponge iron as a coolant in BOF steelmaking. *J. Metals, N.Y.*, **23**, Aug. 1971, 27–32.

We note that the sulphur content of 0·2% of the Queensland coals mentioned by Dr. Worner is even lower than generally found in the western Canadian coals.

Dr. I. G. Sayce Mr. A. W. Fletcher (p. 293) has raised the question of residence time of particles in the plasma. This is of considerable importance in much of Thorpe's work, and I should prefer to leave this mainly to him to answer; but I should like to make two points. First, there are difficulties, resulting from the flow patterns within the gas, and its high viscosity, in getting particles of solid materials into the plasma. The nature of these effects as they apply to the induced plasma torch has been discussed by Chase,[1] and in order to overcome them in such a torch it is necessary to introduce the powder via a water-cooled probe, which itself enters the fireball as described by Charles et al.[2] Secondly, at NPL we have circumvented the retention problem in much of our work by adopting an alternative approach. By using the centrifugal furnace[3] to hold the material to be vaporized we can contain the material, in a thermally efficient manner, for any desired retention time. Thus, the material is held in contact with the plasma until it vaporizes, and only in that way can it leave the plasma zone.

To answer Dr. T. R. Shelley (pp. 293–4), voltage drops down an argon plasma column emerging from a torch used in the transferred mode are generally in the range 2–5 V/cm. A gradient of 4 V/cm is quoted for the 'Plasmarc' furnace[4] and one of 2 V/cm has been reported for the NPL expanded arc furnace described by Whyman.[5] I would expect the voltage drop in an argon plasma flowing from a hollow carbon electrode to be within this range, provided that vaporized species did not seriously affect the arc. In our experience the use of a laminar plasma jet in transferred-arc fuming of melts does give less wander than when a simple carbon electrode is employed. The plasma column is well defined and has an intrinsic 'stiffness', which opposes movement of the arc root off the axis. As the gas flow is reduced, however, there is an increasing tendency of the arc root to wander, much as observed with the carbon electrode.

With regard to my reference to thermal fuming in the very interesting work reported by Shelley and Charles,[6] I regret that in the interests of brevity my comment was badly phrased. The authors did indeed indicate that thermal fuming made a significant contribution to the net yield in certain arc electrolysis experiments. However, in considering development of their process they appear to have placed their main emphasis on the electrolytic aspects of the technique. From our own work at NPL I consider that the thermal effect may be of equal or greater importance. We have fumed tin oxide from tin-containing slags on a small scale by use of a plasma jet. We have observed both electrolytic and thermal fuming, but find that in suitably designed apparatus thermal fuming can predominate: indeed, we have obtained fume rates comparable with those produced electrolytically with non-transferred arcs. Since thermal fuming will be favoured on scaling up the apparatus, and since pure ionic conduction may be impossible to achieve with slags of commercial interest, I feel that greater attention should be paid to the importance of non-electrolytic plasma fuming in any consideration of the industrial application of these studies.

References

1. See reference 43 on page 272.
2. See reference 83 on page 273.
3. See references 51–53 on page 272.
4. See reference 44 on page 272.
5. See reference 26 on page 271.
6. See reference 118 on page 274.

M. L. Thorpe In reply to Dr. M. W. Davies (p. 293), our zircon costs relate to heat affection of solid particles in a plasma. Basically, this is a relatively inefficient process, utilizing about 30% of the heat available in the plasma for actual melting of the particles in the plasma. TiO_2, on the other hand, is an efficient gas–gas exothermic reaction requiring only enough power input to bring the reactants up to reaction temperature; hence, the power requirements are much less.

Mr. A. W. Fletcher's questions (p. 293) centre around the problems of retention of materials in the plasma (retention time–residence time) and how these problems could be solved. Three years ago efficient heating of particles was a serious problem in all plasma generators. When one attempted to inject materials through the arc region, plugging and contamination of both the cathode and anode spots resulted. On the other hand, when one injected downstream, thermal efficiencies were considerably reduced and powers in the range of 5–10 kWh/lb were required to melt materials. Ionarc has overcome this by injecting materials directly into the arc region and ensuring intimate, uniform injection. This technical solution resulted in two process improvements. Because of the higher temperature in the arc region, thermal efficiencies were improved so that, depending on the material, 0·5–1 kWh/lb was all the energy required to completely melt the feedstock (up to 200–300 μm in diameter). This brings up another point—it is absolutely essential in some processes that every particle be heat-affected; for example, in our zirconia process if non heat-affected zircon gets through in the feedstock, this produces a silica contamination, which is undesirable. Thus, it is extremely important that uniform heat affection is achieved.

In the case of induction plasmas the induction arc can be visualized as the shell of an egg, the upstream portion being the larger end. When powders are dropped on to the surface it is observed that they 'bounce' off as if hitting a solid object. There are many explanations set forth regarding the cause of this phenomenon and they will not be discussed here; however, the problem can be overcome by actually introducing a water-cooled probe through the surface of the arc at this point, injecting materials into the centre ball of the plasma. In contrast, the sides of the plasma ball eggshell are not 'hard' and powders can be easily injected at this point.

Dr. T. R. Shelley (pp. 293–4) enquired about the voltage drop in the arc columns of various arcs, i.e. plasma arcs versus carbon arcs, hollow cathode arcs, etc. He was apparently concerned that there would be a great difference between these kinds of devices, and this, in turn, might present some operating problems. It has been our experience that there is a considerable (conventional) voltage drop at both the anode and the cathode; however, the voltage in the arc column normally is in the range 1–2 V/cm, and as long as adequate open voltage is available on the power supply the sustaining of long arcs is not a problem.

Session 5

Pneumatic processes

Chairman
Dr. S. E. Woods

Prognostic in disease

Chairman
Dr S E Mende

Gas lancing in metal refining: an air–water model study

A. E. Wraith B.Sc., Ph.D.

Department of Metallurgy, University of Newcastle upon Tyne

669.014.74:669.054

Synopsis

Gas lancing is widely used in metal refining as a technique for gaseous reactant addition, for gas flushing and as a means of agitation. The liquid seal depth is characteristically small and gas flow rates may be high, with uncertain manual control.

In deep-seal systems large bubbles formed at a submerged orifice will break down within two or three bubble diameters above the point of injection. Shallow-seal depths may allow bubbles to break surface before fragmentation appreciably enhances the gas–liquid contact area. An isothermal study of air lancing in water, using high-speed cine photography, shows that the volume of bubbles, V, formed at a lance tip is given by $V \cong 1 \cdot 14 Q^{6/5} \, g^{-3/5}$, where Q is the gas flow rate. Coalescence is observed between successive bubbles, and gas can be channelled directly to the surface, limiting gas–liquid contact further.

It is evident that lancing may be an inefficient phase-contacting device; effective operating conditions are suggested. An alternative injection technique is proposed in which multiple high-velocity gas jets are generated at the lance tip.

The submerged gas lance is widely used in liquid metal refining to inject reactant or flushing gases and as a means of agitation. In small-scale operations the lance is a convenient manual equipment for intermittent use, where it has the advantage of simplicity and retractability. For similar reasons the lance is also valued in some large-scale operations, such as copper fire-refining and aluminium degassing.

Major factors in the use of the submerged lance, namely convenience and simplicity, may offer some cost advantage provided that gas–liquid contacting is effective. A general feature of liquid metal process plant is the shallow liquid seal depth, which must impose a limitation on gas bubble contact time as well as providing too short a rise path to allow adequate breakdown of injected gas streams into an effective bubble population and size distribution. If contacting is inefficient, there will be gas wastage and process times will be prolonged.

There is now a useful understanding of the relationship in deep-seal, relatively narrow, liquid-filled columns between gas injection rate, system geometry, mean bubble size and size distribution, where the gas is injected upwards. Downward injection into shallow, broad pools is a major departure from those desirable conditions. In this paper an indication of the nature of gas–liquid contacting in submerged lancing is obtained by means of an isothermal water–air model, and the performance of the simple lance is briefly compared with that of other bubble-forming devices in shallow systems.

The simple lance

Theory*

Suppose the gas lance tip is a diffuse point gas source located in a low-viscosity liquid of large extent, with no surface nearby. Then, provided that the gas flow rate is sustained, a radially expanding envelope will form at the source. When the gas injection rate is high, so that the radial velocity, dr/dt, and the radial acceleration, d^2r/dt^2, are large, the envelope may be treated conveniently as a 'rigid' expanding sphere.[1, 2] The radial velocity and acceleration are given by

$$\frac{dr}{dt} = \frac{Q}{4\pi r^2}$$

$$\frac{d^2r}{dt^2} = -\frac{Q^2}{8\pi^2 r^5}$$

where Q is the volumetric gas flow rate and r the instantaneous bubble radius.

The bubble, initially at rest, will begin to move upwards under gravity as it expands. In a low-viscosity liquid viscous drag may be neglected in this initial motion, so bubble movement is dictated by a balance between gravity and inertial forces. The latter arise from the kinetic energy imparted to the liquid by the expanding rising envelope. The Newtonian force balance is then

$$V\rho_1 g = \frac{d}{dt}\left(\tfrac{1}{2} V\rho_1 \frac{ds}{dt}\right) \tag{1}$$

where V is the envelope volume at an instant during expansion, $\tfrac{1}{2}V\rho_1$ the effective or 'virtual' mass of the bubble apparent from liquid-phase kinetic energy, s the displacement of the bubble centre from the gas source and ρ_1 the liquid density. The gas density, ρ_g, is neglected since $\rho_1 \gg \rho_g$.

To solve equation 1 the following simplifying assumptions are made: (1) the envelope remains spherical throughout growth and (2) the gas flow rate is constant. On the basis of (2), we may write

$$V = Qt \tag{2}$$

where t is the time of envelope growth from initiation. Substituting relation 2 in equation 1, a simple equation in s is obtained:

$$2gt = \frac{d}{dt}\left(t\frac{ds}{dt}\right) \tag{3}$$

* Definitions of the symbols used in this paper appear on page 315.

Setting $s = ds/dt = 0$ when $t = 0$, integration twice gives

$$s = \frac{gt^2}{2} \tag{4}$$

which is the relation obtained by Walters and Davidson[2] for the upward-acting free-standing nozzle on the basis of similar assumptions.

The bubble will rise and grow until its base meets the lance tip (Fig. 1, (i)–(iv)). If the gas supply to the envelope is assumed to be cut off when the source breaks through the envelope, the size of the bubble formed in this way will be given by setting $s = r$, and the bubble volume is derived as a function of flow rate by further substitution for t from relation 2 in equation 4.

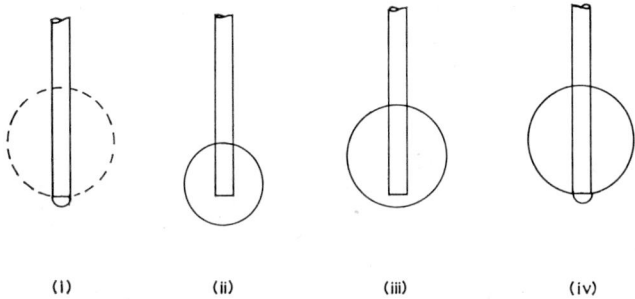

(i)   (ii)   (iii)   (iv)

Fig. 1 Configuration of bubble formation at a submerged lance ((iv) shows the postulated cutoff position when the lance tip breaks through the bubble base)

Fig. 1 shows the lance enveloped by the growing bubble. The buoyant volume of bubble will therefore be smaller than the value derived from the actual bubble radius by an amount equal to the volume of the enveloped lance. Incorporating the lance volume when $s < r$, the bubble radius is

$$r = \left[\frac{3Qt}{4\pi} + \tfrac{3}{4}r_o{}^2 r + \tfrac{3}{4}r_o{}^2 s \right]^{1/3} \tag{5}$$

and when the bubble base meets the lance tip, that is, when $s = r$, equation 5 becomes

$$s = \left[\frac{3Qt}{4\pi} + \tfrac{3}{2}r_o{}^2 s \right]^{1/3} \tag{6}$$

Assuming the virtual mass of the bubble is unaffected by the penetrating lance, substitution for s from equation 4 into equation 6 gives

$$\left[\frac{3Qt}{4\pi} + \tfrac{3}{4}gr_o{}^2 t^2 \right]^{1/3} = \frac{gt^2}{2} \tag{7}$$

or

L

$$\frac{g^3 t^5}{8} - \tfrac{3}{4} r_o^2 g t - \frac{3Q}{4\pi} = 0 \tag{8}$$

Further substitution for t from relation 2 gives an equation in V, the volume of gas in the bubble, and Q

$$\frac{g^3 V^5}{8Q^6} - \tfrac{3}{4} r_o^2 g \frac{V}{Q^2} - \frac{3}{4\pi} = 0 \tag{9}$$

Equation 9 reduces to

$$V = 1{\cdot}138\,.Q^{6/5} g^{-3/5} \tag{10}$$

when $r_o = 0$; this is the straightforward solution of equation 4 applicable to an upward-acting free-standing nozzle. The gas bubble volume given by equation 9 is therefore slightly larger than that given by relation 10 when r_o is finite, but equation 9→relation 10 when Q is large.

Experimental

Experiments were done to study equation 9. Since liquid-phase density and surface tension do not appear in equation 9, it is reasonable to suppose that air–water might be an acceptable model for a liquid metal system. Furthermore, neglect of viscosity is justified in studies of bubble growth in low-viscosity liquids on the basis of previously published observations from other gas injection systems. Close agreement[2] has been observed between experiment and theory for relation 10, and there are other experimental studies of the growth of large bubbles in water where viscosity is seen to play a negligible part.[3, 4] The motion of air bubbles in water after detachment from the gas source is affected by viscous forces where the rise path is lengthy, but there is no appreciable influence on the detachment process. Thus, an air–water system may provide a feasible model of this aspect of liquid metal lancing.

In the present experiments bubble formation at a submerged lance was investigated by using such a system. Lance tubes 1·50 cm and 2·82 cm in external diameter and 1 mm in wall thickness were used to inject air into a water-filled glass-walled tank 75 cm wide × 40 cm front to back × 90 cm deep. The lances were supported rigidly and carefully aligned vertically. The apparatus is shown schematically in Fig. 2. There were two types of lance tip. In one type, used with both tube sizes, a converging–diverging metering nozzle was brazed into the lance near the submerged end (Fig. 2). At an upstream pressure greater than 2 atm the metering tip became a sonic nozzle, which stabilized the air flow by damping the downstream pressure changes during bubble growth and detachment. The other lance type was simply the plain tube; the injection speed was smaller and downstream pressure changes could therefore be communicated to the gas volume of the delivery system. The larger lance tube (2·82 cm in diameter) was used in this form. The air flow rate was indicated by standardized variable-area meters, and the delivered volume was corrected to ambient conditions at the lance tip. In practice, the temperature correction was negligible.

Bubble formation was recorded by high-speed cine photography, and by flash photographs of rising envelopes. By the use of a motion analysis projector, bubble volumes were calculated from the dimensions of scaled, projected bubble images. Accurate time-scaling was provided by a neon marker incorporated in the camera, and framing rates were generally in the range 200–300 pictures per second.

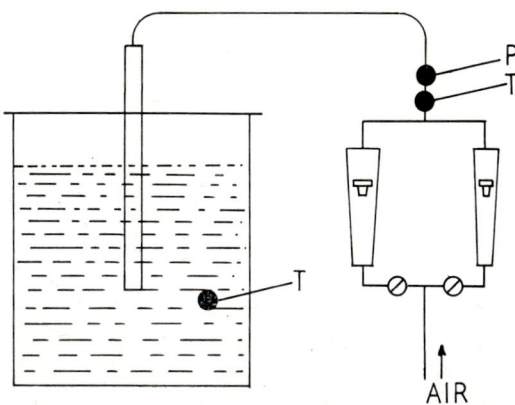

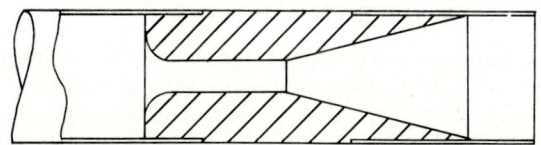

Fig. 2 Schematic view of injection apparatus and details of nozzle tip. Points of pressure and temperature measurement are denoted by *P* and *T*

Bubble observations

Bubble volumes were determined at the instant the bubble base met the lance tip. Mean values are shown in Fig. 3 together with relation 10 for the two lance sizes. There is clearly good agreement at low flow rates for the smaller metering tips and for the plain lance. It is evident at once that gas bubbles formed in this way are remarkably large. Photographs (Fig. 4) taken from cine film show an additional and vitally important feature: as the bubble rises past the cutoff position postulated in the theory, it can be seen that the gas flow is not actually interrupted. A gas-filled annulus forms when the lance tip penetrates the bubble base (the instant $s = r$) that links bubble and source. This connecting stem lengthens as the bubble rises until it is nipped or 'pinched off' near the lance tip.

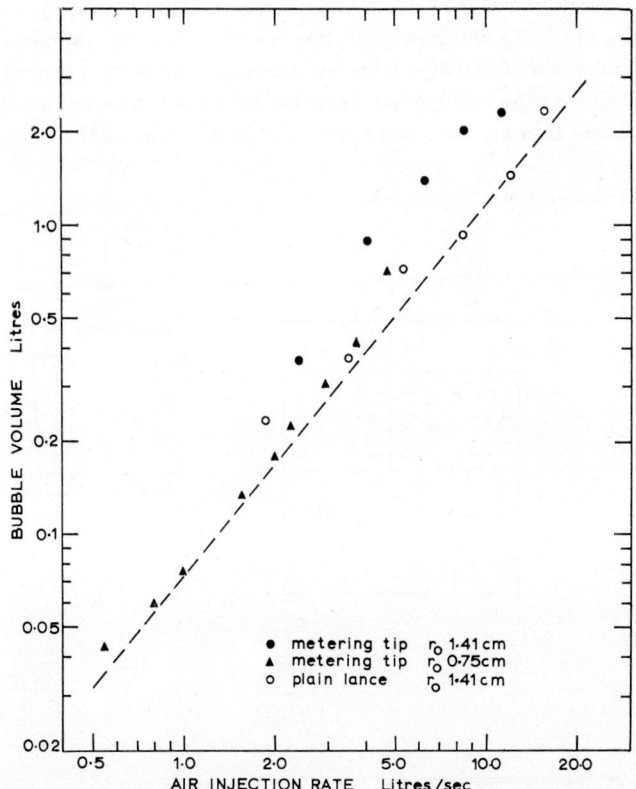

Fig. 3 Volume of bubbles formed at a lance; the volumes were measured at the instant shown in Fig. 1 (iv). The broken line represents relation 10

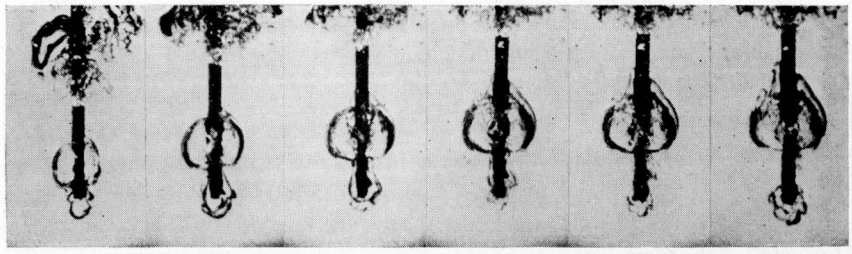

Fig. 4 Sequence of cine film frames showing stem formation and bubble growth. $Q = 1.59$ l/sec; $r_o = 0.75$ cm (metering nozzle tip)

In this way the bubble continues to grow after the base leaves the gas source. The final severed volume is therefore larger than the values plotted in Fig. 3. With increasing flow rate the annular stem grew more persistent, until, eventually, pinching off no longer occurred and the formation of severed bubbles became rare. There is an important general difference in bubble formation behaviour between the metering tip and the plain lance. The high gas kinetic energy associated with high-speed flow through the metering tip gave much deeper penetration and produced a protrusion below the bubble base during growth (Fig. 5). This had the effect of prolonging contact between bubble and lance tip, so the bubble volume measured at the theoretically postulated cutoff instant was larger at high flow rates than that predicted by equation 9. With the plain lance the protrusion effect was apparent only at the highest flow rates. The divergence for both lance types can be seen in Fig. 3.

Sonic injection speeds at high flow rates produced a highly turbulent jet below the lance which formed small bubbles that were projected downwards and

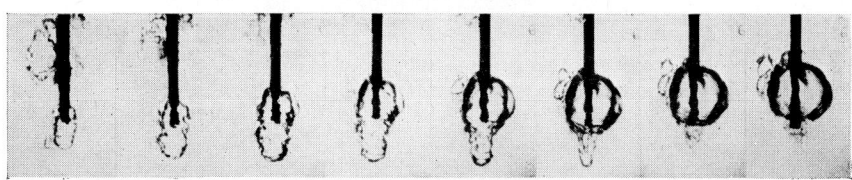

Fig. 5 Downward protrusion formation and retraction. $Q = 4.71$ l/sec; $r_o = 0.75$ cm (metering nozzle tip)

laterally (Fig. 6). Under these conditions the large envelopes formed around the lance were masked by foam generated lower down. It was clear, nevertheless, that the principal bubbles were unstable and began to disintegrate during growth, giving a more dispersed gas column than that of the plain lance.

Bubble motion

Large severed gas bubbles formed at an upward-acting nozzle disintegrate within a rise path of about three bubble diameters to produce a turbulent column of smaller bubbles. Disintegration is the outcome of an asymmetric pressure distribution around the bubble as it accelerates upwards after severance from the gas source. Walters and Davidson[2] demonstrated the effect for bubbles in water, where the initial acceleration is $2g$, showing clearly how the bubble base is depressed and penetrated by a tongue of liquid that renders the bubble unstable, leading to fragmentation. Growing bubbles accelerate and deform more slowly and, even where there is vertical distortion induced by gas kinetic energy at upward-acting orifices,[4] disintegration is inhibited until the bubble is severed from the source.

Observations of bubble formation at the plain lance show similar behaviour. Disintegration is retarded until the annular stem pinches off. From this instant the bubble accelerates and a spray of liquid penetrates the base. As the spray impinges on the internal bubble surface fragmentation begins; the effect increases in vigour with increasing bubble size. But it must be stressed that at relatively shallow seal depths the mixing promoted by fragmentation may not develop fully before the main body of gas in the bubble reaches the surface. In this way agitation at the surface as the bubble breaks through may become a principal source of gas–liquid dispersion.

Channelling

The air–water model reveals two characteristics of the plain gas lance that minimize its effectiveness as a gas–liquid contacting device: one is the large

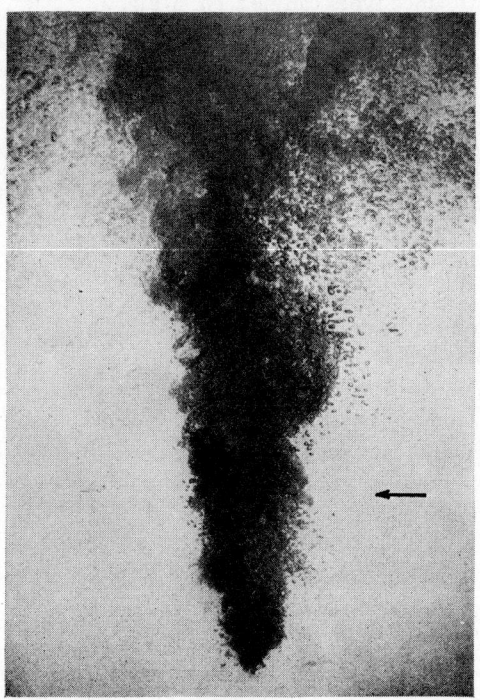

Fig. 6 Turbulent downward protrusion. $Q = 11.3$ l/sec; $r_o = 1.41$ cm. Lance tip position is indicated by arrow

bubble size; the other the tendency to stem formation, stabilized perhaps by the presence of the lance. Together, these give an initially stable bubble shape near the lance tip and therefore more effective gas–liquid mixing is confined to levels nearer the liquid surface.

The formation of an annular stem in the lance process at high gas injection rates may be expected from recent studies of upward-acting submerged nozzles.[4,5] As with other gas sources, the bubble formed at a lance tip moves upwards about half the bubble radius before the stem is pinched off, and this displacement is observed to be approximately independent of flow rate. So the lance tip must be at least $(2+\frac{1}{2})r$ below the liquid surface if a complete cycle of bubble growth to pinch-off is to take place. When the immersion depth is less than this, the bubble formation mechanism will break down, and gas will be channelled directly to the surface through a series of incompletely formed envelopes.

For the plain lance the bubble radius at cutoff is derived from equation 4 by setting

$$t = \frac{1}{Q}(\tfrac{4}{3}\pi r^3 - 2\pi r_o{}^2 r)$$

and inserting the dimensionless cutoff position, s/r, to give, on rearrangement,

$$\left(\frac{s}{r}\right)^{1/2}(2g)^{-1/2}\frac{Q}{\pi} - \tfrac{2}{3}r^{5/2} + r_o{}^2 r^{1/2} = 0 \tag{11}$$

where s is the displacement of the bubble centre above the lance tip at pinch-off. The bubble volume at this instant can be derived at once from the r values of equation 11. When Q is large, the term in r_o becomes negligible and equation 11 simplifies to

$$r = 0.648 \left(\frac{s}{r}\right)^{1/5} Q^{2/5} g^{-1/5} \tag{12}$$

Setting $s/r = 1.5$, the bubble volume at pinch-off follows directly:

$$V = 1.453\ Q^{6/5} g^{-3/5} \tag{13}$$

Comparing relations 10 and 13, it can be seen that, ideally, the volume will increase by at least 28% while gas is supplied through the lengthening annular stem.

In reality, channelling takes place at greater immersion depths than $2\frac{1}{2}r$. The bubble is still coherent at this position. The process of fragmentation begins there and continues over an appreciable rise distance, so the bubble retains much of its coherent bulk for at least a further bubble diameter. Several other factors enter the estimate of an acceptable immersion depth. At the higher injection rates examined, pinch-off did not take place regularly, so bubbles continued to grow at s/r values >1.5, though the envelopes began to distort rapidly beyond this position. There was also coalescence between ascending and growing bubbles. Both of these effects delayed fragmentation. Further, as gas packets approached the surface, protrusions were seen to erupt rapidly upwards from the rising envelope (Fig. 7).

In view of these effects a realistic immersion depth might be three times the minimal, namely $h_D = 7.5r$. At this depth the model indicates that fragmentation will approach completion before the bulk of gas breaks through the surface. With some approximation, the criterion can be interpreted from relation 12, whence

$$h_D \cong 5.25\ Q^{2/5} g^{-1/5} \tag{14}$$

The relation for h_D gives a guide to the highest desirable injection rate for a given bath depth when a freely suspended lance is used. In view of the non-isothermal injection conditions likely in practice, relation 14 may well under-estimate h_D.

At this point the characteristics of very high injection speed might be briefly re-examined. The effect of a protrusion below the bubble during formation at high gas velocities is to prolong growth and to generate inordinately large gas packets. This is accompanied by turbulence promoted below the lance, by the generation of clouds of small bubbles in that region and by instability induced in the main gas packet during growth. It is, nevertheless, evident from the model that the large gas-filled envelopes inherent in lancing represent a somewhat

Fig. 7 Upward protrusions and multiple-stem coalescence leading to channel-ling to surface. $Q = 0.785$ l/sec; $r_o = 0.75$ cm (metering nozzle tip). Immersion depth is 15 cm, corresponding, at that flow rate, to $h_D = 5.5\,r$

restricted gas-contacting process. It is therefore constructive to consider ways to improve gas dispersion from lances and to briefly examine alternative bubble-forming devices appropriate to liquid metal service.

Lateral gas injection

Converter processes rely on the highly energetic injection of oxidizing gases into a liquid bath and, in recent years, much interest has developed in the dynamic behaviour of the injected gas jet. Themelis and co-workers have analysed horizontal and inclined jets in model studies of the Peirce–Smith converter and have published valuable data describing the trajectory of gas jets in liquids.[6, 7, 8]

With horizontal and upward-acting nozzles very high injection velocities produce a lengthy, turbulent two-phase jet cone that increases in density along its trajectory as liquid is entrained. The formation of individual envelopes at the nozzle tip, familiar at lower flow rates, is not feasible because gas kinetic energy provides the major and highly directional force in the initial contact between gas and liquid. Mixing takes place progressively along the trajectory, producing a compact gas dispersion.

Evidence of a similar turbulence was seen with the sonic lance in the present model, but, because the lance was aligned vertically downwards, the gas kinetic energy was rapidly dissipated in the lance axis. Even greater retardation might be expected in a liquid metal. Despite some dispersion around the jet below the lance tip, large envelopes continued to form in the rising backflow of gas. By mounting the lance tip horizontally, the gas kinetic energy might, alternatively, be dissipated within an upward-curving jet cone that carries the dispersion clear of the lance stem. This would inhibit the formation of large gas packets.

The effect was demonstrated by injecting air into water through an orifice in the wall of a vertical lance that had been sealed at the tip (a simple alternative to rotating the lance axis). Fig. 8 shows lateral jets formed at a 5-mm diameter

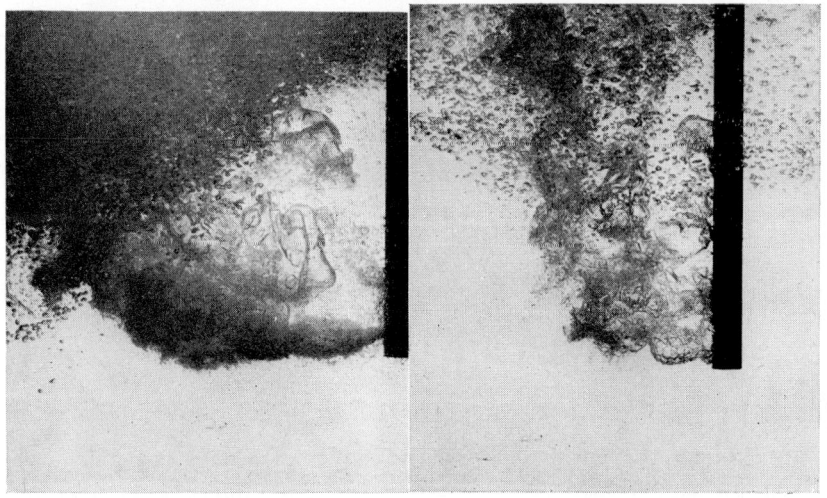

Fig. 8 Horizontal jets formed at 5-mm diameter orifice: *(a) (left)* $Q = 8.18$ l/sec; *(b) (right)* $Q = 2.90$ l/sec

orifice—the extent of the dispersion can be seen at once. The boundaries and axes of the dispersions conform quite closely to those predicted for water from the data of Themelis and co-workers.[8]

The degree of gas liquid mixing can be represented, perhaps simplistically, by the volume fraction of liquid incorporated into the expanding jet cone. From

L*

the data of Themelis and co-workers the liquid volume fraction for the lance arrangement of Fig. 8 in a liquid metal bath is estimated to be about 10%. This notably small value may be acceptable in a converter where there is vigorous agitation and reaction throughout the melt, but it does not suggest useful mixing conditions for the physical and chemical situation in which the retractable lance is used. It is desirable to carry the gas stream clear of the lance stem if large bubbles are to be inhibited, yet lateral jetting produces a lean, compact two-phase column. The liquid volume fraction increases appreciably as buoyancy forces begin to dominate the jet;[7] it seems reasonable to suppose that a less compact bubble column might be generated if the gas momentum were dissipated at a deep level within the melt. This may be assisted by directing the jet downwards at an acute angle, so producing an appreciable opposing buoyancy force component in the jet direction.

Figs. 8 and 9 show horizontal and inclined jets at comparable flow rates. There

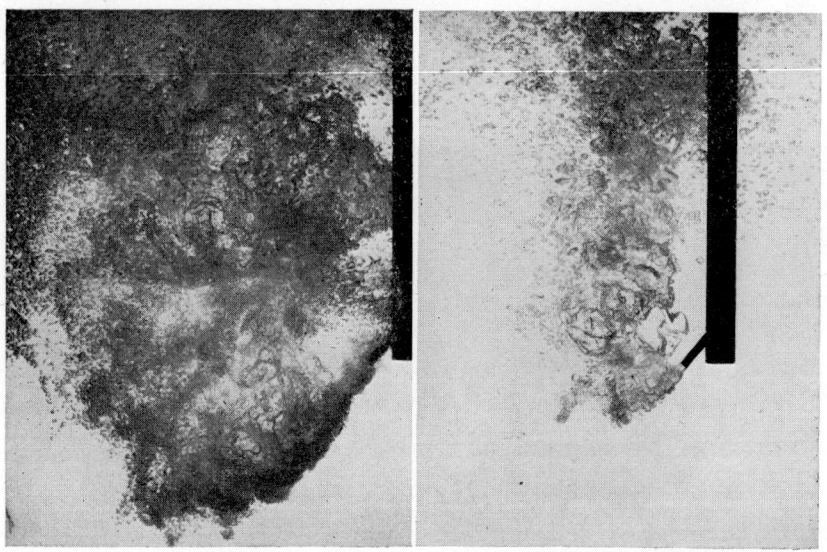

Fig. 9   45° jets at 5-mm diameter orifice (flow rates as Fig. 8)

is little difference in the state of dispersion between the two types of jet at the lower flow rate, although it is clear that the bubble stream is being carried clear of the lance stem. Differences are more marked at the higher flow rate, which is a sonic jet. First, it is self-evident that for a comparable nozzle position the inclined jet gave deeper penetration. Second, it appears that the inclined nozzle produced a rather more diffuse dispersion. It was also observed, but could not successfully be conveyed pictorially, that surface agitation was less localized with the inclined jet as against the horizontal jet for comparable penetration depths. Further investigation of such high-speed jets is in progress.

It is apparent that submerged jetting may produce a better mixing mode than the plain downward-acting lance. By using a multiple-hole lance radiating jet cones through 360°, liquid entrainment could be extended over a greater area of the bath than is possible with a single source. It must be made clear, however, that the differences in jet behaviour between water and liquid metals, particularly regarding penetration distance, limit the relevance of the water model. There is evidence from the model of a potential advantage; larger-scale studies are required to verify it.

Summary

It is clear from an isothermal air–water model that the downward-acting plain lance produces large gas bubbles that may reach the surface of a shallow liquid seal before breaking down into an acceptable bubble dispersion. To avoid the possibility of direct gas channelling from lance tip to surface the tip should be immersed to a depth

$$h_D \ngtr 5{\cdot}25\ Q^{2/5} g^{-1/5}$$

This suggests a maximum flow rate in terms of seal depth h_S for which bubbles generated at a freely suspended lance tip may be expected to disperse before reaching the surface:

$$Q \ngtr 0{\cdot}016\ h_S^{5/2} g^{1/2}$$

Injection rates greater than this might be accommodated by increasing the number of lances.

A proposal is put forward that gas–liquid contacting might be made more effective if the injected gas were jetted from radially positioned nozzles at the submerged lance tip. Where a high injection rate is required, this would overcome the need to use multiple lances.

Symbols

g	Acceleration due to gravity, LT^{-2}
$h_D,\ h_S$	Lance immersion depth, seal depth, L
Q	Volumetric gas flow rate, $L^3 T^{-1}$
r	Bubble radius, L
r_o	External lance radius, L
s	Distance of bubble centre above lance tip, L
t	Time, T
V	Bubble volume, L^3
ρ_g	Gas density, ML^{-3}
ρ_l	Liquid density, ML^{-3}

References

1. MILNE-THOMSON L. M. *Theoretical hydrodynamics* (London: Macmillan, 1949), 600 p. (p. 405)
2. WALTERS J. K. AND DAVIDSON J. F. The initial motion of a gas bubble formed in an inviscid liquid. *J. fluid Mech.*, **17**, 1963, 321–36.

3. QUIGLEY C. J. JOHNSON A. I. AND HARRIS B. L. Size and mass transfer studies of gas bubbles. *Chem. Engng Progr., Symp. Ser.*, **51,** no. 16, 1955, 31–45.

4. WRAITH A. E. Two stage bubble growth at a submerged plate-orifice. *Chem. Engng Sci.,* **26,** 1971, 1659–71.

5. WRAITH A. E. AND KAKUTANI T. The pressure field beneath a growing rising bubble. Paper submitted for publication.

6. THEMELIS N. J. AND TARASSOFF P. Gas–liquid momentum transfer in a copper converter. *Trans. Am. Inst. Min. Engrs,* **245,** 1969, 2425–33.

7. THEMELIS N. J. AND SCHMIDT P. R. Deoxidation of liquid copper by a submerged gas jet. *Trans. Am. Inst. Min. Engrs,* **239,** 1967, 1313–8.

8. THEMELIS N. J. TARASSOFF P. AND SZEKELY J. Gas–liquid momentum transfer in a copper converter. *Trans. Am. Inst. Min. Engrs,* **245,** 1969, 2425–33.

Slag fuming by the use of liquid fuel

G. Abrashev Eng.

Non-Ferrous Metals Works, Plovdiv, Bulgaria

669.054.822:669–63

Synopsis

Various aspects of the **Non-Ferrous Metals Works'** slag-fuming operation in Bulgaria are described. The development of the technique of injecting liquid fuel *(mazut)* into the slag bath—in order to eliminate the use of coal—is outlined. The operation is considered in relation to fuming practice, oil injection, effect of sulphur content, combustion of the mazut and interaction of the gas mixture with the slag.

The results of a series of tests are given, and possible future developments are suggested.

Slags from non-ferrous metals contain zinc, lead, copper, tin, cadmium, germanium, indium, thallium, selenium and other elements. Over the years various smelters have amassed enormous amounts of by-product slags, containing thousands of tons of various non-ferrous metals. Hence, treatment of currently produced liquid slags, and those from existing heaps remaining from the extraction of copper, lead and tin, represents a considerable source of additional metal values, thus improving the complex utilization of primary raw materials. Moreover, treatment of such slags leads to a lowering of production costs and an improvement of the various technical and economic parameters. One of the most economical ways for the treatment of slags appears to be the fuming process.

From its inception to the present time the fuming process has undergone a number of improvements, both with regard to the basic process and in the equipment. In general, however, the process has preserved its original essentials: grinding of coal to a predetermined size and air-blowing the coal dust into the liquid slag bath. Attempts to replace coal by liquid fuel in the hope of achieving a simplification of the process, with a corresponding reduction in costs, have, to date, been unsuccessful and are still at the laboratory and pilot-plant stage.

In 1965 a group of Bulgarian engineers from the Non-Ferrous Metals Works 'D. Blagoev' in Plovdiv developed a method and equipment for injecting liquid fuel into the slag bath, thereby dispensing with the use of coal.

In the paper the main features of the use of liquid fuel in the fuming process are considered. In Bulgaria the process is carried out with the use of a variety of

317

liquid fuel called *mazut*; this term is applied throughout to indicate liquid fuel.

The fuming of lead slags with mazut differs significantly from that which is performed with coal dust. The differences start with the composition of the liquid fuel, pass through its chemical behaviour and its reactivity, and end with the atomization and combustion techniques employed. The considerable reactive ability of the atomized mazut and its high hydrogen content lead to a change in the chemical activity of the gases and, hence, to the process flow.

The interaction between the components of the gas phase and the liquid slag are evaluated here. A solution to this problem is needed in order to answer a basic question in the fuming process: Is equilibrium reached between the gases and the slag, and is the chemical potential of the burning gases utilized to the maximum extent? From the answer to this question various possibilities for the intensification of the process and for design improvements will emerge.

A criterion of equilibrium will be the partial pressure of the gaseous phase. Bearing in mind that the theoretically calculated partial pressure of zinc vapour is substantially higher than that which is obtained in practice, there are obviously considerable opportunities in the process for improvement of performance.

Some of the particular features of the fuming process with mazut are examined.

Survey of fuming with liquid fuel

The use of mazut in slag fuming has enormous practical application in that in a number of areas where slags are being treated there is an abundance of liquid fuel and a shortage of coal.

According to Kostelov, Verner and Baimakov,[1] the use of coal dust is not always sensible, as it is one of the most expensive fuels (Table 1). Thus, the use of mazut offers the possibilities of both improving and reducing the cost of the fuming process. Furnace maintenance is considerably simplified, and the effectiveness of labour is increased.

The first attempts to use mazut for the removal of zinc from slags were made in the U.S.A. while a technique for the treatment of copper–zinc concentrates was being sought.[2] It was concluded, however, that its use was not worth while.

In 1955 Bell, Turner and Peters[4] published their studies on the fuming of zinc from lead blast-furnace slags. They reviewed the various types of fuels which, eventually, would lead to an increase in the rate of fuming and a decrease in the cost of fuel, concluding that the use of mazut or natural gas would result in a higher rate of fuming and a lower fuel cost per unit of zinc produced. They went no further than this, however, and their findings remained in the realm of theory.

Investigations and experimental work carried out in the U.S.S.R. into the substitution of mazut for coal dust in the fuming process have shown the feasibility of its use, but no definitive results have been attained, the investigations remaining at the stage of pilot-plant testing.

Okounev, Kostianovskii and Donchenko[3] stated that the successful use of mazut in the fuming process requires a tuyère system that will permit atomization and turbulence of the mazut in the slag bath.

As was mentioned above, a group of Bulgarian engineers have developed a method and equipment for slag fuming with mazut.*

The plant installed at Plovdiv has been working for almost seven years with mazut alone, with no injection of solid fuel in the molten slag bath. This is a considerable advantage of the method and seems to prove the contention that the gases are the main reducing agent in fuming. At present Bulgaria is the only country in which fuming is performed exclusively with mazut.

Mazut is also used for fuming tin slags in Novosibirsk, but, contrary to the claim by Gnatovskii *et al.*[6] that fuming with mazut has been implemented in the smelter, it is, in fact, used only as a fuel, reduction of ZnO being effected by virtue of the CO originating from the solid coal fed to the bath. The mazut burns at $\alpha = 0.95-1$, whereas solid fuel is injected into the bath at the rate of 5–7% of the weight of the slag.

Table 1

Fuel	Calorific value, kcal/kg (kcal/Nm^3)	Price, Roubles/t (m^3)	Cost of 1000 kcal of heat, Kopecks
Coal dust	6500	24·0	0·37
Mazut	9800	25·0	0·25
Natural gas	8000	0·014	0·17

Fuming practice at Plovdiv

In the Non-Ferrous Works in Plovdiv a fuming furnace is installed with a cross-section in the tuyère zone of 5·85 m^2. In addition to being fired with mazut, the furnace has the distinction of being the only one to work continuously. Details of the furnace are given below.

Productive capacity   48–56 t/m^2/24 h
Consumption of air   1160–1230 Nm/t of slag
Slag composition before fuming   12·5–14% Zn; 1·2–1·6% Pb; 36–38% FeO; 10–12% CaO; 21–23% SiO$_2$; 5–6% Al$_2$O$_3$; 1·5% MgO; 2% BaO; 0·7% Cu; 1·5% S
Slag composition after fuming   2–2·5% Zn; 0·1% Pb
Consumption of mazut   15·0–16·5% per t of slag

Fig. 1 shows the slag fuming flowsheet.[7] Slag from the shaft furnace (1) is tapped continuously through the slag siphon (2) into the electric settler (holding furnace) (5). The opening (3) for the periodic tapping of slag is used to start the furnace, or in cases of emergency; (4) is the lead siphon.

* The process has been patented in various countries.

The slag siphon (Fig. 2) is constructed entirely of refractories and has no cooling elements.

The electric settler has a 9-m³ capacity and serves for the initial filling of the fuming furnace and for settling the lead entrained by the slag. Moreover, the slag temperature in the electric settler is increased by 60–80°C. The slag leaves the electric settler through the overflow (6) and enters the fuming furnace

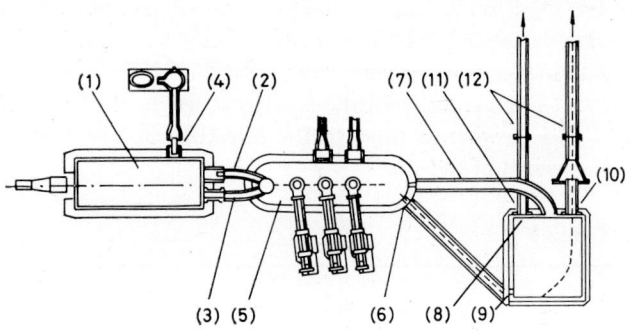

Fig. 1

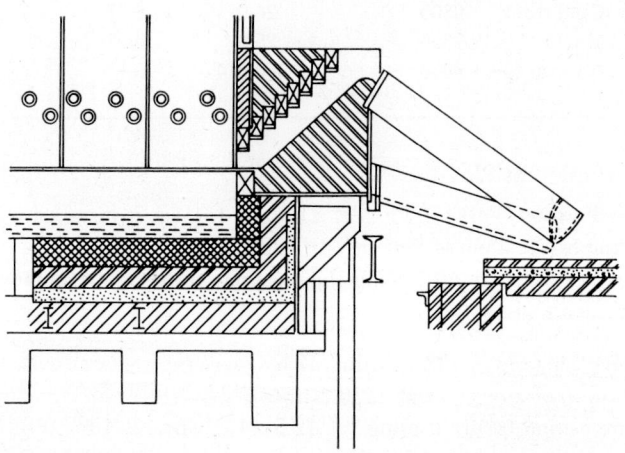

Fig. 2

through opening (9). Fumed slag runs out through overflow (10) into the chute for granulation. Chute (7) serves for the initial filling of the furnace. Outlet (11) serves for emergency discharge of the furnace. The slag passes through a chute (12) into a settling shaft.

Fig. 3 shows the design of a tuyère for preparing the air–mazut mixture. Mazut enters the nozzle (3) via (1) and (4) and is pulverized in the stream of incoming air from opening (2). The mixture enters the slag bath via pipe (5).

The ball-valve (6) enables cleaning of the nozzles and the tuyères to be carried out while work is in progress.

The mazut for the furnace, pumped at a rate of 5·4 m³/h and a pressure of 40 atm, has the following characteristics.*

C   86·8%
H_2 9·3%
N_2 0·5%
O_2 0·2%
S   3·5%
Viscosity (Engler)   Up to 11
Sulphur content   Up to 3·5%
Water   Not more than 2%
Freezing point   Not more than 15°C
Ignition temperature of vapour   Above 110°C
Heat capacity of dry mazut   9560 kcal/kg
Flash point   500–600°C
Ash   Not more than 0·3%
Specific density at 80°C   0·966

Oil injection

For atomization of the mazut, and its injection into the slag bath, a tuyère system has been designed as shown in Fig. 3. The system is notable for its simplicity of construction and ease of operation. The stem injecting the mazut is located

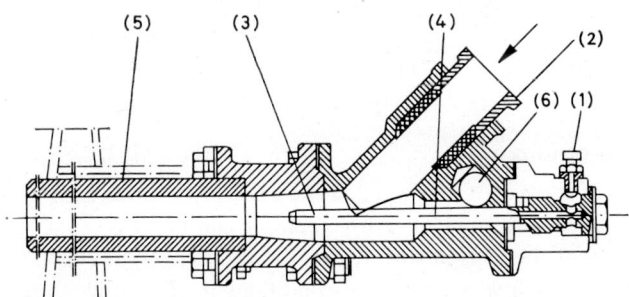

Fig. 3

along the tuyère axis, its special nozzle atomizing the oil very finely. The quality of the fuming process depends wholly on the performance of the nozzles. Unlike standard tuyères, in the Bulgarian system air enters through only one inlet, the concepts of primary and secondary air therefore being eliminated. Air is heated to 180–200°C—a shortcoming of the process; but the present air heater is to be modified in due course.

* These characteristics meet the Soviet Standard GOST 1502–52, brand 60. The nearest British and American equivalent oil is Shell 830.

A special testing stand has been designed for calibration and 'tuning' the nozzles. Any nozzle can be slightly drawn out of its tuyère and cleaned during operation. The temperature of the mazut gives an indication of the inlet of mazut in the tuyère. The special system of temperature controls maintains the mazut temperature in the range 65–80°C, which ensures adequate pulverization of the oil.

Following the successful use of mazut in the fuming installation, the coal-dust preparation section has been closed; a 30% saving in the labour force has been achieved; working conditions have been improved; tuyère and pipeline wear as a result of the abrasive action of the coal dust has been eliminated: conditions have been created for the complete automation of the fuel intake and the maintenance of a strictly determined mazut/air ratio; fuel costs per ton of slag have been reduced; and conditions have been created for the intensification of the process by decreasing the time of air blowing.[8]

The rate of fuel consumption (15·0–16·5%) obtained may well, by the introduction of air heating to 450–500°C and further modifications, drop below 12%.

By intermittent fuming with mazut the fuel consumption is in the range 11–12%.

Effect of sulphur content in mazut on fuming process

In September, 1966, an investigation was carried out into the effect of sulphur in the mazut on the zinc content in the fumed slag. It was found that sulphur in the mazut exerts a substantial influence on the composition of the slag. A series of tests was carried out with mazut containing up to 0·5% sulphur and with mazut up to 3·5% sulphur. When low-sulphur fuel was used, a substantial decrease of the zinc content in the slag was achieved.

A special unit is now being constructed adjoining the fuming installation for the low-sulphur mazut only. This will further increase the effectiveness of the process.

Combustion of mazut

Combustion of the mazut is effected at the expense of the oxygen in the air and through reactions with some oxygen-containing constituents of the slag. Assuming interaction of the oxygen with the mazut at a temperature of 1600°K and at 1 atm, which is in line with normal conditions in the furnace, mazut having the composition C 86·8%, H_2 9·3%, N 0·5%, O_2 0·2% and S 3·5%, and a consumption of air and mazut of 16 000 Nm^3/h and 2100 kg/h, respectively, with $\alpha = 0·71$, a gas mixture would be obtained having the composition CO_2 6·9%, CO 5·8%, H_2 2·1%, H_2O 6·1% and N 79%. This estimate is made ignoring the interaction between the mazut and slag oxygen. According to Haralampiev,[9] carbon in the solid state is not involved in this gas mixture.

Interaction of gas mixture with slag

The basic chemical reactions between the gases and the slag are

$$CO + H_2O \rightleftharpoons H_2 + CO_2 \tag{1}$$

$$ZnO + CO \rightleftharpoons Zn + CO_2 \tag{2}$$

In the gas phase, however, the following reaction takes place:

$$ZnO + H_2 \rightleftharpoons Zn + H_2O \tag{3}$$

We shall not consider the interaction of the gases with FeO, as it is known from thermodynamic analysis that at the conditions given (gas composition and temperature) this interaction does not take place.

As was stated above, in order to determine whether equilibrium is reached between the gas and slag, the partial pressure of the zinc vapour in the gas phase should be considered as the criterion. Making use of calculations by Haralampiev,[9] it is first necessary to provide data for the activity of ZnO in molten slags. Okounev and co-workers[3] stated that the activity coefficient of zinc oxide changes, and for a 3% zinc oxide in a slag we have

$$\gamma = 0.45$$

From data by Richards and Thorn[3] the ratio

$$\gamma_{ZnO} : \gamma_{FeO} = \sim 1.4$$

The ratio remains constant, CaO/SiO_2 changing from 0.12 to 0.74. With the composition of the Bulgarian slags this ratio is ~ 0.35–0.5.

Lakernik,[3] on the basis of experimental data, has formulated an equation for the dependence of the activity coefficient of FeO in a slag on its composition at 1600°K:

$$\gamma_{FeO} = 0.971 - 0.0145\% \ Fe + 0.634 \frac{CaO}{SiO_2}$$

By use of the Richards and Thorn ratio and our own value we obtain

$$\gamma_{ZnO} = 1.4 \times 0.727 = \sim 1$$

From calculated equilibrium constants and the composition of the gases Haralampiev[9] has worked out sets of equations. The equilibrium partial pressure of the zinc vapour for the reactions with CO_2 and H_2 is equalized when the gas phase satisfies the reaction

$$CO + H_2O \rightleftharpoons CO_2 + H_2$$

The bases of the assumption of a reaction determining the equilibrium are that (1) the reaction is homogeneous and proceeds in a very turbulent environment: diffusional limitations are not, therefore, to be expected; and (2) the temperatures at which these processes take place are sufficiently high for any kinetic restrictions to be absent. It can therefore be concluded that the equilibrium of this reaction is established much more rapidly than that of the other two.

In his numerical solutions Haralampiev[9] assumed a zinc oxide content in the slag of 3%. By various transformations and substitutions he arrived at the equation

$$x + \frac{M \cdot x}{k_3 a(x+Q)+x} + \frac{N \cdot x}{k_2 a(x+Q)+x} = P$$

where x = moles of zinc vapour passing into the gas phase per unit time as a result of the reduction with CO and H_2, M = moles of hydrogen introduced into the system with the mazut per unit time, N = moles of carbon introduced into the system with the mazut per unit time, k_2 and k_3 are equilibrium constants of the reactions of the zinc oxide in the slag with carbon oxide and hydrogen, respectively, a is activity (thermodynamic concentration) of the zinc oxide in the slag, Q = moles of hydrogen, carbon and nitrogen blown with the mazut in unit of time and P = moles of carbon dioxide and hydrogen in the initial gas mixture (before interaction with the slag).

The equation thus deduced may be solved for conditions given in each particular case, different numerical solutions being reached for each of the values of the respective equilibrium constant and activity coefficient of zinc oxide. It should be mentioned that in presenting the results certain logical considerations have been taken into account, such as excluding negative roots, etc. It has been assumed that the activity of the zinc oxide in the slag towards carbon dioxide and hydrogen is the same and that in the gas phase the partial pressure of the zinc is common for both reactions.

In taking into consideration the amount of the gases obtained by vaporization of 15–16·5% mazut with 1160–1230 Nm^3 of air per ton of slag and the reactions with the slag, a partial pressure is reached in the gas mixture of 1·5–1·8% by volume. Comparison with the results obtained by calculation shows that the gases in the best case contain only 50% of the zinc theoretically possible. This justifies the belief that the assumption of the non-existence of diffusional restrictions is not correct, that an equilibrium in the fuming process is not reached and that in the process there exist conditions for improving various indices. These improvements should be sought in a new equipment design for the process and in optimizing the diffusion and kinetic factors.

To elucidate some pertinent factors, in the period 2–5 February, 1970, some tests were conducted on the industrial scale on intermittent fuming with mazut. The average results of the tests are given in Table 2.

By increasing the per-hour expenditure of mazut and air, the zinc in the fumed slag is decreased from 2·32 to 1·10%. Moreover, the specific expenditures of air and mazut (per ton of slag) are decreased—again confirming the fact that in the process there exist diffusional restrictions in the internal diffusion zone. Since Kellogg has very carefully expressed his opinion on the subject of equilibrium,[5] and Gnatovskii et al.[6] have retreated from their categorical statement that equilibrium is reached, it may be said that the fuming process can be considered as a typical mass-transfer process, obeying the laws of mass transfer.

In December, 1970, the fuming installation was completely reconstructed and modernized. Of special importance was the fact that the size of the furnace was reduced from 8·9 to 5·85 m^2. The expenditures of air and of mazut, however,

Table 2

Test no.	Time of blowing, min	Fumed slag Lead, %	Fumed slag Zinc, %	Specific air, Nm^3/ton	Specific mazut, %	Amount of slag in furnace, t	Coefficient of expenditure of air, α
1	100	0·16	2·32	935	12	25	0·70
2	85	0·15	1·10	910	11·6	25	0·75
3	100	0·14	0·57	1070	11·3	25	0·70

were retained, remaining the same for the reduced furnace size. The results of these modifications, under continuous fuming conditions, can be seen in Table 3. There are considerable overall improvements.

Future trends

Undoubtedly, one of the major means of improving the fuming process arises from an increase in the temperature of the air blown to 450–600°C. The use of cheap oxygen and enrichment of the air blown are also desirable.

The quantity of energy introduced has a marked beneficial effect, and it has a direct relation to the rate of blowing. Rates of 180–200 m/sec are favourable.

Table 3

Period	Specific air, Nm^3/ton	Specific mazut, %	Zinc in the fumed slag, %	Specific capacity of furnace, t/m^2/24 h	Furnace capacity per hour, t	Furnace capacity per day, t	Number of tuyères
June–Aug., 1970	1600	18·8	2·61	27	10	240	28
Jan.–Feb., 1970	1230	15·7	2·04	53·3	13	312	22

What remains now is to verify the effect of the rate of air blown in the range 200–300 m/sec, as at this point there are opportunities for decreasing the specific expenditures of mazut and air.

The use of mazut with a sulphur content below 1% is also potentially beneficial for continuous and periodic fuming. The use of mazut in periodic fuming might well shorten the blowing time by 10–15%. Likewise, the use of low-sulphur mazut would reduce blowing time by another 10–15 per cent. In reducing the time of blowing alone, there is a possible saving of 20–30%.

Important to the further improvement of the fuming process is the equipment layout. The present installations are not entirely satisfactory and many improvements should be sought here. Research and experimental investigations recently carried out will lead to significant new developments in the fuming process.

Conclusions

No attempt has been made to consider and examine all the problems that relate to fuming; rather, some aspects of fuming by mazut have been reviewed. The paper reflects a part of the practice of the fuming installation in Plovdiv. It is hoped to present further data in the near future as a result of the extensive programme of research now in progress.

The advantages of continuous fuming with mazut over the classical method of fuming are very clear. As far as intermittent fuming with mazut is concerned, it can be added very easily to any existing fuming installation. Change to a continuous process, however, requires the cascade arrangement of the aggregates. Continuous fuming with mazut provides a high degree of mechanization and automation, simplifies maintenance and permits considerable economies to be made.

References

1. KOSTELOV V. V. VERNER B. F. AND BAIMAKOV A. YU. Fuming process in non-ferrous metallurgy. *Trudy Proek. Nauch.-Issledovatel. Inst. Gipronikel* no. 9 1961, 116 p. (Russian text)
2. RALSTON O. C. FOWLER M. G. AND KUZELL C. R. Recovering zinc from copper smelter products. *Engng Min. J.*, **136,** April 1935, 167–9.
3. OKOUNEV A. I. KOSTIANOVSKII I. A. AND DONCHENKO P. A. *Slag fuming* (Moscow: Metallurgia, 1966), 259 p. (Russian text)
4. BELL R. C. TURNER G. H. AND PETERS E. Fuming of zinc from lead blast furnace slag. *J. Metals, N.Y.*, **7,** 1955, 472–7.
5. KELLOGG H. H. A new look at slag fuming. *Engng Min. J.*, **158,** March 1957, 90–2.
6. GNATOVSKII E. S. *et al.* Improving the slag fuming process. *Tsvet. Metally, Mosk.,* **43,** no. 5 1970, 27–30. (Russian text)
7. YANEV Y. Continuous fuming of lead slags with mazut at NFM Works 'D. Blagoev', Plovdiv. Report presented at the Exposition of Bulgarian Inventions, Moscow, 1969.
8. ABRASHEV G. I. Improvement of the fuming of lead slags. Report presented at Conference on processing of slags in non-ferrous metallurgy, Moscow, 1967.
9. HARALAMPIEV G. A. On some basic processes in fuming with mazut. Report presented at the Second National Conference on non-ferrous metallurgy, Plovdiv, 1970.

Roasting of flotation pyrite in a fluidized bed: residence times and kinetics

Tor Lindstad Siv. ing.

SINTEF (The Engineering Research Foundation), Technical University of Norway, Trondheim, Norway

622.784:622.765.4:622.7–366.121

Synopsis
Most fundamental work on fluidization has been done on fairly uniformly sized particles. Metallurgical fluidization processes, however, usually deal with particles of a wide size distribution.

In the work described flotation pyrite is roasted in a continuous bench-scale fluidization reactor. The gas velocity is so high that the greater part of the particles from the feed are elutriated from the bed and recovered in the cyclones: the bed therefore consists of coarser particles than the feed.

Roasting experiments have been carried out at varying gas velocity, feed rate of pyrite, air/pyrite ratio, bed height and temperature and for different types of flotation pyrites (with different size distribution and impurity contents). The cyclone product, as well as the bed material, is fractionated by test sieving. The mean residence times in the bed are determined for each fraction.

If, at a chosen gas velocity, the diameter of the greatest particle that can be entrained is defined as d_e, particles smaller than d_e have a significant mean residence time (0·5–10 min) in the bed. The mean residence time of such particles is strongly affected by gas velocity, but little affected by any of the other operational parameters. The air/pyrite ratio does not seem to have any direct influence on the mean residence times, but these are somewhat shorter for roasting to magnetite than to hematite, probably due to interparticle forces.

Total sulphur, sulphide sulphur and sulphate sulphur are determined for each particle size fraction. Diagrams of the percentage of sulphide sulphur and of sulphate sulphur are drawn as functions of residence time and with particle size range, temperature, air/pyrite ratio and type of pyrite as parameters. The type of rate-controlling mechanism is discussed.

The usefulness of the results with regard to the full-scale roaster is considered.

Introduction

Although prices of sulphur are very low at the present time, it is thought that pyrite-based sulphuric acid plants will still be economic in the future, especially in pyrite-producing countries. The value of pyrites depends on the quality of the pyrite cinder, which is used as a raw material for iron production. A large amount of pyrites is produced by gravity concentration. The product contains all the metal sulphides present in the ore. To be acceptable for iron production, compounds of copper, zinc and other heavy metals must be extracted from the cinder: this is done by chloridizing roasting, followed by leaching.

By means of differential flotation it is possible to produce a pyrite concentrate containing 0·05–0·1% Cu, 0·2–0·4% Zn, 0·02–0·05% Pb and 3–5% gangue minerals. For the sake of brevity we shall call such a pyrite concentrate a flotation pyrite. Improved techniques enable the differential flotation of ores that could not previously be treated in such a way. These techniques involve milling the crushed ore to very fine particles—70% of the particles finer than 325 mesh is not unusual in modern flotation practice. The amount of metal impurities in the cinder, obtained by roasting a flotation pyrite, will be relatively low. Nevertheless, it will often pay to purify this cinder too, which can be done by chlorination.

At present roasting of flotation pyrites in a fluidized bed is the main process used in Norway and Sweden to produce SO_2 for use in sulphuric acid plants.

Published information on pyrite roasting is, in the main, restricted to a coarser spectrum of particles than that of flotation pyrite; moreover, the range of particle size examined is frequently quite narrow. Although such experiments have provided important information on the chemistry of the roasting process, they are not easily applied in the design of an industrial roaster for a flotation pyrite of a wide particle size range. A fluidized bed of particles of mixed sizes behaves differently from a bed of single- or narrow-sized particles. In the roasting of fine flotation pyrites most of the feed is small enough to be elutriated from the bed, and the bed will consist of the coarser particles. Even in this case, however, the fine particles will have a measurable residence time in the bed.

The first aim of the experiments described was to measure the concentration of the various particle size fractions in the bed and calculate the mean residence time in the bed of each size fraction. The second aim was to find a relation between the degree of roasting, as measured by the content of sulphide and sulphate sulphur, and the mean residence time for each particle size fraction.

Bubbling-bed model

A smooth or particulate fluidization is typical for the liquid–solid system, whereas bubbling or aggregative fluidization is typical for the gas–solid system. In analysing the results obtained in the present work, the bubbling-bed model has been chosen for interpretation. Here the bed is considered as a two-phase system consisting of a particulate (emulsion) phase, in which the gas velocity is equal to that at minimum fluidizing conditions, and a bubble phase, which carries all gas in excess of the gas velocity at minimum fluidization. An outline of the bubbling-bed model is given in Appendix 1.

Kinetics

The reaction mechanism depends on the temperature. In the present work the temperature range 700–950°C is of main interest. The reactions that take place are

$$FeS_2 \rightarrow FeS_{1+x}+S_2$$
$$S_2+O_2 \rightarrow SO_2$$
$$FeS_{1+x}+O_2 \rightarrow Fe_3O_4+SO_2$$
$$SO_2+O_2 \rightarrow SO_3$$
$$Fe_3O_4+O_2 \rightarrow Fe_2O_3$$

Previous investigations on roasting flotation pyrites in a fluidized bed by Schytil,[1] Malets[2] and Safiullin[3] agree that gas diffusion is the rate-controlling factor.

Experimental procedure

Fig. 1 shows a sketch of the roasting apparatus. Certain features of this design have been taken from Vian and Romero.[4]

The reactor is made of heat-resistant steel and is surrounded by a furnace (not shown in Fig. 1). The furnace is divided at mid-height into two compartments. Propane burners are used in the furnace, one in the bottom of each compartment. The outside walls of the furnace, as well as the division between the compartments, are built of bricks.

A screw, operating at a constant speed (rev/min) for a given setting, provides the feed of pyrite to the reactor. A small stream of nitrogen into the feed tube, about 1% of the air stream supplied to the roaster, prevents clogging. Overflow tubes from the bed are placed 29 and 57 cm above the distributor plate. These tubes and the tube from the cyclone are provided with valves. Erlenmeyer flasks of glass, connected to the tubes by rubber stoppers, are used as receivers.

The air enters the bed through a 3-cm thick distributor plate made from olivine sand ($-10 +25$ mesh) and water-glass hardened with CO_2 at room temperature. This plate is placed on a stainless steel plate with holes 2 mm in diameter. The roasting gas goes from the top of the reactor to a cyclone. From the cyclone a continuous gas stream is branched off to a SO_2 meter, which works on the principle of measuring the heat conductivity of the gas mixture.

The pressure drop through distributor plate and bed, and through the whole system, is measured by U-type manometers. The temperature is measured at four points in the reactor with thermocouples, the measurements being recorded on a multi-channel potentiometric recorder.

At the start of an experiment, when sufficient bed material is present in the reactor, the air stream and heating are switched on. When the temperature in the bed has reached about 600°C, the feeding of pyrite starts. The feed variator and the air valve are set to the desired feed rate and air-flow rate, and the burners are adjusted to give the desired temperatures in the bed and in the compartment above—usually, these temperatures are identical. At constant feed and air-flow rate the SO_2 meter will, after some time, show a constant SO_2 content in the gas. The test period starts when samples taken intermittently from the bed show

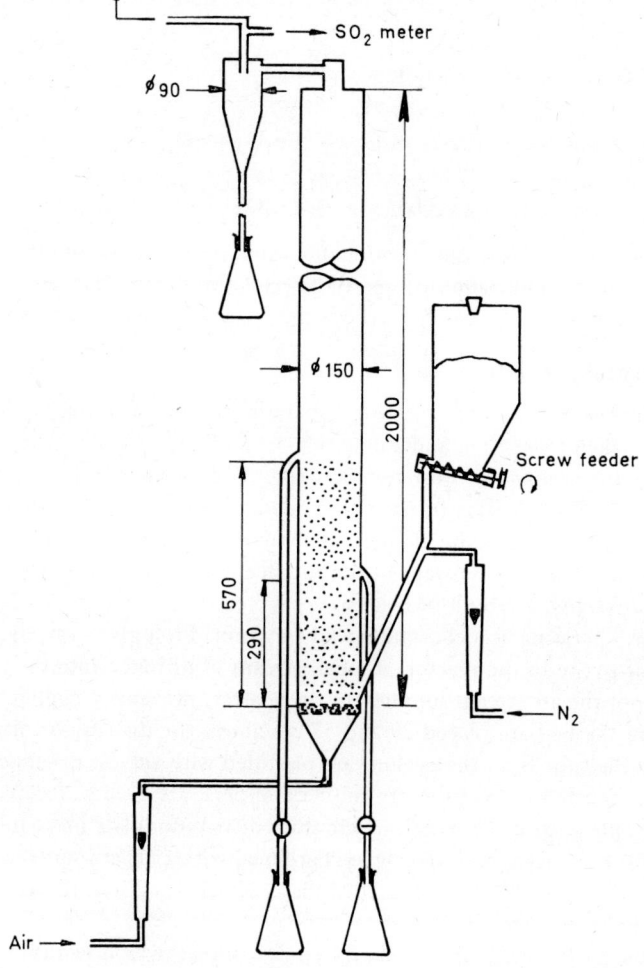

Fig. 1 Roasting apparatus

that a reasonably constant particle size distribution has been obtained.

The test period usually lasts $\frac{1}{2}$–1 h. All material separated in the cyclone or entering the overflow during the test period is collected in the receivers. When operating at 57-cm bed height, samples of the bed are taken intermittently by opening the 29-cm overflow valve. When operating at 29-cm bed height, a sample of the bed can be obtained by taking out the whole bed after the experiment. Any material collected in the cyclone after the feeding has been stopped belongs to the bed material.

The cyclone material, overflow material and bed material are split to give average samples of each, the samples being fractionated by sieving. Total sulphur and sulphide sulphur are determined in the samples before fractionation and, in most of the sieve fractions, by means of the combustion method, but sulphide sulphur after sulphate sulphur has been leached out with water. The sulphate sulphur is obtained by difference. The content of magnetite is measured by a magnetic method. The results of all analyses are given in weight per cent.

Flotation pyrites

Roasting experiments have been performed on two different Norwegian flotation pyrites (*A* and *B*). Fig. 2 shows the particle size distribution of these pyrites.

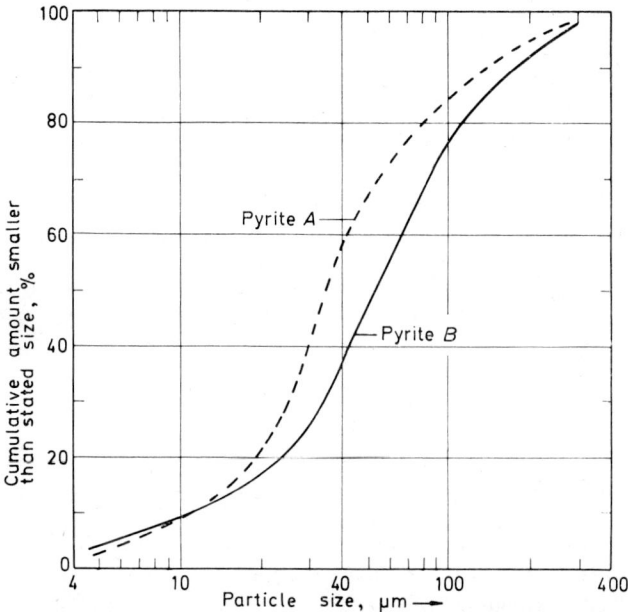

Fig. 2   Particle size distribution for pyrites

Pyrite *B* came fresh from the flotation process, whereas *A* had been stored for about two years after mining and flotation. It will be seen from Table 1 that sulphate has been formed in this pyrite during the storing period.

Experimental results*

Table 2 summarizes the experimental conditions for the 16 runs. The temperature was held at about 800°C, except for the last four runs, when it was 900°C. In most cases the percentage of stoichiometric air (for the formation of Fe_2O_3, CuO, ZnO and SO_2) was about 125. Three different gas velocities were tried in these runs, about 0·45, 0·9 and 1·4 m/sec. Runs 9 and 10 were conducted at 280 and 150% of stoichiometric air to explore the effect of varying the feed rate

---

* Definitions of the symbols used in this paper appear on pages 358–9.

Table 1   Analysis of flotation pyrites*

%	Pyrite A	Pyrite A, soluble in water	Pyrite B
S_{total}	50·3	0·87	48·1
Fe	44·3	0·64	43·7
Cu	0·19	0·09	0·10
Zn	0·30	0·18	0·42
Pb	0·04		0·14
Ca	0·45	0·43	0·05
Mg	0·007		0·16
SiO_2	0·57		3·4

* All results are reported on a water-free basis and in weight per cent. The pyrite fed into the reactor held 1·5% H_2O *(A)* and 0·9% H_2O *(B)*.

at a constant gas velocity. Runs 15 and 16 were conducted with less than 100% of stoichiometric air, giving a large percentage of magnetite in the cinder.

It appears that runs 1 and 5, 2 and 6, 3 and 7 and 4 and 8 are parallel except for the type of pyrite. Runs 1 and 3, 2 and 4, 5 and 7 and 6 and 8 are parallel but for the bed height.

Size distribution of bed and cyclone material

Preliminary experiments have shown that the particle size distribution in samples drawn through the 29-cm overflow valve, when operating at 57-cm bed height, is equal, within 10%, to that determined on samples split from the total amount of bed material.

Fig. 3 presents a Schytil diagram[1] for the particles when roasting to hematite at 800°C. The line Fr_{mf} represents the conditions at minimum fluidization, whereas the line Fr_e represents the minimum conditions for entrainment above the transport disengaging height. The diameter of the biggest spherical particle that can be entrained at a given gas velocity u_o is termed d_e.

So far, the effect of radial and axial velocity distribution for the gas flow above the bed has not been discussed. These quantities are related to the Reynolds numbers (Re_r), presented in Table 3 for the experimental reactor (0·15-m diameter) and for an industrial unit of 6-m diameter for comparison. The distance after inflow where the transition to laminar flow is practically complete is calculated by an equation quoted by Prandtl.[5]

$$L = 0·03 \, D_r Re_r \tag{1}$$

With the large reactor the Reynolds numbers are definitely in the turbulent-flow region, and the time-averaged gas velocity is almost constant across the

Table 2 Summary of experimental conditions

Run no.	Type of pyrite	Feed rate, kg/h	Feed rate per unit area, kg/m² h	Percentage of stoichiometric air, %	Mean temperature, °C In bed	Mean temperature, °C Above bed	u_o, m/sec	Bed Height, m	Weight, kg
1	A	2·85	156	122	805	805	0·47	0·57	6·6
2	A	5·6	300	123	805	780	0·94	0·57	4·9
3	A	2·82	153	123	810	815	0·47	0·29	3·6
4	A	5·6	300	123	800	810	0·94	0·29	2·5
5	B	2·70	146	123	820	810	0·43	0·57	6·6
6	B	5·6	300	123	795	790	0·90	0·57	4·9
7	B	2·70	146	123	820	805	0·43	0·29	3·6
8	B	5·6	300	123	800	790	0·90	0·29	2·5
9	B	2·46	133	276	805	795	0·90	0·57	5·9
10	B	4·6	250	147	800	795	0·90	0·57	6·3
11	B	8·9	480	123	810	805	1·42	0·57	4·6
12	B	8·9	480	123	805	600	1·42	0·57	4·2
13	B	5·4	290	126	905	900	0·97	0·57	4·9
14	B	8·3	450	130	905	905	1·56	0·57	3·2
15	B	8·3	450	97	900	900	1·17	0·57	3·9
16	B	5·7	310	96	905	910	0·78	0·57	5·1

reactor. The d_e read from the Schytil diagram (Fig. 3) will represent the largest spherical particle that can be entrained (if the freeboard is sufficiently high, see later).

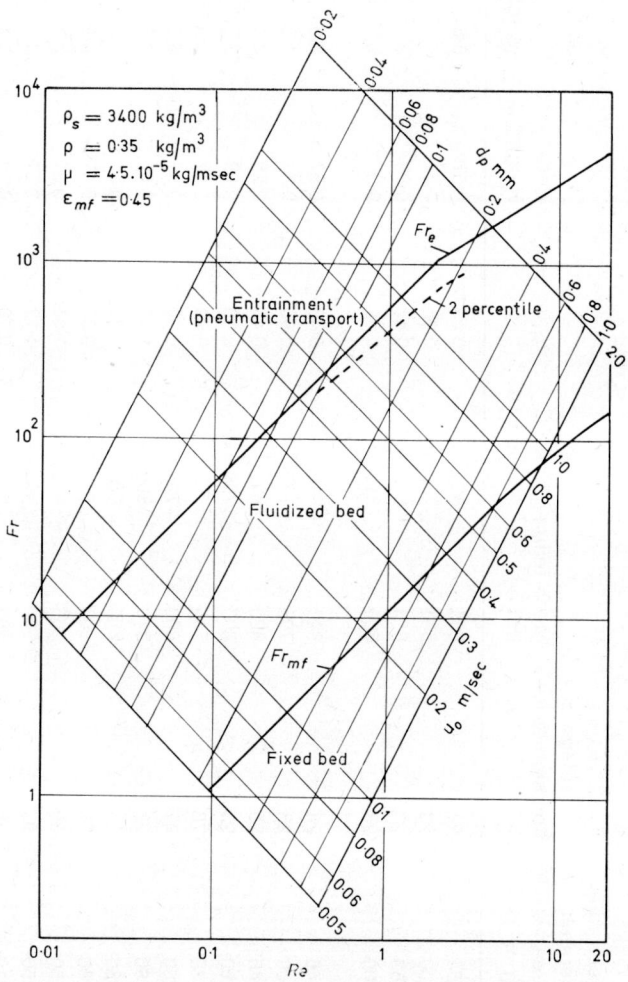

Fig. 3 Schytil diagram for roasting at 800°C

In the case of the reactor used in the present experiments the Reynolds numbers lie in the region of laminar flow ($Re_r < 2000$). At laminar flow there is a parabolic velocity distribution across the reactor, the velocity in the axis being twice the average velocity. The freeboard over the reactor is 1·4 or 1·7 m, and it appears that we are not far from laminar flow at the top of the reactor at $u_o = 0·45$ m/sec. But at the higher velocities tried (0·9 and 1·4 m/sec) the flow is far from laminar, even at the top of the reactor.

Table 3 Reynolds number and transition lengths _(L)_ for gas flow in 0·15- and 6-m diameter reactors: $\rho = 0·35$ kg/m³; $\mu = 0·45$ kg/m sec

	$D_r = 0·15$ m		$D_r = 6$ m
u_o, m/sec	Re_r	L, m	Re_r
0·45	525	2·4	$2·1 \times 10^4$
0·9	1050	4·7	$4·2 \times 10^4$
1·4	1600	7·2	$6·5 \times 10^4$

Two factors which will probably lengthen the transition distance are not discussed further—the time variation of gas velocity, because of the bursting bubbles, and the influence of the particles entrained on the gas flow. It is likely, however, that there is a practical velocity distribution across the reactor with a maximum at the axis. The result of this is that even spherical particles greater than d_e can be entrained. It is assumed that the freeboard height is greater than the transport disengaging height (see later).

In the experiments it was found that the cyclone material held a few per cent of material greater than d_e. About 2% of the cyclone material is greater and 98% smaller than the dotted line (2 percentile) in Fig. 3. This result is as could be expected, because of the higher gas velocity in the centre of the reactor and because the pyrite particles are not spherical.

The bed material contained 1–4% of material small enough to be elutriated eventually.

Mean residence time

The mean residence time in the bed has been calculated for all the experimental runs. By use of the symbols indicated in Fig. 4, the mean residence time in the bed for a fraction n (with mean particle size d_p) is given by

$$\bar{t}(d_p) = \frac{W x_{w,n}}{F_o x_{F_o,n}} \tag{2}$$

where $x_{w,n}$ is weight per cent of sieve fraction n in the bed material and $x_{F_o,n}$ is weight per cent of sieve fraction n in the feed. The equation assumes that the feed rate F_o is expressed as the rate of pyrite cinder equivalent to the pyrite feed rate. The following example shows how the equation is used.

EXAMPLE: CALCULATION OF MEAN RESIDENCE TIME FOR SIEVE FRACTION 44–74 μm IN RUN 3

Feed rate of pyrite, 2·82 kg/h
$F_o = 1·92$ kg/h (pyrite cinder)

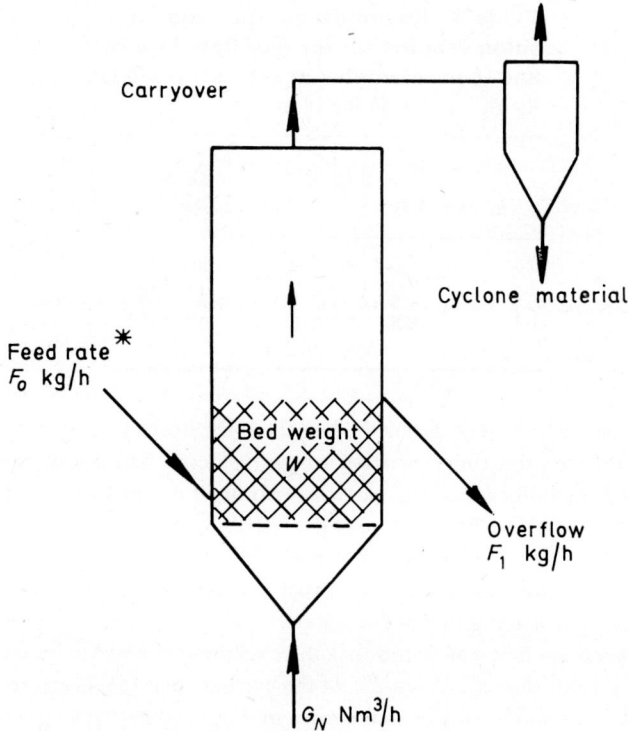

Carryover

Cyclone material

Feed rate *
F_0 kg/h

Bed weight
W

Overflow
F_1 kg/h

G_N Nm³/h

* Expressed as kg pyrite cinder/h

Fig. 4 Flowsheet of fluidized-bed system

$x_{Fo}, 44\text{–}74\,\mu m = 15\cdot1\%$
$W = 3\cdot6\,\text{kg}$
$x_W, 44\text{–}74\,\mu m = 0\cdot8\%$

$$\bar{t}\,(57\,\mu m) = \frac{(3\cdot6\,\text{kg})\,(0\cdot8)}{(1\cdot92\,\text{kg/h})\,(15\cdot1)}\,(60\,\text{min/h}) = 6\cdot0\,\text{min}$$

The error in the calculated mean residence time is estimated to be within 20%.

In Fig. 5 mean residence time, $\bar{t}(d_p)$, is plotted against particle size, d_p. Curves are drawn to show the relation between d_p and $\bar{t}(d_p)$ at different gas velocities (or feed rates) and bed heights. On the three curves drawn for the different gas velocities, d_e (the diameter of the largest spherical particle that can be entrained at a given gas velocity) taken from Fig. 3 is plotted, and a curve is drawn between the three points that result. The particle sizes to the left of this curve will mainly report to the cyclone, whereas the particle sizes to the right will report mainly to the overflow flask.

Fig. 5 shows that the particles in the cyclone material have a considerable residence time in the bed before they are elutriated. The mean residence time is

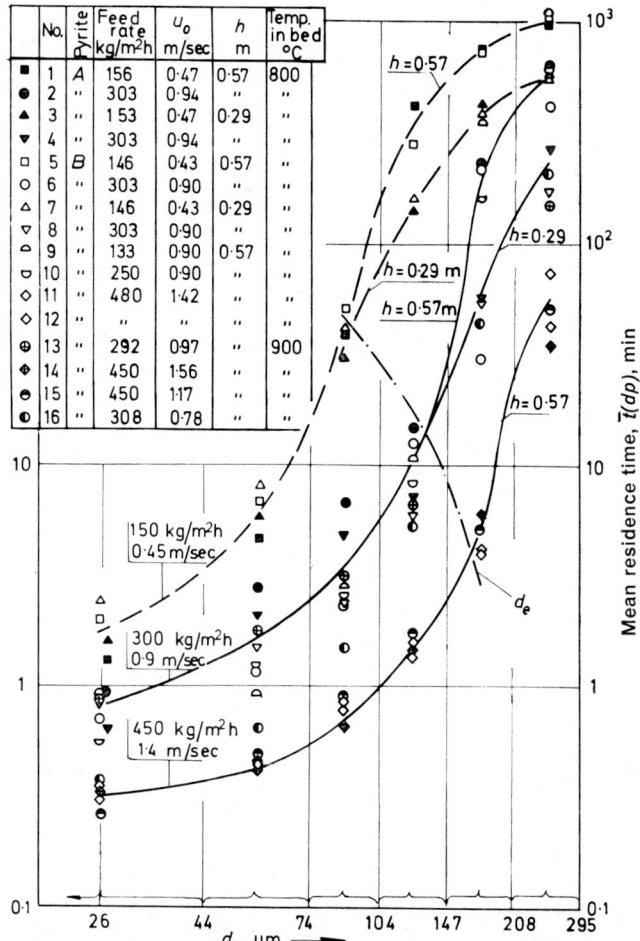

	No.	Pyrite	Feed rate kg/m²h	u_0 m/sec	h m	Temp. in bed °C
■	1	A	156	0·47	0·57	800
●	2	''	303	0·94	''	''
▲	3	''	153	0·47	0·29	''
▼	4	''	303	0·94	''	''
□	5	B	146	0·43	0·57	''
○	6	''	303	0·90	''	''
△	7	''	146	0·43	0·29	''
▽	8	''	303	0·90	''	''
⌂	9	''	133	0·90	0·57	''
⊽	10	''	250	0·90	''	''
◇	11	''	480	1·42	''	''
◇	12	''	''	''	''	''
⊕	13	''	292	0·97	''	900
◆	14	''	450	1·56	''	''
◉	15	''	450	1·17	''	''
◖	16	''	308	0·78	''	''

Fig. 5 Mean residence time in bed versus particle size

0·5–2 min, depending on the gas velocity, for the sieve fraction $< 44\ \mu m$, and about 4–40 min for particles of size d_e. At first sight this result is surprising, since particles of diameter less than d_e would not be expected to stay for more than a few seconds.

One explanation for the relatively long residence times observed could be interparticle forces, which make the particle behave more or less as agglomerates. Baerns[6] fluidized fine-grained particles of various materials and observed a minimum fluidization velocity many times greater than the calculated value from the ordinary equations (used, for example, in the construction of Fig. 3). As an example, aluminium oxide of a particle size range 6–34 μm (95 weight % of particles within this range) first fluidized at a velocity about 200 times the calculated minimum fluidization velocity. Baerns explained his results by

M

interparticle forces, which, for fine particles, can be greater than gravitational forces. The ordinary equations for the calculation of minimum fluidization velocity take gravitational and drag forces into account, but not interparticle forces. No attempt has been made in the present work to measure interparticle forces at roasting temperatures.

Some experiments have been made, however, in fluidizing pyrite cinder at 800°C in air at low gas velocities. It was, for instance, not possible to fluidize a pyrite cinder of about $75\% - 44$ μm with gas velocities below 10 cm/sec, even if this cinder, theoretically, should have a minimum fluidization velocity about 0·1 cm/sec. Somewhat coarser pyrite cinders, containing about $50\% - 44$ μm, could be fluidized at velocities down to 5 cm/sec, whereas the theoretical minimum fluidization velocity is about 0·3 cm/sec. In these experiments the bed consisted of more than 50% of particles smaller than d_e. These observations confirm that interparticle forces have an appreciable effect on the fluidization of fine-grained pyrite cinder. Furthermore, residence times about 30 min have been observed for the fraction below 44 μm at a gas velocity 0·3 m/sec, whereas it is about 2 min at 0·45 m/sec. This great difference between 0·3 and 0·45 m/sec indicates that the size of the agglomerates is around 60–80 μm (they are entrained at these velocities).

It is interesting, in this connexion, to note that the roasting was considerably worse at 0·3 than at 0·45 m/sec with the same percentage air supply. As is known from previous investigations, and shown in the present paper, combustion rate decreases with increasing particle size. These results indicate that the bed acts as if the particle sizes were much greater at a gas velocity of 0·3 m/sec than at 0·45 m/sec.

Nevertheless, the main explanation for the long residence times, both at low (10–30 cm/sec) and at high velocities (45–150 cm/sec), should be sought in the behaviour of the gas–solid bed, as explained by the bubbling-bed model. Calculations on this basis are shown in Appendix 2. Run 5 has been chosen as an example because the gas velocity is low in this case (0·43 m/sec). The calculation indicates that the volume fraction of bubbles in the bed is about 0·5, that the absolute rise velocity of bubbles (u_b) is 0·82 m/sec and that the relative velocity (u_e) between upward-percolating emulsion gas and downward-flowing solid is $-0·14$ m/sec. These calculations are not thought to give a complete description of the system. This is due to several factors: the values used for some of the variables are estimates, the bubbling-bed model is presently not developed to give quantitatively correct results, and it is uncertain how far the model can be applied to beds of a wide range of particle sizes, especially when some of the particles will eventually be elutriated.

The results of the calculation are, nevertheless, of interest—in particular, that u_e certainly is negative, which means that the gas flows downward in the emulsion phase. Since a run with the lowest gas velocity was chosen in the example, it follows that the direction of the gas flow in the emulsion phase is downward in all the runs. Consequently, particles can only be entrained in the gas stream and leave the bed by the gas stream by means of the bubbles. In the present paper entrainment refers to the removal of solids from the bed by the fluidizing gas. Some of these are particles greater than d_e and they will fall again at some height above the bed. Above a certain height in the bed, called the transport disengaging height, the entrainment is constant, and the gas stream only contains particles smaller than d_e. Elutriation refers to the removal of fines (particles smaller than d_e) from the bed. The elutriation rate decreases some-what with increasing freeboard above the bed. The reason for this is that part of the fines leaving the bed are probably agglomerates being entrained by the gas bubbles, and these agglomerates will tend to fall down again as such. Also, a fine particle going upwards can be caused to reverse its direction by the impact of a larger particle falling downwards. There seem to be two possible causes for the particles being entrained by the bubbles. The first is associated with the wake following the bubble when the bubble bursts on top of the bed: this wake will be ejected upwards from the bed at a starting velocity u_b which is higher than the gas velocity u_o above the bed. In run 5 u_b was calculated as 0·82 m/sec and u_o was 0·43 m/sec. Secondly, it is assumed that the 'roof' over the bubble will be ejected when the bubble bursts. The energy for this can be produced by the retardation of the bubbles when they burst. Which of the proposed mechanisms will pre-dominate cannot be inferred; at any rate, however, only particles in contact with the bubbles can be entrained. On these grounds the observed mean residence times of 0·5–10 min for the fines appear reasonable.

So far, the results have been discussed in a rather general way. The effect of the parameters, freeboard (H), bed diameter, gas velocity (u_o), feed rate per unit area, bed height (h), temperature (t), type of roasting (to hematite or to magne-tite) and type of pyrite used, is now discussed. It is assumed, first, that the type of pyrite used has no effect on the elutriation of a given sieve fraction, as long as flotation pyrites are used. The validity of this assumption is discussed later.

Effect of freeboard on mean residence times

The reactor, in the present experiments, was constructed with a freeboard height of 1·4 m (1·7 m when operating at the lower bed height), which was thought to be higher than the transport disengaging height (TDH). Experiments were conducted to confirm this. Pyrite cinder was fluidized in air at 700°C, and an-other pyrite cinder, with approximately the same particle size distribution as pyrites A and B, was fed into the reactor. In these experiments the freeboard could be shortened by putting a circular plate (148-mm diameter), with a 40-mm diameter outlet tube leading to the cyclone, into the reactor, freeboard heights of 0·55, 0·98 and 1·4 m being obtained. The amount of material per minute collected by the cyclone was plotted against the freeboard for each gas velocity, and the TDH is then the height where this amount becomes independent of the freeboard. The results obtained (Table 4) show that the freeboard was suffi-ciently high in the roasting experiments with gas velocities up to 1·17 m/sec (run 15).

Table 4 TDH for pyrite cinder in 0·15-m reactor with air at 700°C

u_o, m/sec	TDH, m
0·45	0·7
0·9	1·2
1·3	1·5 (by extrapolation)

Feed rate, 3·3 kg/h pyrite cinder (45% <44 μm; 30% 44–74 μm; 15% 74–104 μm; 10% >104 μm).

In runs 11, 12 and 14, with gas velocities of 1·42–1·56 m/sec, the TDH is somewhat higher (about 1·6 m) than the freeboard. This means that particles greater than d_e are entrained in the gas leaving the reactor. This applies especially to particles only a little greater than d_e. For the 147–208 μm fraction the observed mean residence time is probably 20–40% less than the time that could be expected in a bed with TDH equal to 1·6 m. For the fractions smaller than 147 μm the effect on the mean residence time of the freeboard being a little shorter than the TDH is negligible.

Effect of bed diameter on mean residence times

The effect of varying the bed diameter has not been studied. When operating with the top of the reactor removed, it was observed that the gas bubbles erupting were smaller than the bed diameter—they were 5–10 cm in diameter.

Effect of feed rate per unit area on mean residence times

Table 5 shows that for particles smaller than about 150 μm (or smaller than d_e) the mean residence time is independent of the feed rate per unit area. As was mentioned previously, the mean residence times are determined for a test period that starts when samples taken intermittently from the bed show that a reasonably constant particle size distribution has been obtained. Neglecting the small amounts of fines in the overflow, the amount of fines carried off with the gas equals the amount of fines in the feed:

$$u_o A_t \alpha (1 - \varepsilon_{mf}) \rho_s x_{wk,\text{fines}} = F_o x_{Fo,\text{fines}} \qquad (3)$$

where A_t is cross-sectional area of bed, α is ratio of wake volume to bubble volume, ρ_s is density of solids, and $x_{Fo,\text{fines}}$ and $x_{wk,\text{fines}}$ are the percentages of material smaller than d_e in the feed and in the wake, respectively. The void fraction of the emulsion phase (including the wake) is equal to ε_{mf}. This equation assumes that the amount of solids in the bubbles is negligible compared with the solids in the wake. For all the present experiments α, ε_{mf} and ρ_s are constant or almost constant, and equation 3 can then be written

Table 5   Mean residence time at varying feed rate per unit area but constant gas velocity ($u_o \simeq 0\cdot9$ m/sec), bed height ($h = 0\cdot57$ m), temperature ($t \simeq 800°C$) and roasting to hematite

Run no.	Feed rate per unit area, kg/m² h	$\bar{t}(d_p)$, min for fraction, μm					
		<44	44–74	74–104	104–147	147–208	208–295
9	133	0·9	0·9	2·8	11	350	1080
10	250	0·6	1·3	2·6	9	170	630
2	303	0·7	1·2	2·3	13	210	420

$$A_t u_o \gamma x_{wk,fines} = F_o x_{Fo,fines} \tag{4}$$

where

$$\gamma = \alpha(1 - \varepsilon_{mf})\rho_s \tag{5}$$

γ is the weight of solids in the wake region per volume of bubbles in the bed, and is a constant in all the present experiments.

A mean residence time for all fines, i.e. particles smaller than d_e, can be calculated by equation 6:

$$\bar{t}(\text{fines}) = \frac{W x_{W,fines}}{F_o x_{Fo,fines}} \tag{6}$$

Eliminating $F_o x_{Fo,fines}$ from equations 4 and 6 gives

$$\bar{t}(\text{fines}) = \frac{W x_{W,fines}}{u_o A_t \gamma x_{wk,fines}} \tag{7}$$

This equation does not include F_o, and therefore conforms with the observation that the mean residence time for particles smaller than d_e is independent of the feed rate per unit area.

Effect of gas velocity on mean residence times

It is apparent from Table 6 that the mean residence time for the sieve fraction 74–104 μm is strongly dependent on the gas velocity. This is as would be expected, because d_e is about 90 μm at 0·45 m/sec and about 140 μm at 0·9 m/sec. For the sieve fraction 208–295 μm the mean residence time is independent of gas velocity, also as expected. The difference observed for the fraction 147–208 μm seems somewhat too large, although a great part of the difference is explained by non-spherical particles greater than d_e being elutriated. For the sieve fraction <44 μm, where the particles are definitely smaller than d_e, the mean residence time is roughly proportional to the reciprocal gas velocity, which is in accordance with equation 7.

Table 6 Mean residence time at varying gas velocity but at almost constant feed rate per unit area ($\simeq$ 140 kg/m² h), constant bed height ($h = 0.57$ m), temperature ($t \simeq 800°C$) and roasting to hematite

Run no.	Feed rate per unit area, kg/m² h	u_o, m/sec	$\bar{t}(d_p)$ min for sieve fraction, μm					
			<44	44–74	74–104	104–147	147–208	208–295
1	146	0.43	2.0	6.9	50	290	770	1060
5	156	0.47	1.5	4.7	39	420	770	1010
9	133	0.90	0.9	0.9	2.8	11	350	1080

Effect of bed height on mean residence times

It appears from Table 7 that for particles smaller than d_e the mean residence time is independent of bed height. Even if this result, at first sight, is surprising, it is possible to explain it by an extension of the bubbling-bed model. When the bubbles are formed at the bottom of the bed, the wake material carried along has the same size distribution as the emulsion phase. As the bubbles rise upwards in the bed, there is a continuous interchange of solids between wake and emulsion. If then the wake has a preference to retain the finest particles and release

Table 7 Mean residence time at two bed heights, at two pairs of constant gas velocity and feed rate per unit area, at constant temperature ($t \simeq 800°C$) and roasting to hematite

Run no.	Bed height, m	Feed rate per unit area, kg/m² h	u_o, m/sec	$\bar{t}(d_p)$ min for sieve fraction, μm					
				<44	44–74	74–104	104–147	147–208	208–295
1	0.57	146	0.43	2.0	6.9	50	290	770	1060
3	0.29	146	0.43	2.4	8.2	43	160	350	560
2	0.57	303	0.90	0.7	1.2	2.3	13	210	420
4	0.29	303	0.90	0.8	1.5	2.5	5.8	53	170

the coarser particles, the wake material becomes finer as the bubble rises upwards, and an increase in bed height will increase the entrainment of fine particles. Returning to equation 7, since W is roughly proportional to the bed height, the results indicate that the ratio $\dfrac{x_{wk, fines}}{x_{W, fines}}$ is roughly proportional to the bed height.

Effect of temperature on mean residence times

By examining runs 6, 11, 12, 13 and 14 (see Fig. 5), it is found that an increase of temperature from 800 to 900°C does not seem to have any appreciable effect on the mean residence times—at any rate, this is the case for particles smaller than d_e.

Effect of type of roasting on mean residence times

By examining runs 13, 14, 15 and 16 (see Fig. 5), it is found that the mean residence time for particles smaller than d_e is somewhat shorter when roasting to a more magnetic cinder. This is probably due to the influence of interparticle forces.

Effect of type of pyrite on mean residence times

So far, the type of flotation pyrite has been assumed to be without significance. A comparison is made between the four pairs of runs, 1 and 5, 2 and 6, 3 and 7 and 4 and 8 (see Fig. 5), pyrite A being used in the first of each pair and pyrite B in the second. Within the precision of measurement the type of flotation pyrite seems to have little effect on the residence time.

Elutriation

Mean residence time $\bar{t}(d_p)$ is used in the present paper to quantify the retention of particles in the bed. One of the elutriation constants

$$\kappa = \frac{1}{\bar{t}(d_p)} \tag{8}$$

or

$$\kappa^* = \frac{W}{A_t} \kappa \tag{9}$$

might also be used. The mean residence time was chosen mainly because of the more direct connexion obtained between residence time and roasting than that between elutriation rate and roasting.

In Table 8 the elutriation rates are calculated from the results in the present work for the 26-μm particle size (median of -44-μm fraction) and for the 57-μm particle size (geometric mean of 44–74 μm fraction). These elutriation constants are compared with those calculated by the correlation given by Yagi and Aochi.[7] Their correlation is given graphically on a log–log scale. The correlation can be represented by the equation

$$\phi = \frac{\kappa^* d_p}{\mu} \frac{g d_p}{(u_o - u_t)^2} = 9\cdot0 \times 10^{-3} \left(\frac{d_p u_t \rho}{\mu} \right)^{1\cdot24}$$

$$\text{for } 0\cdot5 \leqslant \frac{d_p u_t \rho}{\mu} < 10^2 \tag{10}$$

Table 8 Comparison between elutriation rate constants obtained in present work and calculated by correlation of Yagi and Aochi[7]

d_p, μm	u_o, m/sec	Present work			Correlation of Yagi and Aochi
		κ, 1/sec	W, kg†	κ^*, kg/m² sec‡	κ^*, kg/m² sec
26	0·45	$9·3 \times 10^{-3}$	6·6	3·3	0·3
	0·9	$2·1 \times 10^{-2}$	5·4	6·1	1·5
	1·4	$5·4 \times 10^{-2}$	4·4	12·9	3·8
57	0·45	$2·8 \times 10^{-3}$	6·6	1·0	0·08
	0·9	$1·04 \times 10^{-2}$	5·4	3·0	0·6
	1·4	$4·2 \times 10^{-2}$	4·4	10·0	1·7

† 0·57-m bed height.
‡ $A_t = 1·85 \times 10^{-2}$ m².

For $\dfrac{d_p u_t \rho}{\mu} < 0·5$ the slope of the curve decreases, ϕ being 9×10^{-4} at

$$\frac{d_p u_t \rho}{\mu} = 10^{-1} \text{ and } 3·5 \times 10^{-4} \text{ at } \frac{d_p u_t \rho}{\mu} = 2 \times 10^{-2}.$$

The correlation of Yagi and Aochi gives much lower elutriation rates than those observed—probably because the correlation does not apply to highly aggregative fluidization with about half the bed volume taken up by bubbles.

Summary of results for residence time

The conclusions drawn on the effect of the variables on the mean residence time when roasting flotation pyrites may be summarized as follows.
(1) The mean residence time for particles greater than d_e is inversely proportional to feed rate per unit area, proportional to bed height and independent of gas velocity.
(2) The mean residence time for particles smaller than d_e is independent of feed rate per unit area and of bed height, but decreases rapidly with increasing gas velocity.
(3) Whether the temperature is 800 or 900°C seems to be insignificant.
(4) The residence time for particles smaller than d_e is somewhat shorter when roasting to a more magnetic cinder than to hematite (at equal gas velocity)—indicating a probable effect of interparticle forces.
(5) The type of flotation pyrite used does not seem to have any influence on the mean residence time (for a given sieve fraction).

Roasting

Fig. 6 shows per cent sulphide sulphur in cyclone material versus feed rate per unit area. The individual runs are identified by the same symbols as were used in Fig. 5. Curves drawn with the percentage stoichiometric air as a parameter show that the sulphide content increases with increasing feed rate per unit area.

A similar graph of per cent sulphate sulphur in cyclone material versus feed rate per unit area shows that, when the roasting produces hematite, the sulphate content decreases with increasing feed rate per unit area. This graph is not presented, but a check can be made from the data given in Appendix 3, together with the feed rate data presented in Fig. 5.

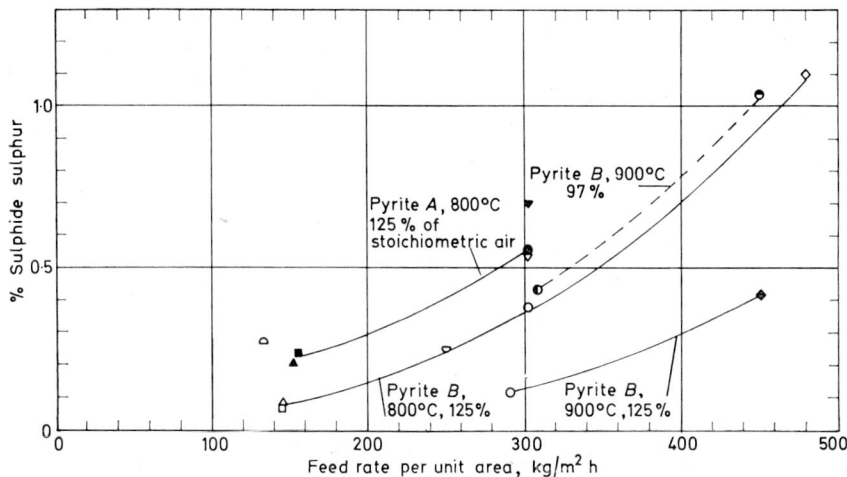

Fig. 6 Sulphide sulphur in cyclone material versus feed rate per unit area

As has already been mentioned, analyses of total sulphur and sulphide sulphur, giving sulphate sulphur as the difference, have been made of various sieve fractions of bed material, overflow and cyclone material from all the runs. The following discussion is based on these results.

Afterburning in roaster shaft

A comparison between sulphide and sulphate sulphur in bed (or overflow) material and in cyclone material shows that there is no significant oxidation of sulphide nor any significant formation of sulphates in the roaster shaft (freeboard above bed). At the highest gas velocity (1·4 m/sec) the mean residence time in the bed is 20–30 sec for the <44-μm and 44–74 μm sieve fractions, compared to about 1 sec in the shaft. For the lower gas velocities the residence time in the shaft would account for even less of the total residence time. This result for afterburning is not representative for industrial roasters, as they often have a considerable shaft height (for example, 7 m) and also often have a shaft with an enlarged cross-sectional area (compared with the bed) to promote afterburning.

M*

Sulphide sulphur in sieve fractions of cyclone material

As was stated above, reaction in the shaft was small. It was therefore concluded that it was relevant to discuss the sulphide and sulphate content in sieve fractions of cyclone material as functions of mean residence time in the bed. The reason why cyclone material was chosen rather than overflow or bed material is the higher content of fines in the former, which made it easier to obtain sufficient material for analysis.

Fig. 7 presents a graph of per cent sulphide sulphur in cyclone material versus mean residence time in the bed. Lines are drawn of per cent sulphide sulphur as a function of $\bar{t}(d_p)$ for the different sieve fractions, with temperature and percentage of stoichiometric air as parameters. The combustion rate for the sulphide increases with decreasing particle size, increasing temperature and increasing

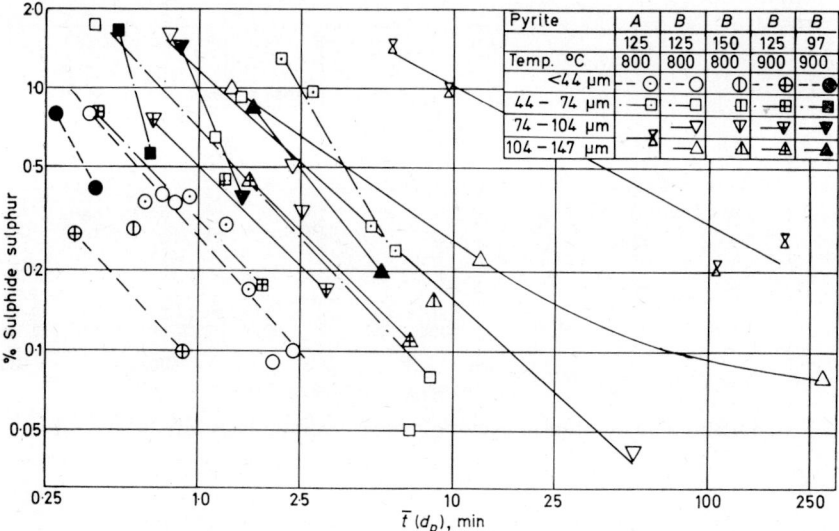

Fig. 7 Sulphide sulphur in sieve fractions of cyclone material versus mean residence time $\bar{t}(d_p)$ in bed

percentage of stoichiometric air. There is no difference between pyrite A and B for the -44-μm fractions, but for greater particle sizes pyrite B burns more slowly.

Bed height was also tested as a parameter, but was not found to have any significant effect. Both runs at 0·29- and 0·57-m bed height are therefore plotted in Fig. 7, no differentiation in symbols being made.

The results obtained on the conversion of sulphide sulphur were tested in five different kinetic models for the rate-controlling step: mass transfer from bubble to solid surface or backwards; continuous reaction model; unreacted core models; thermal conduction through product layer; diffusion in product layer; and chemical reaction.

MASS TRANSFER FROM BUBBLE TO SOLID SURFACE OR BACKWARDS

Equations to calculate this mass transfer were given by Kunii and Levenspiel[8] (chapter 7). The possible total mass transfer from bubble to solid surface will increase with increasing residence time of bubbles in the bed. As no effect of bed height on conversion of sulphide was observed, it can be concluded that mass transfer from bubble to solid surface or backwards is not rate-controlling. The same reasoning can be applied to heat-transfer processes to or from the solid surface, and therefore these cannot be rate-controlling.

CONTINUOUS REACTION MODEL

The reactant gas enters and reacts throughout a solid particle at all times. In this case the conversion at a given time will be the same in all particles, regardless of particle size. The results obtained (Fig. 7) show that the conversion depends substantially on particle size, and the model does not fit.

UNREACTED CORE MODELS

The present results were obtained in a continuous fluidizing reactor. For this case Kunii and Levenspiel[8] gave equations for the three unreacted core models. The equations are given for conversion of solids of uniform size. In the present paper similar equations are used for conversion of solids of non-uniform size. In these equations each sieve fraction is treated individually. The equations suppose that the exit age distribution for each sieve fraction is given by

$$\mathbf{E}(d_p, t) = \frac{1}{\bar{t}(d_p)} e^{-t/\bar{t}(d_p)} \tag{11}$$

where $\bar{t}(d_p)$ is the mean residence time for the sieve fraction with mean particle size d_p.

The conversion, when $\theta(d_p) > 5$, for all three unreacted core models is expressed by the equation

$$1 - \overline{X}_B(d_p) \simeq \frac{n}{\theta(d_p)} \tag{12}$$

where $\overline{X}_B(d_p)$ is the mean conversion of solid reactant B, for the sieve fraction with mean particle size d_p

$$\theta(d_p) = \frac{\bar{t}(d_p)}{\tau(d_p)} = \text{dimensionless} \tag{13}$$
$$\qquad\qquad\qquad \text{mean residence}$$
$$\qquad\qquad\qquad \text{time for particle}$$
$$\qquad\qquad\qquad \text{size } d_p$$

$\tau(d_p)$ is the time required for complete conversion, for particle size d_p, and n is the dimensionless coefficient.

The expressions to be used for $\tau(d_p)$ (which is a function of d_p and a factor M), n and M depend on the type of unreacted core model, and are presented in Table 9.

Table 9 n, $\tau(d_p)$ **and** M **to be used in equations 12 and 13**

Type of rate control	Thermal conduction through product layer	Diffusion in product layer	Chemical reaction
n	$\frac{1}{5}$	$\frac{1}{5}$	$\frac{1}{4}$
$\tau(d_p)$	Md_p^2	Md_p^2	Md_p
M	$\dfrac{\rho_B(-\Delta H_R)}{24k_s\,\Delta t}$	$\dfrac{\rho_B}{24bDC_{As}}$	$\dfrac{\rho_B}{2bk_cC_{As}}$

THERMAL CONDUCTION THROUGH PRODUCT LAYER

At lower temperatures thermal conduction may possibly be rate-controlling, but in the present case, where the temperature in the bed is at least 100° above 690°C (at which the decomposition pressure of pyrite reaches 1 atm), this seems hardly possible. The effect of the percentage of stoichiometric air corresponding to the concentration (C_A) of oxygen found by comparing the results of the experiment conducted at 150% of stoichiometric air with those at 125% confirms this statement.

DIFFUSION IN PRODUCT LAYER AND CHEMICAL REACTION

The data in Fig. 7 (at 125% of stoichiometric air) have been used in these two models. As is shown in Appendix 4, calculations give the M factors. If a model is correct, the M factor will be constant (independent of particle size at a constant temperature). If the same model fits at two different temperatures, the M factor will decrease greatly for the reaction control model, whereas it will decrease only slightly for the diffusion control model. Looking at the variation of the calculated M factors with varying particle size, the model found to agree best for pyrite A is that for diffusion in product layer. For pyrite B both diffusion and chemical reaction seem to be rate-controlling. On the basis of the M factors for pyrite B with the chemical reaction model, the activation energy has been calculated to be 20 000 cal/g mole. This activation energy is too high to fit the diffusion in the product layer model, and implies that in the range 800–900°C there will be a substantial degree of chemical reaction control. No attempt has been made to discuss the various types of chemical reaction control.

In the discussion so far the particle sizes used in the equations have been averages of each sieve fraction: this may not be correct. When discussing residence time, interparticle forces were shown to have an appreciable effect. The results indicated that the small particles behaved as agglomerates with an approximate size at 60–80 μm. This indicates that an 'apparent' rather than an actual particle size should have been used in the calculation of M factors. Probably the 'apparent' particle size to be used in the calculation increases somewhat, though not as much as the sieve fraction average, with increasing 'true' particle size. This will give M factors for diffusion control which vary less with particle size than the M factors calculated in Appendix 4. In other words, the diffusion in the product layer model fits better.

The storing of pyrite A for two years may have had some influence on the roasting of this pyrite, both indirectly through an effect on the interparticle force and/or more directly on the rate-controlling mechanism. Possibly such a great difference in rate as is found between A and B would not be observed between 'fresh' pyrites.

The exit age distribution (equation 11) used in these calculations assumes an ideal back-mix flow of solids in the bed. This is probably almost true, but with the short times needed for complete conversion it should be remembered that the pyrite in the experiments was fed into the bottom of the bed and cannot leave faster than the bubbles, which in Appendix 2 were found to have an absolute rise velocity of about 1 m/sec. Consequently, this gives a minimum residence time in the bed of at least 0·6 sec (with 0·57-m bed height). This means that the 'real' time needed for complete conversion is some tenths of a second larger than that calculated in Appendix 4, but will not affect the general conclusions on the rate-controlling mechanism.

Sulphate sulphur in sieve fractions of cyclone material

Fig. 8 shows a graph of per cent sulphate sulphur in cyclone material versus mean residence time in the bed. Lines are drawn of per cent sulphate sulphur as functions of $\bar{t}(d_p)$ for the different sieve fractions, with temperature as parameter. Because of the high sulphate content in pyrite A, the results obtained with this are not included. It appears that the reaction rate for the formation of sulphate increases with decreasing particle size. The effect of temperature is uncertain, especially as the equilibrium content of sulphates is lower at 900°C than at 800°C. Of the possible sulphate compounds only $CaSO_4$ is thermodynamically stable in roaster gas (partial pressure of oxygen about 0·04 atm) at 900°C, whereas both $CaSO_4$ and $ZnSO_4$ are stable at 800°C.

The results for sulphate formation are thought to be too few and too uncertain to justify an argument such as that used for the conversion of sulphide.

The value for sulphide sulphur in Fig. 7 can be added to the value for sulphate sulphur in Fig. 8, resulting in a similar graph of per cent total sulphur versus mean residence time. Curves of per cent total sulphur as a function of $\bar{t}(d_p)$ can be drawn for the different sieve fractions. These curves will have a minimum at some optimal mean residence time for each sieve fraction. This is not shown in the present paper, but can easily be verified by simply adding the values.

Summary of the results for roasting

(1) The afterburning in the shaft is not found to be significant in a bench-scale roaster with only 1·4-m freeboard.

(2) The connexion between mean residence time and the roasting efficiency

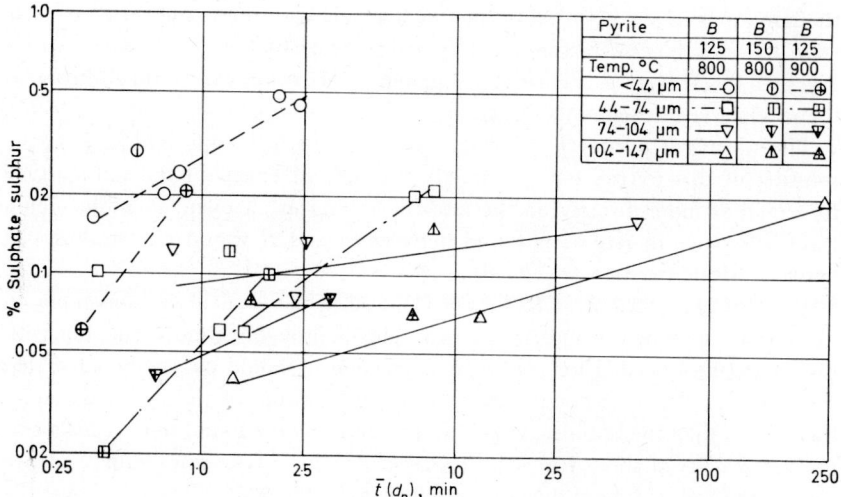

Fig. 8 Sulphate sulphur in sieve fractions of cyclone material versus mean residence time $\bar{t}(d_p)$ in bed

(measured by the per cent sulphide sulphur and per cent sulphate sulphur in the cinder) is shown in Figs. 7 and 8 for various values of the parameters percentage of stoichiometric air and temperature. The lines for pyrite B are probably representative of all pyrites produced by differential flotation.

(3) Both diffusion in the product layer and chemical reaction are rate-controlling in the combustion of pyrite (conversion of sulphide).

(4) The results for sulphate formation are too few to justify a discussion of the rate-controlling mechanism for this reaction.

Full-scale roaster

It would have been of considerable interest to have conducted a similar investigation to that described above for mean residence times and conversions for the different sieve fractions in a large pilot-plant or a full-scale roaster. This was not done, nor has any literature reference to such an investigation been found. The conclusions that can be drawn on roasting in industrial roasters are therefore only tentative.

The feed of pyrite to a full-scale roaster is mostly either as pulp or dry powder fed into the roaster at or above the top of the bed. But even if the feed is dry, the pyrite stream will probably go to the bottom of the bed before being distributed through the bed.

Wall effects in the bench-scale roaster ought to be considered, although the bubbles were observed to be smaller than the reactor diameter. In a full-scale roaster the bubbles might grow somewhat larger, but it is not thought that this would affect significantly the mean residence times.

Lateral mixing of solids probably constitutes a greater problem when scaling up. In the bench-scale roaster there is probably no significant variation in particle size distribution across the bed, whereas a variation is to be expected in a full-scale roaster, which usually has only one feed point. The concentration of fines can be expected to decrease as one moves away from the feed point: hence, the mean residence time for the fines will be shorter in a full-scale roaster.

The connexion between mean residence time and roasting will be the same as that found in the bench-scale unit, but in the full-scale unit the graphs of per cent sulphide sulphur and per cent sulphate sulphur versus residence time apply for the overflow and the entrained particles as they leave the bed. After-burning in the roaster shaft will have greater significance in the full-scale roaster. Although only a small fraction of the total sulphur burns in the shaft, this is important because it especially applies to the particles with a very short residence time in the bed.

Acknowledgment

The author wishes to thank the Norwegian Pyrites Producers' Association for financial support and for permission to publish this paper. In addition, he thanks Mr. A. Rein for valuable assistance in carrying out the experimental work and Mr. S. E. Olsen, Professor N. Christensen, Professor M. B. Müller and Professor T. Rosenqvist for helpful discussions and comments on the manuscript.

References

1. SCHYTIL F. The principles of fluidised solids roasting. *Metallgesellschaft*, no. 1 1959, 13–29. (English text)
2. MALETS A. M. Kinetics of roasting ferrous sulfide in fluidized beds. *Khim. Nauka Prom.*, **2**, 1957, 530–1; *Chem. Abstr.*, **52**, 1958, 3620.
3. SAFIULLIN N. SH. Kinetics of roasting of flotation pyrite in a fluidised bed. *Zh. prikl. Khim.*, **38**, no. 1 1965, 34–43; *J. appl. Chem. USSR*, **38**, no. 1 1965, 29–37.
4. VIAN A. AND ROMERO A. Feinkornbildung bei der Wirbelschichtröstung von Pyrit. *Aufbereitungs-tech.*, **6**, 1965, 367–73.
5. PRANDTL L. *Essentials of fluid dynamics* (London: Blackie, 1952), 452 p.
6. BAERNS M. Effect of interparticle adhesive forces on fluidization of fine particles. *I&EC Fundamentals*, **5**, 1966, 508–16.
7. YAGI S. AND AOCHI T. Paper presented at the Society of Chemical Engineers (Japan), Spring Meeting, 1955. Cited in reference 8, p. 323.
8. KUNII D. AND LEVENSPIEL O. *Fluidization engineering* (New York: Wiley, 1968), 556 p.

Appendix 1   Brief outline of bubbling-bed model

The bubbling-bed model, as formulated by Davidson and Harrison*, considers the bed as a two-phase system consisting of a particulate (emulsion) phase in which the gas velocity is equal to that at minimum (incipient) fluidizing conditions and a bubble phase which carries all the gas in excess of the gas velocity at minimum (incipient) fluidization. The model is based on the following postulates: (1) a gas bubble is solid-free and spherical in shape; (2) as the bubble rises, the particles move aside, as would an incompressible inviscid fluid of bulk density $\rho_s (1-\varepsilon_{mf})$ (ρ_s is density of solids (including inner pores) and ε_{mf} is void fraction in bed at minimum fluidization); (3) the gas flows in the emulsion phase as an incompressible viscous fluid.

Kunii and Levenspiel† extended the model to the emulsion phase. This model is best described by Fig. 1, which shows the movements of solids and gases in the bubbling-bed model. Kunii and Levenspiel's model is based on several postulates, the most important of which are (1) that every rising bubble

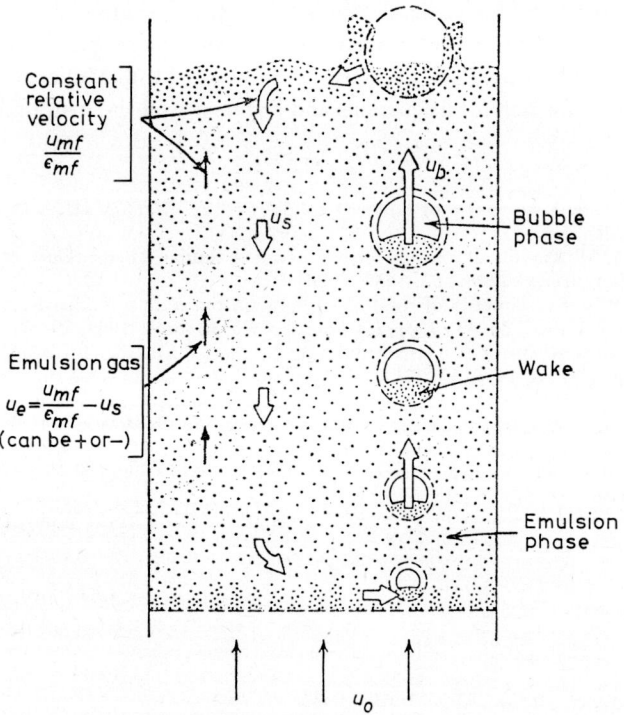

Fig. 1 Main features of solid movement and gas flow as visualized in bubbling-bed model. From Kunii and Levenspiel†

* DAVIDSON J. F. AND HARRISON D. *Fluidised particles* (London: Cambridge University Press, 1963), 156 p.
† KUNII D. AND LEVENSPIEL O. *Fluidization engineering* (New York: Wiley, 1968), 556 p.

drags behind it a wake of material: the void fraction of the wake is like that of the emulsion phase; (2) just above the distributor solid is entrained by rising bubbles to form the bubble wake: the solid is carried up through the bed at velocity u_b and there is a continuous exchange of solid between the wake and the emulsion phase as the bubble rises; at the top of the bed this wake solid rejoins the emulsion to move down the bed at velocity u_s; (3) the relative velocity between upward-percolating emulsion gas and downward-flowing solid u_s is given by the minimum fluidizing condition

$$u_e = \frac{u_{mf}}{\varepsilon_{mf}} - u_s \tag{1}$$

This expression shows that if the downward velocity of solids is sufficiently high, the emulsion gas will reverse its direction of flow. This will often be the case in a roasting process where the bed is vigorously bubbling.

Appendix 2   Some calculations according to the bubbling-bed model

Run 5 is chosen for the calculation.

A_t = Cross-sectional area of bed = $1 \cdot 85 \times 10^{-2}$ m^2
ρ_s = Density of solids (including inner pores) = 3400 kg/m^3
h = Height of bed = 0·57 m
W = Weight of solids in bed = 6·6 kg
u_o = 0·43 m/sec

d_m = 200 μm = 2×10^{-4} m, calculated by $\dfrac{1}{d_m} = \dfrac{1}{100} \sum \dfrac{x_{W,n}}{d_p(n)}$

u_{mf} = 0·04 m/sec (from Fig. 3, p. 334)
ε_{mf} = 0·6 (estimated)
V = Volume of solids in bed

$V = \dfrac{W}{\rho_s}$

$V = \dfrac{6 \cdot 6 \text{ kg}}{3400 \text{ kg/m}^3} = 1 \cdot 94 \times 10^{-3}$ m^3

ε_f = Average bed voidage

$\varepsilon_f = \dfrac{hA_t - V}{hA_t}$

$\varepsilon_f = \dfrac{0 \cdot 57 \, (1 \cdot 85 \times 10^{-2}) - 1 \cdot 94 \times 10^{-3}}{0 \cdot 57 \, (1 \cdot 85 \times 10^{-2})} = 0 \cdot 815$

δ = Volume fraction of bubbles in bed
$1 - \delta$ = Volume fraction of emulsion

$1 - \delta = \dfrac{1 - \varepsilon_f}{1 - \varepsilon_{mf}}$

$$1-\delta = \frac{1-0\cdot815}{1-0\cdot6} = 0\cdot46$$

$$\delta = 0\cdot54$$

This indicates that a little more than the half of the bed volume is bubbles—seemingly, too much. A probable explanation is that the voidage is greater in the upper part of the bed where the bubbles burst. The true δ is estimated to be 0·5.

$$\frac{u_o}{u_{mf}} = \frac{0\cdot43}{0\cdot04} \simeq 10$$

This shows that the bubbles are large, with negligible clouds, and that they move rapidly (Kunii and Levenspiel*).

u_b = Absolute rise velocity of bubbles

u_b is given by the equation*

$$u_b \simeq \frac{u_o-(1-\delta)u_{mf}}{\delta}$$

$$u_b = \frac{0\cdot43-(1-0\cdot5)0\cdot04}{0\cdot5} \text{ m/sec} = 0\cdot82 \text{ m/sec}$$

u_s = Downward velocity of solids in the emulsion: this velocity is also expressed by an equation from Kunii and Levenspiel*

$$u_s = \frac{\alpha\delta u_b}{1-\delta-\alpha\delta}$$

α = Ratio of wake volume to bubble volume

According to data from Rowe and Partridge,† α is 0·2–0·25 for irregular sand particles of particle size from 70 to 500 μm. α is estimated to be 0·2 in the present example.

$$u_s = \frac{0\cdot2\,(0\cdot5)\,(0\cdot82 \text{ m/sec})}{1-0\cdot5-0\cdot2\,(0\cdot5)} = 0\cdot205 \text{ m/sec}$$

$$u_e \simeq \frac{u_{mf}}{\varepsilon_{mf}} - u_s \quad \text{(equation 1, Appendix 1)}$$

$$u_e = \frac{0\cdot04 \text{ m/sec}}{0\cdot6} - 0\cdot205 \text{ m/sec} = -0\cdot14 \text{ m/sec}$$

* Kunii D. and Levenspiel O. *Fluidization engineering* (New York: Wiley, 1968), 556 p.
† Rowe P. N. and Partridge B. A. An X-ray study of bubbles in fluidised beds. *Trans. Instn. chem. Engrs*, **43**, 1965, T157–75.

Appendix 3 Analysis of cyclone material, overflow and gas

Run no.	Cyclone material			Fe$_3$O$_4$, %	Overflow			Gas
	% Total sulphur	% Sulphide sulphur	% Sulphate sulphur		% Total sulphur	% Sulphide sulphur	% Sulphate sulphur	% SO$_2$ in gas after cyclone
1	1·13	0·23	0·90	6	1·46	0·46	1·00	11·9
2	1·20	0·56	0·64	11	1·03	0·41	0·62	11·9
3	1·06	0·20	0·86	7	1·13	0·37	0·76	11·7
4	1·30	0·70	0·60	13	1·02	0·60	0·42	12·0
5	0·40	0·07	0·33	6	0·42	0·17	0·25	11·7
6	0·55	0·38	0·17	8	0·50	0·25	0·25	
7	0·40	0·08	0·32	4	0·39	0·11	0·28	12·0
8	0·68	0·55	0·13	10	0·32	0·20	0·12	11·6
9	0·50	0·27	0·23	6	1·99	0·14	1·85	4·3
10	0·52	0·31	0·21	7	1·05	0·12	0·93	9·0
11	1·16	1·09	0·07	13	0·48	0·13	0·35	11·6
12	1·94	1·77	0·17	16	0·36	0·12	0·24	12·2
13	0·26	0·12	0·14	5	0·23	0·18	0·05	11·5
14	0·54	0·42	0·12	10	0·13	0·09	0·04	11·8
15	1·07	1·05	0·02	42	0·08	0·06	0·02	16·7
16	0·46	0·43	0·03	42	0·11	0·07	0·04	16·7

Appendix 4   Calculations of conversion of pyrites according to diffusion in product layer model and chemical reaction model

The relation

$$\frac{[\text{Percentage of sulphide sulphur}]\ 55\cdot85}{32\cdot06\ [\text{Percentage of iron}]}\ \text{gives}\ \frac{\text{g atom S}}{\text{g atom Fe}}$$

In pyrite cinder it is about 67% Fe; e.g. 1% sulphide sulphur then gives

$$0\cdot026\ \text{g atom S/g atom Fe}$$

The starting point for the diffusion control model is assumed to be pyrite with

$$\frac{49\times55\cdot85}{32\cdot06\times44}\ \text{g atom S/g atom Fe} = 1\cdot94\ \text{g atom S/g atom Fe}$$

1% sulphide sulphur gives

$$1-\overline{X}_B(d_p) = \frac{0\cdot026}{1\cdot94} = 0\cdot0134$$

The starting point for the reaction control model is assumed to be a pyrrhotite $FeS_{1\cdot1}$.

1% sulphide sulphur gives

$$1-\overline{X}_B(d_p) = \frac{0\cdot026}{1\cdot1} = 0\cdot0236$$

Data from Fig. 7 (p. 346) at 125% of stoichiometric air are calculated by use of equations 12 and 13 (p. 347) and the expressions in Table 9 (p. 348), giving the results presented in Table 1.

Table 1

Pyrite	Temp., °C	Sieve fraction, μm	$d_p \times 10^3$, cm	% Sulphide sulphur	$t(d_p)$, sec	Diffusion in product layer				Chemical reaction			
						$1-X_B(d_p)$	$\theta(d_p)$	$\tau(d_p)$, sec	$M \times 10^{-4}$, sec/cm²	$1-X_B(d_p)$	$\theta(d_p)$	$\tau(d_p)$, sec	M, sec/cm²
A	800	44	2·7	0·4	42	0·00536	37·5	1·12	15·3	0·00944	26·5	1·59	590
				0·2	79	0·00268	75	1·05	14·4	0·00472	53	1·49	550
		44–74	5·7	1·0	150	0·0134	15	10·0	31	0·0236	10·6	14·1	250
				0·2	390	0·00268	75	5·2	16·0	0·00472	53	7·4	130
B	800	44	2·7	1·0	19	0·0134	15	1·27	17·4	0·0236	10·6	1·79	660
				0·1	150	0·00134	150	1·00	13·7	0·00236	106	1·41	520
		44–74	5·7	1·0	43	0·0134	15	2·86	8·8	0·0236	10·6	4·1	720
				0·1	400	0·00134	150	2·67	8·2	0·00236	106	3·9	680
		74–104	8·8	1·0	72	0·0134	15	4·8	6·2	0·0236	10·6	6·8	770
				0·1	1020	0·00134	150	6·8	8·7	0·00236	106	9·6	1090
B	900	44	2·7	0·2	27	0·00268	75	0·36	5·1	0·00472	53	0·51	187
				0·1	53	0·00134	150	0·35	4·9	0·00236	106	0·50	185
		44–74	5·7	0·5	38	0·0067	30	1·27	3·9	0·0118	21·2	1·79	310
				0·2	96	0·00268	75	1·28	3·9	0·00472	53	1·81	320
		74–104	8·8	0·5	60	0·0067	30	2·00	2·6	0·0118	21·2	2·83	320
				0·2	160	0·00268	75	2·13	2·7	0·00472	53	3·0	340
					Fig. 7 (p. 346)	Equation 12 (p. 347) $n = \frac{1}{3}$	Fig. 7 (p. 346)	Equation 13 (p. 347)	$\dfrac{\tau(d_p)}{d_p^2}$	Equation 12 (p. 347) $n = \frac{1}{4}$		Equation 13 (p. 347)	$\dfrac{\tau(d_p)}{d_p}$

Symbols

A	Gaseous reactant (oxygen)
A_t	Cross-sectional area of bed, cm^2, m^2
B	Solid reactant
b	Stoichiometric coefficient $= \dfrac{\text{moles of } A \text{ reacting}}{\text{moles of } B \text{ reacting}}$
C_A	Concentration of A, g mole/cm^3
C_{As}	Concentration of A at surface of solids, g mole/cm^3
D	Diffusion coefficient, cm^2/sec
D_r	Reactor diameter, m
d_e	Diameter of biggest spherical particle that can be entrained, μm
d_m	Mean particle size in bed, μm
d_p	Particle diameter; for non-spherical particles, diameter of sphere having the same volume as the particle. In the present paper d_p is also used to indicate mean particle diameter of a sieve fraction, μm, cm
$\mathbf{E}(d_p,t)$	Exit age distribution function for sieve fraction with mean particle size d_p, sec^{-1}
F_o	Feed rate (expressed as pyrite cinder), kg/h
F_1	Overflow, kg/h
Fr_e	Froude number at entrainment, dimensionless
Fr_{mf}	Froude number at minimum fluidization, dimensionless
G_N	Gas flow rate, Nm^3/h
g	981 cm/sec^2, acceleration of gravity
H	Freeboard, m
h	Bed height, m
ΔH_R	Enthalpy of reaction, cal/g mole
k_c	Rate constant for first-order surface reaction, cm/sec
k_s	Thermal conductivity of solids, cal/cm sec °C
L	Transition length for laminar flow, m
M	Factor used in Table 9, sec/cm^2 or sec/cm
n	Coefficient in equation 12, dimensionless
n	Number on a sieve fraction
Re	Reynolds number for particles, dimensionless
Re_r	Reynolds number for reactor, dimensionless
TDH	Transport disengaging height, m
t	Temperature, °C
Δt	Temperature difference through product layer, °C
t	Time, sec
$\bar{t}(d_p)$	Mean residence time for sieve fraction with mean particle size d_p, sec, min
$\bar{t}(\text{fines})$	Mean residence time for particles smaller than d_e, sec, min
u_b	Absolute rise velocity of bubble, m/sec
u_e	Relative velocity between upward-percolating gas and downward-flowing solid (equation 1, Appendix 1), m/sec

u_{mf}	Superficial gas velocity at minimum fluidizing conditions, m/sec
u_o	Superficial gas velocity (measured on empty reactor basis), m/sec
u_s	Mean downward velocity of solids, m/sec
u_t	Terminal velocity of falling particle, m/sec
V	Volume of solids in bed, m^3
W	Weight of solids in bed, kg
$\overline{X}_B(d_p)$	Mean conversion of solid reactant for sieve fraction with mean particle size d_p
$x_{Fo,n}$	Weight % of sieve fraction n in feed
$x_{Fo,\text{fines}}$	Weight % of particles smaller than d_e in feed
$x_{W,n}$	Weight % of sieve fraction n in bed
$x_{W,\text{fines}}$	Weight % of particles smaller than d_e in bed
$x_{wk,\text{fines}}$	Weight % of particles smaller than d_e in wake material
α	Ratio of wake volume to bubble volume, dimensionless
γ	Weight of solids in the wake region per volume of bubbles in bed, g/cm^3, kg/m^3
δ	Volume fraction of bubbles in bed, dimensionless
ε_f	Average bed voidage, dimensionless
ε_{mf}	Void fraction in bed at minimum fluidization, dimensionless
$\theta(d_p)$	Dimensionless mean residence time, for sieve fraction with mean particle size d_p
κ	Elutriation constant, sec^{-1}
κ^*	Elutriation constant, g/cm^2 sec
μ	Viscosity of gas, g/cm sec, kg/m sec
ρ	Gas density, g/cm^3, kg/m^3
ρ_B	Molar density of component B in solids, g mole/cm^3
ρ_s	Density of solids (including inner pores), g/cm^3, kg/m^3
$\tau(d_p)$	Time required for complete conversion for sieve fraction with mean particle size d_p, sec

DISCUSSION

Dr. A. E. Wraith introduced his paper briefly, summarizing its principal contents.

G. Abrashev introduced his paper briefly, summarizing its principal contents.

T. Lindstad, in introducing his paper, said that the work described was part of a larger project on the utilization of flotation pyrites sponsored by the Norwegian Pyrites Producers' Association and the Royal Norwegian Council for Scientific and Industrial Research.

At present a large amount of pyrites was produced by gravity concentration, the product containing all the metal sulphides present in the ore. Improved techniques, however, enabled the differential flotation of ores that could not previously be treated in such a way. Those techniques involved milling the ore to very fine particles—70% of the particles finer than 325 mesh was not unusual in modern flotation practice.

Published information on pyrites roasting was, in the main, restricted to a coarser spectrum of particles than that of flotation pyrite; moreover, the range of particle size examined was frequently quite narrow. A fluidized bed of particles of mixed sizes behaved differently from a bed of single- or narrow-sized particles. In the roasting of fine flotation pyrites most of the feed was small enough to be elutriated from the bed, and the bed would consist of the coarser particles. Even in that case, however, the fine particles would have a measurable residence time in the bed.

The primary aim of the experiments was to measure the concentration of the various particle size fractions in the bed and calculate the mean residence time in the bed of each size fraction. The second aim was to find a relationship between the degree of roasting, as measured by the content of sulphide and sulphate sulphur, and the mean residence time for each particle size fraction. The experiments were conducted in a bench-scale, 15-cm diameter fluidized-bed roasting reactor. Flotation pyrites with 40–60% − 325 mesh were used.

In Fig. 5 (p. 337) the mean residence time, $\bar{t}(d_p)$, was plotted against particle size. Curves were drawn for different gas velocities and bed heights. The diameter of the biggest spherical particle that could be entrained at a given gas velocity u_o was termed d_e. Even particles smaller than d_e had a considerable mean residence time—of the order of magnitude of minutes—in the bed. At first sight that result was surprising, but it could be interpreted by means of the bubbling-bed model.

The effect on mean residence time, $\bar{t}(d_p)$, of various operational parameters, the most important being gas velocity, feed rate per unit area, bed height and free-board, was discussed.

For particles smaller than d_e the mean residence time was found to be independent of feed rate per unit area, independent of bed height and roughly proportional to the reciprocal gas velocity.

360

Fig. 7 (p. 346) showed per cent sulphide sulphur in cyclone material versus mean residence time in the bed. Lines were drawn for the different sieve fractions, with temperature and percentage of stoichiometric air as parameters. The combustion rate for the sulphide increased with decreasing particle size, increasing temperature and increasing percentage of stoichiometric air.

The results obtained on the conversion of sulphide sulphur were tested in five different kinetic models. Mass transfer from bubble to surface did not seem to be rate-controlling. The conversion depended substantially on particle size and, therefore, the continuous reaction model did not fit. Thus, only the unreacted core models remained to be discussed, and both diffusion in product layer and chemical reaction seemed to be rate-controlling. The activation energy was calculated to be 20 000 cal/g mol—implying a substantial degree of chemical reaction control. Because of interparticle forces, however, the smaller particles tended to behave as agglomerates, which seemed to have an approximate size of 60–80 μm. If such an 'apparent' particle size were used in the calculations, the diffusion in the product layer model fitted better.

Tentative conclusions were drawn on roasting in industrial roasters.

W. Drummond* said that the Bulgarians were to be congratulated on being the first to adopt oil fuming on a commercial scale. Figures were given for oil consumption, but none for coal consumption: perhaps the author would give corresponding figures on a dry ash-free basis. He usually found that coal comparisons could be made on a heat value basis and from the author's oil figures he guessed that that simple basis might be extended to oil: the author's comments would be welcomed.

Great store seemed to have been laid on good atomization of the oil, and that lined up with coal practice in that better results were attained with finer pulverized fuel. Did the author have any quantitative information on drop sizes? The paper showed clearly the importance of adequate slag depth in that the deeper the slag the better was the fuming efficiency: could the author state the minimum undisturbed slag depth that he would recommend?

Operating the furnace continuously resulted in much poorer fuming efficiency, which was to be expected, and the unit size was too small to be compartmentalized. What advantages other than easier maintenance and constant steam output were there in that method to offset the extra force of fuel? Had natural gas been tried—that was cheaper still than oil?

Could the author give some details of the type of furnace, boiler, air heater, etc., used on the fuming plant.

P. A. Wright† said that he wished to congratulate Mr. Abrashev on his very interesting paper, which raised several points. The design of the tuyère was very elegant and made for ease of cleaning without loss of the atomizing power of the

* Babcock and Wilcox, Ltd., London.
† Consolidated Tin Smelters, Ltd., London.

nozzle by bringing it into the air stream at an oblique angle. It appeared that lead–zinc slag fuming furnaces, all of which (except the Bulgarian) used powdered coal, rarely needed any tuyère punching, whereas tin slag fuming furnaces, all of which, so far as he knew, used oil, did need quite frequent punching on account of the formation of balls of frozen magnetite or slag on the nose of the tuyère. In order to settle the question as to whether it was the fuel or the basic process which gave rise to those accretions, he would like to ask the author whether he found tuyère punching necessary.

In discussing the interaction of gas mixture with slag the author stated that the reaction proceeded in a very turbulent environment: was it so turbulent that the slag was suspended in a fluidized bed, or was the gas the dispersed phase?

It would be interesting to compare the rate constants

$$k = \frac{1}{t} \log \frac{Zn_0}{Zn_t}$$

where t was time of fuming, Zn_0 zinc content of input slag ($t = 0$) and Zn_t zinc content of discard slag, under the various conditions described in Table 2 (p. 325) and to extrapolate k to the conditions of continuous fuming described in Table 3 (p. 325). By that means it should be possible to calculate whether the rate of fuming of zinc in continuous fuming was that to be expected at the zinc content of the discard slag or whether the furnace might be regarded as having one or more 'theoretical weirs' between which the slag had an average zinc content greater than that of the discard slag.

In order to carry out that calculation it would be necessary to know the zinc content of the input slag in each case: perhaps the author would give that information.

He would have expected the coefficient of expenditure of air (α) to be related to the specific air/mazut ratio, but that did not appear from Table 2. Could the author explain that more fully?

Professor T. R. A. Davey* said that anyone who had been concerned with slag fuming must be full of admiration for the Bulgarian development of the continuous process, which required tremendous courage, since the handling of streams of molten slag was a very difficult business. He was not sure whether the substitution of liquid for solid fuel was done first by the Bulgarians or the Russians, who used oil for fuming tin from slags; that was also an interesting development, although careful economic analysis was necessary in a particular location to see whether the use of oil was on the whole cheaper than the use of coal.

Abrashev stated positively that fuming with oil as fuel was a first-order reaction with respect to zinc, and that was what would be expected when fuming with coal as well. The first analysis of slag fuming was done by Bell, Turner and

* Colorado School of Mines, Golden, Colorado, U.S.A.

Peters at Trail, and they used a cyclical argument in which they assumed that equilibrium was reached between slag and gas, and then showed that the zinc elimination curve indicated the correctness of their assumption. Something was wrong with their calculations, which indicated that the slag was saturated with ZnO at a content of about 16% Zn, whereas it was now known that the true solubility for ZnO was much greater than that.

Quarm* stated that the form of the zinc elimination curve (linear dependence of log Zn versus time) showed that equilibrium was *not* reached between slag and gas, and that the reaction was rate-controlled.

There was no doubt that the elimination of zinc proceeded *as if* the reaction were first-order with respect to zinc, and that fact was used at Trail as a means of determining the end-point of economic fuming, for plant control purposes. On the other hand, Professor H. H. Kellogg had produced a computer model of slag fuming, based on establishment of equilibrium at all stages during the operation, and the model correctly predicted the effects of changes in operating conditions. The model had been adapted at Port Pirie for optimization purposes, and was said to work extremely well there.

Kellogg took the view that, although one could well expect the reaction to be rate-controlled, his model, based on the establishment of equilibrium, *worked*. If they admitted the possibility that there might be a difference between conditions with the use of liquid or solid fuels, he wondered if the author could offer any *evidence* that equilibrium was not achieved when coal was being used instead of oil?

C. F. Harris† said that he found Lindstad's paper very interesting, but was worried about the applicability of the work to a commercial unit. Fig. 1 (p. 330) showed that the laboratory reactor had a diameter of 150 mm and bed depth of 290 and 570 mm. Thus, the apparatus was working with a bed height/diameter ratio of 2 or 4. From the literature and from personal experience in working on fluidization within a glass tube of similar size, he would expect bubbles to form of the approximate diameter of the tube, thus causing slugging.

He thought that the reason that the author had measured 50- to 100-mm bubbles in his 150-mm tube was due to the shape of the bubbles rising. Those were, in fact, domed, and the bubble collapsed through the dome as it broke surface, giving the impression of a smaller diameter when viewed from the surface. That would be expected to affect elutriation.

There was a comparison (p. 344) of the present results with the correlation of Yagi and Aochi. The author observed that his rates were much the lower and suggested that that was due to highly aggregative fluidization. The situation postulated above seemed to support that view. He did not think that that type of bed action occurred normally in commercial installations.

* QUARM T.A.A. The slag fuming process. *Min. Mag., Lond.*, **113**, 1965, 114–23.
† Imperial Smelting Corporation, Ltd., Avonmouth.

Dr. K. J. Reid* said that Lindstad stated that the size distributions of samples obtained from the 29-cm overflow valve were 'within 10%' of those determined from samples split from the total bed material. That was a rather loose way to compare two size distributions. Could a more precise comparison be made and, if possible, could a tabulation or plot be given of the actual size distributions observed?

Was there any change in particle size due to passage through the bed—either by attrition or reaction? An alternative way of framing the question was to ask if a comparison of total feed and total product size distributions was carried out, and, if so, how good was the overall mass balance? The answer to that question was, of course, important in relation to the method of calculating the mean residence time of each screen fraction.

Contributed remarks

Dr. J. H. E. Jeffes†　On page 329 the oxides of iron listed as possible products of the roasting of pyrite are Fe_3O_4 and Fe_2O_3. Since the process was carried out in the temperature range 700–950°C, it seems probable that the first oxide produced may well be wustite, which is stable in this temperature range.

T. A. A. Quarm‡　Abrashev is to be congratulated not only for the development of a means of burning fuel oil in the fuming furnace but also for making the process continuous. His achievement with fuel oil is particularly appreciated by one who was associated some years ago with an attempt to replace part of the coal feed to a standard furnace by injecting fuel oil directly into the tuyères. That experiment was soon halted by an irate smelter superintendent when he found that unburned carbon in the gas stream had made the zinc oxide black.

Having long held that equilibrium is not attained in the fuming furnace,[1,2] I was especially interested in the author's evidence in support of this conclusion. The general reluctance to question the assumption that a system must be in equilibrium because the temperature is high is curious. In a paper on slag fuming at Trail[3] mention was made of tests that indicated that volatile matter in coal escaped from the slag bath and burned above it; nevertheless, equilibrium between slag and gas was assumed, notwithstanding the premise of the original study[4] that all carbon and hydrogen in the coal took part in the combustion and reduction reactions. At the same time a straight-line plot of log per cent zinc versus time, which in itself provided necessary and sufficient evidence of a first-order kinetic reaction, was employed for process control. It is also worthy of note that automatic processing of plant data at Boliden[5] produced a mathematical model of the form

$$\%Zn_t = \%Zn_0 . e^{-kt}$$

* Nchanga Consolidated Copper Mines, Ltd., Zambia.
† Department of Metallurgy, Imperial College, London.
‡ Bechtel Corporation, San Francisco, California, U.S.A.

in which t is in minutes. This equation describes the graph plotted at Trail.

It would be helpful if the author would provide the additional data for each test that would permit calculation of reaction rates. For the purposes of discussion they can be estimated from the data given by assuming the slag feed to contain 14% zinc. For ease of calculation the equation is used in the form

$$2 \cdot 303 \log (Zn_0/Zn_t) = kt$$

Then the values of k for the three tests in Table 2 would be 0·018, 0·030 and 0·032, respectively. For comparison, the value computed from data in the Trail paper was 0·028.

To compute k for the continuous tests in Table 3 the residence time in the furnace must be known. It would appear to be 60 min for the large furnace, in which case k would be 0·028. Then it would follow that the residence time in the small furnace would be

$$60 \times 10/13 = 46 \text{ min}$$

and the value of k would be 0·042. This is markedly higher than the values normally encountered in slag fuming and indicates that the author has achieved a significant increase in fuming rate.

References

1. QUARM T.A.A. The slag fuming process. *Min. Mag., Lond.*, **113,** 1965, 114–23.
2. QUARM T.A.A. Slag fuming—kinetic or thermodynamic? *Engng Min. J.*, **169,** Jan. 1968, 92–3.
3. YURKO G.A. Slag fuming process at the Cominco smelter, Trail, British Columbia. In *Extractive metallurgy of lead and zinc* (New York: AIME, 1970), 330–47.
4. BELL R.C. TURNER G.H. AND PETERS E. A thermodynamic study—fuming of zinc from lead blast furnace slag. *Trans. Am. Inst. Min. Engrs*, **203,** 1955, 472–7.
5. SUNDSTRÖM O.A. The slag fuming plant at the Rönnskär works of the Boliden Aktiebolag, Skelleftehamn, Sweden. *J. Metals, N.Y.*, **21,** June 1969, 15–21.

B. S. Andrews,* A. J. Moore* and Dr. Howard K. Worner* As part of the WORCRA process development staff of the C.R.A. Research Division have also been studying air–water models of submerged gas lancing. This work has included both subsonic and sonic gas injection velocities with submerged lances at various angles. Our observations are in agreement with those of Dr. Wraith, particularly with respect to the better gas dispersion produced by downward-angled jets of sonic velocities.

These studies have assisted in explaining the position and shape of splash patterns observed in the converting zone of the U-shaped semi-commercial WORCRA copper smelting furnace. Good agreement has been found between other phenomena observed in the operating furnace and those seen in and photographically recorded in model studies.

Within a model of the WORCRA furnace converting zone we have found that when the lances are correctly positioned, better gas–liquid contact is obtained by

* Conzinc Riotinto of Australia, Ltd., Melbourne, Australia.

opposed downward-angled submerged lances entering from opposite sides of the furnace. As compared with non-opposed downward-angled lancing, this arrangement achieves greater liquid turbulence in the centre of the furnace and away from the walls. It also results in increased depth and degree of dispersion of the fragmented gas bubbles.

We believe that the greater fragmentation of gas bubbles results mostly from the increased shear between the mixing vortices generated by the opposed-jet systems. From other studies related to WORCRA continuous steelmaking we believe that this opposed-jet technology could be beneficially applied in the argon degassing of slowly flowing streams of steel, as well as in the WORCRA counterflow slag steel refining practice.

AUTHORS' REPLIES

G. Abrashev   In reply to Mr. W. Drummond (p. 361), I would stress that the installation in Plovdiv works on a continuous basis and with fuel oil only. The data shown for oil consumption refer to this type of operation.

When the installation was working on an intermittent basis with coal, the consumption of coal dust was 25–28%, the coal having the following content: 6800–7200 kcal, 15–17% ash and 13–15% volatile matter.

In order to effect a comparison with the fuel consumption of other units working on coal, I think that the calorific content could be accepted as the basis for comparison.

Considerable attention is indeed paid to atomization. For that purpose the special testing stand (see page 322) was installed. Each tuyère is subjected to special testing before being mounted.

I have no information on drop sizes, but they are such that when the tuyères are being tested with oil, only a fine mist can be observed.

The minimum undisturbed slag depth under our conditions of working is 850 mm.

The efficiency of the fuming is not poorer than had been expected. No extra fuel is forced into the furnace—only that amount which is required for the fuming process, and it does not exceed the amount used with the periodic process.

The furnace is rectangular, having a configuration nearing a square, with a cross-section $5 \cdot 89$ m^2 in the tuyère zone. The boiler is model UKCM 15/4, made in the U.S.S.R.

Tuyère punching due to accretions, queried by Mr. P. A. Wright (pp. 361–2), has not been found to be necessary. Sometimes the need arises to take out the stem of a nozzle to prevent clogging with solid particles carried by the oil (the nozzle appertures are very small). A drop in oil temperature in a tuyère is indicative of clogging, and this is a convenient means of control. In a 6-h period the need arises to clean one or two nozzles.

The equation given on page 324 contains the basic dependent variable—the content of zinc vapours in the gas phase, determined by the parameters of process and thermodynamic characteristics, equilibrium constants and activity of ZnO in the molten slag. The equation should be regarded as a description of the state of equilibrium of the system gas–slag. The actual state of the system may, more or less, approximate its equilibrium state, depending on the kinetic and hydrodynamic parameters of the process. Thus, it may be said that the expected rate of fuming has been reached at the zinc content of the spent slag, i.e. no theoretical limitations exist.

The amount of oil, G, can be determined by the amount of air, according to the relationship

$$G = \frac{\%O_2}{2 \cdot 16\alpha}$$

where $2 \cdot 16$ is the amount of oxygen for the complete burning of 1 kg of oil, α is the coefficient of expenditure of air and O_2 is the content of oxygen in the air. Evidently, the relationship between $\%N_2$ and $\%O_2$ is

$$\%N_2 = 100 - \%O_2$$

As far as Table 2 is concerned, the values of α are those calculated under experimental conditions.

In reply to Professor T. R. A. Davey (pp. 362–2), it is contended that under the conditions of continuous fuming with oil equilibrium is not reached. Evidence of this is the fact that with the same fuming parameters, when the dimensions of the furnace were reduced, the parameters of the process sharply improved. Of course, the rate of air-blowing had been increased, which is a decisive factor.

As far as intermittent fuming with coal dust is concerned, in this field too there are ample opportunities for new developments and an intensification of the process.

On the question of equilibrium raised by Mr. T. A. A. Quarm (pp. 364–5), it was stated (p. 323) that the equilibrium partial pressure of the zinc vapour for the reactions with CO_2 and H_2 is equalized when the gas phase satisfies the reaction

$$CO + H_2O \rightleftarrows CO_2 + H_2$$

Explicitly, for this reaction, at the fuming temperature, equilibrium is reached much sooner than for the remaining two—if equilibrium is, in fact, reached for them. In the paper it was shown that for the reactions

$$ZnO + CO \rightleftharpoons Zn + CO_2$$
$$ZnO + H_2 \rightleftharpoons Zn + H_2O$$

equilibrium is not reached, and that there are hidden possibilities in the process.

As for the reaction

$$CO + H_2O \rightleftharpoons CO_2 + H_2$$

it is indisputable that equilibrium is reached quite soon at fuming temperatures. Perhaps it was not quite clear that the statement was concerned with this reaction.

With the large-size furnace the capacity was 25 tons of liquid slag—15 tons after the reduction in size. The residence time was considerably decreased, and Mr. Quarm's deduction for k is therefore logical.

T. Lindstad I fully agree with Mr. C. F. Harris (p. 363) that the bed diameter is perhaps somewhat small. The laboratory reactor is a compromise between the desirable and the practical. A large diameter will necessitate a longer preheating period and the handling of more material. The bed height of 570 mm was chosen to give the gas a residence time similar to that of a commercial roaster.

It is not quite clear what significance Mr. Harris attaches to the bed height/ diameter ratio. I think that this ratio itself has no influence on the quality of fluidization. But, of course, the bed height and the diameter are both of importance.

As the bubbles rise upwards in the bed they coalesce until they either reach a maximum stable bubble size or are restricted by the wall from the attainment of maximum stable bubble size. As a result of coalescence the remaining bubbles may be too far apart for further coalescing; this, however, is not likely in the present experiments with so high a fraction of the bed consisting of bubbles.

The method given by Davidson and Harrison* to calculate the maximum stable bubbles size is based on the assumption that the upward velocity of gas through a large rising bubble is roughly equal to the rising velocity of the bubble, u_{br}. If u_{br} is greater than the terminal velocity of the particles, u_t, the particles will be drawn into the bubble from the wake below, and the bubble will break up. This method gives the maximum stable bubble size as a function of particle size and the difference between the densities of the solid and the gas. Since the method supposes a narrow particle size range, what then if the bed has a wide particle size range, as in the roasting of flotation pyrite? As far as I know, this problem has not been dealt with in the fluidization literature. Presumably, we cannot use the mean particle size of the bed, d_m. Probably a particle size, below which only a few per cent of the bed is found, should be used in the calculation. However, it is not possible to calculate a reliable maximum stable bubble size. We therefore have to base the discussion of the quality of fluidization on the observed frontal diameter d_f of the bursting bubbles. This diameter was observed in the bed with a 0·57-m bed height. At $u_0 = 0·45$ and $0·9$ m/sec, d_f was about 5 cm, and at 1·4 m/sec it was about 10 cm (the velocities were omitted in the original paper). These observed frontal diameters agree fairly well with bubble diameters calculated from the rising velocities of the bubbles. The observations of bubble diameters lead to the conclusion that for velocities $\leqslant 0·9$ m/sec the wall effect has some, but not much, influence on the fluidization. At 1·4 m/sec the wall effect probably predominates, i.e. slug flow exists. The bubbles are domed, but I cannot quite agree that the diameter of the bursting bubbles when

* DAVIDSON J. F. AND HARRISON D. *Fluidized particles* (London: Cambridge University Press, 1963), 156 p.

viewed from the surface is smaller than the real frontal diameter of the bubbles. At least, that depends on how the observation is done.

The elutriation rate constants found in the present experiments are four to ten times greater than those calculated by Yagi and Aochi. An explanation for this is the seeming preference of the wake to retain the finest particles so that an increase in bed height will increase the entrainment of fine particles (p. 342). But bed height was not included in the elutriation correlation of Yagi and Aochi.

In reply to Dr. K. J. Reid (p. 364), by saying that the size distribution of one sample is within 10% of another sample, I mean that comparison of any sieve fraction from the two samples will show that the difference in weight per cent of that sieve fraction between the two samples is equal to or less than 10% (for example, the difference between 8·0 and 8·8% is 10%).

A comparison of total feed and total product size distribution was carried out for some of the experimental runs. Table 1 is representative. As before, all amounts of material are expressed as the equivalent amount of pyrite cinder.

Table 1

	Sieve fraction, μm						
	Total	> 208	147–208	104–147	74–104	44–74	< 44
	g	g	g	g	g	g	g
Total feed*	26 900	4910	2520	2390	3580	4080	9420
Total product†	26 900‡	6700	1750	1660	3080	3860	9850‡
Total feed − total product		0	−1790	770	730	500	220	−430
$\dfrac{\text{Total feed} - \text{total product}}{\text{Total feed}}$ 100%		−36%	30%	30%	14%	5%	+5%

* Total feed includes bed at start.
† Total product includes bed at end.
‡ The amount of product found was actually 25 560 g, the difference (1340 g) between total feed and product being assumed to be losses in the cyclone and to consist only of particles smaller than 44 μm.

It appears from Table 1 that the mass balance is valid for the −104-μm sieve fractions. Above 104 μm the mass balance is not as good since there seems to have been an agglomeration of particles in the 104–208 μm size range.

The remarks by Dr. J. H. E. Jeffes (p. 364) give me the opportunity to present an equilibrium diagram for the Fe–S–O system (Fig. 1). For the sake of brevity this was omitted from the original paper. I have chosen to use the Kellogg type of diagram at a temperature of 800°C. In addition to the lines

N

describing equilibria between the condensed phases, the three parallel dashed lines represent the equilibrium $\frac{1}{2}S_2 + O_2 = SO_2$ at partial pressures of S_2, p_{S_2}, equal to $1\cdot0$, $0\cdot1$ and $0\cdot01$ atm. The total pressures, p_{S_x}, of sulphur are shown at these p_{S_2}. For simplicity FeS and FeO are used in the diagram instead of $Fe_{1-x}S$ and $Fe_{1-y}O$.

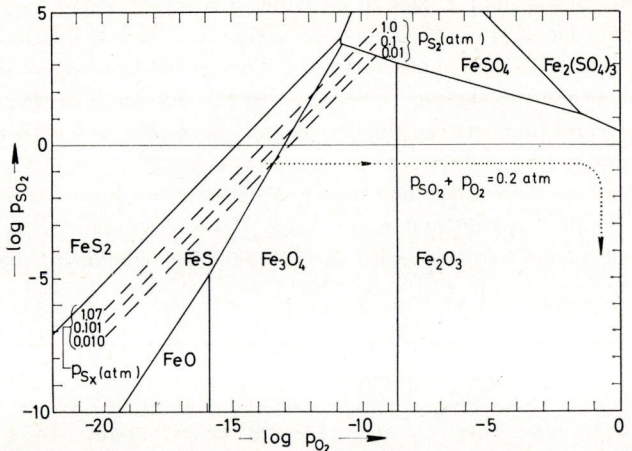

Fig. 1 Kellogg diagram of Fe–S–O system at 800°C. Free energy data used are from *JANAF thermochemical tables*,* except for FeS, FeS$_2$, S$_2$, S$_4$, S$_6$ and S$_8$, which are from Kubaschewski and co-workers†

In the roasting process FeS$_2$ first decomposes to FeS and S$_2$. Furthermore, at equilibrium conditions most of this sulphur will oxidize to SO$_2$ before any iron oxides form. Since roasting is carried out in air, the sum of partial pressures of SO$_2$ and O$_2$ is about 0·2 atm. This means that the conditions during roasting will be described by the dotted line in Fig. 1. Following this line FeS will be oxidized directly to Fe$_3$O$_4$ at equilibrium conditions. The predominance area for FeO is far away from equilibrium conditions. This does not rule out the possibility of FeO being formed as an intermediate product at non-equilibrium.

* *JANAF* (*Joint Army–Naxy–Air Force*) *thermochemica ltobles* (Washington, D.C. National Bureau of Standards, 1965 (with addenda, 1966 and 1967), PB 168 370.
† KUBASCHEWSKI O. EVANS E.LL. AND ALCOCK C.B. *Metallurgical thermochemistry, 4th edn* (Oxford, etc.: Pergamon, 1967), 495 p.

Session 6

The use of oxygen
Molten salt electrolysis

Chairman
Dr. T. W. Farthing

Use of oxygen-enriched air at the Metallurgie Hoboken–Overpelt smelter

P. J. Lenoir Ing.A.I.Lg.
J. Thiriar* Ing.A.I.Br.
C. Coekelbergs Ing.A.I.Ms.

All of Metallurgie Hoboken–Overpelt, Hoboken, Belgium

662.611.25:669.3/.4(493)

Synopsis

The use of oxygen-enriched air is discussed with specific reference to (1) the water-jacketed blast-furnace during lead and lead–copper charges, (2) the converter section, where oxygen is employed in the Hoboken siphon converter, and (3) the sintering plant, where oxygen is employed in downdraught, 2-m wide Dwight–Lloyd machines with gas recirculation.

The present is a critical time for non-ferrous pyrometallurgy: under the pressure of changing social and economic factors, the metallurgist is looking for new extractive processes which require minimum power and fuel, are easy to control automatically, provide good working conditions and, last but not least, are as free as possible from pollution.

As regards the extraction of lead, future development is difficult to forecast.[1] On the one hand, there are many new processes that could, in principle, be used for extracting and refining lead; on the other, as Davey and Bull[2] have indicated, even the classical pyrometallurgical processes for simple lead concentrates have not been made as efficient and profitable as they could be. It is therefore worth conducting chemical and technological research along both orthodox and unorthodox routes. This is especially true for custom smelters such as Metallurgie Hoboken–Overpelt, who handle complex Pb–Cu concentrates—increasing amounts of secondary materials and scrap from which, as well as Pb and Cu, it is necessary to recover many other metallic values and the precious metals. The use of pure oxygen seems to offer some ways of improving the technological efficiency of existing processes, while keeping investment costs at a minimum. This paper therefore gives a brief description of what has been done with oxygen at Hoboken in attempts to improve operation throughout the smelter.

Three uses of oxygen have been investigated: blast enrichment at the blast-furnace, oxygen lancing at the siphon converters and oxygen enrichment at the

* Now Canadian Copper Refiners, Ltd., Montreal, Canada.

downdraught sintering machine. The results obtained are described below. A full description of the smelter has been given elsewhere;[3] explanation of the smelter itself is only given when necessary for describing the experiments.

O₂ enrichment at the lead blast-furnace

For some years the use of oxygen-enriched blast has been considered for the lead blast-furnaces at the Hoboken plant on account of encouraging results published by other smelters. Enrichment appeared attractive because it was known that the blast-furnace would later prove to be the bottleneck in the treatment of concentrates and secondary materials. Moreover, there was the possibility of taking oxygen directly from a pipeline running from Mons to Antwerp, and planned by a major oxygen producer for 1970.

Preliminary experiments

Preliminary experiments were made in early 1967, the oxygen coming from a liquid oxygen tank. The O₂ contents of the blast were between 23·0 and 25·1%, and experiments were made on the two furnaces described in Table 1. The results

Table 1 Dimensions of blast-furnaces used in oxygen trials

Blast-furnace no.	3	4
Number of tuyères	36	40
Tuyère diameter, mm	80	80
Width at tuyère level, m	1·13	1·30
Length at tuyère level, m	5·55	6·00
Surface at tuyère level, m²	6·27	7·80
Smelter column height, m	3·81	4·60
Furnace blast flow, Nm³/h*	9000–10 500	10 000–13 000
Blast pressure, mm wg	1700–2000	1800–2000
Forehearth, m²	2·2 × 1·1	2·2 × 1·1

* Depending on charge porosity.

obtained are given in Table 2. These results show that the increases in smelting rate depended on the nature of the charge being smelted and were especially interesting for the Pb–Cu charge (both Pb and Pb–Cu charge have been described earlier[3]). Although decreases in coke consumption were relatively low, the improvements obtained in smelting rates, as well as in the operating conditions (see below), were sufficient to show that the oxygen was economically worthwhile for both types of charge.

In addition, the following observations were made.
(1) The operating conditions improved: the molten products left the furnace at a higher temperature, so tapping was easier. There was less blocking of the tuyères and less hanging of the charge within the shaft.

Table 2   Blast enrichment—preliminary tests

Furnace no.	Type of charge*	Test no.	Test period, days	Smelting conditions					Operating parameters				
				Blast, Nm³/h	O₂ in blast, %	Smelting rate, t/day	Coke consumption t/day	Coke consumption % Charge	Relative enrichment†	Coke/O₂ ratio, kg coke/ Nm³ O₂	Relative coke rate, %	Relative smelting rate, %	Relative coke consumption, %
3	Pb	Reference	‡	10 476	20·9	435	54·86	12·62	100·0	1·040	100·0	100·0	100·0
		Test I	7	10 476	25·1	529	65·21	12·33	120·1	1·040	118·9	121·6	97·7
		Test II	4	10 476	25·1	497	59·69	12·01	120·1	0·942	108·1	114·3	95·2
3	Pb–Cu	Reference	‡	10 307	20·9	380	53·08	13·97	100·0	1·025	100·0	100·0	100·0
		Test III	17	10 411	25·4	528	68·95	13·06	126·3	1·045	123·0	139·0	93·5
3	Pb–Cu	Reference	‡	9827	20·9	357	46·66	13·07	100·0	0·950	100·0	100·0	100·0
		Test IV	30	9973	26·3	453	62·10	13·71	125·8	0·990	133·1	126·9	104·9
4	Pb–Cu	Reference	‡	12 617	20·9	468	59·33	12·68	100·0	0·940	100·0	100·0	100·0
		Test V	87	12 978	25·1	682	75·70	11·10	120·2	0·970	128·0	145·7	87·5

* For charge description see Leroy and co-workers.[3]
† (Oxygen in blast/oxygen in air)×100.
‡ Reference smelting period between 1 and 2 months.

(2) The temperatures of the exit gases were decreased, as was the quantity of dust produced.

(3) The temperature of the cooling water was increased. With 25·1% O_2 in the blast, the figures were

Molten products	1150–1170°C	(20–30°C increase)
Exit gases	100–135°C	(50–65°C decrease)
Cooling water	55–60°C	(5–7°C increase)
Dust production	1·87%	(1·1% decrease)

Prolonged experiments with liquid oxygen

It was then decided, while waiting for the oxygen pipeline, to make prolonged tests with liquid oxygen. The oxygen content of the blast was held for 12 months at about 24·2%, which was the maximum possible concentration with the supply available.

Table 3 compares the results (mean yearly values) obtained with two furnaces during this period with those of the preceding year, when there was no enrichment.

Table 3

Furnace no.	3		4	
	Smelting rate, t/day	Coke, % charge	Smelting rate, t/day	Coke, % charge
Reference period	397	12·11	517	10·94
Period with oxygen	427	12·84	591	11·29

During this period furnace no. 3 treated mainly Pb charges and no. 4 Pb–Cu charges. The smelting rates for the latter were increased by 14·4% (7·6% for the former).

It is difficult to conclude anything from the coke figures because, during the test period, the size and quality of the coke supplied were considerably less satisfactory than during the reference period. It can only be said that oxygen enrichment, owing to the increased smelting rates, more than compensated for the lower quality of the coke.

During the first months of the oxygen period good-quality coarse coke (>60 mm) was difficult to obtain. To avoid fluctuations in coke quality, coarse coke was therefore blended with about 16% finer coke of the same quality (20–40 mm) and 8% of petroleum coke (>40 mm). Very satisfactory results were obtained with Pb–Cu charges at furnace no. 4 with 24·5% O_2 in the blast and 10·8% total coke consumption. This blending was then adopted for both furnaces and was still used when (after four months' operation at 24·5% in the blast) higher enrichment experiments were made with the same Pb–Cu charges.

Higher enrichment experiments

In 1970, when the oxygen pipeline was completed, prolonged experiments were planned with oxygen contents of up to 26–27%. Operation at both furnaces, however, became very difficult.*

Owing to accretion formation, the furnaces had to be cleaned almost daily with explosives. The smelting rate fell drastically (even excluding interruptions), and reduction became very erratic, giving very high and very low levels of lead in the slag. The temperature of the top gases fell for some periods as low as 30°C, the coke addition being between 10·3 and 11·5% at no. 4 furnace and between 11·2 and 13·5% at no. 3. It was clearly established that for the Pb–Cu charge and the coke used at this time there was an upper limit for useful enrichment and that it was desirable to obtain a better understanding of the different factors influencing the smelting rates.

Theoretical aspects

The results all indicated that a complex relationship existed between the chemical and physical properties of the charge and the coke, the coke consumption and the smelting rate. Attempts have therefore been made to develop a simple model in order to correlate the different parameters involved. This model has been based on an experimental thermal balance established during stable operations at furnace no. 4 with a Pb–Cu charge and with 23·5% O_2 in the blast. During these operations the variation of temperature and gas compositions with height in the furnace had been measured and had confirmed that the furnace could be divided, like an iron blast-furnace, into three operating zones, over which separate heat balances could be made.

From the calculations it may be concluded that with our existing furnaces and charge preparation the useful limit of oxygen enrichment is restricted by the combustion properties of the coke and by the efficiency of heat transfer between the gas and the charge. For high enrichments the adjustment of coke rate at a constant degree of reduction becomes critical owing to the profound effects of quality and size of the coke on heat transfer to the charge from the gas phase. Close monitoring of gas outlet temperatures and composition is necessary in order to adjust the coke rate to the enrichment and the quality of the charge so as to obtain an optimum smelting rate. The calculation also suggests that oxygen enrichment is not the best means of lowering the coke consumption; the percentage coke decrease per added per cent O_2 in the blast falls drastically as the per cent O_2 in the blast increases.

Conclusions

In the light of the calculations and the earlier experiments it was decided to limit enrichment to 24·5–25·0% and to maintain the coke rate at no less than 10·5%

* The earlier data[3] relating smelting rate, coke consumption and enrichment were based only on relatively short runs. They gave only a rough idea of possible performances and did not forecast the difficulties encountered at high oxygen levels.

N*

at no. 4 furnace and 11.5% at no. 3. Very satisfactory results have been obtained over a period of about 6 months with both Pb and Pb–Cu charges (Table 4). Smelting rates have increased, pressure drops in the furnaces are lower than during the earlier periods of oxygen enrichment, the tuyères remain brighter and cleaning of the furnace shaft has become exceptional. It should, perhaps, be added that, even if it were possible to achieve an increased production rate by means of a higher blast rate, the oxygen-enriched blast at the present flow rate would be preferred on account of the easier and steadier operation.

Table 4   Some recent smelting performances (see Table 3 for comparison without enrichment)

Charge	Furnace no.	Blast flow, Nm^3/h	O_2 in blast, %	Smelting rate, t/day	Coke consumption, %
Pb–Cu	3	10 500*	25·0	500	11·5
	4	11 500*	24·3	620	10·5
Pb	3	10 600	24·16	475	12·09
	4	11 800	24·73	588	10·81

* The blast flow rate was reduced because the drossing and slag treatment plants were saturated.

Oxygen in copper converting

The influence of O_2 on converting is much less complex than on the lead blast-furnace. O_2 enrichment increases the rate of converting and results in shortened operating cycles and higher rates of heat evolution. Larger additions of solid material are needed to maintain a constant bath temperature. Enrichment can be justified economically because converting and melting costs are lowered; in addition, enrichment can help to solve some pollution problems because the increased SO_2 content of the converter gases makes it possible to dilute them with poor SO_2-containing gases from other parts of the plant.

Oxygen can be introduced into a copper converter (1) by enriching the air blown through the tuyères, (2) by lancing through the surface with a submerged lance in a horizontal converter and (3) by top blowing through a nozzle type of lance in a vertical converter. The method selected depends on the type of converter being used and on the type of charge being treated. Although method (1) is the only method so far used for matte blowing, it has been found to be impractical at Hoboken because the corrosive lead-bearing mattes which have to be treated attack the lining next to the tuyères excessively. Thus, method (2) has been tried with pure oxygen, air being blown through the tuyères to maintain mixing and turbulence.

The siphon converter

The Hoboken-type converter has already been described and compared with the conventional Peirce–Smith units.[4] Briefly, it consists of a cylindrical shell, fitted at one end with a 'goose' neck or inverted U duct, called the siphon, which allows the gases to escape (Fig. 1). The converter and duct can be freely rotated about its horizontal axis. Fumes finally pass through a fixed vertical duct *en route* to the sulphuric acid plant. The connexion between the rotating U duct and the fixed vertical one is made by a specially designed seal.

In this unit, by controlling the air blow and the fume flow by means of fans and dampers, it is possible to prevent the escape of SO_2 to the atmosphere and also dilution of the converter gases by the air intake at the converter mouth. As the mouth is freely accessible throughout the operations, it is possible to charge large quantities of liquid or solid materials during blowing. This, together with the Hoboken converting practice previously described,[4] in which slag is tapped and matte is added five or six times during each cycle, allows for maximum efficiency of the converter, i.e. operation at maximum matte height and tuyère depth with a thin slag layer. The progress of the operation can be controlled at any time during the blow by spooning samples out of the bath from a platform located near the converter mouth.

Oxygen in the siphon converter

The purpose of the trials was to attain an increased capacity in order to match the improved smelting rates now obtained with oxygen in the blast-furnace. At Hoboken there is little advantage in the use of oxygen at the converters from the standpoint of pollution because, even with air blowing, the SO_2 content of the converter gases is rather high ($\sim 8.5\%$).

Because the oxygen needed to give the required rates of converting was relatively small (less than 15 Nm^3/min per converter), it was decided to use consumable refractory-coated steel lances. In the trials a single lance was introduced along the centre line of the converter at an angle of about 30° from the vertical so that the tip was submerged to a depth of about 60 cm (Fig. 1). The lance was moved up and down by a simple mechanical drive and was connected through conventional fittings and a flexible pipe to the O_2 feeding system.

The converter was charged in the usual manner,[4] blowing was started through the tuyères, and, as soon as the converter was in the blow position, the lance was inserted with oxygen flow at its full rate. The Hoboken schedule consisted of a number of short blows of about 90 min, after each of which slag was tapped. Liquid matte was added after slagging and during blowing. All solid cooling materials were added during blowing.

In the preliminary trials measurements were made of the rates at which lances were consumed. This was found to be between 1·5 and 2·5 m/h, depending on the composition of the bath. It was therefore possible to make lances which would last for one blow, and to change them when slag was tapped. It was also found possible to maintain the lance tip at a constant depth by recording the oxygen flow (supplied at a fixed pressure) and positioning the lance so as to keep the flow as nearly constant as possible. The position of the tip within the bath is important because corrosion of the lining has to be minimized and oxygen should not be blown into the slag. Temperatures were controlled by adding properly selected cold materials to the bath. The temperature of the bath was measured with a dip thermocouple through the mouth of the converter at various times during blowing. This is an operation which is easy with the siphon design and which is vital for proper control when the cold materials are variable in form and composition.

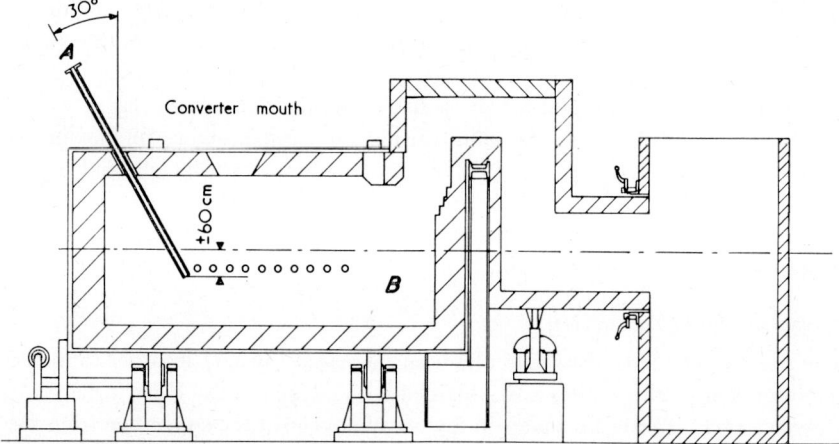

Fig. 1 Oxygen lancing in siphon converter. Oxygen lance in blowing position. *A*, oxygen lance: ¾-in internal diameter; flow rate, 10–15 Nm³/min; *B*, level of conventional tuyères

It is clearly desirable to recover the SO_2 as completely and at as high a concentration as possible. To avoid dilution from entrained air, as well as blowout of gases from the converter, the suction has to be maintained constant in the U duct. Besides the usual fan draught adjustment, air flow through the tuyères must be adjusted to the oxygen blow through the lance in order to keep the total gas flow in the U duct constant. The SO_2 content has been recorded in the vertical duct very close to the converter. Typical instantaneous records with and without oxygen lancing are shown in Fig. 2.

The rather high fluctuations in the instantaneous SO_2 contents are caused by the varying amounts and nature of the cold additions. Fig. 2 suggests that proper sizing of the cold materials and more continuous additions could lead to steadier operation, which might well improve both the mean per cent SO_2 concentration and its stability.

Considerable evolution of fume occurs in the converter. Nevertheless, visual inspection during lancing is quite possible, and one can see that, with proper depth of immersion, the lance causes neither splashing nor foaming of the slags.

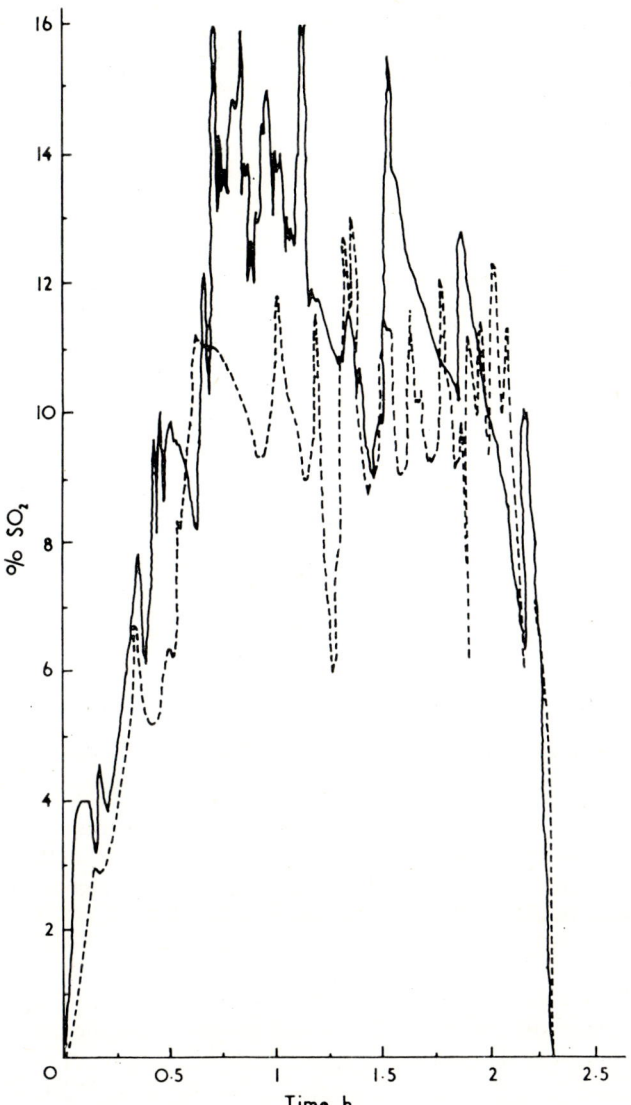

Fig. 2 Oxygen lancing in siphon converter. SO_2 content of the fumes in the cooler. Full line, with oxygen lancing (air, 175 Nm^3/min; O_2, 10 Nm^3/min); broken line, with conventional air blowing (180 Nm^3/min)

Converting rates obtained with O_2 lancing

During the first experimental period two converters (10 ft × 20 ft) were operated for matte blowing. One was lanced with oxygen and the other was conventionally blown so as to provide a reference. The oxygen flow rate was maintained at

$10 \, Nm^3/min$ throughout the experiments. This corresponds stoichiometrically to a 25·1% oxygen blast through the tuyères. No difficulties have been encountered other than those arising from handling increased amounts of cold materials and from training the operators. During the first trials the O_2 flow had to be cut from time to time to avoid too high temperatures, but this was mainly the result of lack of experience concerning temperature control. Under these conditions the O_2 blow time did not exceed 35–50% of the total available time. After a few weeks' training about 60% was achieved, the limitation being caused by the unbalanced blowing cycles of the two converters and resultant difficulties in maintaining a regular supply of SO_2 to the acid plant. Fig. 3 compares typical

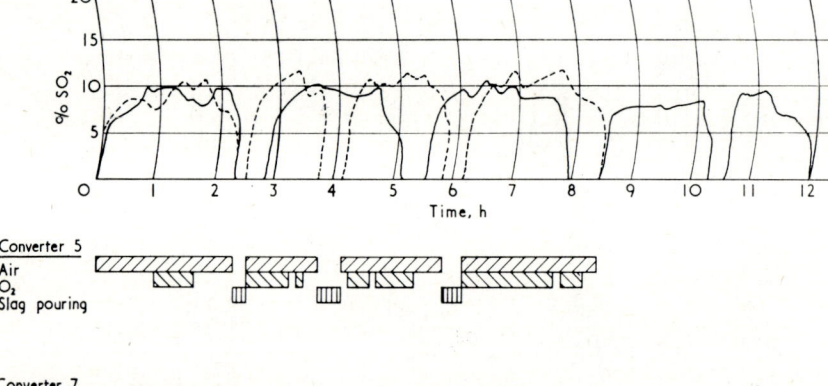

Fig. 3 Comparison of experimental O_2 lanced and conventional air-blown converting cycle. O_2 lancing (broken lines): $10 \, Nm^3/min \, O_2$ in lance, $175 \, Nm^3/min$ air at tuyères; O_2 blowing time utilization, 60%; production rate, 15·7 t/h; conventional blowing (full lines): $180 \, Nm^3/min$ air; 12·8 t/h

converting cycles achieved with and without O_2 lancing. With 60% blowing time production was increased from 12·8 t/h to 15·7 t/h. The solid–liquid charge ratio increased from about 0·57:1 to 0·87:1, mostly by the increased addition of scraps to keep the temperature between 1250 and 1300°C. The SO_2 content of the gases coming from the oxygen-lanced converter was measured continuously at the acid plant. A mean value of about 9·6% was found with O_2 lancing (8·3% without). During some blows O_2 was lanced during about 98% of the time, the SO_2 mean content reaching about 10·2%. No significant increase in the MgO content of the slags has been found—indicating no excessive corrosion of the lining.

After these very promising results it was decided to stop the experiments in order to provide lancing equipment for a second converter and to make improvements to the driving equipment for the lance. With two converters being lanced it will be possible to operate full time with oxygen, and so obtain information

concerning the gains in smelting and converting capacity and in SO_2 content
likely to arise over a prolonged period.

Oxygen enrichment during sintering

Increased sintering capacity is needed at Hoboken for a number of reasons. These
include the increased smelting capacity of the blast-furnaces brought about by
the use of oxygen, the possible advantages of increasing the percentage of
sinter in the blast-furnace charge and the advantage of avoiding multi-hearth
furnace roasting. The sintering plant has been described elsewhere.[3] It is
composed of two Dwight–Lloyd machines, with downdraught gas recirculation,
2 m wide and 35 m long.

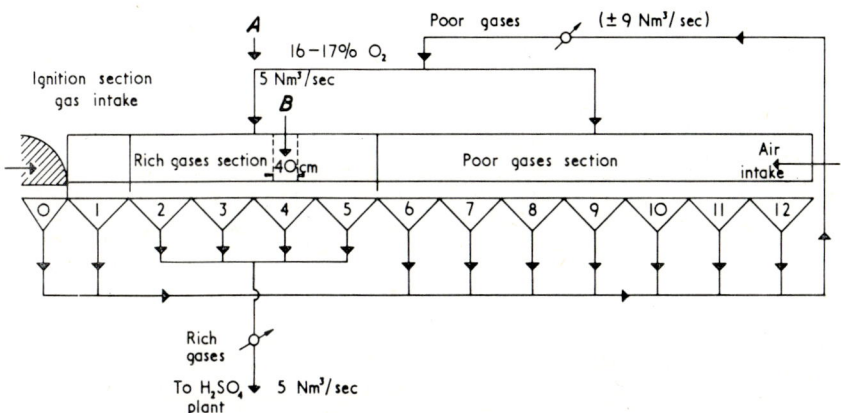

Fig. 4 Oxygen enrichment at sinter plant. Pure oxygen intake for trial 1 at A and
for trial 2 at B. O_2 flow rate, 700 Nm^3/h

Although more capacity might be obtained by updraught sintering, this
change would involve a substantial investment. So, other alternatives have been
considered. The simple theory of sintering suggests that oxygen enrichment
should not improve significantly the sintering rates, but, with the availability of
oxygen at Hoboken, it was decided to carry out some production-scale tests.

Fig. 4 shows a flowsheet of the gas circuit with the usual recirculation of the
poor SO_2 gases coming from the ignition box and the sinter cooling section.
Two types of tests were made, each for 12 h. During test 1 oxygen was introduced into the rich gas inlet flue (point A) and so divided between the different
boxes of the rich gas section according to the porosity of the bed above each box.
During test 2 the O_2 flow was concentrated on the fourth rich gas box at point B.
Oxygen was introduced between two dead-plates, so preventing the gases from
spreading out of the 40-cm wide section.

For both tests an O_2 flow rate of about 700 Nm^3/h was adopted. This corresponded, for the first test, to a local increase of 3·75% in the oxygen concentration.

Table 5 Results of O_2 enrichment at sinter plant on lead–copper charge

Test	Raw feed, % S	SO₃	Sinter, % S	SO₃	Flow, Nm³/h Rich gases outlet*	Poor gases outlet†	O₂ inlet	Gas analysis, % Rich gases SO₂	O₂	Poor gases SO₂	O₂	Strand speed, m/min	Production, t/h
1	6·56	4·86	2·96	5·54	19 656	31 860	—	5·97	8·70	1·46	15·30	1·35	45·6
	6·40	4·83	2·76	3·72	18 648	32 400	700	6·19	11·20	1·18	16·60	1·35	45·3
2	7·08	5·59	2·70	4·57	17 928	33 300	—	6·14	8·49	0·8	15·00	1·05	37·5
	6·92	5·71	2·36	4·01	17 712	30 240	700	7·43	11·67	1·44	14·74	1·15	41·6

* From boxes 2–5 inclusive.
† From all other boxes.

For the second test, assuming an equal draught in the four rich gas boxes, the increase at the fourth box should have reached 15%. Table 5 summarizes the results of both experiments. During the first, no significant change was observed; during the second, the results were more interesting. It was found possible to increase the strand speed and to obtain a better level of sulphur removal, better SO_2 content of the gases and a higher production rate. But the increase of about 10% in the production rate is far from significant when it is compared with test 1, and it is hardly worthwhile in view of the amounts of oxygen required.

It is now felt that better results may be obtained by improving the preparation of the charge prior to sintering, because, at present, owing to local conditions, it is poorly sized and liable to channel.

Conclusions

Twelve months after receiving a piped supply of oxygen, oxygen enrichment and pure oxygen lancing has become standard practice for the blast-furnace and the converter. Oxygen is undoubtedly a useful and profitable reagent for both these operations.

Nevertheless, there are technological and economical limitations to its use. At the blast-furnace its use is economically justified by the increased smelting rate. The decrease of coke consumption is only a secondary effect. Obviously, without fuel or steam injection, too high a flame temperature could become a limitation because of jacket maintenance problems and possibly because of excessive zinc circulation. Furthermore, specific smelting rate cannot be increased indefinitely.

At Hoboken these factors are not critical at present. But physical and chemical properties of the charge should be improved in order to obtain more homogeneous gas flow through the furnace. The need remains for further measurements on the blast-furnace in order to discover which parameters must be controlled and how to adjust them when higher enrichments are used.

With the converters the only likely limitation to an increase in the use of oxygen is that arising from the rate of cold additions to control the temperatures. A proper blowing technique, avoiding local superheating of the refractories, is of major importance. Although top blowing above the bath could be considered as practical at Hoboken, owing to the relatively thin slag layer, lancing is, nevertheless, preferred because it is easy and safe to operate.

Oxygen requirements at the converters differ from plant to plant. But, taking into account the materials to be treated, simple thermal balance calculations can provide the information on which to decide whether oxygen blowing is profitable or not. The choice between an oxygen-enriched converter and a larger air-blown converter depends on such calculations, and each has advantages in different situations. For these reasons, in parallel with its oxygen lancing investigations, Metallurgie Hoboken–Overpelt is developing a larger siphon converter. Both sizes of siphon converter and oxygen lancing may help to solve production problems arising from capacity and pollution problems.

References

1. BEILSTEIN D. H. AND WORCESTER A. W. Review of the processes; projections for the future: lead. Paper presented at 100th AIME Annual Meeting, New York, 1971.

2. DAVEY T. R. A. AND BULL W. R. Process research on lead and zinc extraction. In *AIME World Symp. on mining and metallurgy of lead and zinc* (New York: AIME, 1970), vol. 2, 1009–29.

3. LEROY J. L. LENOIR P. J. AND ESCOYEZ L. E. Lead smelter operation at N.V. Metallurgie Hoboken S.A. In *AIME World Symp. on mining and metallurgy of lead and zinc* (New York: AIME, 1970), vol. 2, 824–52.

4. LEROY J. L. AND LENOIR P. J. Hoboken type of copper converter and its operation. In *Advances in extractive metallurgy* (London: Institution of Mining and Metallurgy, 1968), 333–43.

Application of oxygen to the smelting and refining of lead

J. L. Harrison F.I.M., M.Inst.F.

The British Oxygen Company, Ltd., Leeds

662.611.25:669.43/.44

Synopsis

Work carried out in various countries on the application of oxygen to primary and secondary lead smelting is reviewed, and studies on the use of oxygen in sintering are summarized.

Oxygen-enriched blast in primary and secondary lead blast-furnaces results in improved output rates and coke savings. Although lead manufacture may not be regarded as having a high growth rate, the improvements in output obtained from oxygen can be of value in that at some plants fewer units may be employed. Solid fuel costs continue to rise and, in addition to the known savings from oxygen-enriched blast, further economies may be possible by use of substitute hydrocarbon fuels, together with oxygen, to reduce coke rates.

Work on the use of oxygen-enriched air in updraught sintering and the enrichment with oxygen of recirculated gases in updraught sintering machines is discussed. In the latter, higher concentrations of SO_2 in the waste gas are obtained, plus a higher lead content in the sinter in a two-stage recirculating system.

Reference is also made to slag fuming by use of oxygen-enriched air.

In Britain secondary smelting is a highly important industry and a number of companies are believed to have adopted oxygen enrichment in their blast-furnaces. There are also possibilities for oxygen in the remelting of scrap in reverberatory-type furnaces by use of flame-enrichment techniques or supplementary oxygen-fuel burners.

It is perhaps a matter for some regret that the producers of oxygen were not better acquainted with the early Egyptians, Greeks and Romans, or even the Cornishmen, as this paper might well have been written some 25 centuries ago! History cannot be recalled, and it was left to nineteenth- and twentieth-century man first to discover the means of separating oxygen from the atmosphere in large enough quantities, and at economic costs, and then for the metallurgist to take advantage of the situation to utilize this cheap oxygen in pyrometallurgical extractive and refining processes which rely on the combustion of a fossil fuel or the oxidation of one or more elements present in the crude metal. Oxygen also

387

has a contribution to make to extractive metallurgy in that it can be used to produce high-temperature reducing gases by the partial oxidation of liquid or gaseous fuels containing carbon and hydrogen. Immense changes in ironmaking techniques in the coming years, based on this feature, are likely.

Uses of lead

When one is considering what may be described as 'new' techniques, and particularly factors which might have a bearing on the production rate of any commodity, it is highly important to ascertain whether there is a growing demand for the particular product. Unfortunately, domestic consumption appears to have been replaced largely by copper, and lead sheathing of electric cables also appears to have suffered at the hands of the plastics manufacturers.

Judging from the recent international conference *Lead and zinc through the 70s*, the battery industry now seems to be the yardstick by which future consumption may be extrapolated. Reasbeck[10] showed that, as far as vehicle batteries were concerned, six countries—the U.S.A., Japan, Britain, Germany, France and Italy—account for 76% of the world's vehicle population. He indicated a 22·5% total growth to 1975 and 40% to 1980, with Japan, Italy and Britain taking the lead, in that order. Gautschi forecast a threefold increase in the next 5 years for the use of lead sheet for insulation.[11]

It does seem, however, that the average growth rate is not going to be spectacular—probably of the order of 3·0–3·5% per annum in the foreseeable future. It is interesting to note that in the free world, with the exception of the U.S.A., the larger consuming countries rely on the importation of lead bullion, refined lead and the recovery of scrap to supply their needs. Few have extensive domestic resources of lead-bearing ores. Western European countries, e.g. France, West Germany and Britain, are concerned partially with primary extraction methods but, more deeply, with secondary refining and recovery techniques. In all of these, however, oxygen can and does play an important role.

Methods of production

Often, lead and zinc are mined together, and extraction plants may have to deal with both minerals via separate routes—of course, this excepts the Imperial Smelting process, which, one hopes, will one day be a large consumer of oxygen. Although there are important quantities of oxide ores, the major source of lead is from the sulphide ore, galena, found separately or in association with carbonates, sulphates and other minerals, e.g. silver, vanadium, arsenic, antimony, etc. The sulphide ores need to be sintered to form oxides, followed by smelting in a blast-furnace, although hearth smelting is still practised in some plants. Further purification follows by remelting in reverberatory or large under-fired pots, the impurities being oxidized or removed by sulphur and iron. The slag from lead blast-furnaces may be further treated by fuming in order to vaporize the zinc, which oxidizes and is collected as fume.

Use of oxygen in sintering

Interest in the use of oxygen in sintering processes appears to have been taken in Russia during 1958, when laboratory trials were undertaken at the Institute of Metallurgy and Enrichment of the Academy of Sciences of the Kazakh S.S.R.[1] The work was conducted on an experimental sintering unit with 14- to 16-kg samples. The unit consisted of a cylindrical sintering vessel, a reversible air blower, a receiving vessel and an instrument panel. Three thermocouples were inserted in the 200-mm high sinter bed, which was similar to the high melting point and high consumption charge used at the Ust-Kamenogorsk lead plant. The sinter rested on a fire grate and the top of the cylindrical sintering vessel was sealed with a water seal, into which was fitted a pipe through which a calculated volume of air was sucked. The pipe was also fitted with the oxygen inlet tube. The charge was ignited with coke fines, charcoal and shavings and, after ignition, a vacuum was created below the grate of 30–60 mm wg. The air flow was equal to 0.32 m^3/sec/m^2 and the humidity was 7.5%.

The charges consisted of two grades

	Pb	Cu	Zn	Fe	SiO$_2$	CaO	S	
A	32·3	2·5	7·09	14·7	10·4	5·0	6·45	(14 experiments)
B	31·2	2·06	6·6	18·0	10·9	4·1	5·9	(6 experiments)

and the fusing agents had the following composition:

	Fe	CaO	SiO$_2$
Iron ore	43·0	7·0	14·0
Quartz	6·0	2·5	77·0
Limestone	3·0	50·0	3·0

During the experiments tests were run with oxygen-enriched air up to 35.5%, and two types of oxygen trial were used: first, oxygen was used during the second half of the process and, secondly, during the whole of the experiment. The latter was found to be more satisfactory. Increasing the oxygen from 21 to 34% increased the vertical combustion speed from 10 to 15.7 mm/min, and the specific output of sinter from 17.8 to 42.7 ton/m^2/day. The sulphur yield rose from 0.86 to 1.2–1.46 ton/m^2/day at 30% oxygen. The maximum temperature with enriched air did not exceed 1000–1050°C (compared with normal figures of 800–900°C). The highest yield and quality of sinter was obtained during continuous enrichment. The best results were obtained with the continuous use of 30% oxygen blast, when the specific yield of suitable sinter was 31 ton/m^2/day (20 ton/m^2/day with air blast) and 1.5 ton/m^2/day of sulphur (cf. 0.9 with air). The cost reduction with oxygen was calculated as 7.73 roubles.

It would appear that practical work was done in a production updraught sintering unit in which normal operation was compared with the recirculation of the offtake gases and also with oxygen added to the offtake gases.[2] A plant was used having eight chambers, with a total area of 8 m^2. The sinter plant operated under a normal throughput of offtake gas of 12 220 Nm^3/h, containing 315·9

Nm^3/h SO_2 and an SO_2 content of 2·59%. Table 1 gives details of the results obtained.

Table 1 Summarized data of sintering experiments

	Without gas recirculation	One stage of gas recirculation	Two stages of gas recirculation	Two stages of gas recirculation + oxygen
Specific charge capacity, ton/m²/day	39·80	32·50	34·70	40·20
Sulphur in crude charge, %	14·00	14·00	14·65	13·85
Lead in crude charge, %	40·60	40·50	40·40	44·75
Sulphur in final charge, %	7·17	7·29	7·30	7·25
Lead in useful sinter, %	44·30	45·30	44·50	47·10
Specific capacity for useful sinter, ton/m²/day	13·10	10·60	10·10	13·16
Specific capacity for separating sulphur, ton/m²/day	1·71	1·38	1·37	1·67
Specific air consumption per m² of blast area, Nm³/min	2500	1000	750	750
SO_2 in offtake gas, %	2·59	4·81	6·13	8·50
Specific air consumption per ton of sinter, Nm³/ton	4600	2300	1700	1700
Temperature of offtake gas, °C	250–280	160–200	200–290	240–270
Specific oxygen consumption, Nm³/m²/h				48

There was an increase in SO_2 in the offtake gas of 64 Nm^3/h compared with the two-stage recirculating system.

It was concluded that oxygen-enriched blast at the gas recirculation stages (made possible with 50 $Nm^3/m^2/h$) intensified the roasting process to the level of the process when no recirculation was used, but increased the sulphur dioxide in the offtake gas from 2·59 to 8·50%.

During July, 1969, the author visited the East Helena plant of The American Smelting and Refining Company. The concentrates are pelletized on a 12-ft diameter disc and sintered on an 8-ft wide, updraught sinter strand which treats 1350 short ton/day. The initial charge of sinter is about 1 in in depth and is ignited by overhead natural gas burners. A second conveyor then deposits a further 14-in layer on top of the ignited sinter. Prior to this visit trials had been conducted with oxygen from cylinders at a rate of 60–70 ft^3/min. This preliminary work showed an appreciable improvement in sinter throughput, resulting in a 2·5-in diameter oxygen main being installed to provide enriched air to the first four air inlets on the strand. At that time it was the intention to use oxygen to regulate the output of sinter in accordance with fluctuations in blast-furnace demand, but a recent communication indicates that no further work has been carried out.

Oxygen enrichment in lead blast-furnaces

Honours for being the first user of oxygen-enriched air in a lead blast-furnace must go to Cominco at Trail, British Columbia. This plant was blessed with an oxygen supply available as a by-product from the Chemical & Fertiliser Division. Work first began in 1933 in zinc roasting and later commenced at the lead smelter for both blast enrichment and slag fuming for zinc recovery. The earlier report of 1949 by McNaughton et al.[3] was brought up to date by Landucci and Fuller[4] in 1961. The present author visited this plant in July, 1969. In the intervening period the number of furnaces had been reduced from four to three; two are in operation at any one time. The dimensions are given in Table 2.

Table 2

	1969	1961
Length, in	180–273	180–253
Width at tuyères, in	65–74	65–86
Width at top of shaft, in	83–89	83–101
Hearth width, in	60–76	
Bosh width, in	95–96	
Height of tuyères to charge plate, in	216	192–203
Number of tuyères		48–80
Blast pressure, oz/in²	42	42
Blast volume, ft³/min, NTP	10 000	10 500

The lead smelter has priority for the available oxygen and it may be divided between the two furnaces or all of it used on one, depending on current conditions, particularly if the furnace temperature falls. The oxygen is fed into the bustle pipes of the blast-furnaces.

Landucci and Fuller reported that the average oxygen usage was 725 ft³/min, equal to 26·1% oxygen in the blast, and gave a 22·2% increase in output in no. 10 furnace (length 250 in, width 65 in) and an increase of 25% in no. 12 furnace (length 253 in, width 74 in). Theoretical studies on no. 12 blast-furnace based on material and heat balances predicted that for every 100 ft³ of added oxygen the throughput should rise by 1·2 ton/h. In practice, the value was between 1·0 and 1·3 ton/h. The figures quoted in Table 3 were given.[4]

During the 1969 visit the coke rate was quoted as 9·5% and the production rate per furnace per day as 320 short tons.

The next reported work, from Russia, recorded work done at the Ust-Kamenogorsk lead and zinc plant.[5] No details of the dimensions of the furnace were given. Oxygen enrichment to give up to 26·5% oxygen in the blast was used

Table 3　Effect of oxygen on blast-furnace operation

Oxygen addition, ft³/min	300	600	900	1150
Oxygen in blast, %	23·2	25·3	27·2	28·8
Throughput				
No. 10 furnace, ton/op.h	31·3	33·9	36·5	38·7
No. 12 furnace, ton/op.h	33·2	36·3	39·5	42·2
Coke in charge				
No. 10 furnace, %	11·6	11·1	10·7	10·3
No. 12 furnace, %	11·0	10·9	10·8	10·7
Lead in slag				
No. 10 furnace, %	2·4	2·9	3·5	3·9
No. 12 furnace, %	2·3	2·9	3·5	4·2

and, at this level, the furnace output rose by 27%. At 26·5% oxygen content the amount of air used fell by 34% and there was a corresponding reduction in the flue gas volume, which lowered the gas cleaning cost. There was also a reduction in flue gas temperature from 286°C to 120–130°C. Figures as low as 60–80°C were obtained over a long period. The dust content of the gas fell from 2·0–2·5 to 1·5–1·7 g/m³ and there was an increase in metallic yield. At 25% oxygen blast the coke rate fell by 13·4%. No base figures were quoted. Lead losses to the slag fell from 2·05 to 1·21%.

Further work reported[6] from the Ust-Kamenogorsk Combine claimed that with 30–31% oxygen in the blast the coke consumption was reduced by 35%, fluxes were reduced by 54%, which led to an increase in the lead content in the sinter from 36·1 to 42–47% and a reduction in slag yield of 37·7%. No production figures were quoted. The same paper recorded work from the Chimkentsky lead works showing an increase in production of 33% and a reduction in coke of 17·5%.

Hase[7] reported results obtained at the East Helena plant of Asarco in 1962. The furnace has a double set of 3-in tuyères, 46 on the bottom row and 35 on the top row. It is 5 ft wide at the bottom tuyères and 9 ft wide at the top tuyères; the length is 20 ft. These dimensions have been increased in more recent years. The oxygen was introduced so that the air to both rows of tuyères was enriched to give 24 and 26% oxygen in the blast.

In the first test, with 24% oxygen blast, the results presented in Table 4 were obtained. A second series with 26% oxygen blast gave the results presented in Table 5.

It was observed that there was a relationship between the coke charged and the dust and fume losses. With a reduction of 7·5% in coke rate, the dust produced/ton charge fell by 7·5% at 3% enrichment.

Table 4   Use of 3% oxygen in lead blast-furnace[7]

	Normal	3% enrichment
Charge, ton/day	772·1	968·6
% Increase		25·5
lb coke/ton		227
% Decrease		9·9
lb dust/ton charge	107	68
% Decrease		36·4
% Pb in slag	1·5	1·4

Table 5   Use of 5% oxygen in lead blast-furnace[7]

	Normal	5% enrichment
Charge, ton/day	748·1	1144·1
% Increase		52·9
lb coke/ton	256	215
% Decrease		16·0
lb dust/ton charge	112	61
% Decrease		45·5
% Pb in slag	0·96	1·30

Oxygen in slag fuming

Many plants which use oxygen in lead blast-furnaces also use oxygen-enriched air for the removal of zinc from the lead blast-furnace slag. McNaughton et al.[3] described the operation at Trail, in which air and pulverized coal are blown through premelted slag in a furnace 10 ft wide × 24 ft long × 10 ft high. It is fitted with 36 2-in tuyères on each side. The molten slag is at a temperature of 1200°C, and the ZnO is reduced to Zn. This volatilizes and reoxidizes above the bath to ZnO and is collected in a bag filter system after cooling by a waste-heat boiler. The published results show that when air containing 23–24% oxygen is used, the zinc content falls from around 16–17% to 1·6–2·2% in about 2 h 15 min, compared with 2 h 40 min. The recovery of zinc is greater. The figures show an increased recovery rate of 8–25% with 23·4% oxygen blast.

At the Ust-Kamenogorsk plant it was not possible to use oxygen for slag fuming to the fullest extent, but enrichment of the blast to 24–25% increased the reclamation of zinc from sublimates from 73·2 to 82–84%, with a fuel decrease of 12%.

Use of oxygen in secondary lead recovery

The recovery of metals from scrap, dross, etc., is an important part of the economy of all countries where plants have been developed to deal with steel, cast iron, aluminium, copper, brass and, of course, lead. In the U.S.A. approximately 50% of 1×10^6 ton lead produced in 1964 arose from secondary sources, and it would seem that the proportion in the United Kingdom is not dissimilar. Therefore, this is an important industry and one which should be giving serious thought to methods of improving outputs and reductions in fuel rates in the blast-furnaces and reverberatory furnaces used for recovery and refining. Fuel prices for both coke and oil continue to rise, and there are many applications where oxygen can be used to effect economies both for the benefit of the individual companies and of the nation.

Few, if any, results of work have been published in Britain, although it is thought that experimental work has been done which may have led to the permanent use of oxygen in some plants.

Cogen,[8] in his paper dealing with plant-scale tests carried out in the U.S.A., proved that oxygen enrichment provided both technical and economic benefits in an industry which is characterized by high operating costs. How much more must this be true at the present time with inflationary trends due to high wage costs and the price and shortage of good-quality metallurgical coke.

The author pointed out that the main source of scrap in the secondary lead industry is battery plates, comprising 65% of the total, other metallic sources yield 12% and the remainder comes mainly from dross. This situation may not necessarily be true in Britain in 1971 because of the growth in demand for vehicle batteries, and it is likely to have altered the proportions of metal recovered by blast-furnaces and reverberatory-type furnaces because of the ability of the latter process to deal directly with 100% charges of such scrap by the use of what one would expect to be a cheaper capital cost furnace capable of employing more readily available and cheaper oil as the fuel.

Cogen compared the relative proportions of each raw material used in primary and secondary blast-furnaces (Table 6). At first sight, it would seem that coke

Table 6 Charge comparison in primary and secondary lead blast-furnace smelting

	Primary, %	Secondary, %
Lead in charge	40·0	60·0
Iron in charge	1·5	5·5
Coke rate	12·0	5·0

reduction, which was reported particularly by the Russians in primary smelting, is not so important in secondary smelting, but Cogen reported a 15–20% saving, which would reduce the consumption to 4·25–4·00%, which is well worth saving.

Most of the work done by Cogen was with a blast containing 24% oxygen, although tests up to 26% oxygen showed a straight-line relationship between the derived benefits and the percentage oxygen in the blast. Production increases lay between 25% and 50%, and lead recovery was improved by reduced dust losses, losses to the slag and dry dross formation. He quoted normal dust losses for air practice of up to 15% and a reduction of 30–35% was attained with oxygen. When a charge containing 60% lead was used, there was a lead saving of 3 ton/100-ton charge: this was attributed to the reduction in gas velocity in the furnace arising from a lower total blast volume/ton charge. There was also a reduction in the top gas temperature ranging between 50 and 150°F (10–66°C). Owing to higher slag temperatures, the slag losses fell by 0·5–1·0%, and the dry dross formation was reduced from 6 to 5%.

Oxygen enrichment was also used to accelerate the start-up of the blast-furnace. Normally, with air operation this took 8–12 h, but with 26% oxygen in the blast the time was reduced to 2–4 h.

This company operated reverberatory furnaces for the recovery of dross. A lead dross reverberatory furnace does not appear much different in design from those used in the aluminium and brass industries or in the lead industry for the remelting of recovered battery plates and other scrap. These are usually end-fired with air–oil or air–natural gas burners. The practice is different when drossing, as it is necessary to remove such metals as copper, arsenic, antimony, sulphur, etc.: this is done by melting the raw materials and separating various metals or their compounds according to their relative specific gravities. Such reverberatory furnaces are smaller than those used in direct lead scrap melting.

Cogen pointed out that the main restrictive factor to performance improvement is the combustion volume. He showed that combustion stoichiometrically of 1 Sft^3 natural gas requires 10 Sft^3 air and gives a total waste gas volume of 11 Sft^3, whereast he same volume of natural gas requires only 2 Sft^3 oxygen and produces 3 Sft^3 waste gas. Per 1000 Btu thermal input the waste gas volume is reduced by 73%. The elimination of nitrogen also increases the theoretical flame temperature from 3500 to 4900°F (1925 to 2700°C). Cogen used a single oxygen-fuel burner of 30×10^6 Btu/h capacity mounted through the roof at the crown of the arch. It was angled 20° from the vertical, fired towards the exhaust end of the furnace and positioned to impinge upon the dross pit. Between 15 and 30% of the total fuel input was used via the roof burners. The improvements achieved were a production gain of 35–50%, decreased fuel consumption (25–33%) and a reduction in the dross recycling from 20 to 25% to 10 to 12%. These figures are particularly impressive and a pointer to what could be achieved in the United Kingdom, where fuel costs are relatively higher. The roof burner method may not be the only way of achieving the same results. No mention was made of the effect of such techniques on roof life, which might be severe, particularly with the over-ambitious use of roof burners. It may be that the injection of oxygen below the normal burners alone, or a combination of oxygen-fuel roof burners plus end burners, might show a more satisfactory result, especially where oil firing is used with the consequent higher flame velocity.

An excellent paper was presented in the U.S.A. in February, 1970, on work done in a blast-furnace at the Murph Metals Southern Lead Co. smelter.[9] The blast-furnace is water-jacketed, having a diameter of 48 in at the tuyères and 52 in at the top. Antimonial lead alloys are produced from reverberatory furnace slags, battery scrap, antimony ore and various by-products. The furnace is well instrumented and close laboratory control is maintained over the charge components and furnace products.

The paper describes the method of charging and starting up of the furnace from cold. Metallurgical coke (3 in × 5 in) is used, and fines are avoided.

The need for increased furnace production in 1964 prompted the use of oxygen-enriched air blast, which was originally fixed at 24%, i.e. 3% enrichment. Decided improvements in production and coke rates became evident and, as a result of a study of Russian data which claimed that increased oxygen enrichment gave increased production, better recoveries, lower coke consumption and lower fume production in direct proportion to the amount of increase up to 33% total oxygen, Murph decided to increase the enrichment to 30%, but decreased the total blast rate to 1000 ft³/min to improve the smoke-handling problem at the furnace feed hole. The experience of the Russians was substantiated, except for the decrease in coke requirement, and it was also shown that above 25% oxygen the decrease was not proportional to the increase in production and dust loading. The Murph results are summarized in Table 7.

Table 7 Furnace production at Murph Metals with varying oxygen content

Total oxygen content, %	21	24	30
Total blast air + oxygen, ft³/min	1500	1250	1016
Total oxygen added, ft³/min	0	50	116
Average back pressure, oz	10–35	15–30	15–25
Average top gas temperature, °C	260–650	204–427	150–260
Average production of clean metal, short ton/day	30	38	45
Average % coke of charge	10·0	7·5	7·3
Average dust production, % of metal	21	17	8
Average metal content of slag, %	5·9	4·3	2·95
Average tin content of slag, %	1·50	0·90	0·33
Average dross production, % of metal	23	21	19
Averages represented operating time, months	1	30	24

Murph and Pinkston indicated that with the use of oxygen at 30% in the blast the increase in production was 50%, fume decreased by 63% and coke consumption decreased by 27%. There were also decreased tin, antimony and lead losses in the slag.

Blast air was supplied from a Roots-Connersville blower controlled by a Foxboro air-weight controller. Oxygen was introduced between the blower and the tuyères. Gaseous oxygen was provided by evaporation from liquid oxygen and controlled by pressure adjustment on a critical orifice flow meter. It would appear from these results that liquid oxygen can be used economically in lead blast-furnaces.

Although the company was planning to install a larger furnace to meet increased production demands, it was their intention to use oxygen in it, the amount being determined by experimentation.

Possible new developments

As far as the author is aware, some of the newer techniques, such as flash-smelting, have not been widely applied to primary lead smelting. Flash-smelting is practised in Finland by use of preheated air, and, recently, oxygen has been introduced as a means of increasing the capacity of a copper flash-smelter. It has been used at the INCO plant for many years in the treatment of copper concentrates. Given the right conditions, e.g. a desire to increase production or a plant operating on a low lead/high sulphur concentrate, it might well be that autogenous oxygen flash-smelting of lead may one day become a viable process. Doubtless, the greater recovery of sulphur (as elemental sulphur, liquid SO_2 or sulphuric acid) would have an important bearing on the economics of such a process.

Another possibility might be the use of a hydrocarbon fuel injected with oxygen, as previously mentioned in ironmaking. Normally, cold air is used in lead blast-furnaces, and the endothermic cracking of oil or natural gas would thus have a harmful effect on the heat balance and also might lead to an undesirable heightening of the high-temperature zone unless oxygen were used. Recently, work has been done in ironmaking in which the hydrocarbon is partially oxidized in a separate gas cracker with oxygen to produce a high-temperature reducing gas mixture of CO and H_2. This is introduced into the zone of the blast-furnace where the main indirect reduction of iron oxide by CO is proceeding at a temperature around 850–1000°C. As the reduction of PbO is mainly by CO, such a technique might be suggested for primary lead blast-furnaces. If necessary, the reducing gas temperature could be reduced by introducing a suitable modulator, e.g. air, steam or recirculated top gas. The gains in output and reduction in fuel consumption in the iron blast-furnace are considerable and the process should be considered for lead production.

References

1. MILENTYEVA V. I. AND GNATYSHENKO G. I. Experiments on the use of oxygen in the

sintering of lead charges. *Tsvet. Metally, Mosk.*, **31,** no. 5 1958, 38–44. (Russian text)
2. MIKHEEV V. A. AND GOUBAIDULLIN G. S. Agglomerating roasting of lead charges on an up-draught sintering machine, with recirculation of gases and the use of oxygen. *Tsvet. Metally, Mosk.*, **36,** no. 4 1963, 27–35; *Tsvet. Metally, N.Y.*, **4,** no. 4 1963, 26–34.
3. McNAUGHTON R. R. *et al.* The use of oxygen enriched air in the metallurgical operations of Cominco at Trail, B.C. *Trans. Am. Inst. Min. Engrs*, **185,** 1949, 446–50.
4. LANDUCCI L. AND FULLER F. T. Oxygen-enriched air in lead and zinc smelting. *J. Metals, N.Y.*, **13,** 1961, 759–63.
5. VARTANYAN A. M. AND KOPTCHENKO D. S. The experimental use of oxygen in the lead smelting shaft furnaces. *Tsvet. Metally, Mosk.*, **32,** no. 5 1959, 46–9. (Russian text)
6. GETSKIN L. S. SAGINBAEV E. F. AND BUTENKO R. S. The technical and economic effectiveness of the employment of oxygen in the lead and zinc industries of the USSR. *Tsvet. Metally, Mosk.*, **41,** no. 10 1968, 1–4; *Tsvet. Metally, N.Y.*, **10,** no. 10 1968, 1–5.
7. HASE E. A. Oxygen enriched blast at Asarco's lead smelter. *J. Metals N.Y.*, **17,** 1965, 1334–7.
8. COGEN L. L. Oxygen in the secondary lead industry. In *Pyrometallurgical processes in nonferrous metallurgy* (New York: Gordon and Breach, 1967), 319–31. (*Metall. Soc. Conf.* vol. 39)
9. MURPH D. B. AND PINKSTON J. L. Current blast furnace practice at Murph Metals Southern Lead Company smelter. Paper presented at AIME Annual meeting, Feb. 1970.
10. REASBECK P. Contribution to discussion on 'What is the future for lead consumption?' In *Lead and zinc through the 70s* (London: Lead Development Association, 1970), 6–7.
11. GAUTSCHI E. Contribution to discussion on 'What is the future for lead consumption?' In *Lead and zinc through the 70s* (London: Lead Development Association, 1970), p. 7.

Development of a pilot-plant cell for electrorefining lead in fused-chloride electrolytes

E. H. Amstein Ph.D., B.Sc., A.R.C.S.
W. D. Davis B.Sc., A.R.C.S.
C. Hillyer B. Tech.

*All of Research Laboratories, Associated Lead Manufacturers, Ltd.,
Perivale, Middlesex*

669.054.72.001.4:669.447

Synopsis

A number of laboratory studies have demonstrated that certain impurity elements may be concentrated in the anode when lead is electrorefined in fused-chloride electrolytes. The separation of gold, bismuth and antimony is especially clean, copper and silver are appreciably concentrated, and tin electrolyses with the lead. No commercial use appears to have been made of this principle, and the present work was directed towards developing a practical cell.

The design described contains a horizontally disposed diaphragm, consisting of flexible vitreous alumina–silica fibres, which is completely resistant to thermal shock. The cathode lead is deposited underneath the diaphragm, and is tapped continuously; the anode alloy lies above the diaphragm and is tapped at intervals when the impurities in it reach the desired concentration. The operating current density is between 2 and 3 A/cm² and the current efficiency of lead deposition is 100%. The largest scale of operation to date is 3500 A (13·5 kg/h or $2\frac{1}{4}$ tonnes of lead per week). The overall dimensions of this cell are 68 cm × 68 cm × 30 cm ($26\frac{1}{2}$ in × $26\frac{1}{2}$ in × 12 in).

The fibres forming this diaphragm are liable to attack by oxide ions present in the fused electrolyte, but it has been found possible to prevent damage by including in the electrolyte the chlorides of elements capable of precipitating oxide ion as an insoluble oxide.

A cell as described running at or near 3 A/cm² has a maximum terminal voltage of 2·5 V, corresponding to a power requirement of 650 kWh/t, and attains an anode temperature of 700°C.

Depending on the separations being made and on the composition of final anode desired, there is the possibility of reducing the current density and, hence, the power consumption. The corresponding figure for aqueous lead baths is about 200 kWh/t.

The cell has also been applied to the refining of solder and it might prove to be useful for other low-melting metals.

399

A number of metals are produced commercially by fused-salt electrolysis, the outstanding example being aluminium. The cell reactions typically consist of the decomposition of a halide or oxide with a gas as the anode product. There are, however, hardly any commercial processes employing electrorefining (in the sense of the dissolution of an element at an anode and the deposition of the same element at the cathode in a purer form) with liquid metal electrodes and a fused-salt electrolyte. This appears to be due to the engineering difficulties of separating two liquid electrodes and still providing a current path of reasonably low resistance between them. These difficulties are overcome very elegantly in the 'three-layer' process for aluminium,[1] in which the density of the impure (anode) aluminium is increased by alloying with copper to make it heavier than the fused-salt electrolyte, which, in turn, contains barium halides to make it heavier than the pure (cathode) aluminium, which consequently floats on the electrolyte and forms the top layer. Aluminium is electrolysed from the bottom to the top layer, where it can be tapped as it is formed and fresh anode feed is added to the lower layer via a forehearth. The same principle has been investigated on a pilot scale for refining magnesium,[2] but does not appear to have been adopted in full production.

Plutonium is electrorefined on a small batch scale in cylindrical ceramic cells containing an interior cylindrical compartment for the molten anode. The pure cathode is collected in the annulus surrounding the anode compartment, and is recovered by allowing the whole to solidify and breaking up the container and contents.[3]

No commercial use of fused-salt electrorefining seems to have been established for the lower-melting heavy metals, e.g. lead, although the successful development of such a process would offer certain advantages. For example, the high current densities that can be employed (as compared with those in aqueous electrorefining plants) would result in space savings. The fact that both anode and cathode are molten eliminates any difficulties with anode slime accumulation and with dendritic or uneven deposits, and there can be a clean separation between the molten metal and molten salt with no 'drag-out' of electrolyte with the deposit. Nevertheless, the high operating temperature seems bound to increase the power requirement of the cell itself, although there may be savings in the energy requirements for casting and recasting electrodes.

The electrorefining of lead in fused chlorides has been the subject of a number of laboratory studies, mainly by use of cells consisting of one crucible inside another, by Delimarskii and his co-workers.[4] These showed that, at current densities of 1 A/cm^2 (1000 A/ft^2) and above, the concentrations of antimony and bismuth in the cathodes are very low, in the 0·0001–0·001% range, even when the concentrations of these elements in the anode are allowed to rise to considerable percentages.

Arsenic, when present, was also eliminated, although there was probably some volatilization of the trichloride from the electrolyte. Gold was completely retained, and silver almost completely retained in the anode. The behaviour of copper, however, was disappointing, in that the amount of copper in the cathode was appreciable even when only modest accumulations of copper in the anode had taken place.

The results of Delimarskii and his co-workers were published without any theoretical analysis, except for correlating the results with the potentials of the various metal–metal ion electrodes in fused chlorides, but a more sophisticated analysis of the process has been attempted by Hart, Hills and Tomlinson.[5] They assumed that thermodynamic equilibrium exists between both electrodes and the adjacent electrolyte and applied the friction coefficient theory of Laity[6] to the relative rates of transport of the major element and impurity metal ions across the cell. They thus arrived at a 'refinability parameter' for each impurity (in lead as major element) such that values below unity correspond to accumulation of the impurity in the anode and values above unity to preferential deposition on the cathode. Their treatment makes a number of simplifying assumptions, but the order of their refinability parameters does correspond with the observed behaviour of different impurities. In particular, their estimated parameters for bismuth, silver, and copper in lead are, respectively, 10^{-8}, 0·16 and 2·7 and, in practice, the retention of these impurities in the anode can be classed as excellent, good and poor. Unfortunately, no estimate of the parameter is given for antimony. The possibility of effectively producing a pure lead cathode product from anti-monial lead, and, incidentally, of removing bismuth from the secondary lead circuit, is of special importance to secondary lead producers, and the excellent performance in bismuth removal may be of interest to primary producers.

Laboratory studies[7] have demonstrated that when the anode metal contains an appreciable percentage of tin as well as lead, the cathode product is a lead–tin alloy, but antimony, bismuth, precious metals and some copper are retained in the anode. It is thus also possible to refine secondary solder in a fused-chloride cell, and, recently, the U.S. Bureau of Mines[8] have described a successful experiment on the concentration of gold contained in scrap solder by this method.

A few publications have described attempts to carry out the process on a pilot-plant scale. A very interesting pioneer attempt was made by Borchers.[9] His cell was externally heated and worked at the rather low current density of 0·1 A/cm². In recent years Pavlenko and Grinyuk[10] have described experiments with rigid porous diaphragms, permeable to the electrolyte but not to molten metal, for separating the electrodes. They concluded that existing materials were inadequate to the task. Delimarskii and his colleagues[11] have worked on refractory-lined cells with the anode metal lying on the bottom, and vertical graphite plates as cathodes. The cathode metal is collected in horizontal troughs just under the cathode, but at a higher level than the anode metal surface. This design would appear to have the disadvantage of a long and non-uniform current path.

The present paper is an account of work carried out over the past five years in the Central Research Laboratories of Associated Lead Manufacturers, Ltd. The

o

object of the work was to develop, if possible, a metal refining cell capable of operating economically, on a reasonable scale, under industrial conditions.

The distinctive features of the cells described in the following section have been made the subjects of patent protection.

Experimental

Because of the difficulty of providing impervious containers for fused electrolytes, it was regarded as imperative, from the start, to use the ohmic heat generated in the cell to maintain the working temperature. This avoidance of external heating enables the container to be made from as many separate water-cooled metal plates as convenient, because as long as these meet fairly closely the joints between them are readily sealed with solidified electrolyte and a layer of solidified electrolyte prevents chemical interaction between the container and the fused electrolyte. It may be said, in fact, that the fused electrolyte is contained by the solidified electrolyte.

Given the necessity of generating enough ohmic heat to maintain temperature, it is clear that the required wattage should be the product of the highest possible current, and the lowest possible cell voltage, to maximize the rate and minimize the cost of electrolysis. It follows from this that the electrode area should be as large and the interelectrode distance as small as possible, and the problem becomes one of keeping two large pools of molten metal near each other, but separated from each other, with the separation as uniform as possible to keep the current density uniform. The geometry of the three-layer aluminium refining cell is ideal in this respect, but because there is no possibility of formulating a fused electrolyte of higher density than lead, or even antimony, this geometry is only possible if a diaphragm can be provided which is permeable by the electrolyte but not by the molten metal.

Diaphragm cells, as we have seen,[3, 9, 11] are, however, not the only possible solution to the problem, but these other suggestions involve either long and tortuous current paths, or great difficulties in scaling up. The diaphragms which have been tried to date have consisted of rigid, porous ceramics, which have also suffered from formidable disadvantages, especially when large industrial units are required. In recent years, however, flexible 'blankets' made from inorganic fibres have been developed and sold as heat-insulating materials. It was decided to try such a material as a diaphragm, since its flexibility would ensure that it could not crack in use, and because it was already available in large continuous areas there would seem to be no serious limitation to the size of cell.

A 'blanket' material available when this work was started has the trade name 'Triton', and consists of alumina–silica vitreous fibres. It has the obvious advantages mentioned above, but there was, of course, no indication that it could retain a sufficient head of metal or that it would be sufficiently inert under the very unusual conditions to which it would be subjected in this work.

It was decided right from the start to reverse the geometry of a three-layer aluminium refining cell and have the cathode as the lower and the anode as the upper molten electrode. This was because it was judged easier to arrange a continuous feed of cathode metal from the lower half of the cell and also easier to replenish the anode pool from above. Another very early decision was to maintain, if possible, a layer of molten electrolyte above the anode metal. The original reason for this was to prevent oxidation of the anode metal, but, as is shown later, this layer plays an important part in maintaining the hydraulic balance in the cell and also in the protection of the diaphragm fibres from chemical degradation.

An anode of lead–antimony alloy was indeed concentrated to 96% Sb, at quite an early stage, in a 200-A cell made in a cylindrical copper vessel. This had a horizontal diaphragm resting on a graphite disc, which served as the cathode, and the lead deposited by electrolysis flowed along radial grooves to the centre and left via a hollow graphite rod which formed the cathode conductor. This design almost immediately revealed two difficulties. The first was that of satisfactorily sealing the anode compartment to prevent anode metal from running over the edge of the diaphragm disc into the lower parts of the cell. This was readily solved by using the flexibility of the blanket to turn up the edges of the diaphragm and make a shallow container for the anode metal, or, rather, a combined diaphragm and anode container. More important, cells in which the diaphragm rested on a graphite plate were very liable to short-circuit failure as a result of what came to be called 'penetration'.

This consisted of the impregnation of parts of the diaphragm by lead actually electrodeposited in the pores. This starts in the pores next to the cathode plate; surface tension prevents this metal from leaving the pores and these metal-filled pores, being nearer the anode, attract to themselves a disproportionate share of the current so that a 'front' is developed with a strong tendency to move through the diaphragm towards the anode, eventually causing a short circuit.

If the above explanation is correct, then a possible remedy for penetration would be to keep a thin layer of 'free' electrolyte between the undersurface of the diaphragm and the surface of the cathode metal. This, in its turn, made it necessary to devise a form of multi-point support for the diaphragm, and also to pay close attention to maintaining the level of the cathode metal surface constant. One form of cell which was used at this point is shown diagrammatically in Fig. 1. The scale of operation at this time was 800 A at about $4\frac{1}{2}$ V.

The cathode of this cell was a graphite block machined to give a recess 25 mm deep by 175 mm square with a central boss into which was screwed a metal cathode conductor. The recess was fitted with four, square 'support plates', each consisting of a stout zircon rim supporting a 3-mm thick zircon plate drilled with a number of 6-mm holes to provide about 40% of open area for electrolysis.

The top surfaces of the support plates were flush with the raised outer flange of the graphite block, which was covered with thin zircon plates to insulate it from the diaphragm. One layer of blanket was laid flat over the support plates and the outer flange, and a frame of insulating bricks was pressed lightly on to the outer edges so as to delineate an anode compartment equal in area to the recess. A second layer of blanket was moulded into the anode compartment to form a container for the anode metal. A graphite anode conductor was employed. The recess in the graphite block was filled with pure lead, and the level of the inter-

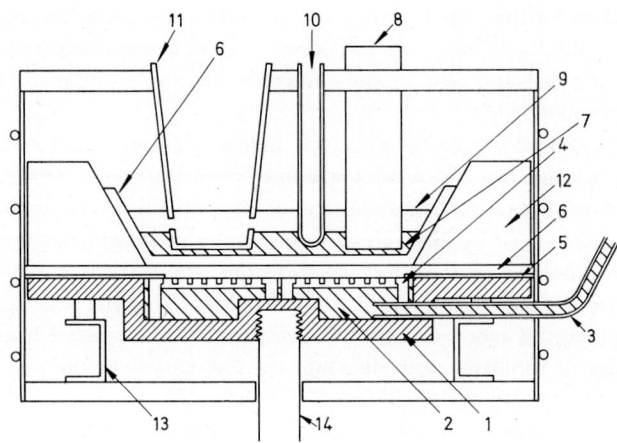

Fig. 1 Diagram of 800-A cell with graphite cathode plate. 1, Cathode plate; 2, cathode metal; 3, siphon tube; 4, zircon support plate; 5, zircon insulator plate; 6, diaphragm; 7, anode metal; 8, anode conductor; 9, electrolyte; 10, thermocouple sheath; 11, baffle crucible; 12, ceramic block; 13, support; 14, cathode conductor

face between the cathode lead and the electrolyte could be regulated by a siphon formed from an angled stainless steel tube screwed into the vertical wall of the cathode recess. This was heated at the outer end in order to maintain a free path for molten lead to leave the cell as it was electrodeposited.

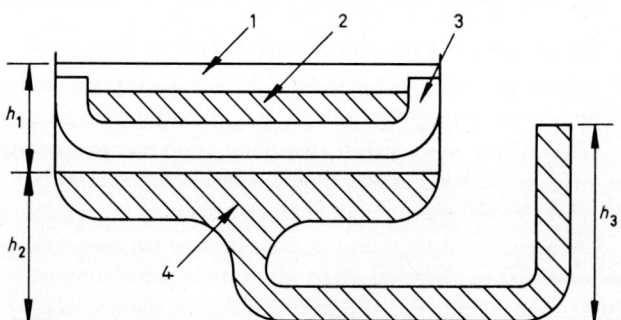

Fig. 2 Diagram illustrating hydraulic balance in cell. 1, Electrolyte; 2, anode metal; 3, diaphragm; 4, cathode metal

At this point it is appropriate to indicate what are believed to be the hydraulic considerations prevailing in a cell with a diaphragm supported clear of the cathode metal surface, and with an upturned vent tube for the cathode metal. A diagrammatic representation is given in Fig. 2. The diaphragm is represented as forming a container for the anode metal, but because it is permeable to electrolyte, the electrolyte layers above and below the diaphragm form one deep layer for hydraulic purposes. The cell and the cathode vent tube then form a 'U'-tube.

If h_1 is the difference in level between the cathode–electrolyte interface and the surface of the electrolyte above the anode, h_2 is the height of the cathode–electrolyte interface above the lowest point of the 'U' and h_3 is the height of the cathode outlet above the lowest point, the equilibrium value of h_2 is given by

$$h_1\rho_e + h_2\rho_m = h_3\rho_m$$

where ρ_e and ρ_m are the densities of the electrolyte and of the cathode metal, respectively.

In a given cell and over a short period h_1 is a function of the total amount of the electrolyte present, and is, in principle, constant. It can be seen that adjustment of h_3 (in practical terms rotation of the outlet tube in its mounting) can be used to regulate h_2. It is important, however, to note the function of the anode metal: this participates in the hydraulics by displacing electrolyte. An addition of anode metal therefore increases h_1 and so reduces h_2. The surplus cathode metal thus leaves the cell via the outlet until equilibrium is re-established. Conversely, as anode metal is consumed and cathode metal leaves the cell, h_1 is gradually reduced and h_2 increases again. Consequently, in a properly adjusted cell, an addition of anode metal causes a brief, rapid feed of cathode metal. Afterwards the rate of feed of cathode metal lags a little behind the electrolytic rate until the shortfall is made good by the next addition of anode metal.

Over a long period, therefore, the integrated feed from the cathode is equal within errors of measurement to the electrolytic rate. The behaviour predicted above is observed in a practical cell and movement of the cathode–electrolyte interface is shown by a small increase in resistance, due to the increased depth of free electrolyte under the diaphragm immediately after topping up the anode.

Although some encouraging results were obtained with cells of the type shown in Fig. 1, there were still difficulties due to penetration tracks being initiated from the graphite flange surrounding the cathode recess, in spite of the zircon plates interposed between the flange and the diaphragm.

The final design selected for testing on a larger scale avoided many of the drawbacks encountered with graphite cathode plates and lends itself much better to enlargement of scale. The 800-A (nominal) version is illustrated in Fig. 3. Four shaped zircon or other suitable refractory blocks are combined in a square water-cooled container to form a 175 mm square cathode well or recess 25 mm deep, a shallow shelf to locate the diaphragm support, and an upper compartment with concave walls sloping back towards the water-cooled outer plates at the top. The diaphragm supports consisted at one time of drilled sillimanite plates, but these have been replaced by parallel grids made from elliptical-section aluminous porcelain thermocouple sheaths 7 mm wide. The spaces between these are aligned with grooves in the interior faces of the blocks forming the anode compartment. Experience has shown that a certain amount of gas, believed to be hydrogen, is liberated from the cathode surface during electrolysis, particularly in the early stages, and it is essential to provide a means for this to escape. The continuous gaps between parallel support rods, when aligned with grooves in the inner faces of the ceramic blocks, are much better adapted for this purpose than separate holes in drilled plates. The satisfactory solution of the problem of gas escape has been one of the more important practical steps forward in the development of working cells.

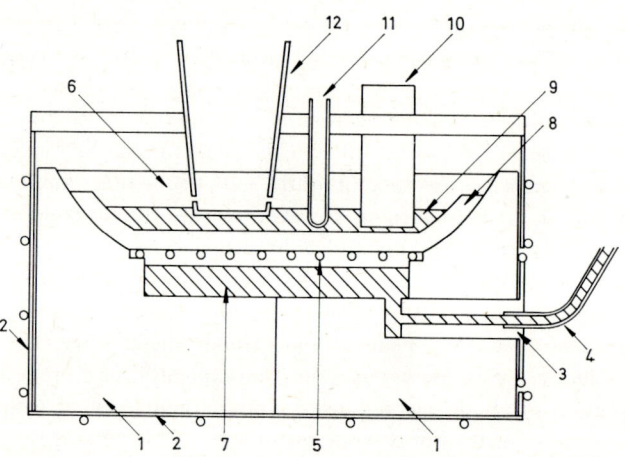

Fig. 3 Diagram of 800-A cell with ceramic block lining. 1, Ceramic block; 2, water-cooled plate; 3, cathode conductor; 4, siphon tube; 5, support rods; 6, electrolyte; 7, cathode metal; 8, diaphragm; 9, anode metal; 10, anode conductor; 11, thermocouple sheath; 12, baffle crucible

Other features illustrated in Fig. 3 include the baffle crucible, which is used for replenishing anode metal. It is an ordinary fireclay crucible with some radially drilled holes near the base, and it serves to protect the diaphragm from damage by the repeated impact of streams of molten metal. The cell is fitted with an asbestos–cement composition lid, which, in addition to the baffle crucible, carries a thermocouple sheath and the anode conductors, which may be of graphite, or of metal sheathed in graphite, and are normally gripped in water-cooled clamps (not shown) which rest on the lid and are connected to the positive dc supply. Some attention has to be paid to the thermal balance in these conductors. Normally, they are designed so that the ohmic heat generated by the passage of the working current through them balances the heat conducted out of the cell by them by virtue of the temperature gradient between the bottom end, which is in the anode metal, and the top end, which is water-cooled. The higher thermal conductivity of graphite makes it necessary to dissipate more electrical energy in the anode conductors (if thermal balance is to be satisfied) than when metals are used, with the consequence that the total cell voltage is increased. On the other hand, most metals and alloys are corroded to some extent by molten antimony; recourse to graphite-sheathed chromium steel with careful attention to avoiding undue contact resistance may therefore offer the best compromise.

The problem of the removal of cathode lead from a cell made from ceramic blocks has been solved by combining the cathode conductor and molten lead outlet as shown in Fig. 4. A stainless steel bar with a 9-mm axial bore is inserted

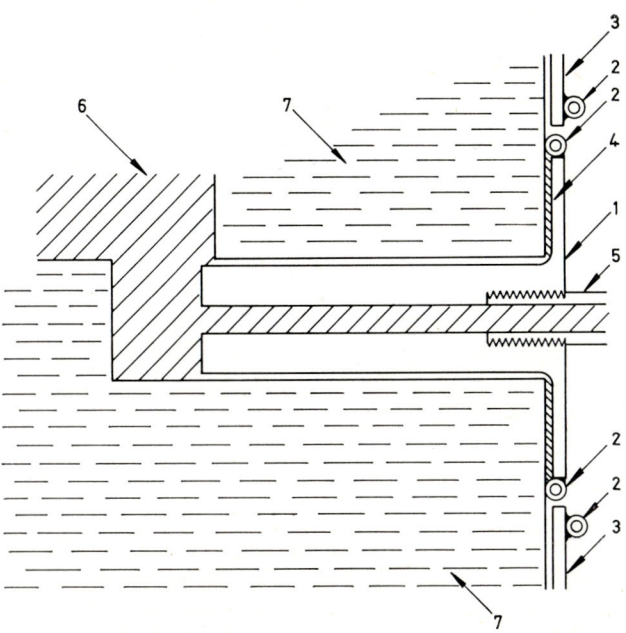

Fig. 4 Combined cathode conductor and vent tube. 1, Stainless steel bar with welded flange; 2, cooling coil; 3, water-cooled side wall of cell; 4, packing; 5, siphon tube; 6, cathode metal; 7, ceramic block

through a hole in one of the ceramic blocks which connects with a small cavity extending downwards from the main cathode well. At the outer end a stainless steel disc is welded to the bar, and round the periphery of this is brazed a ring of copper pipe carrying cooling water and connected also to the negative busbar. A 9-mm outer diameter stainless steel outlet tube, bent as shown, is fastened by a direct thread, or a union, to the centre of the bar in such a way that it can be adjusted by rotation to vary the height h_3 of Fig. 2. The centre of the disc is kept hot because the current flowing radially across it generates enough heat to compensate for that conducted outwards along the radial temperature gradient between the hot centre and the cold periphery of the disc. The temperature at the centre is thus kept high enough to allow molten lead to leave the cell via the outlet tube. This tube is provided, if necessary, with some auxiliary heating by a small gas flame, and the union can be lagged.

The water-cooled outside plate of the cell is provided with a circular hole to correspond with the disc, and three screws on suitable mountings (not shown) hold the disc hard against the outer surface of the ceramic block. The gap between the disc and block is packed with ceramic fibre and heat-resisting cement, and any electrolyte or metal which finds its way through flaws in this packing is halted by solidification when it reaches the edge of the water-cooled disc: thus, the contents of the cell are effectively retained.

The structural features which have provided a basis for trials with scaled-up cells have now been outlined, but it is necessary also to refer to the question of the chemical stability of the fibres forming the diaphragm. In the early stages of the development there were many instances of rapid failure of diaphragms. This was found to be due to chemical attack whereby the fibres were converted to a mass of crystals lacking the resilience of the original fibres.

A programme of laboratory work established that a typical chloride electrolyte, say, the ternary eutectic $PbCl_2$ 79% wt–KCl 15% wt–NaCl 6% wt, is quite inert to the vitreous alumina–silica forming the fibres when it is pure. If any oxide, however, such as PbO, is dissolved in the fused-chloride mixture, it attacks the fibre substance and converts it to lead–aluminium silicate, $PbAl_2Si_2O_7$. It would seem that it is impossible, in practice, to maintain a lead chloride–alkali chloride electrolyte in a working cell free from oxide. Oxide is formed slowly by the action of atmospheric oxygen on the fused chloride, and even if a cell were operated in an atmosphere of inert gas, some oxide would be bound to be introduced with the feed metal supplied to the anode. This serious difficulty was solved by the observation that the oxides of certain elements are insoluble in lead chloride based electrolytes, with the consequence that the presence of the chloride of such an element in the electrolyte ensures that any oxide, either present originally or introduced later, is precipitated. If the 'precipitating' chloride is in fair excess, the common ion effect makes the final equilibrium concentration of dissolved oxide ion very small indeed.

A number of elements can be introduced (as chlorides) into the electrolyte to act as oxide precipitators, for example, magnesium, thorium, chromium and tin. The generally most effective and economical appears to be chromium. This is introduced into fresh electrolyte (for example, the ternary $PbCl_2$–KCl–NaCl eutectic referred to above) by adding metallic chromium. An exchange reaction takes place whereby chromium chloride is released into the electrolyte and metallic lead is formed. Traces of oxide present give a precipitate of chromia, and more is precipitated during the life of the cell. The layer of electrolyte lying on the anode metal, apart from its hydraulic function, has already been stated to play a part in the protection of the diaphragm; it does so by providing a reservoir of protective chloride.

Although the precipitating chloride consumed as oxide is absorbed by the electrolyte, either from fresh anode feed or by reaction with the atmosphere, it is always possible to reconvert some oxide precipitate to dissolved chloride by stirring some solid ammonium chloride into the electrolyte. Some of the ammonium chloride fumes away unchanged, but there is some reaction, e.g.

$$Cr_2O_3 + 6NH_4Cl \rightarrow 2CrCl_3 + 3H_2O + 6NH_3$$

Long-term trials will be required to test the effectiveness of this regeneration, but at least some possibility exists that it will not be necessary to add fresh precipitating chloride to a cell already running, however long the duration of the run.

One of the effects of having a precipitate of chromia in the electrolyte is that the interface between the molten metal anode and the electrolyte above it cannot be seen. This has made it necessary to develop a simple electrical probe system to locate the interface and to give warning when more anode metal is required.

It has been mentioned that tin is an element capable of precipitating oxide. The introduction has made it clear that, in chloride media, lead and tin are not separable by electrolysis. However, in a cell in which a lead–tin alloy is being transferred from anode to cathode, as in scrap solder refining, the automatic maintenance of an equilibrium distribution of lead and tin between the metal phases and the electrolyte ensures that some stannous chloride is always present in the electrolyte and replenishment of tin consumed by precipitation of oxide (in this case as stannous oxide) is assured. Even here, though, ammonium chloride treatment may be useful in checking the accumulation of large amounts of oxide precipitate.

The satisfactory cell life, extended to a month or more, conferred by solving the problems of gas escape and of preventing the chemical deterioration of the diaphragm, has made it possible to assess the refining performance of the design. One cell, whose operating conditions are set out in the centre column of Table 1, was operated for about six weeks, the antimony content of the anode metal being maintained between 70 and 80% for most of the time. The cathode metal over this period showed antimony contents of the order of 0·001%. On a number of occasions electrolysis was continued without the addition of fresh lead to the anode until the lead was exhausted, leaving molten antimony. This point is easily recognizable by a fall in current and obvious evolution of antimony trichloride fumes. The spot concentration of antimony in the cathode at an 'antimony point' is of the order of 0·01–0·02%. The analyses also show negligible bismuth in the cathode lead, but, as indicated above, the process is not very effective in removing copper.

One of the advantages of the ceramic-block type of construction is that larger cells can readily be made by assembling together as many as necessary of a limited number of standard shapes. Thus, a number of cells have been made for a nominal current of 3200 A, i.e. with a cathode well four times the size of that just described, by assembling together four base blocks, four corners and eight sides. Four of the 'side' blocks, disposed opposite one another, have gas escape grooves, and the other four are plain, and the rod supports lie at right angles to the grooved sides as just described. The current is distributed between two anode and two cathode conductors, but, normally only one outlet tube is used to remove the cathode lead, the other being held as a spare. The cathode well in such a cell measures 355 mm × 355 mm × 25 mm (14 in × 14 in × 1 in). One of the

O*

Table 1   Typical working details for nominal 800- and 3200-A cells

Nominal current rating, A	800	3200
Electrolyte	$PbCl_2$ 79%, KCl 15%, NaCl 6% reacted with $2\frac{1}{2}$% of its weight of metallic Cr	$PbCl_2$ 92·5%, NaCl 7·5% reacted with $2\frac{1}{2}$% of its weight of metallic Cr
Working current, A	820	3100
Current density, A/cm²	2·5	2·3
Voltage drops, V		
(i) total	4·3	2·4
(ii) across diaphragm	3·2	1·4
(iii) in anode conductor	0·9	0·7
(iv) in cathode conductor	0·2	0·3
Anode temperature, °C	650	650
Current efficiency	100% within errors of measurement	100% within errors of measurement
Anode feed	Secondary antimonial lead with Cu and Bi impurities	Antimonial lead
Cathode product	Lead containing 0·001% Sb, rising to 0·01% when the anode is concentrated to antimony. Bi content less than 0·0005% Cu *ca* 0·01% Cu, dependent on Cu content in anode	Lead containing 0·001% Sb or less
Production rate	3·17 kg/h (0·53 t/week)	12 kg/h (2 t/week)

effects of increased size is that a lower wattage per unit area will maintain the required working temperature—hence, a larger cell will function at a lower voltage. This has been achieved partly by using electrolyte compositions of higher conductivity, such as the lead chloride–sodium chloride eutectic ($PbCl_2$ 92·5%–NaCl 7·5%) and partly by taking advantage of an observation that in a ceramic-lined cell with no solid conductors, such as graphite, in contact with the diaphragm penetration is much less a problem. The cell voltage can be minimized, once a newly started cell has settled down, by temporarily blocking the cathode lead outlet tube, allowing the lead level in the cathode well to rise, and plotting the cell resistance at 5-min intervals. The observed resistance falls until the lead interface reaches the diaphragm and then remains steady. The outlet tube is then adjusted by rotation to fix the interface just below the point corresponding to minimum resistance. The right-hand column of Table 1 shows typical operating conditions for a nominal 3200-A cell.

Studies are now in progress on the best means of removing antimony from the anode compartment once an adequate quantity has been accumulated. Certainly, vacuum methods will be used and matters of detail remain to be settled. The other problem, that of combating the corrosion of anode conductors by molten antimony, has already been mentioned.

Laboratory studies on various alloys are in progress and it cannot be said at this moment that graphite sheathing of anode conductors will be the final solution.

Discussion and conclusions

The next step in the development of the process will be the design of 8000-A cells, perhaps run with several in series. Each of these should produce 5 t of lead per week.

It is of interest in conclusion to compare cells of the type described with those of an aqueous electrolytic lead refinery.[12] These run at a current density between 0·015 and 0·025 A/cm^2, compared with 2·0–2·5 A/cm^2 in a fused-salt cell, so the potential savings of space offered by the fused-salt method are obvious. The cell voltage in the aqueous plant can vary between 0·35 and 0·70 V, and the practical energy consumption between 100 and 200 kWh/t of lead. The theoretical energy consumption of any electrolytic cell producing lead is 260 kWh/t for every volt, so a cell running at 2 V would take 520 kWh/t. Although it is clear that fused-salt cells will always have a greater energy consumption than aqueous cells, the fused-salt method may have lower energy requirements in the auxiliary processes. Thus, casting and recasting electrodes, and anode slime treatments, are all unnecessary. The point at which increased power cost ceases to be justified by the compensating advantages of a fused-salt installation will vary according to conditions, especially scale and the appreciation in value of the anode concentrate, but, obviously, a reduction in voltage is desirable.

It may be pointed out that cells concentrating the anode metal to antimony have to run at a temperature of at least 650°C. If bismuth were the final product, a temperature of, say, 450°C would be tolerable, and this could be obtained by reducing the current density and, hence, the voltage. The voltage drop in the anode conductors could be reduced in a cell working at a lower anode temperature by increasing the cross-section to a point at which they withdraw a controlled amount of heat from the cell content instead of generating enough heat to prevent heat loss. Also, unsheathed high-chromium steel would probably have a satisfactory life and would save power. It may be conjectured from these facts that a large cell concentrating bismuth could be operated at not more than 1·5 V.

Although the emphasis of this work has been laid on the refining of lead and of lead–tin alloys, cells constructed on the same principle might be useful in refining other low-melting metals in which most of the impurities are noble to the major metal. Indium and zinc come to mind as possible examples, and it is interesting to note that Pokrovskii and co-workers[13] have reported some encouraging results in laboratory studies on the refining of zinc by electrolysis at 500°C in a zinc chloride–potassium chloride electrolyte.

Acknowledgment

The authors are indebted to the Directors of Associated Lead Manufacturers, Ltd., for permission to present this paper, and to B. Baker and P. Boatwright, who have been actively associated with the work described.

References

1. PEARSON T. G. and PHILLIPS H. W. L. The production and properties of super-purity aluminium. *Metall. Rev.*, **2**, 1957, 305–60.
2. LEBEDEV O. A. TATAKIN A. N. AND SVALOV G. N. Energy balance of an experimental-industrial electrolyzer for the three-layer refining of magnesium alloy scrap and waste products. *Tsvet. Metally, Mosk.*, **38**, no. 7 1965, 62–6; *Tsvet. Metally, N.Y.*, **6**, no. 7 1965, 71–5.
3. MULLINS L. J. AND LEARY J. A. Fused-salt electrorefining of molten plutonium and its alloys by the LAMEX process. *I&EC Process Design Develop.*, **4**, 1965, 394–400.
4. DELIMARSKII YU. K. TUROV P. P. AND GITMAN E. B. Electrochemical separation of lead from the binary lead alloys with bismuth, antimony, arsenic, and tin in molten electrolyte. *Ukr. khim. Zh.*, **21**, no. 6 1955, 687–93. (Russian text)
DELIMARSKII YU. K. AND PANCHENKO I. D. Electrolytic refining of lead in molten salts. *Ukr. khim. Zh.*, **25**, 1959, 458–62. (Russian text)
GITMAN E. B. AND DELIMARSKII YU. K. Electrolytic separation of binary alloys of lead with silver and arsenic. *Zh. prikl. Khim.*, **32**, 1959, 578–82; *J. appl. Chem. USSR*, **32**, 1959, 607–10.
5. HART P. F. HILLS A. W. D. AND TOMLINSON J. W. Electrorefining using molten salt electrolysis. In *Advances in extractive metallurgy* (London: Institution of Mining and Metallurgy, 1968), 624–51.
HART P. F. Mass transfer in the electrolysis of fused salts. Thesis, University of London, 1969.
6. LAITY R. W. Interionic friction coefficients in molten salts. *Ann. N.Y. Acad. Sci.*, **79**, 1959–60, 997–1022.
7. DELIMARSKII YU. K. *et al.* Electrolytic refining of lead–tin alloys in molten salts. *Ukr. khim. Zh.*, **31**, 1965, 687–93. (Russian text)
8. KLEESPIES E. K. BENNETTS J. P. AND HENRIE T. A. Gold recovery from scrap electronic solders by fused-salt electrolysis. *J. Metals, N.Y.*, **22**, Jan. 1970, 42–4.
9. BORCHERS W. Elektrolytische Scheidung leicht schmelzbarer Metalllegierungen. *Z. Elektrotech. Elektrochem.*, **1**, 1894, 13–5.
10. PAVLENKO I. G. AND GRINYUK A. P. Electrolytic processing of lead in melts using a porous diaphragm. *Ukr. khim. Zh.*, **29**, 1963, 868–73. (Russian text)
11. ROMS YU. G. BELENKII B. S. AND DELIMARSKII YU. K. Semi-industrial electrolytic cell for producing and refining heavy non-ferrous metals in fused salts. *Tsvet. Metally, Mosk.*, **41**, no. 7 1968, 34–8; *Tsvet. Metally, N.Y.*, **9**, no. 7 1968, 46–51.
12. FRENI E. R. Electrolytic lead refining with sulphamic and fluosilicic electrolyte. In *Symposium on sulfamic acid and its electrometallurgical applications, Milan 1966* (Milan: Edito della Associazione Italiana di Metallurgia, 1969), 367–71.
13. POKROVSKII V. V. SAMODELOV A. P. AND SKOROBOGAROV A. A. Electrochemical refinement of crude zinc in salt melts. *Tsvet. Metally, Mosk.*, **38**, no. 2 1965, p. 86; *Tsvet. Metally, N.Y.*, **6**, no. 2 1965, p. 94.

Electrodeposition of the refractory metals

D. Inman B.Sc., D.I.C., Ph.D., D.Sc., A.R.C.S., F.R.I.C., A.M.I.M.M.
R. Spencer B.Sc., D.I.C., Ph.D.

Both of the Nuffield Research Group in Extraction Metallurgy, Department of Metallurgy, Imperial College, London

669.054.72:669.283

Synopsis

Attention is focussed on some recent advances in the understanding of the fundamental mechanisms of the processes used to electrodeposit refractory metals. This understanding has been used to establish principles which should allow better processes to be devised and/or existing processes to be improved.

Cathode deposits are usually of three main forms—dendritic, powdery and coherent. The form is very dependent on the mechanism and, hence, on the kinetics of the overall electrode reaction; the nature of the rate-controlling step is particularly important. 'Fast', i.e. mass-transfer rate-controlling, processes generally lead to dendritic deposits, whereas other rate-controlling mechanisms generally lead to either coherent or powdery deposits.

The electroreduction of molybdenum(III) in molten chloride, with and without added fluoride ions, has been studied in detail by means of chronopotentiometry. The chloride solvent melts used were lithium chloride–potassium chloride eutectic at 567°C and sodium chloride 20 mole %–potassium chloride 80 mole % at 765°C. It was shown that the overall electroreduction process in both melts included a slow-coupled chemical step, involving the slow dissociation of the multinuclear species $[Mo(III)]_n$. At the higher temperature the value of n was shown to be 2. The addition of fluoride ions to the melts caused the overall electroreduction process to become faster (i.e. more reversible). This can be related to a decreasing stability of the multinuclear species.

In this way the formation of coherent electrodeposits conceivably could be facilitated by introducing, and optimized by adjusting the rates of, 'slow' chemical steps coupled to the main electron-transfer process. In addition, it has been shown that the chemical stability of the solution can be optimized by use of a suitable mixture of solvent cations.

The elements of groups IVA, VA and VIA of the periodic table are generally called refractory metals. In 1966 Senderoff[1] summarized their properties and uses, and extensively and critically reviewed the processes for electrodepositing them from solutions of their compounds. The aim of the present paper is to focus attention

413

on some recent advances in our understanding of the fundamental mechanisms of these processes and to attempt to use this understanding to establish the principles for devising better processes and/or improving existing processes.

The well established and successful (non-electrolytic) processes for the isolation of these metals are often rather complex. Electrolytic methods for the extraction of metals are, in principle, more straightforward and could lend themselves to continuous or semi-continuous processes with purer products. The many electrolytic routes, employing non-aqueous solvents, for the extraction and refining of the more exotic metals, which have been worked out in the laboratory and, in many cases, developed to the pilot-plant stage will probably compete strongly with the existing commercial processes if the cost of electrical power for the commercial user decreases as more nuclear power stations are introduced. In any event, if the quality of the environment becomes an overriding factor, clean (e.g. electrolytic) processes may have to be introduced even if they are rather expensive in conventional economic terms. For example, the electron is a much more powerful reducing agent than hydrogen: in principle, therefore, direct electrolytic reduction could be used to advantage in place of existing processes which employ roasting to oxidize sulphides to oxides (leading to SO_2 pollution) prior to hydrogen reduction. In addition, if it were possible to employ the ores themselves as electrolytes, transport costs could be cut by processing 'on site', hydroelectric power, where available, being used. In other areas the costs of electrolytic processes could be reduced if off-peak electrical power were used. The present primary ore sources are not inexhaustible. When these run out, leaner ores containing metals, other than the desired metal, in gross amounts will have to be employed. In addition, it will become increasingly necessary to reclaim scarce metals from scrap materials, effluent, etc. Therefore electro-refining operations by use of high-power potentiostats are likely to become more important; a better knowledge of the mechanisms of electrodeposition and electrodissolution processes is also desirable from this point of view.

There are no reports of groups IVA, VA or VIA metals giving rise to electro-deposits containing the metal as the major ingredient, from aqueous or organic media, except in the case of chromium.[1] All these metals, on the other hand, have been electrodeposited, in a powder or dendritic form, from their chlorides dissolved in other molten halides.[2] Coherent (massive) molybdenum deposits have been obtained from potassium hexachloromolybdate (K_3MoCl_6) dissolved in molten lithium chloride–potassium chloride.[2, 3, 4] Coherent (massive) tungsten deposits have been obtained from tungstic oxide (WO_3) dissolved in a melt consisting of one part lithium sodium metaborate ($LiNaB_2O_4$) and six parts lithium sodium tungstate ($LiNaWO_4$).[5] On the other hand, all the metals from groups IVA, VA and VIA can be electrodeposited in a coherent (massive) form* from solutions of their fluorides in alkali metal fluoride solvents[6] although

---

* This form of deposit is desirable because, otherwise, it is difficult to separate occluded melt from the deposits after electrolysis, except by expensive processes which may introduce impurities.

the process is not particularly successful in the case of titanium.[7] Unfortunately, the process does not seem to work (i.e. the deposits are no longer massive) in the presence of varying amounts (depending on the system) of other halides and oxides. Therefore, in the light of present knowledge[1] it would probably be necessary to convert the ores to fluorides before electrolysis if massive metal were the desired product of the electrowinning process. Another disadvantage of molten fluorides is that they need to be handled at rather high temperatures and are very corrosive.

A general long-term aim of our research on the electrodeposition of refractory metals is therefore to try to establish the principles for designing baths to win, refine and form metal in a coherent, massive form in one single-stage operation direct from the ore by use of more easily handleable alkali metal halide solvents, on the basis of a better understanding of the fundamental aspects of the electro-deposition mechanisms.

Electrodeposition

Electrodeposition is carried out for four main purposes: winning, refining, plating and forming. The state of the cathode deposit is not critical in the first two cases so long as the metal is pure and in a recoverable form. The other two processes require a continuous coherent metal deposit. Metal deposits, obtained by electrochemical reduction, are of three main forms—dendritic, powdery and coherent. The condition of the electrodeposit formed is very dependent on the mechanism and, hence, the kinetics of the overall electrode reaction; the nature of the rate-controlling step is particularly important.

Barton and Bockris[8] considered the deposition characteristics of a fast electrode process in which the rate-controlling step is the diffusion of the electroactive species up to the electrode surface. They concluded that for a given diffusion overvoltage the current density, on a spherical electrode, would be greater than at a planar electrode if the radius of the sphere were less than the diffusion layer thickness. At the start of metal deposition the metal will build up on certain growth sites, and these aggregates of metal atoms will be, in effect, very small spherical electrodes with radii less than the diffusion layer thickness. Hence, for a diffusion-controlled process, the current density, i.e. the rate of deposition, will be greater on these spherical metal aggregates than on the surrounding quasi-planar electrode surface. This will lead to the formation of dendrites, which will grow into the bulk of the electrolytic solution where the concentration of depositing metal ions remains high.

If the overpotential associated with the metal deposition process does not arise only from diffusion, then the above situation does not apply. Under these conditions, where the diffusion overpotential is small compared to the total overpotential, one would expect a multilayer coherent deposit, since the rate of deposition is not strictly determined by the micro-geometry of the surface.

In some cases the *working* electrode potential (this is *not* the thermodynamic reversible potential) for metal deposition can become more cathodic than the potential required to reduce the solvent cations. The primary product (e.g. an alkali metal) may then chemically reduce the solute cations around the electrode. The resulting metal deposits will be powdery in form and not necessarily attached to the electrode. This type of deposition is generally described as secondary deposition.*

$$nA^+ + ne \rightarrow nA^\circ \quad [\text{A = solvent cation}]$$
$$nA^\circ + M^{n+} \rightarrow nA^+ + M^\circ$$

Secondary deposition occurs when the electrode process is very irreversible or if the applied current density is very high or if the reversible electrode potential for the solute cation is very close to that for the solvent cation.

The three major factors that affect the nature of metal deposits are (1) the thermodynamic electrode potential for the solute cation; (2) the inherent kinetics of the deposition process; and (3) the rates of deposition of the metal, i.e. the applied current density.

Experimental study

The electroreduction of molybdenum(III) ions in lithium chloride–potassium chloride eutectic with and without added fluoride ions at 567°C has been studied chronopotentiometrically. Chronopotentiometry is voltammetry at constant

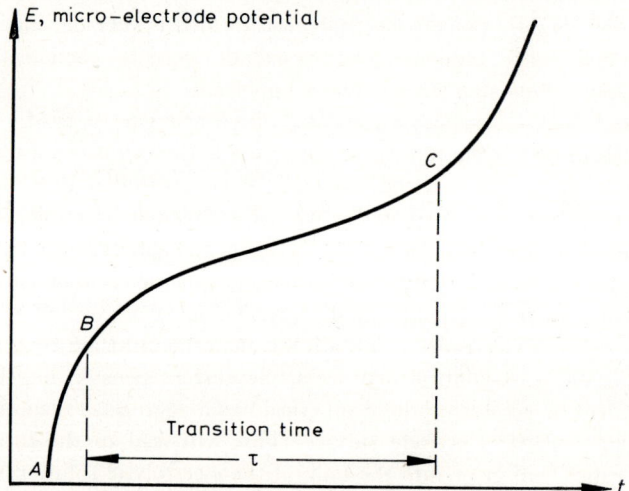

Fig. 1   Chronopotentiogram

current; it has been reviewed by Paunovic.[9] The electrolysis is carried out under the following conditions: (a) the solution is not stirred; (b) the current is carried by a large excess of indifferent electrolyte in order that migration may be neglected; (c) conditions of semi-infinite linear diffusion exist. The important

* Definitions of the symbols used in this paper appear on page 424.

experimental parameter, the transition time, τ, is the time-interval between the onset of constant current electrolysis and the time when the concentration at the electrode surface of the species which is undergoing electron transfer just reaches zero. It is indicated by a sharp increase in the electrode potential. A typical chronopotentiogram is shown in Fig. 1. From point A to point B the potential changes rapidly and the current is used almost exclusively to charge the double layer. Point B corresponds to the potential at which electrolysis becomes appreciable. The potential change from B to C is dependent on the nature of the overall electrode reaction. After C, the concentration of the electro-active species at the electrode surface becomes essentially zero. For a simple diffusion-controlled electrode process, Sand's equation is applicable[9]

$$\tau^{\frac{1}{2}} = \frac{nFC\pi^{\frac{1}{2}}D^{\frac{1}{2}}}{2i} \tag{1}$$

The potential–time relationships for a 'reversible' electrode process in which the activity of the product is variable or unity are described by equation 2 (variable activity) and 3 (unit activity).[10]

$$E = E^\circ + \frac{RT}{nF} \ln \left[\frac{\tau^{\frac{1}{2}}}{t^{\frac{1}{2}}} - 1 \right] \tag{2a}$$

$$E_{\tau/4} = E^\circ \tag{2b}$$

$$E = E^\circ + \frac{RT}{nF} \ln C^\circ + \frac{RT}{nF} \ln \left[1 - \frac{t^{\frac{1}{2}}}{\tau^{\frac{1}{2}}} \right] \tag{3a}$$

$$E_{\tau/4} = E^\circ + \frac{RT}{nF} \ln \frac{C^\circ}{2} \tag{3b}$$

In the case of an irreversible *charge-transfer* process the potential–time relationship for both types of products is given by equation 4.[10]

$$E = \frac{RT}{\alpha nF} \ln \frac{nFC^\circ k^\circ_{fh}}{i} + \frac{RT}{\alpha nF} \ln \left[1 - \frac{t^{\frac{1}{2}}}{\tau^{\frac{1}{2}}} \right] \tag{4}$$

In the present study a single wave was observed for deposition from solutions varying in concentration from $4\cdot87 \times 10^{-3}$ to $3\cdot31 \times 10^{-2}$ M. The wave was stable with time, but did not obey Sand's equation. The product $i\tau^{\frac{1}{2}}$ was found to decrease with increasing applied current density, i, according to the equation

$$i\tau^{\frac{1}{2}}.10^3 = a - b\,10^3.i \tag{5}$$

i.e. a plot of $\tau^{\frac{1}{2}}$ versus $1/i$ had a negative intercept at $1/i$ equal to zero (Fig. 2). This relationship indicates that a slow chemical reaction[10, 11] precedes the charge-transfer process. In this case the value of a should be that given by Sand's equation; hence, a value for the diffusion coefficient may be calculated. Values for a, b and the apparent diffusion coefficient D are listed in Table 1 with respect

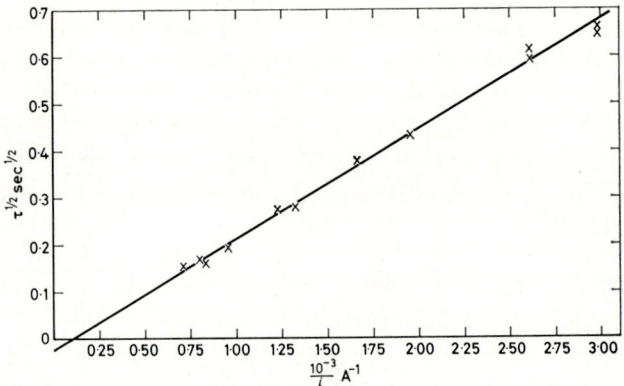

Fig. 2 Mo^{3+} in LiCl–KCl eutectic: $T = 839°K$; micro-electrode area $= 4.52mm^2$; Mo^{3+} concentration $= 8.77 \times 10^{-3}$ M

Table 1

C	a	b	$D \times 10^6$ cm^2 sec^{-1}
4.87×10^{-3}M	2.62	0.199	4.4 ± 0.6
6.82×10^{-3}M	3.83	0.247	4.8 ± 0.7
8.77×10^{-3}M	5.13	0.448	5.2 ± 0.5
9.73×10^{-3}M	5.90	1.03	5.6 ± 0.8
3.31×10^{-2}M	23.0	0.379	7.4 ± 1.3

i, A cm^{-2}; τ, sec; equation 5.

to concentration C. Plots of the electrode potential E versus $\log_{10}(\tau^{\frac{1}{2}}/t^{\frac{1}{2}}-1)$ and $\log_{10}(1-t^{\frac{1}{2}}/\tau^{\frac{1}{2}})$ were both non-linear at long transition times (Fig. 3). At short transition times, e.g. around 20 msec, plots of E versus $\log_{10}(1-t^{\frac{1}{2}}/\tau^{\frac{1}{2}})$ became linear with slopes of about 130 mV (Fig. 4). The addition of 4.44×10^{-2} M fluoride ions to a 3.31×10^{-2} M molybdenum(III) solution gave a value for the product $i\tau^{\frac{1}{2}}$ which was independent of the applied current density, i.e. Sand's equation was obeyed (Fig. 5). The value for the diffusion coefficient in the presence of fluoride ions was $(5.3 \pm 1.5) \times 10^{-6}$ cm^2 sec^{-1}. In the presence of fluoride ions, for a wave of $\tau = 330$ msec, the plot of E versus $\log_{10}(1-t^{\frac{1}{2}}/\tau^{\frac{1}{2}})$ was almost linear with a slope of 58 mV (Fig. 6).

The results of a previous study of molybdenum(III) in molten sodium chloride 20 mol %–potassium chloride 80 mole % at 765°C have been reported elsewhere.[12] The molybdenum species volatilized from the melt, but at a rate which still allowed measurements. At low molybdenum(III) concentrations one chronopotentiometric reduction wave was observed, but at high concentration a further reduction wave appeared at a more cathodic potential. The first wave gave linear E versus $\log_{10}(1-t^{\frac{1}{2}}/\tau^{\frac{1}{2}})$ plots with slopes in the range 160–220 mV. Plots of E versus $\log_{10}(\tau^{\frac{1}{2}}/t^{\frac{1}{2}}-1)$ were not linear. Plots of $E_{\tau/4}$ versus $\log_{10}i$ (when only one wave was present) were linear with slopes of from 45 to 49 mV.

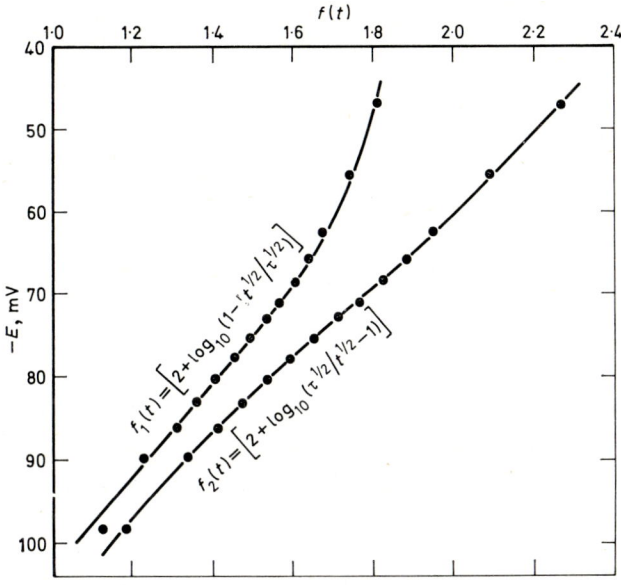

Fig. 3   Mo^{3+} in LiCl–KCl eutectic: $\tau = 505$ msec

The addition of fluoride ions radically altered the shapes of the reduction waves. The plots of E versus $\log_{10}(\tau^{\frac{1}{2}}/t^{\frac{1}{2}}-1)$ approached linearity with slopes of about 150 mV and plots of E versus $\log_{10}(1-t^{\frac{1}{2}}/\tau^{\frac{1}{2}})$ were non-linear.

Discussion

For a slow-coupled chemical step the values of a/C and b (equation 5) should be constant. It can be seen from Table 1 that this was not the case; the values for b and D increase with increasing concentration. This suggested that the kinetic effect was partially compensated by the effect of some other non-diffusion-controlled process. Such a process could be the reduction of a layer of adsorbed molybdenum ions.[9] The most realistic value for the diffusion coefficient should be that corresponding to the lowest concentration, since adsorption would then be at a minimum. This value for the diffusion coefficient is close to that obtained by Senderoff and Mellors[13] at higher temperatures. The non-linearity of the plots of E versus $\log_{10}(\tau^{\frac{1}{2}}/t^{\frac{1}{2}}-1)$ and E versus $\log_{10}(1-t^{\frac{1}{2}}/\tau^{\frac{1}{2}})$ for the chloride at long transition times also indicates that the irreversibility of the electrode process arises from a slow process other than slow charge transfer. At short transition times a slope of about 130 mV for the plot of E versus $\log_{10}(1-t^{\frac{1}{2}}/\tau^{\frac{1}{2}})$ (which is linear in this case) could be interpreted in terms of an irreversible charge-transfer process with a value for αn of 1·3.

In a binary system in which there is only one type of anionic species a kinetic effect can only arise from the slow dissociation of a multinuclear complex species, i.e. $[Mo(III)]_n$. The low value measured for the diffusion coefficient

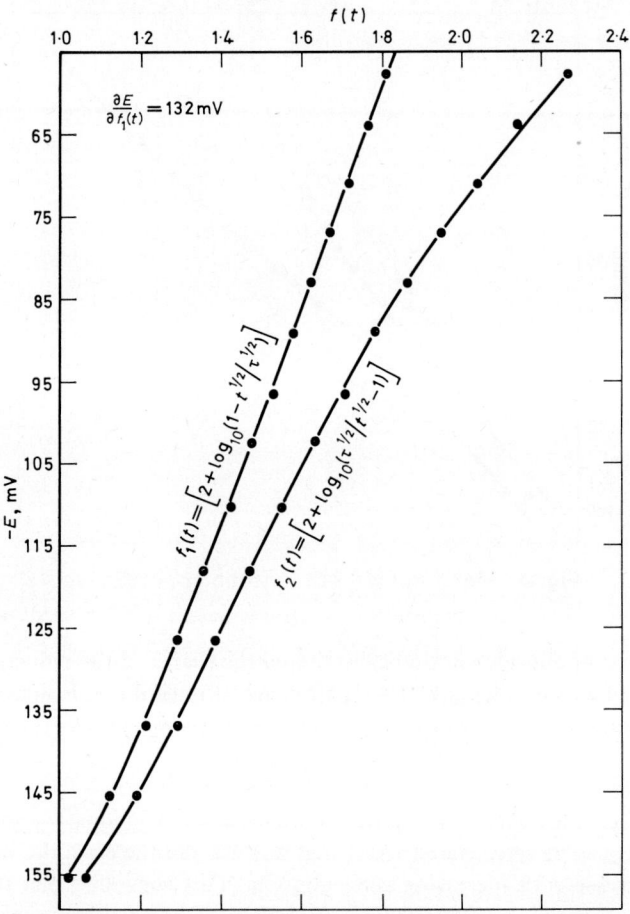

Fig. 4 Mo^{3+} in LiCl–KCl eutectic at 565°C: $\tau = 19$ msec

would be consistent with the formation of large multinuclear species. The irreversibility of the electrode process would then arise from this slow chemical step; the forms of the potential–time relationships are in accord with this model. The presence of adsorption suggests that, at least in part, the chemical step occurs heterogeneously in an adsorbed layer on the electrode.

The addition of fluoride ions led the system to obey Sand's equation, i.e. the reaction became diffusion-controlled. At long transition times plots of E versus

$\log_{10}(1 - t^{\frac{1}{2}}/\tau^{\frac{1}{2}})$ were not wholly linear. The non-linearity took, however, a different form from that observed in the chloride solvent in the absence of fluoride ions and could be explained in terms of interfering artefactual processes, e.g. double layer charging. The slope of the linear portion of the plots, i.e. 60 mV,

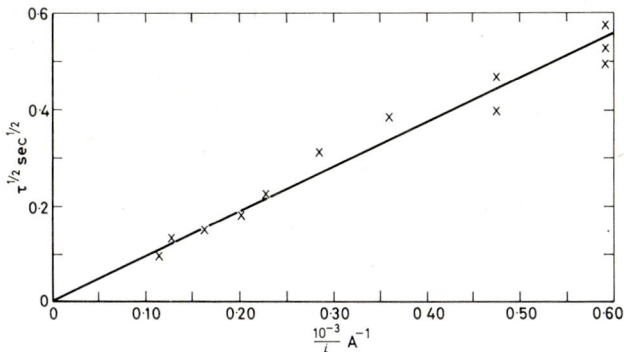

Fig. 5 Mo^{3+} in LiCl–KCl eutectic at 565°C + fluoride

corresponds to a reversible three-electron transfer process, in which the metal is deposited at unit activity. The disappearance of the slow chemical step and the increase in reversibility of the system on the addition of fluoride ions may be explained in terms of the reduction in stability of the multinuclear complex species. If the complex involves chloride ligand bridges, cf. the solid state,[14, 15] then the inclusion of small, 'hard' fluoride ions would lead to a breakdown of the ligand bridges. Hence, if the slow chemical step were ascribed to the dissociation

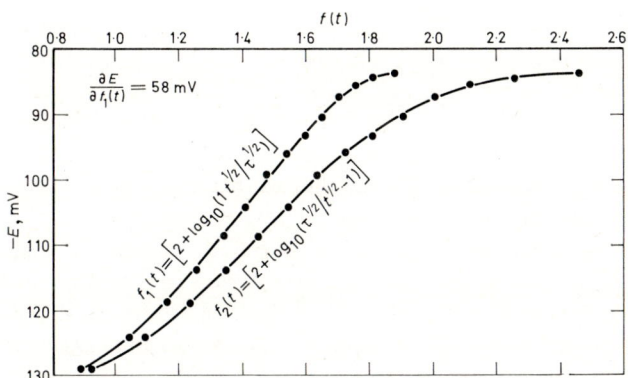

Fig. 6 Mo^{3+} in LiCl–KCl eutectic at 565°C + fluoride: $\tau = 330$ msec

of a multinuclear complex species, the addition of fluoride ions would be expected to increase the reversibility of the electrodeposition process.

In addition, in the previous study[12] of molybdenum(III) in sodium chloride

(80 mole %)–potassium chloride (20 mole %), the differences in the slopes of the plots of E versus $\log_{10}(1 - t^{\frac{1}{2}}/\tau^{\frac{1}{2}})$ and $E_{\tau/4}$ versus $\log_{10} i$ were also not consistent with an irreversible charge-transfer process. The results were interpreted in terms of the slow dissociation of a dinuclear molybdenum(III) species. The second wave was ascribed to the direct reduction of the dinuclear species. The non-linearity of the irreversible relationship E versus $\log_{10}(1 - t^{\frac{1}{2}}/\tau^{\frac{1}{2}})$ and the increase in linearity of the reversible plot E versus $\log_{10}(\tau^{\frac{1}{2}}/t^{\frac{1}{2}} - 1)$ resulting from the presence of fluoride ions was explained in terms of decreased stability of the dinuclear complex species, cf. the lithium chloride–potassium chloride system.

Control of deposition processes

The effect of the kinetics of the electroreduction process on the nature of the electrode deposit was discussed earlier, together with a brief mention of the major factors that affect metal deposition. The four variables available in the design of an electrodeposition system are the solvent cations, the solvent anions, the temperature and the applied current density.

The effects of solvent cations can be considered in terms of their charge densities (ionic charge Z divided by the cube of ionic radius r, that is, Z/r^3). The greater the charge density, the greater the solvent cation–anion interaction, that is, the shorter the solvent interionic distances. An increase in the solvent cation–anion interionic distances should lead to an increase in the solute cation–anion interaction, since there is less competition for the anion from the solvent cation. Hence, for solvent cations of the same charge the stability of complexes of solute cations should increase with increasing solvent cation size. Mellors and Senderoff[7] attempted to relate, with some degree of success, the charge density of the cations in fluoride melts to the type of deposit formed. They suggested that the stability of the complexes would determine the reversibility of the overall electroreduction process and, hence, the type of deposit. Apparently, they managed to predict empirically the limits in solvent cation charge density necessary to obtain coherent deposits, but the effects of thermodynamic electrode potential, which were not taken into account, are equally important. Flengas and Pint[16] measured the thermal stability of solutions of $TiCl_4$, $ZrCl_4$ and $HfCl_4$ in alkali- and alkaline-earth chloride melts, and showed that the lower the charge densities of the solvent cations, the greater is the stability of the solution.

It has already been mentioned that, in general, the refractory metals have only previously been electrodeposited in a coherent form from fluoride melts if other anions, e.g. chlorides, were absent. Coherent molybdenum deposits can be obtained, however, from chloride melts,[2–4] and this has been associated with the presence of a slow chemical reaction coupled to the charge-transfer process proper.[12, 13] The extreme irreversibility of the niobium deposition process in chloride melts, which, in this case, led to secondary deposition,[12] could also perhaps be associated with this type of chemical step, in view of the tendency for many refractory metal chlorides, including niobium chlorides, to form multi-nuclear groupings in the solid state,[17] which is very similar to the molten state for ionic systems. Therefore, by use of a suitable mixture of solvent cations to give a chemically stable solution (i.e. strong solute cation–anion interactions), and a suitable mixture of chloride ions and fluoride ions, it should be possible to optimize multinuclear complex stability to give the best kinetics for coherent metal deposition. Temperature is also an important factor in determining the stability of complex species, but from the economic point of view it is desirable to keep the temperature as low as possible.

Possible electrolytic extraction of molybdenum

Molybdenum is generally produced by the hydrogen reduction of the oxide, which is produced from the ore molybdenite (MoS_2) by roasting. It is not possible to reduce by hydrogen the sulphide ore directly. The hydrogen reduction method involves two inefficient heating processes, i.e. the roasting and the reduction steps. Molybdenum could possibly be directly electrodeposited from the ore dissolved in a chloride melt. In general, electroreduction processes are very efficient users of energy, and if hydroelectric power is employed, that energy is also relatively cheap. Electrolysis also offers the prospect of direct sulphur recovery, thereby avoiding the SO_2 pollution problems associated with roasting. Sulphide ions are, however, strongly surface-active and could well interfere with the electrodeposition process. In principle, their stability in the bulk melts could be enhanced by use of solvent cations of high charge density. Direct electro-reduction from ores could be carried out at the source of the ore. Molybdenite is mined in areas where cheap hydroelectric power is available, e.g. Colorado, U.S.A., and British Columbia, Canada, which makes such a reduction process economically attractive. Other advantages of reduction at the ore source are reduced transport costs and concentration of the industry in the mining area, thereby reducing the area despoiled.

The possible advantages that would accrue from electrolytic methods involving the direct reduction of the ores make the development of such methods highly desirable. The application of fused-salt electrolysis to the winning of niobium and tantalum from their ores has been investigated by Bowles,[18] but success, to date, has been limited.

Acknowledgment

The authors are pleased to acknowledge the support given to them by the former Ministry of Technology Warren Spring Laboratory, Stevenage, Hertfordshire.

References

1. SENDEROFF S. Electrodeposition of refractory metals. *Metall. Rev.*, **11**, 1966, 97–112.
2. SENDEROFF S. and BRENNER A. The electrolytic preparation of molybdenum from fused salts. *J. electrochem. Soc.*, **101**, 1954, 16–38.
3. COUCH D. E. AND SENDEROFF S. The electrolytic preparation of molybdenum from fused salts. V. Electrorefining studies in the presence of tin, iron, copper, silicon and nickel. *Trans. Am. Inst. Min. Engrs*, **212**, 1958, 320–5.
4. SENDEROFF S. Techniques for coating metals with molybdenum. In *The metal molybdenum* (Cleveland, Ohio: American Society for Metals, 1958), 199–213.

5. DAVIS G. L. AND GENTRY C. H. R. The electrodeposition of tungsten. *Metallurgia*, **53**, 1956, 3–17.

6. MELLORS G. W. AND SENDEROFF S. Canadian Patent 688 546, 1964.

7. MELLORS G. W. AND SENDEROFF S. Electrodeposition of coherent deposits of refractory metals. I. Niobium. *J. electrochem. Soc.*, **112**, 1965, 266–72.

8. BARTON J. L. AND BOCKRIS J. O'M. The electrolytic growth of dendrites from ionic solutions. *Proc. R. Soc.*, **A268**, 1962, 485–505.

9. PAUNOVIC M. Chronopotentiometry. *J. electroanal. Chem.*, **14**, 1967, 447–74.

10. DELAHAY P. AND BERZINS T. Theory of electrolysis at constant current with partial or total control by diffusion—application to the study of complex ions. *J. Am. chem. Soc.*, **75**, 1953, 2486–93.

11. REINMUTH W. H. Chronopotentiometric transition times and their interpretation. *Analyt. Chem.*, **33**, 1961, 322–5.

12. INMAN D. SETHI R. S. AND SPENCER R. The effects of complex ion formation and ionic adsorption on electrode reactions involving metals and metal ions in fused salts. *J. electroanal. Chem.*, **29**, 1971, 137–47.

13. SENDEROFF S. AND MELLORS G. W. Electrodeposition of coherent deposits of refractory metals. VI. Mechanism of deposition of molybdenum and tungsten from fluoride melts. *J. electrochem. Soc.*, **114**, 1967, 586–7.

14. MARTIN R. L. AND WINTER G. The metal–metal bond in binuclear di-π-cyclopentadienyl-titanium(III) chloride. *J. chem. Soc.*, 1965, 4709–14.

15. SCHÄFER H. AND SCHNERING H. G. Metall–Metall-Bindungen bei niederen Halogeniden, Oxyden und Oxydhalogeniden schwerer Übergangsmetalle. *Angew. Chem.*, **76**, 1964, 833–49.

16. FLENGAS S. N. AND PINT P. Potential chloride electrolytes for recovering the metals Ti, Zr and Hf by fused salt electrolysis. *Can. metall. Q.*, **8**, 1969, 151–66.

17. COTTON F. A. AND WILKINSON G. *Advanced inorganic chemistry* (New York: Interscience, 1966), 1136 p.

18. BOWLES P. J. Extraction of niobium and tantalum from their ores by molten salt electrolysis. In *Advances in extractive metallurgy* (London: Institution of Mining and Metallurgy, 1968), 600–23.

Symbols

C°	Bulk concentration of species
D	Diffusion coefficient
E	Electrode potential
E°	Standard electrode potential
F	One Faraday
i	Current density
k°_{fh}	Formal forward rate constant for charge-transfer process
n	Number of electrons in charge-transfer process
T	Temperature, degrees absolute
t	Time from onset of process
α	Charge-transfer coefficient
τ	Transition time
$E_{\tau/4}$	Electrode potential at $t = \tau/4$
R	Gas constant

DISCUSSION

P. J. Lenoir, in introducing his joint paper, said that the use of pure oxygen or enriched air had been investigated at the Hoboken plant of Metallurgie Hoboken–Overpelt in relation to the blast-furnace division, the siphon converter department and the sintering plant. Its use appeared to offer ways of improving the technological efficiency of existing processes, investment cost being kept at a minimum. Very encouraging results had been published by other smelters concerning the use of oxygen-enriched air in lead blast-furnaces. The blast-furnace division was, in the Hoboken plant, the bottleneck in the treatment of concentrates and secondary materials. A major oxygen producer had planned to install, in 1970, an oxygen pipeline between Mons and Antwerp, which would pass near the plant.

Preliminary test had begun in 1967, the oxygen coming from a liquid oxygen tank (see Tables 2 and 3, pp. 375 and 376, for results). In 1970, when the oxygen pipeline was commissioned, prolonged experiments were carried out with oxygen blast enrichment up to 26–27%.

The operation of both furnaces, however, became very difficult, it being necessary to clean them almost daily with explosive to avoid the formation of accretions in the shaft. The smelting rate fell drastically and reduction became erratic.

It was clearly established that, for Pb–Cu charges, and with the coke used at that time, there was an upper limit to oxygen enrichment. An experimental thermal balance had confirmed that oxygen enrichment was restricted by the combustion properties of the coke and heat transfer between the gases and the charge. Calculations also showed that oxygen enrichment was perhaps not the best way of lowering the coke consumption in those particular charges.

Finally, it was decided (in 1971) to limit the enrichment to 24·5% and to maintain the coke rate at not less than 10·5%. Very satisfactory results had since been obtained. Smelting rates had increased, pressure drops in the furnace were lower, tuyères remained brighter, and operations were easier and steadier. The need remained for further measurements on the blast-furnace to discover which parameters must be controlled when higher enrichments were used.

Oxygen in copper converting

In ferrous metallurgy and, more recently, in non-ferrous metallurgy converting processes had been evolved in which use was made of oxygen-enriched air or pure oxygen. The most striking advantages were the increase in speed of converting operations, the possibility of treating larger quantities of solid materials for cooling and the possibility of obtaining gases containing more SO_2 from sulphurous materials.

Trials had been made on no. 6 furnace to obtain an increased capacity to match the improved smelting rate obtained with oxygen in the blast-furnace. Already, when blowing with air, the SO_2 content of the converter gases was rather high

(8·5%). The progress of the operations could be controlled at any time during the blow by ladling samples out of the bath from a platform located near the converter mouth. Visual inspection during oxygen lancing was possible. The operator had free access to the bath to add cold matte or scraps or liquid matte during blowing. The average SO_2 content increased from 9 to 11% when oxygen lancing was being used.

They believed that the Hoboken converter was a very convenient vessel for roof lancing with pure oxygen. During the trial the lance was submerged below the slag level away from the walls—to avoid increased refractory wear. Lance life corresponded very well with the different partial blows preceding the white matte final blow. Lances were replaced during slag skimming after each blow, as was current practice with the siphon converter connected to an acid plant for complete recovery of the sulphur in the form of sulphuric acid or as elemental sulphur.

The possibility and the need existed for cold additions during the blow: copper scrap, solid matte or other coolant materials could be added on a large scale and on a continuing basis. The mouth of the converter was always free, and was situated above the hot reaction zone created by the oxygen lance. Turbulence, maintained by the usual immersed tuyères, assisted the heat distribution.

Initial trials had shown an increased rate of production of 25% by lancing 10 Nm^3/min of pure O_2 in a 10 ft × 20 ft siphon converter blowing at a rate of 175 Nm^3 air/min through the tuyères. Higher oxygen rates appeared possible, but further trials were necessary to confirm the limit of up to 50% increase in production rate.

A proper blowing technique, avoiding local superheating of the refractories was of vital importance. Oxygen requirements at the converters differed from plant to plant. The high SO_2 content of the gases of the Hoboken converter made it possible to mix the gas stream containing more than 10% SO_2 (average) with a 1 or 2% SO_2 gas stream from existing reverberatory furnaces or electric furnaces. Rich SO_2-bearing gases could be cooled and cleaned for waste-heat utilization and economic production of sulphuric acid or elemental sulphur.

The development of larger siphon converters, with or without oxygen lancing, could contribute to the abatement of atmospheric pollution by providing existing or new smelters with an economic method of recovering more than 95% of the sulphur present in concentrates and secondary materials.

J. L. Harrison introduced his paper briefly, summarizing its principal contents.

C. F. Harris* said that the papers by Lenoir and his colleagues and by Harrison were extremely interesting, particularly with regard to the application of oxygen in sintering and in blast-furnace practice. Considering the sintering case first, he

* Imperial Smelting Corporation, Ltd., Avonmouth.

would advise caution in the use of oxygen-enriched air. E. W. Voice and Dr. R. Wild of BISRA, working on iron ore sintering, had demonstrated that the gas volume required for sintering was primarily determined by the heat-transfer process. With carbonaceous fuel they demonstrated that the greatest fuel economy would result from the use of air with significantly less oxygen than the normal 21%. It was obvious that nitrogen enrichment would not be a financially viable method of achieving fuel economy.

The importance of the heat-transfer process was more obvious in carbon-fuelled sintering than in sulphide-fuelled sintering. Nonetheless, the heat-transfer process was still of paramount importance and the rate of combustion had to be matched to the rate of heat transfer. With highly reactive sulphide fuels an increase in the sulphide content of the feed mix was necessary, when oxygen-enriched air was being used, to achieve matching rates. Information on that subject had been published.* In view of that, it was not surprising to him that conflicting results from the use of oxygen in sintering were obtained at Hoboken.

The Russian results described by Harrison were very difficult to understand. He quoted maximum temperatures of 1000–1050°C with enriched air compared with 800 to 900°C with normal air. He wondered if those were sinter bed temperatures. If so, they did not ring true. He had measured sinter bed temperatures in excess of 1000°C in lead sinter beds with normal air, and such temperatures had been reported in publications from B.H.A.S. He would not expect to make good sinter with such low temperatures as 800 or 900°C.

Summarizing his views on oxygen enrichment in sintering, it was possible to use oxygen with benefit to the sulphur dioxide content of the roaster gas, so long as the fuel content of the bed was increased to keep the heat-transfer and combustion processes in reasonable match. Unless there were plenty of very cheap oxygen, however, he doubted if that was profitable practice.

Turning to the blast-furnace, he would stress once again the importance of the heat-transfer process. His understanding of iron blast-furnaces was that for many purposes increased blast preheat could be regarded as interchangeable with increased oxygen content of blast. Beyond a certain level of blast preheat, in excess of 1000°C, operation of a blast-furnace could become difficult, and there was a similar result with oxygen enrichment. Simultaneous injection of fuel with the blast countered the difficulties, and for that reason fuel injection and oxygen enrichment usually went hand in glove.

Oxygen could be used in the Imperial Smelting Furnace, but, in general, the cheapest way of improving output and efficiency had been to increase the blowing rate and the blast preheat. Because there had been concern over the possible bad effect on zinc condensation of excessive amounts of water vapour in the furnace gas, the use of fuel oil injection had been avoided. In his view it was the combined use of fuel-oil injection and oxygen enrichment in blast-furnaces which had the greatest attraction.

* Woods S.E. and Harris C.F. Heat transfer in sinter roasting. In *Chemical engineering in the metallurgical industries* (London: Institution of Chemical Engineers, 1965), 77–86.

J. S. Jacobi* said that he would like to congratulate those at Hoboken for their workmanlike and concise account on the use of oxygen in their extensive operations. He had also read with undiminished fascination the persuasive arguments brought up by Harrison in favour of the use of that expensive commodity. With regard to blast enrichment for shaft furnaces, on his company's copper furnace, which was smaller than the Hoboken units, their observations had been rather similar: they achieved a marginal reduction in coke and a marginal improvement in smelting rate. However, once one drove the furnace beyond about 2·5 tons charge per hour per square metre of hearth area other factors begin to impose limitations, such as the coke 'quality'. He thought that one could be more specific and mention coke grading and reactivity. The paper said nothing about the effect of oxygen on metal losses in slags. Their own impression had been that those were increased when blast enrichment was practised—certainly the slag came out of the furnace nice and hot. It also dissolved more copper and that loss was only partially balanced by a lesser amount of metallic copper prills in the slag.

It would be appreciated that the question of whether to use blast enrichment or not was largely one of economics, and there was always blast preheat as a cheaper competitor. Maybe they would one day apply all those aids to shaft furnace smelting, namely blast preheat, oxygen enrichment and fuel injection. If each of those contributed a fuel saving—as was claimed by the enthusiasts— of about 35%, they would use no coke at all! As, presumably, the whole would be better than the sum of the individual parts, they would actually start to produce coke in the furnace! When one considered present coke prices and metal quotations, that might be very good business.

Dr. D. A. Temple† said that Harrison had expressed the hope (p. 388) that the zinc–lead blast-furnace process 'will one day be a large consumer of oxygen'. Although the subject of enrichment of the furnace air blast by oxygen had been the subject of two papers,‡ it might be interesting, for the sake of completeness, to outline the development work on that subject carried out in 1965 at the Swansea ISF. Test work, which lasted for 6 weeks, showed that O_2 in blast up to 27% volume could be satisfactorily used without any adverse effects on furnace performance (either in the shaft or in the condenser), the overall effect being to increase productivity by about 35%. The conclusion reached by Gray and Woods on the relative merits of increasing production capacity by blowing with more air compared with oxygen enrichment had been summarized as followed: metallurgically and economically, blowing more air was preferable so long as

---

* IMI Refiners, Ltd., Walsall, Staffordshire.
† Imperial Smelting Processes, Ltd., Avonmouth, Bristol.
‡ MORGAN S.W.K. AND TEMPLE D.A. The place of the Imperial Smelting Process in non-ferrous metallurgy. *J. Metals, N.Y.*, **19**, Aug. 1967, 23–9.
GRAY P.M.J. AND WOODS S.E. Production capacity of the Imperial Smelting Furnace. In *Mineral processing and extractive metallurgy* (London: Institution of Mining and Metallurgy, 1970), 853–77. (*Proc. 9th Commonw. Min. Metall. Congr. 1969, vol. 3*)

development of shaft and condenser operation could enable high efficiencies to be maintained. Oxygen enrichment enabled productive capacity to be increased with less capital investment if the tonnage oxygen plant itself were not included in the capital cost. It also avoided the necessity to develop operating technology to cope with high-velocity gases and must be considered as a means of extending the smelting capacity beyond whatever limits to air blowing were eventually reached.

Dr. Howard K. Worner* said that in addition to the applications of oxygen in more conventional lead smelting and refining, outlined by Harrison, he believed that there was a promising field for development in oxygen-assisted *direct smelting–converting* of good-quality concentrates. It might be of interest to record that the first pilot-plant trials of WORCRA continuous smelting–converting took place with Broken Hill lead concentrates at Cockle Creek, New South Wales, at the beginning of 1963.

The dried concentrates were injected into the smelting zone of the furnaces entrained in air or air enriched with oxygen. Some of the finely particulate PbS became oxidized to PbO or $PbSO_4$ and a continuing 'roast reaction' was induced in the smelting zones, e.g.

$$2PbO + PbS \rightarrow 3Pb + SO_2$$

Residual PbS in the bath was 'lanced' out sequentially with air or air enriched with oxygen as the metal flowed slowly into and through the converting zone. A crude bullion was tapped at that end of the furnace. The converter zone slag, containing PbO, was obliged to flow back countercurrently to the S-containing 'matte', and, in the process, was stripped of much of its PbO. The 'cleaned' slag passed slowly through a settling zone and then flowed out of the furnace remote from the lead taphole.

As in other approaches† to direct smelting–converting of lead concentrates, considerable fume was generated that could be collected and recirculated to the smelting zone.

The WORCRA smelting–converting of lead concentrates, although promising, was discontinued when even more promising results were achieved with copper concentrates. Those could be smelted and converted directly to copper with much less expensive hooding and fume-collection equipment.

Professor T. R. A. Davey‡, commenting on the paper by Lenoir and co-authors, congratulated the authors on a fine paper and a fine piece of work; his question was not intended as a reflection on that. He would like to know why so much

---

* Conzinc Riotinto of Australia, Ltd., Melbourne, Australia.

† ELVANDER H.I. The Boliden lead process. In *Pyrometallurgical processes in nonferrous metallurgy* ANDERSON J.N. AND QUENEAU P.E. eds (New York: Gordon and Breach, 1967), 225–45. (*AIME Metall. Soc. Conf.* vol. 39)

FULLER F.T. Process for direct smelting of lead concentrates. *J. Metals, N.Y.*, **20**, Dec. 1968, 26–30.

‡ Colorado School of Mines, Golden, Colorado, U.S.A.

attention was devoted to producing elemental sulphur from SO_2 rather than to finding other ways to render it innocuous.

The only conceivable large-scale use for sulphur was as sulphuric acid, and the man-made SO_2 from coal- or oil-burning and non-ferrous metal production was many times the amount needed for sulphuric acid production, and likely to be so for the foreseeable future. Within a decade or so most of the SO_2 from power generation would probably be required by law to be captured. It was not conceivable that the sulphuric acid demand could be expanded to absorb that additional sulphur.

There were, in principle, two ways in which the SO_2 could be treated—an expensive process aimed at producing a product which could be stored (e.g. sulphur) and cheaply converted to sulphuric acid later on; or a cheap process aimed at spending little money now to produce an innocuous product that could be stored (e.g. $CaSO_4$), although the conversion of that product to sulphuric acid at a later date, if required, would be relatively expensive.

He wondered why, apparently, so much attention was paid to the former method and so little to the latter, in view of the fact that, considering the world as a whole, it seemed certain that sulphuric acid must be in oversupply for generations.

Dr. E. H. Amstein, in introducing his joint paper, pointed out that although electrowinning processes which made use of fused-salt electrolytes were quite well known, refining processes on an industrial scale were very rare. The only outstanding example of electrorefining in fused salts was the well known three-layer process for aluminium. In spite of the lack of industrial applications, however, a considerable amount of work had been published on electrorefining in fused salts, and one early paper referring to lead was published more than 70 years ago.

He then went on to consider the advantages of the process and the reasons for its failure to achieve any wide applications on an industrial scale. As compared with aqueous electrolytic refining, fused-salt electrolytes had very high conductivities, and if both the anode and the cathode consisted of liquid metals, then there were obviously no difficulties due to either the formation of dendritic deposits on the cathode, or to the formation of anode slimes, loss of conductivity and other difficulties which could arise with anodes in aqueous electrolytic refining.

Those advantages could easily be demonstrated on the laboratory bench, but the real difficulty in applying the process lay in the problem of scaling up. The essence of that problem was the difficulty of opposing two liquid metal electrodes of large area so that they had a minimum linear separation. That was obviously necessary in order to achieve a large current-carrying capacity with a minimum voltage drop. There proved to be two simple geometric solutions to the problem: one was to separate two pools of metal by an impermeable wall, which was immersed in the electrolyte ('semi-wall'); and the second solution was to use a diaphragm permeable to the electrolyte, but not to either of the liquid metal electrodes. Both methods had been made to work on a small scale, but both revealed formidable difficulties on even a pilot-plant scale.

Up to the present time solid porous refractories had been used as diaphragms, and they had proved to be quite unreliable in practice. The solution to the problem proposed in the present paper was to use newly developed materials, which were based on ceramic fibres, as diaphragms. Work was described on one such material, which consisted of a felt of ceramic fibres, and which had originally been developed for heat insulations.

Dr. Amstein then described a cell designed to take advantage of that new material.

The diaphragm was substantially horizontal, but curved upwards at the edges to form a saucer shape. The saucer contained the anode metal, and in that way the problem of sealing the edge of the diaphragm was eliminated. The body of the cell was specially shaped from refractory blocks, which contained a well beneath the diaphragm in which the cathode metal collected. The cathode metal was continuously tapped from that well by means of a siphon. In the course of the work it became apparent that the diaphragm fibres were being attacked by the electrolyte and diaphragm lives could vary from 2 h to 2 weeks. That variability indicated that some impurity in the electrolyte might be responsible, and it was eventually shown that oxygen ions caused rapid attack of the ceramic fibres.

The problem was eventually overcome by incorporating in the chloride electrolyte the chloride of an element which had an oxide which was insoluble in the electrolyte. Chromium had been found to be one element whose compounds met that requirement very well. As a result of the development work it had proved possible to build cells which would operate for 100 days or more. The initial work was done with cells which took 200 A, and that was followed by 800-A cells. There was now a pilot-plant cell, taking 3000 A, which produced 2 tons of lead per week; slides demonstrated the construction and operation of one such cell.

The process had been applied to the refining of both lead and solder, and it gave extremely good separations for bismuth, antimony and gold, and fairly good separation of silver, but it had little effect on copper. There seemed no reason, if it were thought desirable, why that type of cell should not be applied to any metal which melted below about 700°C.

Dr. D. Inman, in introducing his joint paper, said that although electrochemical processes had a lot to offer, e.g. selection of reaction, control of rate, etc., large-scale electrometallurgical operations had often not been developed from the many successful laboratory and pilot-plant experiments. In certain cases, however (e.g. the Hall–Héroult process for the extraction of aluminium at high temperatures and the electrorefining of copper at low temperatures), electrometallurgical operations had been eminently successful. Thus, of the three branches of extractive metallurgy, electrometallurgy would still appear to be the

'Cinderella'. Many circumstances operating at the present time, however, were likely to change that state of affairs in due course.

He felt that it was the job of academics to produce ideas, establish principles, keep a broad mind and not involve themselves in a too specific way with industrial processes. They should also not try to blind technologists with the excessive erudition of their highly specialized science! It was the purpose of the present paper to skate along the interface between the pure and applied aspects of the subject, and perhaps scatter a few ideas in so doing.

Thus, they hoped that their model study of molybdenum deposition would emphasize the principles which could be employed to design molten salt electrolyte baths for electrodepositing refractory metals in massive, coherent form at temperatures at which they could not be deposited in the liquid state. In order to clarify the conclusions, the detailed electrochemical arguments had been omitted.

G. W. Mellors and S. Senderoff, in a noteworthy series of papers, had shown that the overall electrodeposition process had to be rate-controlled by some process occurring at the metal–melt interface (chemical or electrochemical control) rather than mass-transfer controlled in order to obtain coherent non-dendritic deposits. On that basis they were able to design successful molten fluoride baths for a whole range of refractory metals. Molybdenum was exceptional inasmuch as it could be deposited in that form from a chloride bath.

The present authors' general aim was to examine whether other baths (e.g. fluoride–chloride mixtures), which might be less corrosive than the pure fluorides, could be used for that purpose, and, particularly in mixtures, to look at the slow rate-controlling steps in detail to see whether more sophisticated process control might be possible.

A. B. Suttie,* commenting on the paper by Inman and Spencer, asked why a constant-current method had been used. A controlled-potential method, preferably with the use of a potentiostat, would be simple, and deposition kinetics, prior chemical reactions, mass transfer, etc., would be easier to analyse.

Dr. D. J. Fray,† commenting on the paper by Amstein, Davis and Hillyer, congratulated the authors on the development of their novel cell. When the anode was concentrated to antimony, how pure was the final product, and was the anode pool agitated in any way? At the high current densities used in the cell it was possible that the surface of the anode became depleted of lead at lead concentrations below 1%, transfer of lead from the bulk of the anode to the anode surface being slower than the removal of lead by electrolysis. If that occurred, antimony would be electrolysed. Did that, in fact, happen?

Dr. Howard K. Worner said that, with reference to the problem of achieving a coherent cathode deposit of metals, such as titanium, he would draw attention

* Capper Pass and Son, Ltd., North Ferriby, Yorkshire.
† Department of Metallurgy, University of Cambridge.

to a paper* which described a 'hot-spot cathode' technique which achieved a type of sintering of the dendrites deposited from an electrolyte consisting of titanium trichloride in the KCl–LiCl eutectic.

AUTHORS' REPLIES

J. L. Harrison In reply to the comments made by Mr. C. F. Harris (pp. 426–7), I agree that the Russian results are difficult to understand, but this is not unusual in reports emanating from such sources. The method employed in expressing results is often difficult to follow and translation difficulties often arise. The temperatures of 1000–1050°C with oxygen compared with 800–900°C without oxygen were taken in the sinter bed, but it must be remembered that these are laboratory results taken during experiments on a small scale with a fixed bed of only 200-mm height with charges of 14–16 kg.

Regarding the use of enriched air in iron blast-furnaces, I agree that oxygen additions have a similar effect to blast preheat. Ridgion has stated that the effect of a blast containing 25% oxygen is $2\frac{1}{2}$ times that of a 100°C increase in blast temperature. The operating difficulties experienced with increasing blast temperatures over 1000°C are usually associated with the type of burden and the degree of preparation, but as far as I am aware, no similar difficulties are experienced with oxygen enrichment. In Germany, Russia and Japan blast temperatures as high as 1100–1200°C with oxygen contents of 28–32% are being successfully employed, along with oil injection. The results are lower coke rates and appreciable increases in productivity.

Mr. J. S. Jacobi (p. 428) raised the question of the cost of oxygen—a very important factor in the economics of blast-furnace operation. The price of oxygen bears a direct relationship to the quantity consumed, but the economics are related to the advantages obtained in increased output and decreased solid fuel costs. The value of the end-product may also have a bearing on whether or not oxygen can be used economically. If the end-product cost is high, it may be able to tolerate the added cost of a modest amount of oxygen at the upper or medium range of the price scale, but if the end-product cost is low, as in iron-making, low-priced oxygen must be available to warrant its use. Fortunately, because of the large volumes required at low pressure, oxygen is for tonnage plants proving economically viable in iron blast-furnaces. In the case of lead smelting, the demand is less because of the smaller units employed, but in many instances oxygen in the form of liquid has proved to be economically advantageous, despite the higher oxygen cost. Where the demand is greater, as in medium- or large-size lead smelters, and particularly if there are other uses for oxygen, such as slag fuming, there are available small on-site plants, or plants

---

* BETT F. L. *et al.* Some investigations into the extraction of titanium by fused salt electrolysis. In *Extraction and refining of the rarer metals* (London: Institution of Mining and Metallurgy, 1957), 381–95.

which generate gaseous oxygen by the use of cold from a proportion of the oxygen imported as liquid, which provide oxygen in the intermediate price range.

In reply to Dr. D. A. Temple (pp. 428–9) on the question of the viability of oxygen in the ISF, the oxygen supply companies are prepared to install oxygen plants or supply facilities by use of their own capital resources and to supply oxygen under an agreed contract without involving the customer in capital expenditure. The oxygen cost would thus be entirely an operating cost, unless trade conditions were very exceptional.

Dr. E. H. Amstein, W. D. Davis and C. Hillyer   In reply to Dr. D. J. Fray (p. 432), the antimony produced by electrolysing all the lead from a lead–antimony anode contains 96–99% Sb, depending partly on the content of other elements in the original feed alloy. All the bismuth and some silver and copper remain with the antimony, but very little lead is left. An example of an anode residue alloy from very impure scrap lead analysed 96·4% Sb and 2·8% Bi, and a 99·7% Sb anode residue has been obtained from a pure antimonial lead feed.

There is no deliberate agitation of the molten lead–antimony anode, but there is some stirring, partly electromagnetic in origin, and partly due to thermally induced convection. This stirring has been observed to be very vigorous in short-life 200-A cells with exposed anode metal, and it must take place in the larger cells also.

It is true that when the lead in the anode alloy becomes exhausted, continued passage of current will cause the ionization of antimony atoms. However, because of the high volatility of antimony trichloride, hardly any antimony remains in the electrolyte to deposit with the lead at the cathode; nearly all of it leaves the cell in the white fume mentioned in the paper as marking an 'antimony point'. This fuming gives immediate warning of the exhaustion of the lead, and it ceases as soon as fresh lead is fed to the anode.

Dr. D. Inman and Dr. R. Spencer   In principle, we agree with Mr. A. B. Suttie (p. 432) that it is better to 'select', by potential control, an electrochemical process for study than to control the overall rate of, perhaps, several processes occurring in parallel. In our case we employed the constant-current technique primarily because of the simplicity of its instrumentation.

We feel that the best approach is to use a range of electrochemical techniques, an approach which has been adopted by one of us (D.I.) and Mr. M. Weaver in a current study of rather complex electrode processes in melts involving the deposition of sulphur from sulphide ions.

Session 7

Process control

Chairman
M. J. Cahalan

Development of an electrochemical method for the determination of copper in molten slags

D. G. Winter A.R.I.C.
P. J. Bowles B.Sc., Ph.D., D.I.C.

Both of the Mineral Science and Technology Division, Warren Spring Laboratory, Department of Trade and Industry, Stevenage, Hertfordshire

543.25 : 546.56 : 669.046.584

Synopsis

The viability of rotating-electrode voltammetry as a technique for the quantitative determination of copper and silver in the KNO_3–$NaNO_3$ eutectic at temperatures up to 350°C has been demonstrated. In attempts to extend the use of the technique to silicate systems at temperatures of 1000–1200°C the reduction of solute cations has been characterized by peaks rather than plateaux in the current-voltage curve because of the high viscosity of the melts so far studied. Use of a tungsten rotating-disc electrode has resulted in a linear variation of the peak potential for the reduction of a given solute with the concentration of that solute. It is considered that the occurrence of both these phenomena should be eliminated before the voltammetric technique can be successfully applied to the on-line analysis of molten slags.

Although pyrometallurgical processes were comparatively slow batch operations, taking, for example, in open-hearth steelmaking, many hours for their completion, the control of these processes in terms of following composition changes in metal and slag could be effected by discontinuous sampling techniques by use of comparatively slow analytical methods. Originally, both slag and metal samples were analysed by classical methods—a very lengthy operation—and, even with the replacement of these by faster spectrometric techniques, a time-delay occurs between sampling and receipt of results.

With the development of fast pneumatic techniques in steelmaking, and continuous methods such as the WORCRA process, applicable to both copper and steel production, discontinuous analytical techniques have become less suitable for the effective control of these processes. A need exists for on-line methods for both metal and slag analysis where the change in concentration of solute elements can be monitored continuously during a pyrometallurgical process. Progress has already been made in the continuous determination of oxygen in both molten steel and copper by use of solid electrolyte probes. Of the physico-chemical methods available for on-line slag analysis, the electrochemical technique of voltammetry appears to offer considerable potential in the case, for example, of calcium aluminosilicate slags, because these liquids, when molten, are ionic conductors.

The technique of voltammetry involves measurement of the current passing between a working and a secondary electrode immersed in an electrolyte. This current is a function of a linearly varying voltage applied between the working electrode and a third unpolarized reference electrode. If a species capable of being reduced or oxidized is present in the electrolyte, an increase in the current passing through the cell is observed at a potential determined by the Gibbs free energy of the reduction or oxidation reaction. In some cases the same electrode may be used as both the reference and secondary electrode if the current drawn from the cell is so low that the reference electrode is effectively unpolarized. In many investigations, particularly those at high temperatures, this simplification is invalid and a separate reference electrode *must* be used. In controlled-potential voltammetry a noble metal can be used as a quasi-reference electrode because the cell current does not flow through it and, hence, it remains at some constant potential as the current–voltage curve is recorded. The half-wave potential, i.e. the potential at which the current is half its maximum value, as recorded relative to this quasi-reference, is arbitrary for it has the potential of the quasi-reference impressed upon it, but it *is* reproducible. Ideally, the half-wave potential for a particular reduction should be independent of the concentration and, therefore, be a qualitative method of detection of the reducible species. Also, the limiting current should be a linear function of the concentration, giving a quantitative method of determination.

The voltammetric techniques which can be applied to on-line analysis are the dropping metal electrode, rotating-disc electrode (RDE) and voltammetry in a flowing electrolyte with electrodes so designed that a laminar flow régime exists. The dropping mercury electrode is the most widely used technique in aqueous solutions, but the application of a dropping metal electrode to high-temperature systems has met with very limited success on account of the reactivity of the electrode material and the difficulty of keeping it in the molten state. Voltammetry in flowing electrolytes, though attractive to pilot-scale operations, is very difficult to operate on a laboratory scale at high temperatures. In addition, the theory of these systems has not been analysed to the same extent as the dropping metal and rotating-disc electrodes. For these reasons a RDE system was chosen for the present study.

Since a number of excellent reviews on electrochemistry in molten salts have been published,[1-7] it is not proposed to carry out a further review here; only the small amount of work involving the RDE will be summarized. The majority of this work has been published by Russian authors and it includes only the minimal amount of experimental detail. It may be noted, also, that the severe experimental difficulties encountered at temperatures above 1000°C have greatly limited the number of investigations.

Bowcott and Plunkett[8] have investigated the deposition of silver on to a RDE from molten $NaNO_3$ and $NaNO_3$–KNO_3 mixtures. Chovnyk and Vashchenko[9] have shown that a RDE could be used for polarographic studies in melts. These workers made a study of the discharge of silver ions from the $NaNO_3$–KNO_3 eutectic and, from their results, calculated a value for the diffusion coefficient of silver, although the value they calculated does not agree with their published experimental data. Panchenko and Shilina[10] have also applied the rotating disc to polarographic work in molten KNO_3–$NaNO_3$ and LiCl–KCl mixtures. They examined the reduction of the chlorides of zinc, lead, cadmium, cobalt and copper and established that the limiting diffusion currents were proportional to the solute concentrations. Esin and co-workers[11, 12, 13] have used rotating-disc voltammetry to determine the diffusion coefficients of iron, manganese, chromium, silicon, vanadium, lead, copper and zinc in oxyanion melts at temperatures between 1200 and 1500°C, but they did not publish any details on setting up the electrode. Okunev and Chumarev[14] used a rotating-disc technique to investigate the reduction of zinc oxide by metallic iron in silicate melts. They showed that the process was diffusion-controlled, but, again, no experimental details were published.

Experimental method

The preparation of experimental materials, construction of apparatus and the working procedure used in the present study are described in detail in the Appendix. A better assessment of the results obtained may, however, be possible if the principles underlying the experimental method are discussed briefly.

As has been stated, the technique of voltammetry involves measurement of the current passing between a working and a secondary electrode, which are immersed in an electrolyte. On the application of a linearly varying voltage between the working electrode and a third unpolarized electrode, reduction of heavy metal impurities in the electrolyte will produce discontinuities in the current–voltage curve, which may obscure the electrode reactions of interest to the slag analyst. Adequate purification of the fused-salt electrolyte is therefore an important preliminary to experiments producing a series of current–voltage curves in a given solvent.

For initial low-temperature studies designed primarily to test the apparatus, an alkali-nitrate eutectic was used, whereas at high temperatures a sodium silicate melt has been used for most work to date. Platinum proved a very satisfactory electrode material for low-temperature studies, but was, unfortunately, attacked by cathodic reduction products at high temperature; it was therefore necessary to use tungsten for work in silicate melts.

Work in both simple silicate and nitrate melts has been carried out in an argon atmosphere, but some preliminary work in an iron-bearing calcium aluminosilicate slag was carried out under an atmosphere of controlled oxygen pressure. The controlled atmosphere was produced by a carbon monoxide–carbon dioxide mixture with the ratio carbon monoxide pressure : carbon dioxide pressure so

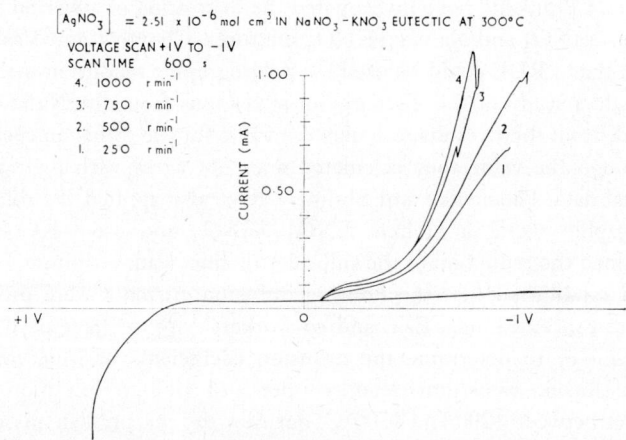

Fig. 1 Typical voltammogram for deposition of silver on platinum rotating-disc electrode at various angular velocities

chosen that the ferrous oxide in the slag was not oxidized to magnetite.

Production of current–voltage curves of the type shown in Figs. 1 and 2 by use of a RDE requires the construction of the electrode assembly to high mechanical standards. Particular care has been taken in the present work to ensure (1) that the electrode surface is as flat as possible and (2) that the electrode rotates with a minimum of eccentricity. A final requirement is that the RDE be surrounded by an electrical insulating sheath which is not attacked by the melt.

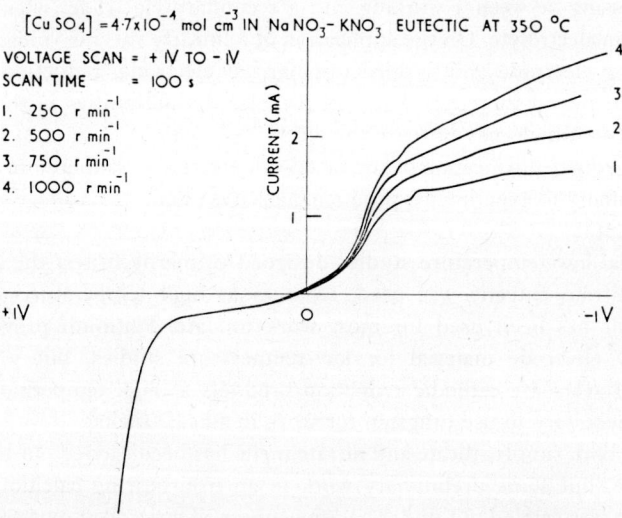

Fig. 2 Typical voltammogram for deposition of copper on platinum rotating-disc electrode at various angular velocities

At temperatures up to 1000°C boron nitride was found to be satisfactory for this purpose, but at 1200°C cracking and warping of this material necessitated its replacement by alumina as the electrode sheathing material.

Determination of silver and copper in a KNO_3–$NaNO_3$ melt

EXPERIMENTAL PROCEDURE

The first system chosen for investigation was that of $AgNO_3$ in equimolar $NaNO_3$–KNO_3. This system was selected because of its relatively low melting point (ca 250°C) and because the silver redox reaction was reversible. An equimolar solvent mixture of KNO_3–$NaNO_3$ was prepared as described in the Appendix and heated to 300°C in the cell, and the electrodes were lowered into the molten salt. The signal generator was set to sweep from $+1.0$ to -1.0 V in a triangular mode where the rate of change of voltage was linear with respect to time and the electrode rotated at 1000 rev min^{-1}. A current–voltage curve was obtained for the solvent and then an accurately weighed quantity of $AgNO_3$ was carefully added, stirred in and a new current–voltage curve recorded, this being repeated for several increasing amounts of $AgNO_3$. At a point when the silver ion concentration was large enough to give rise to an easily measurable limiting current the dependence of the limiting current on the angular velocity of the electrode was determined (Fig. 1). The voltammetric behaviour of anhydrous $CuSO_4$ in KNO_3–$NaNO_3$ containing 1% $KHSO_4$ to minimize precipitation of CuO was investigated in a similar manner (Fig. 2).

RESULTS

Typical current–voltage curves obtained for the reduction of silver and copper in the KNO_3–$NaNO_3$ eutectic are shown in Figs. 1 and 2; also shown is the dependence of the limiting current on the speed of rotation of the disc electrode at constant concentration of the reducible species. This dependence is depicted graphically in Fig. 3. A linear relationship was also found between concentration and limiting current density (Figs. 4 and 5).

Determination of copper in a sodium silicate melt

EXPERIMENTAL PROCEDURE

The Na_2O–SiO_2 melt was prepared and purified as described in the Appendix. The dependence of the peak height and the peak potential on the concentration of CuO was determined at 1000°C with the electrode rotating at 250 rev min^{-1} since, although limiting currents were not obtained, Baak and Frederick[15] had found that voltammograms obtained with a rotating-wire electrode were better defined than those obtained with a stationary electrode. CuO was added by dropping a weighed amount down an alumina tube directly on to the surface of the silicate melt at 1000°C. The melt was then stirred for several hours with an alumina rod and a sample was taken to test the homogeneity of the melt. If the melt was not homogeneous, stirring was continued until it was, and a sample

P*

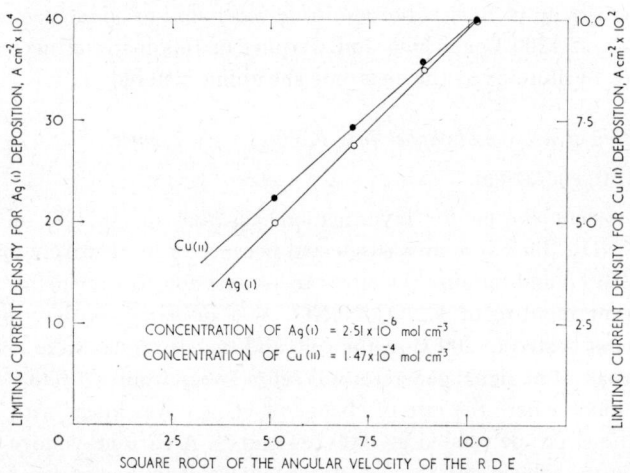

Fig. 3 Dependence of limiting current on angular velocity of rotating-disc electrode

was then taken for analysis. Voltammograms for CuO, ZnO, FeO and SnO_2 at two concentrations in the Na_2O–SiO_2 melt at 1200°C were obtained, the oxides being added and sampled as described for CuO. The electrode was again rotated

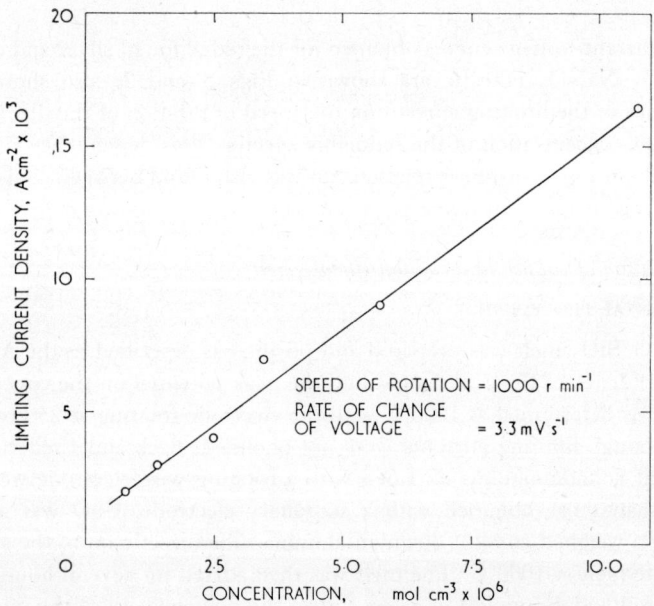

Fig. 4 Dependence of limiting current on the concentration of Ag(I)

at 250 rev min^{-1}, and the dependence of the peak height and peak potential on the voltage sweep rate was determined.

The work described above was carried out under an atmosphere of dry, purified argon. In the case of the calcium aluminosilicate base slag, however, voltammetry was carried out at 1200°C under an atmosphere of controlled oxygen pressure defined by p_{CO}/p_{CO_2} chosen so that the ferrous oxide was not oxidized to magnetite. When other heavy metal oxide solutes are present the p_{CO}/p_{CO_2} ratio will have to be chosen so that inter-oxide oxidation–reduction reactions are suppressed.

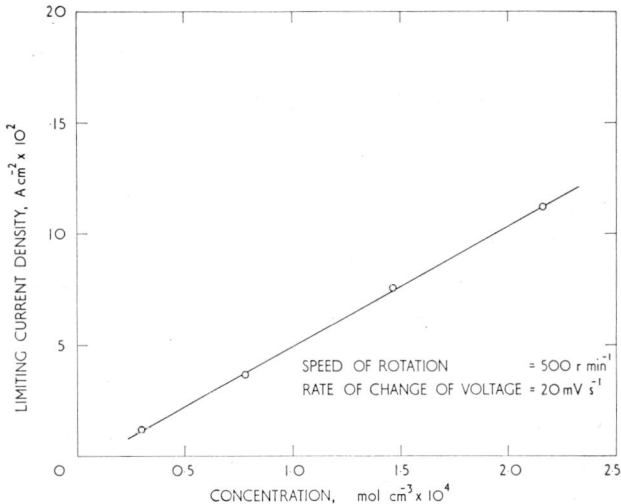

Fig. 5 Dependence of limiting current on concentration of Cu(II)

RESULTS

Attempts to obtain limiting diffusion current voltammograms in the Na$_2$O–SiO$_2$ melt at 1000°C were not successful and current–voltage curves possessing maxima were obtained even though an electrode was used which had previously been found to operate satisfactorily in the KNO$_3$–NaNO$_3$ eutectic. A linear relationship was, however, found between the peak current density and concentration of copper oxide (Fig. 6). It was also found that the peak potential varied in a linear manner with concentration, the potential becoming more cathodic with increasing concentration (Fig. 7) and with the rate of change of voltage (Fig. 8). When the temperature was raised to 1200°C, limiting diffusion currents were still not obtained, maxima being observed for the reduction of oxides of copper, zinc, tin and iron. The peak current density and peak potential were found to be dependent on the same parameters as at 1000°C (Figs. 9 and 10).

At present the work carried out on the iron-rich calcium aluminosilicate slag has been limited to recording the residual current curve (Fig. 11). This has

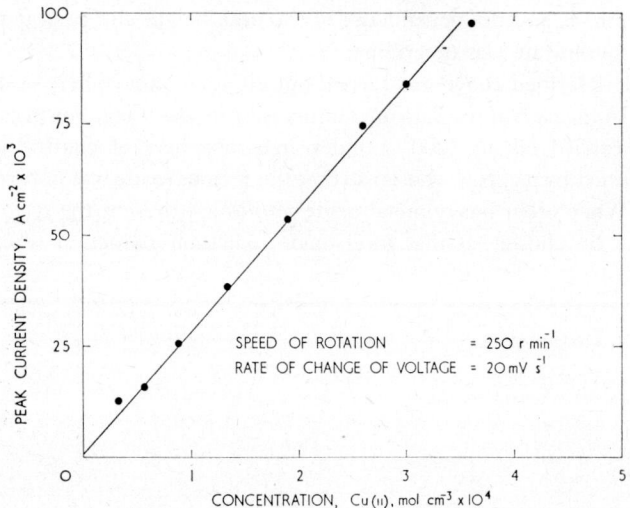

Fig. 6 Dependence of peak current on concentration of Cu(II) in Na_2O-SiO_2 at 1000°C

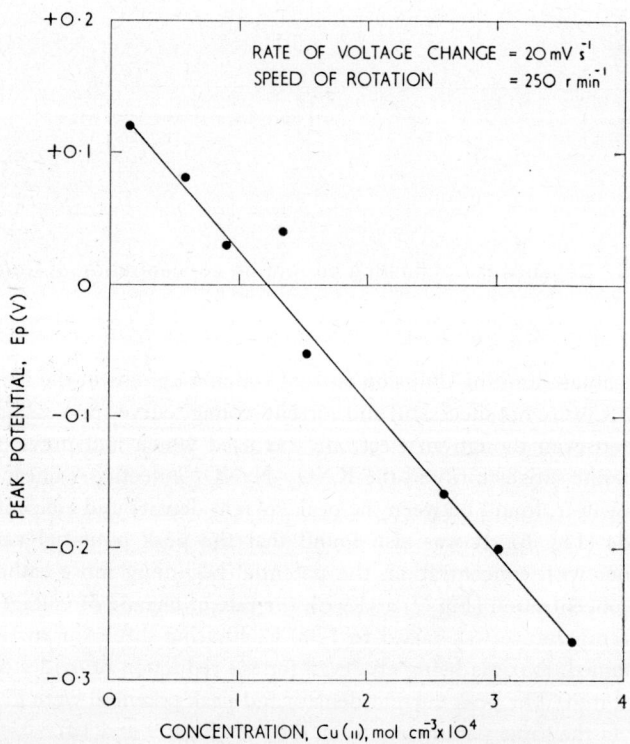

Fig. 7 Variation of peak potential with Cu(II) concentration in Na_2O-SiO_2 melt at 1000°C

indicated that the residual current is of the order of 1 A cm^{-2} at $-0\cdot50$ V, which is extremely high for voltammetric procedures and is probably due to the high FeO ($\simeq 30\%$) content of the slag.

Discussion

Before any voltammetric method could be applied to on-line analysis it was considered that the following three criteria had to be satisfied: (1) the current–voltage curves should possess a limiting diffusion current; (2) there should be a

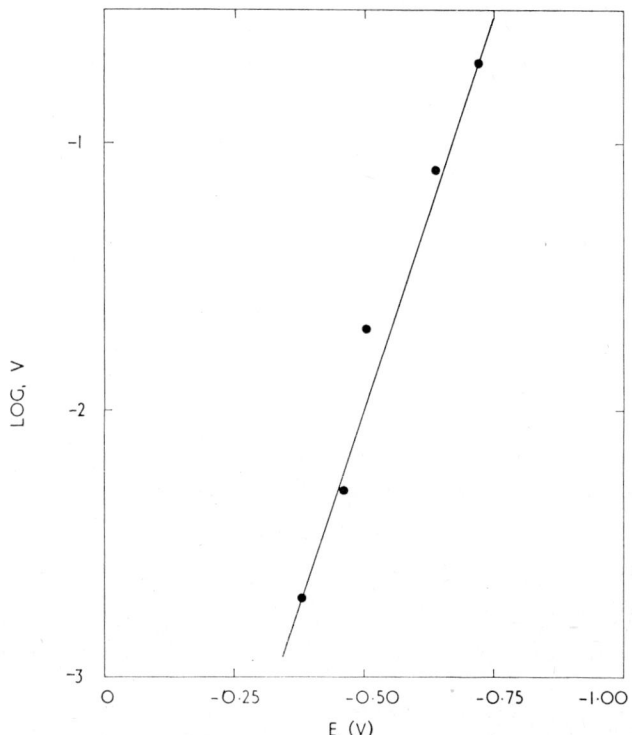

Fig. 8 Variation of peak potential with sweep rate for Cu(II) in Na_2O–SiO_2 melt at 1000°C

linear relationship between the limiting current density and the concentration of reducible species; and (3) the half-wave potential should be constant for a particular species.

The investigations in the nitrate eutectic were intended to provide quantitative information about the design parameters of the RDE and to determine whether the three criteria applied to such a system. Since, for the reduction of both copper and silver, there was a linear relationship between limiting current density and concentration and the half-wave potential was independent of speed of rotation of the electrode and voltage sweep rate, conditions (2) and (3) were satisfied. A more thorough analysis of the limiting current voltammogram was necessary, however, to eliminate the possibility that it was due to instrumental effects.

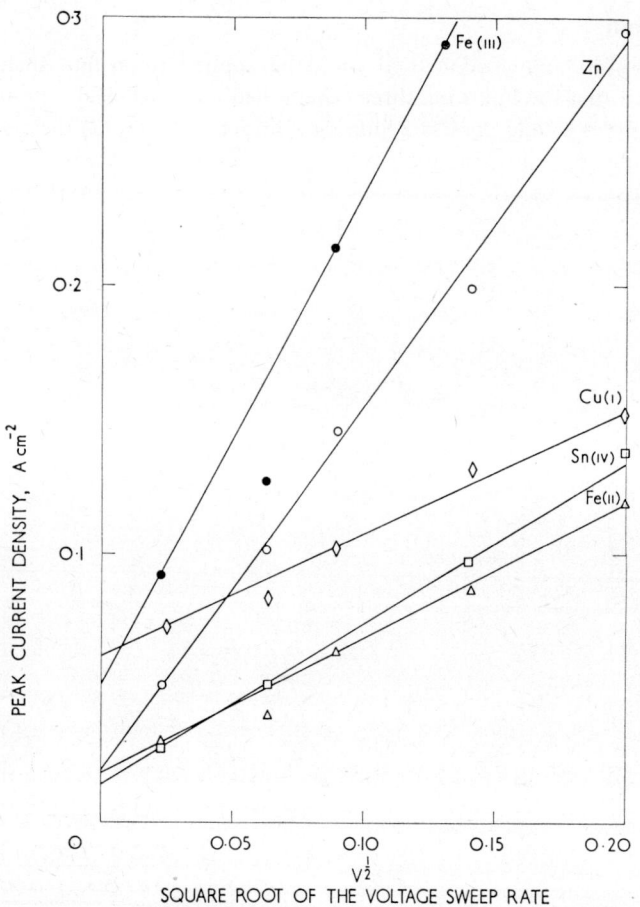

Fig. 9 Variation of peak current with square root of sweep rate for some metal ions in Na_2O–SiO_2 melt at 1200°C

Levich[16, 17, 18] has derived an equation for mass transfer to a disc electrode under conditions of laminar flow and forced convection:

$$i_{lim} = 0.62\, nFD^{\frac{2}{3}}v^{-\frac{1}{6}}\omega^{\frac{1}{2}}C_o$$

where n is the number of electrons taking part in the reduction process, F the Faraday, D the diffusion coefficient of the species undergoing reduction, cm^2 sec^{-1}, v the kinematic viscosity of the bulk electrolyte, cm^2 sec^{-1}, ω the angular velocity of the electrode, radians sec^{-1}, C_o the concentration of diffusing species, mol cm^{-3}, and i_{lim} the limiting current density, A cm^{-2}. Since n can be obtained by an analysis of the rising portion of the current–voltage curve and v from published data,[19, 20] the value of D, the diffusion coefficient, can be calculated. The values found were $4\cdot73\pm0\cdot1\times10^{-5}$ cm^2 sec^1 for Ag(I) at 300°C and $1\cdot04\pm0\cdot1\times10^{-5}$ cm^2 sec^{-1} for Cu(I) at 350°C. The concentrations at which the diffusion coefficients were calculated were $2\cdot5\times10^{-6}$ and $1\cdot47\times10^{-4}$ mol cm^{-3}, respectively. The general agreement between these and published values[21–24] indicated that the limiting current was not due to instrumental effects but to limiting diffusion conditions. These observations showed that the

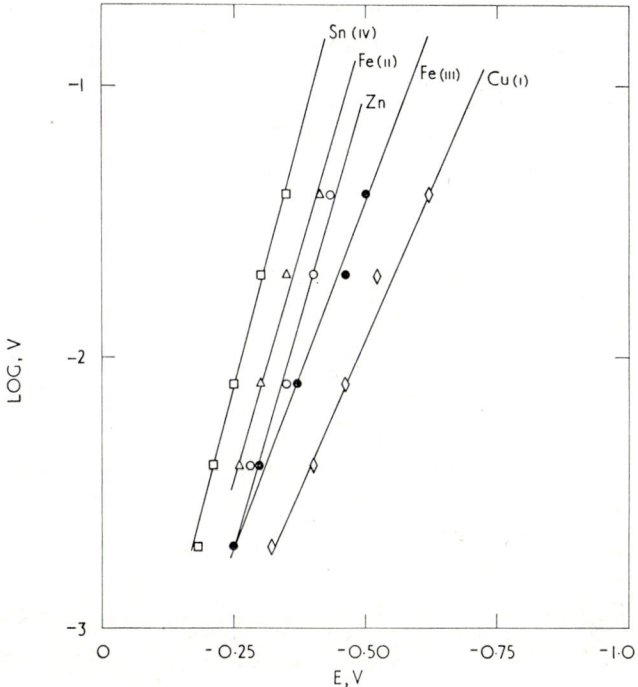

Fig. 10 Variation of peak potential with sweep rate for some metal ions in Na$_2$O–SiO$_2$ melt at 1200°C

RDE was suitable for on-stream analysis of molten salts at temperatures of at least 400°C.

In the silicate melt laminar diffusion conditions were not obtained: instead of a plateau in the current–voltage curve, a maximum was observed of the type obtained at stationary electrodes with a high scan rate. This was, in some respects, expected because the Reynolds numbers achieved in the silicate melt were of the order of 10^{-3}, even at an electrode rotational speed of 1500 rev min^{-1}, whereas the value of 706 was attained in the nitrate melt at 1000 rev min^{-1}. This meant that natural convection prevented laminar flow conditions being attained. Also the boundary surfaces, e.g. crucible walls, secondary electrode, etc., could not be considered to be at an effectively infinite distance from the disc surface. The source of these anomalies was considered to be the high viscosity of the sodium silicate melt. Because, however, the melt contained a high proportion of silica, a characteristic of the majority of blast-furnace slags, but melted at a relatively low temperature for a silicate system, the investigation was continued in order to determine the applicability of the basic electroanalytical principles.

The linear relationship found between the peak current density and concentration of CuO (Fig. 6) in the $Na_2O–SiO_2$ melt at 1000°C indicated that there was a basis for a quantitative method of analysis at these high temperatures.

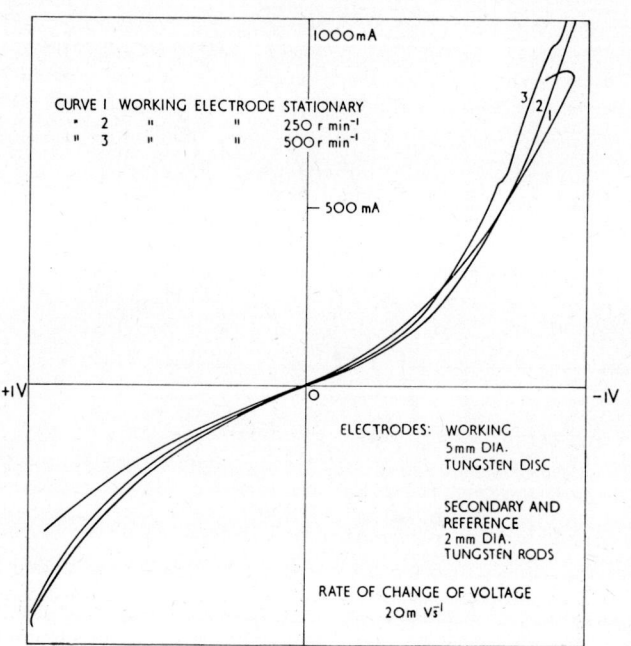

CURVE 1   WORKING ELECTRODE STATIONARY
    2   "   "   250 r min⁻¹
    3   "   "   500 r min⁻¹

Fig. 11 Residual current voltammogram of iron-rich calcium aluminosilicate slag at 1200°C

The observation that the half-wave potential was not constant but a linear function of concentration could, however, cause serious problems in a complex industrial slag containing several reducible metal species. It has been predicted that this type of behaviour occurs when the metal produced by the electrochemical reduction is deposited on the working electrode at unit activity. This observation is supported by the fact that the solid solubility of metals in tungsten, even at temperatures of 1000°C, is very small, whereas platinum alloys readily with many metals at comparatively low temperatures. Thus, in the reduction of silver in the nitrate eutectic silver metal was deposited at less than unit activity, causing the half-wave potential to be independent of concentration. Platinum cannot be used as an electrode material in industrial slags because it is severely and rapidly corroded by metals at the temperatures at which industrial processes operate. For the half-wave potential to remain independent of concentration an electrode metal in which the solubility of deposited metals is intermediate between those of platinum and tungsten is required.

Conclusion

The design of a RDE has been described in quantitative parameters which have been successfully tested by an investigation on the electrochemical behaviour of silver and copper in the KNO_3–$NaNO_3$ eutectic. Current–voltage curves possessing a limiting diffusion current were obtained for the reduction of both cations, indicating that laminar diffusion conditions existed. A linear relationship between concentration and limiting diffusion current density on the speed of rotation of the electrode and the agreement between these and the published values confirmed the viability of the chosen electrode system. In high melting point silicate systems current–voltage curve peaks rather than the more desirable plateaux have characterized the reduction of solute cations. This may be due to either the high viscosity of the metal oxide–silica system or a breakdown in the design parameters caused by inadequate materials. This problem will be investigated by the use of systems with a viscosity similar to that of blast-furnace slags at 1200°C, i.e. 5–10 P, and by selection of more suitable materials for the construction of the electrode. If it is not possible to develop a system which produces current–voltage curves possessing a limiting diffusion current, it may still prove possible to use stationary electrodes for a 'spot-check' system if the voltage scan range and rates are suitably chosen. A linear relationship between $Cu(II)$ concentration and peak current density was observed in the Na_2O–SiO_2 melt at 1000°C, which suggested that the basic electrochemical principles still held at these elevated temperatures.

Linear variation of peak potential with concentration was, however, undesirable in an analytical method because, in an industrial system containing several reducible species, all of unknown concentration, there would be no way of qualitatively identifying the species giving rise to a particular discontinuity in the current–voltage curve. Because this behaviour is primarily a function of the electrode material, future work will be directed to finding a system where the reduction potential is independent of concentration. It is considered essential that this problem be overcome before the method can be applied to the analysis of industrial systems.

References

1. GAUR H. C. AND BHATIA B. B. Electrochemical investigations in molten salt systems: techniques and applications. *J. scient. ind. Res.*, **21A**, 1962, 16–25.
2. GAUR H. C. AND SETHI R. S. Polarography in molten salts. *J. electroanal. Chem.*, **7**, 1964, 474–86.
3. LAITINEN H. A. AND OSTERYOUNG R. A. Electrochemistry in molten salts. In *Fused salts* SUNDHEIM B. R. ed. (New York: McGraw-Hill, 1964), 255–300.
4. LIU C. H. JOHNSON K. E. AND LAITINEN H. A. Electroanalytical chemistry of molten

salts. In *Molten salt chemistry* BLANDER M. ed. (New York: Interscience, 1964), 681–733.

5. DELIMARSKII YU. K. AND MARKOV B. F. *Electrochemistry of fused salts* (Washington, D.C.: The Sigma Press, 1961), 338 p.

6. REDDY T. B. The electrochemistry of molten salts. *Electrochem. Technol.*, **1**, 1963, 325–51.

7. INMAN D. GRAVES A. D. AND SETHI R. S. Electrochemistry of molten salts. *Electrochemistry*, **1**, 1970, 166–222.

8. BOWCOTT J. E. L. AND PLUNKETT B. A. Rotating disc electrode in sodium and potassium nitrate melts. *Electrochim. Acta*, **14**, 1969, 883–7.

9. CHOVNYK N. G. AND VASHCHENKO V. V. Polarography of melts. III. Application of a rotating disc electrode to the polarography of melts. *Zh. fiz. Khim.*, **35**, 1961, 580–7; *Russ. J. phys. Chem.*, **35**, 1961, 283–7.

10. PANCHENKO I. D. AND SHILINA G. V. The rotating disc electrode in the polarography of molten salts. *Zh. anal. Khim.*, **18**, 1963, 920–3; *J. anal. Chem. USSR*, **18**, 1963, 799–802.

11. BORONENKOV V. N. ESIN O. A. AND SHURYGIN P. M. Anodic process on a disk electrode in oxide melts. *Elektrokhimiya*, **1**, 1965, 595–6; *Sov. Electrochem.*, **1**, 1965, 517–21.

12. BORONENKOV V. N. ESIN O. A. AND SHURYGIN P. M. Kinetics of the deposition of metals from molten aluminates on a disc electrode. *Zh. fiz. Khim.*, **38**, 1964, 1148–53; *Russ. J. phys. Chem.*, **38**, 1964, 628–31.

13. SUZOV YU. M. AND ESIN O. A. Use of the disc electrode for determining the diffusion coefficients of lead, copper, and zinc ions in slags in nonferrous metallurgy. *Elektrokhimiya*, **2**, 1966, 974–7; *Sov. Electrochem.*, **2**, 1966, 904–6.

14. OKUNEV A. I. AND CHUMAREV V. M. Kinetics of the reduction of zinc oxide in silicate melts by metallic iron. *Dokl. Akad. nauk SSSR*, **172**, no. 1 1967, 153–5. (Russian text)

15. BAAK T. AND FREDERICK R. L. Polarography in molten sodium disilicate. *J. Am. Ceram. Soc.*, **50**, 1967, 38–42.

16. LEVICH V. G. The theory of concentration polarisation. *Acta phys. chim. URSS*, **17**, 1942, 257–307. (Russian text)

17. LEVICH V. G. Theory of concentration polarisation. *Zh. fiz. Khim.*, **18**, 1944, 335–49. (Russian text)

18. LEVICH V. G. *Physicochemical hydrodynamics* (Englewood Cliffs, N.J.: Prentice-Hall, 1962) 700 p.

19. FAWSITT C. E. Viscosity determinations at high temperatures. *J. chem. Soc.*, 1908, 1299–307.

20. GOODWIN H. M. AND MAILEY R. D. On the density, electrical conductivity and viscosity of fused salts and their mixtures. *Phys. Rev.*, **26**, 1908, 28–60.

21. THALMAYER C. E. BRUCKENSTEIN S. AND GRUEN D. M. Chronopotentiometric determination of interdiffusion coefficients and heats of interdiffusion in molten salts. *J. inorg. nucl. Chem.*, **26**, 1964, 347–57.

22. INMAN D. AND BOCKRIS J. O'M. The application of the galvanostatic potential–time technique to analysis in molten salts. *J. electroanal. Chem.*, **3**, 1962, 126–45.

23. LIU C. H. Electroanalytical techniques in molten lithium sulfate–potassium sulfate eutectic. *Anal. Chem.*, **33**, 1961, 1477–9.

24. LAITINEN H. A. AND FERGUSON W. S. Chronopotentiometric analysis in fused lithium chloride–potassium chloride. *Anal. Chem.*, **29**, 1957, 4–9.

Appendix

Experimental method

MATERIALS

Preparation of solute materials and of alkali nitrate eutectic solvent melt   Analar grade KNO_3 and $NaNO_3$ were dried at $150°C$ under vacuum for 24 h and then mixed in equimolar quantities. The mixture was melted in a Pyrex beaker under a stream of dried argon, after which heavy metal impurities were removed by pre-electrolysis for 6 h by use of platinum flag electrodes with the cathode at $-1·5$ V with respect to a platinum wire reference. Analar $AgNO_3$ was dried as above and anhydrous $CuSO_4$ was prepared by heating $CuSO_4.5H_2O$ at 200°C for 24 h.

Preparation of sodium silicate eutectic solvent melt and of solute materials The lowest melting Na_2O-SiO_2 eutectic has a composition of 25·5 mol per cent Na_2O and melts at 793°C.[1] Technical grade $Na_2SiO_3.5H_2O$ was dehydrated by heating at 600°C for 24 h and the SiO_2 was prepared by crushing pure quartz crystal, leaching with 25% v/v HCl, washing with distilled water and sintering at 1000°C for 24 h. The Na_2SiO_3 (51·4 wt %) and SiO_2 (48·6 wt %) were thoroughly mixed and heated in a large platinum crucible at 1150°C for 48 h. On cooling, a clear glass was formed, there being no opaqueness caused by undissolved SiO_2. The silicate melt was ground to -200 mesh and pre-electrolysed to remove heavy metal impurities in 100-g batches in recrystallized alumina crucibles by use of platinum electrodes. The cathode voltage was maintained at $-1·0$ V with respect to a platinum reference for 8 h, after which time the residual cell current was 2 mA. A sample of each batch of Na_2O-SiO_2 melt was analysed to determine the exact composition. Cupric oxide was prepared by drying Analar grade $Cu(NO_3)_2.3H_2O$ at 120°C for 4 h and then heating to 1000°C for 6 h. Analar grade ZnO and SnO_2 were dried as above and FeO was prepared by adding dried laboratory grade FeC_2O_4 directly to the silicate melt at temperature as required.

Preparation of a base calcium aluminosilicate slag A base silicate slag was prepared to contain FeO, Al_2O_3, SiO_2 and CaO in the same molar ratios as a typical slag from secondary copper smelting.[2] SiO_2 was prepared as above, CaO was prepared by decomposing Analar $CaCO_3$ and FeO was added as FeC_2O_4, which had been dried by heating at 140°C for 48 h under vacuum. These components were thoroughly mixed and put into an alumina crucible (750 cm^3), which was then sealed by a 'Ceramtec' machineable refractory lid fitted with two mullite tubes. The mixture was heated to 700°C under vacuum in an induction furnace and maintained at this temperature until the evolution of gas had almost ceased, indicating that the decomposition of FeC_2O_4 to FeO was nearing completion. The temperature was then raised quickly to 1200°C and the mixture was held at this temperature for 1 h, a positive pressure being maintained, if required, by purified nitrogen. The composition of a typical slag prepared in this way is given in Table 1.

APPARATUS

A schematic diagram of the voltammetry apparatus is given in Fig. 1; also shown is the gas purification system necessary to enable work to be carried out in atmospheres of controlled oxygen pressure, which are required to simulate furnace conditions.

The purification of carbon monoxide and carbon dioxide was followed by mixing in predetermined ratios. Standard procedure was followed to produce an atmosphere in which the oxygen partial pressure was controlled between 10^{-1} and 10^{-9} N/m^2 at temperatures in the region of 1200°C.

After mixing, the gases were passed to the electrochemical cell assembly. A

Table 1   Composition of the synthetic base slag

Compound	Amount added, wt %	Amount found, wt %	Amount present in a typical slag, wt %	Amount present in synthetic slag, wt %
FeO*	40·5	36·4	33·2	29·9
Al$_2$O$_3$	12·2	13·4†	9·9	11·0
SiO$_2$	37·8	37·3	30·9	30·5
Fe$_2$O$_3$	—	4·7‡	—	3·8
CaO	9·5	8·2	7·7	6·7
Total	100·0	100·0	81·8§	81·8§

* Added as dried ferrous oxalate.

† The high alumina content was due to contamination from the crucible.

‡ Fe(III) produced by oxidation of Fe(II) during synthesis and probably during grinding.

§ This percentage is made up to 100 by the addition of 16·6% ZnO, 1·2% Cu and 0·4% Sn.

diagram of the cell head and bush housing is shown in Fig. 2. The body of the head was machined from brass and consisted of two halves. The bottom flange

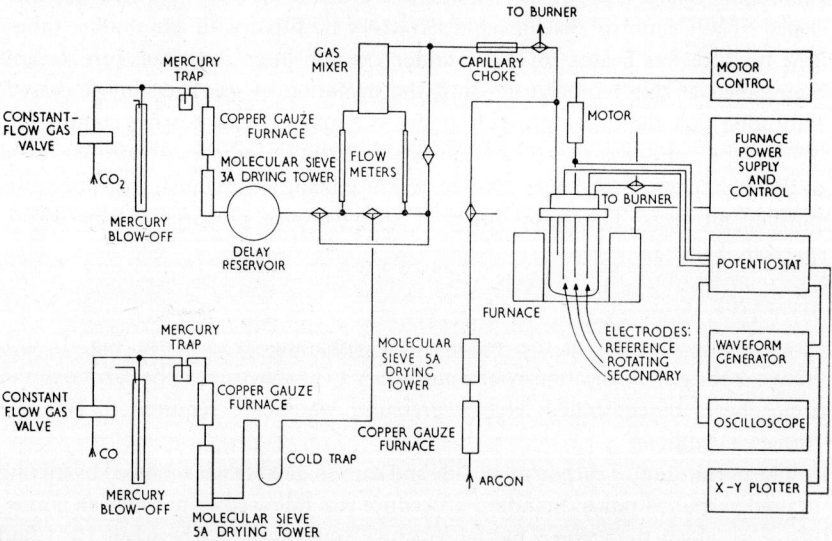

Fig. 1 Schematic diagram of apparatus for electrochemical examination of slags under controlled atmospheres

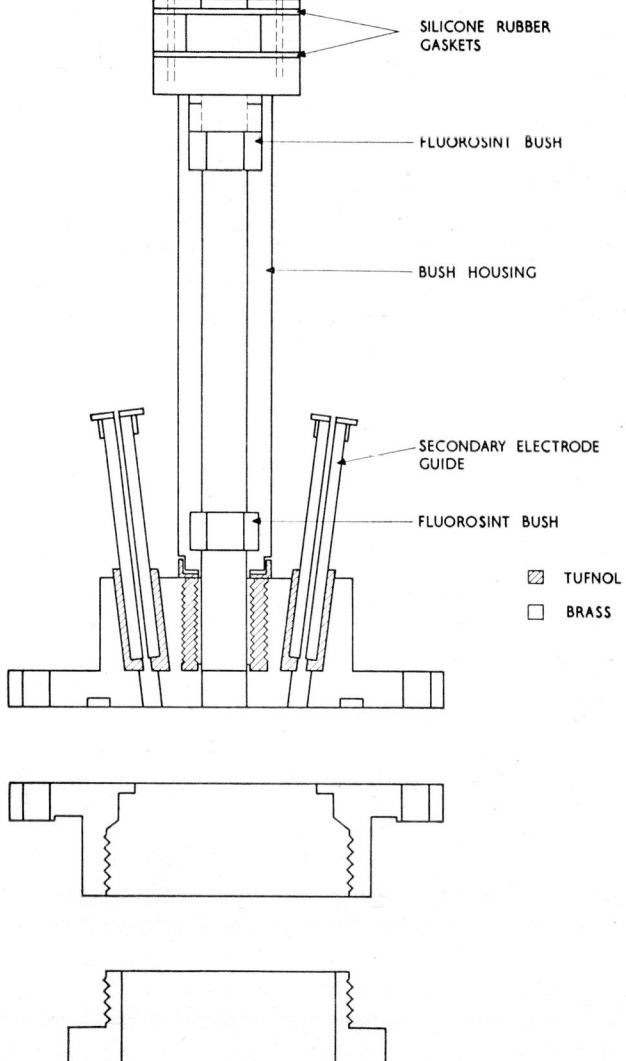

SILICONE RUBBER
GASKETS

FLUOROSINT BUSH

BUSH HOUSING

SECONDARY ELECTRODE
GUIDE

FLUOROSINT BUSH

▨ TUFNOL

☐ BRASS

Fig. 2   Head and bush housing arrangement of electrochemical cell

held a recrystallized alumina tube, 65 mm in outer diameter × 55 mm in internal diameter × 300 mm long, closed at one end.

The electrode guides and bush housing were insulated from the brass head by means of 'Tufnol' inserts. The bush housing screwed into a 'Tufnol' insert and the gas seal was made by means of a Viton 'O' ring. The bushes were carefully machined from 'Fluorosint' (Polypenco, Ltd.), ceramic impregnated PTFE, which had excellent dimensional stability. The gas seal at the top of the rotating shaft was made by two silicone rubber gaskets.

Electrical contact to the shaft was made by means of Ag–C brushes held in a brass collar, and the coupling between the shaft and the drive was made by joining two precision chucks (Jacobs type 8½N) back to back.

The selected range, shape and speed of the voltage scan were determined by a low-frequency waveform generator (Servomex type LF 51 Mk II) and fed to the cell via a potentiostat (Chemical Electronics Co.), the purpose of which was to measure the current passing through the cell during the voltage scan. The resultant curve of current against voltage was recorded by an X-Y plotter (Sefram). A schematic diagram of the current–voltage circuit is shown in Fig. 3.

It had been shown by Riddiford and co-workers[3, 4, 5] that a 'valve'-shaped rotating disc (Fig. 4) was ideal for the laminar flow conditions required if the

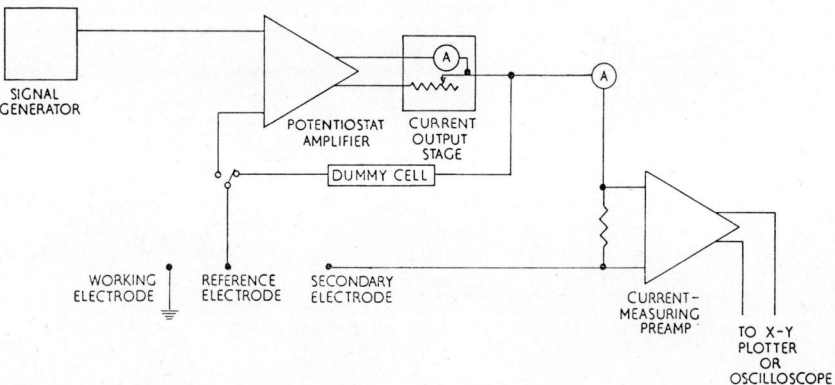

Fig. 3   Schematic diagram of current–voltage supply and measuring circuit

Levich equation was to apply to the system. A 'semi-infinite cylinder' electrode (Fig. 4) may, however, be used provided that the dimensions are correctly chosen. The material problems peculiar to investigations at temperatures above 1000°C in corrosive systems resulted in the latter shape being selected because of its constructional simplicity. The dimensions of the electrode were chosen by a consideration of the limits of laminar flow in terms of the Reynolds number, which, for a rotating disc, is defined as $Re = \dfrac{\omega r^2}{\nu}$, where ω is the angular velocity, radians sec^{-1}, r the radius of the disc, cm, and ν is the kinematic viscosity of the electrolyte, $cm^2\ sec^{-1}$. Since laminar flow exists in the range of Reynolds numbers 10–10^5 the influence of the electrode dimensions on fluid flow may be assessed on the assumption that the electrode is perfectly concentric.

The radius of the electrode at the outer edge of the insulating sheath was chosen so that Reynolds numbers in the range 10^2–10^4 would be attained in the nitrate eutectic for rotation speeds of 250–1000 rev min^{-1}. The electrode should also be so designed that edge effects do not cause turbulence in the laminar and transport boundary layers. The results of Blurton and Riddiford[4] have shown that, provided that the ratio of the radius of the disc at the outer edge of the insulating sheath to the laminar boundary layer is greater than 10, these edge effects may be neglected. In practice, this ratio could be less than 10 because the transport boundary layer is smaller than the laminar boundary layer. The disc must also be mounted horizontally and polished to the extent that surface irregularities are very much smaller than the laminar boundary layer thickness. Thus, theoretically, the smoother the disc, the higher will be the critical Reynolds number for the onset of turbulence. The electrode must be made to run as concentrically as possible for this will determine the importance of edge effects,

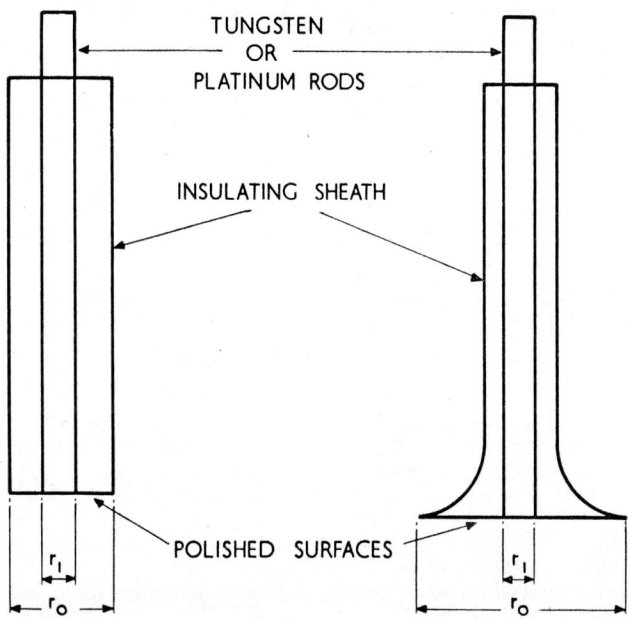

Fig. 4 Diagrams of two types of rotating electrodes: *left*, 'semi-infinite cylinder' electrode; *right*, 'valve' electrode

although the amount of concentricity tolerable is dependent on the ratio of the active radius to the inactive radius. It was concluded that in the present work it would be necessary to work to a tolerance of at least $\pm 25\ \mu$m within the range of Reynolds numbers chosen.

A platinum disc electrode was used for the investigations in the $NaNO_3$–KNO_3 eutectic. The electrode was made by melting the end of a length of platinum wire (75 mm long × 0·5 mm in diameter) into a recrystallized alumina tube (55 mm long × 1·65 mm in diameter). The alumina tube was then pressed into a length of accurately machined boron nitride and sealed in with a boron nitride coating compound. The electrode was set in a brass jig so that it was held in a vertical position, polished with diamond paste and finished on magnesia.

Use of this type of electrode in silicate melts containing heavy metal ions at 1000–1200°C was not, however, possible because platinum alloys rapidly with the reduced metals and the electrode surface becomes pitted. An electrode consisting of a tungsten rod pressed into a boron nitride sheath and polished as before, except that it was finished on 0·25-μm diamond paste, was therefore used. A 2-mm diameter rod was used initially, but at a later stage a high resistance occurred between the disc electrode and the reference and secondary electrodes. This was attributed to a phenomenon analogous to an effect encountered in aluminium production and caused by the inability of the viscous silicate melt to wet the tungsten electrode surface. This effect was overcome by increasing the electrode size to 5 mm in diameter. When the working temperature was raised to 1200°C, it was found that the boron nitride sheath, though not dissolved by the melt, cracked and warped extensively. Alumina was therefore used to replace boron nitride as a sheathing material at this higher working temperature.

Throughout the investigation the reference and secondary electrodes were constructed of the same material as the disc electrode to prevent the complication of thermoelectric effects. Platinum flag electrodes (2 cm²) were used with the platinum disc and tungsten rod (2-mm diameter) electrodes were used with the tungsten discs.

Further details on the experimental method used in the present study have been published previously.[6]

References

1. KRACEK F. C. The system sodium oxide–silica. *J. phys. Chem.*, **34**, 1930, 1583–98.
2. BANKS C. C. Unpublished work. Warren Spring Laboratory, Stevenage, Hertfordshire, 1970.
3. RIDDIFORD A. C. The rotating disc system. *Adv. Electrochem. electrochem. Engng*, **4**, 1966, 47–116.
4. BLURTON K. F. AND RIDDIFORD A. C. Shapes of practical rotating disc electrodes. *J. electroanal. Chem.*, **10**, 1965, 457–64.
5. AZIM S. AND RIDDIFORD A. C. A new type of rotating disk electrode. *Analyt. Chem.*, **34**, 1962, 1023–5.
6. WINTER D. G. The determination of some electrochemical properties of non-ferrous metals in slags. *Warren Spring Lab. Rep.* no. LR 111 (ME), 1969, 31 p.

Developments in the control of iron- and steelmaking processes

J. R. Leigh Ph.D.
R. V. Williams M.A., Ph.D.

Both of BISRA—The Corporate Laboratories of the British Steel Corporation, London

669.012.1 : 669.1

Synopsis
A description is given of the state of development of control and instrumentation in iron and steel manufacture. The control techniques used in the sinter plant, blast-furnace and steelmaking areas of modern works are described with reference to the latest installations. In comparison with rolling mills, applied control is at a very early stage in the iron- and steelmaking areas of steel plants. This is being remedied and the outstanding examples of automatic control in use are described in some detail.

If a plant existed where disturbances were completely absent, each part of the process running exactly according to a preordained schedule, no control would be required. Only when disturbances to the running of the process occur is there need for automatic, or manual, corrective action to be taken. In assessing the control needs of a plant, it is therefore essential to examine the sources of disturbance. In the manufacture of iron and steel, variations occur in raw materials, in plant characteristics and in operating requirements. Control is needed to reduce the effects of all these factors and to ensure that deviations of the product from its specification are at a low level compatible with profitability. In the particular case of the production of steel, large quantities of similar material are manufactured in capital-intensive plants and, hence, the use of automatic control can be particularly profitable.

It is appropriate at this point to describe, very briefly, the various stages in the steelmaking process. Ore from a bedding plant, mixed with coke and fluxes, is treated to produce sintered blast-furnace feed stock. Sinter is mixed in the blast-furnace with metallurgical coke and fluxes and transformed therein to iron saturated with carbon. In modern plants oxygen converters then convert the iron to steel in 300- to 400-ton batches with a tap to tap time as short as 30 min. The liquid steel is cast into ingots or, alternatively, passes to a continuous casting plant for production of billets or slabs. The hot-rolled material is produced by rolling and some products are further cold-reduced. It can be seen that these processes are very different in their nature. The sinter strand is continuous, but subject to frequent operational delays. Even in a well run plant, one stoppage per day is not uncommon. The blast-furnace is also a continuous process, but, in contrast to the sinter strand, generally runs without operational delays. The duration of a blast-furnace campaign is typically measured in tens of months. In contrast, the oxygen converter is a batch process *par excellence*, which, in turn, may have to integrate with a continuous casting plant designed to produce billets or slabs with the minimum delay between the inevitable ladle changes.

This diversity of plant operating modes leads to management as well as technical difficulties, and has to be borne in mind in the design of control systems. Control theory deals with highly idealized situations that cannot be found in a steelworks. It is the task of the control engineer to overcome this gap between control theory and practice, in a situation where insufficient knowledge of the process usually exists, and where accurate reliable measurement is difficult and expensive. This lack of knowledge and difficulty of measurement applies particularly to the oxygen converter; the first accepted theory of the operation of the converter appeared only two years ago, and methods of measurement are still being developed. The efforts of control and instrumentation engineers are therefore orientated towards understanding the process, applying control techniques and developing the necessary sensors.

The sinter plant

In a sinter strand iron ore is sized, screened, mixed with coke breeze and fluxes and then sintered on a moving bed to produce a suitable burden for the blast-furnace. This furnace cannot operate smoothly, producing the right iron of a consistent silicon content, if the sinter is not also of a consistent composition (with special reference to the lime–silica ratio) and also of a consistent mechanical quality, measured in a standard shattering test. If, as is sometimes claimed, the attainment of correct sinter strength is not of obvious importance, it must be remembered that sinter has to withstand large mechanical forces in the 100-ft high blast-furnace. From the control engineer's point of view the sinter strand is an interesting unit. Until very recently there was little instrumentation available for the control of sinter strands or even for the monitoring of its performance by operators: as a result, very little attention has been given by control engineers to the problem of strand control. These deficiencies in instrumentation are being overcome; the present account will therefore be concerned, in the main, with a description of recently available sensors rather than with control applications. Some elementary work has been carried out to translate these measurements into feedback control systems. The application of control to the sinter strand is very much in its infancy, but it should prove to be rewarding over the next few years.

In the monitoring of the input to the plant to ensure consistent chemistry of the output it is necessary to sample the input mix frequently. BISRA—The Corporate Laboratories of the British Steel Corporation—have developed an instrument,[1] known as *OLIVER* (On-Line Investigation via Very Energetic

Radiation), which samples sinter every 5 min, crushes it to a size suitable for analysis and then presents a small pellet of sampled sinter to analysis equipment. The instrument uses a non-dispersive X-ray fluorescence technique, which has been described by Clayton.[2]

At present this instrument is being developed to give a silicon and a calcium analysis simultaneously—these data can be used to adjust the lime additions to the mix. Analysis for these elements is given every 15 min, which is adequate for the comparatively slow-moving sinter strand. The equipment has been tested on a sinter strand over a period of many months in a form shown in Fig. 1. Much development has gone into the mechanical hardware shown, and

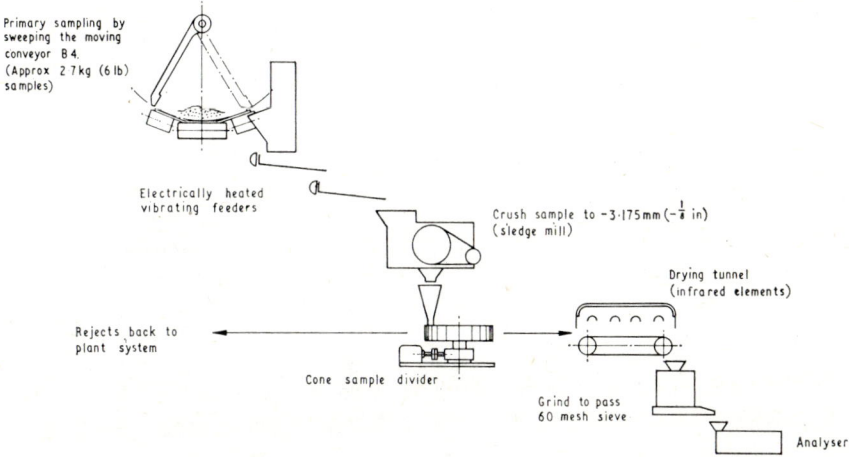

Primary sampling by sweeping the moving conveyor B 4. (Approx 2 7kg (6 lb) samples)

Electrically heated vibrating feeders

Crush sample to ~3·175mm ($-\frac{1}{8}$ in) (sledge mill)

Drying tunnel (infrared elements)

Rejects back to plant system

Cone sample divider

Grind to pass 60 mesh sieve

Analyser

Fig. 1 Schematic arrangement of sampling preparation for sinter mixture analyser

also into the analyser. In the sample preparation part of the equipment, 6 lb of material is swept from a conveyor belt at 5-min intervals and fed to a hammer-mill. A fraction of the mill output flows to a pelletizing unit and so to the analytical system. Lime is analysed by use of a ^{55}Fe radioactive source with a sealed proportional counter as detector of the fluorescent products. Silicon, on the other hand, is analysed by use of a $^{3}H/Zr$ source with a similar sealed detector. Plant trials have indicated an accuracy of the order of ± 0.04 to ± 0.07 of the CaO/SiO_2 ratio (of around 1·3, 1σ value).

The moisture of the mix is manually controlled from a knowledge of the feed rate and, in modern plants, is monitored by a neutron moderation technique. An instrument which uses hemispherical or '2π' geometry, mounted on the side of a surge hopper, is preferred to an insertion neutron probe because of the high rate of abrasion of probe materials by the sinter mix. The accuracy of the equipment associated with the sampling of the mix limits the accuracy of moisture measurement in practice to worse than 2% absolute, and further progress will have to be made to improve this figure. A possible improvement could be made by mounting the sensor underneath a conveyor belt feeding raw mix to the surge hopper or to the strand.

Another important parameter of the sinter mix is the bed air permeability. Workers in Belgium[3] have successfully measured the pre-ignition permeability by use of a very simple pneumatic method. The water content is then completely controlled by this permeability reading. It has been claimed that a considerable improvement in the consistency of strand performance is achieved, in addition

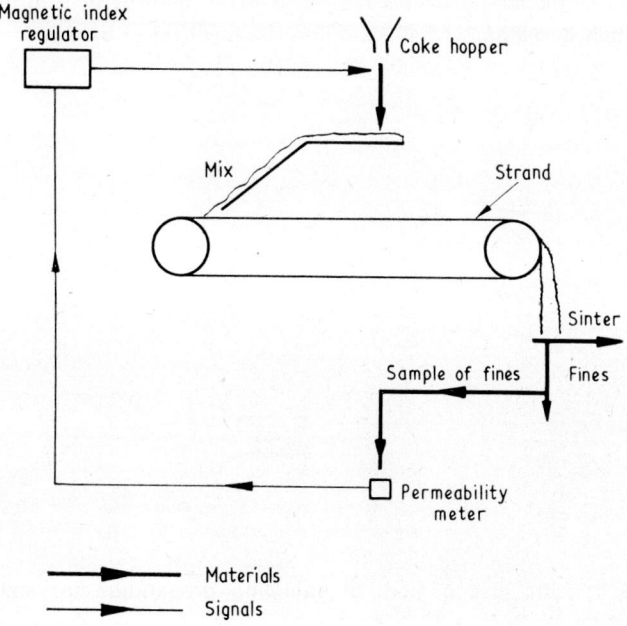

Fig. 2   Control of sinter strand via permeability of returned fines

to a reduction in start-up time after plant shutdown. Luckers *et al.* went so far as to say that moisture measurement, as such, is unnecessary, but, in the opinion of the present authors, even as a diagnostic tool it is desirable to continuously monitor the moisture content of the mix.

It is also important to have a measure of the strength of the final sinter. Its chemistry is determined at the input end, and this is taken account of by the *OLIVER* device described above. Again, workers in Belgium[3] have found a correlation between the magnetic susceptibility of the returned fines and the shatter strength of the sinter. Consequently, a simple analogue loop which uses a measure of magnetic susceptibility (by passing returned fines through a magnetic coil) serves to control the rate of addition of coke breeze to the strand (Fig. 2). The correlation between coke addition and sinter strength allows very consistent shatter strength values to be achieved, as well as the further benefits resulting from rapid stabilization of a strand on start-up after shutdown.

A further simple control loop is fitted to some strands; the materials balance between raw sinter and returned fines from the sinter screens is adjusted by monitoring the level of returned fines in a hopper.

It can be seen that it is possible to fit four simple analogue loops to the sinter strand—one controlling chemistry, one controlling moisture, one controlling coke and additions, and the last monitoring the returned fines/mix ratio. It is not possible, however, to fit all of these without consideration of the interactions between these various control actions. Little is known about such interactions at present, and there is need for further research on this problem. To sum up, the sinter strand now has available several useful diagnostic sensing elements and one or two valuable and simple control loops, but there is a need for study of the control of the system as a whole.

The blast-furnace

Control of blast-furnace operations is best illustrated by an example. In South Wales a modern furnace has been extensively fitted with computer facilities which have been described by Beswick and co-workers.[4] The aims of this scheme are (a) to reduce the variation of silicon content in the iron to a standard deviation of 0.05% about a mean of 0.65%; (b) to improve control of the raw materials; (c) to reduce the coke rate by 0.25 cwt/ton of hot metal; (d) to maximize iron production; and (e) eventually, to control blast stove changeover and to optimize stove efficiency.

It is difficult to monitor the performance of a blast-furnace, as the process is singularly inaccessible. To overcome this difficulty many inferential sensors have been fitted to this pioneer furnace. For example, new orifice plates have been installed at the entries to the electrostatic precipitators to provide a measure of gas flow rate. Continuous top gas analysis equipment has also been fitted, the infrared principle being used. In addition, a katharometer, measuring hydrogen, has been installed. Two alternative sampling systems, both duplicated, provide gas for analysis from before the scrubbers and after the precipitators. Automatic calibration against standard gases is provided and a long-term accuracy of $\pm 0.05\%$ of gas content is achieved. In addition, a sample of the hot blast is taken to an infrared analyser to determine its humidity, and there is a paramagnetic oxygen meter to measure oxygen content. The weighing functions are also extensive.

Information from all sensors and other 'housekeeping' items is fed to a Ferranti Argus 500 with a core store of 24K backed up by disc store size of 640K.

A main aim of the system is to stabilize the silicon content of the metal. This will be achieved by use of an on-line dynamic model of the process capable of predicting the future behaviour of the furnace. Blast-furnace control systems developed by IRSID and CNRM are already in use, but the basic assumption on which these models are built breaks down under other than minor perturbations of the furnace operating conditions. Attempts to add dynamic responses to such models are disappointing, since these perturbations are variably interactive and very non-linear in their effects as the operating conditions of the furnace change. The BISRA/BSC model at the South Wales plant will be supplied with real-time data regarding the blast conditions and burden weights added to the furnace, together with information on the rate of stock descent, cast occurrence and slagging. At intervals, top gas analysis of the furnace will be compared with that indicated by the model. An adaptive routine will be adopted whereby suitable parameters of the model will be changed to bring the model and the plant gas and cast analyses into agreement. At chosen points in the furnace operation the model will be run faster than real time—to predict future iron quality. If this is not satisfactory, control adjustments will be made to selected blast variables and, in extreme conditions, to the burden weights, to produce acceptable cast analyses. Successful implementation will represent a major step towards ensuring truly consistent hot metal output analysis. There are several alternative schemes for blast-furnace control under development around the world, and the next few years will clarify the role that the computer has to play in the control of the blast-furnace.

Oxygen converters

About two-thirds of the world's steel is produced by the basic oxygen furnace process, originally developed in Austria for the conversion of hot metal into steel. This proportion is expected to rise towards 80%, leaving the electric arc furnace to account for the remainder—mainly for the specialist steel market. In the BOS plant oxygen is blown on to the top of a bath of hot metal, through a lance, for a period of about 20 min. The velocity of the oxygen, which is very high, contains sufficient kinetic energy to foam the bath into a slag–metal emulsion, which also contains an oxidizing slag formed by the addition of lime and fluorspar. The slag also contains FeO, MgO, SiO_2 and P_2O_5 from the hot metal. After about 20 min of oxygen blowing, the metalloids contained in the hot metal feed are oxidized, leaving the steel at a desired carbon and temperature level.

The most important control requirement is to achieve correct end-point carbon and temperature simultaneously, with minimum blowing time. It is obvious that the blow has to end at a carbon level within specification, but the relevance of end-point temperature is not so easily understood. In fact, the economic benefits of accurate achievement of temperature target are greater than those of being within the carbon specification range. Wide deviation of temperature will lead to losses, as indicated: (a) too high a temperature will lead to excessive refractory wear and to a necessity for cooling materials to be added, with a time penalty waiting for the vessel to cool; (b) too low a temperature will require reblowing of the vessel, increasing tap to tap time and calling for extra oxygen; and (c) deviations of temperature, whether above or below the target, cause a reduction in the yield obtained from the vessel.

In preparing the vessel for the blow, hot metal, scrap and fluxes have to be added in the correct proportions, such that when blown by a specified quantity of oxygen over a specified time a cast of the correct weight, analysis and temperature will be produced. In order to calculate these quantities a charge control model is used. This consists of a mass balance, heat balance, oxygen balance and lime balance, which are together sufficient to calculate the necessary quantities. The equations are well known and not in dispute, so it appears at first sight that there should be no difficulty in performing the calculations with sufficient accuracy to ensure that all the requirements are met. In fact, there are two main sources of uncertainty. The first concerns the weights and compositions of the raw materials. Some of this uncertainty arises from measurement error or non-homogeneity in the input materials—samples can thus give misleading results. The second uncertainty is that concerning the characteristics of the vessel. As the vessel wears, the amount of heat stored in the walls will vary from heat to heat. Effects such as these can be taken into account by use of adaptive terms in the charge control model: hence, the model virtually learns the changing characteristics of the vessel and counteracts the discrepancies caused by them. As was pointed out earlier, variations in the raw material composition are a source of fluctuation. A study based on simulation has shown that input quantities have to be measured to the accuracy levels quoted in Table 1 to achieve satisfactory end-point temperature. It is particularly important to achieve high weighing accuracy of scrap additions and accurate analysis of the hot metal.

If input variables are determined to the degree of accuracy stated as desirable in Table 1, and a good charge control model with adaptive terms is competently applied, accurate control of the end-point temperature analysis can be achieved. This has been demonstrated in Japanese practice.

It will be realized from what has been said earlier that the control strategy outlined so far is essentially that of attempting to ensure the best possible consistency and repeatability of materials, and then setting the vessel off on its refining path by use of a completely pre-programmed approach with no chance of corrections on the way. This is rather like shooting a projectile at a distance target where the projectile is completely unguided during its journey and all guidance has to be done in a careful setting of the launcher. It will be no surprise that, despite every attempt to ensure highest consistency and repeatability, the steelworks environment ensures that the refining path does deviate from that intended, and the performance achieved still leaves something to be desired. For the best possible performance, therefore, it is necessary to make adjustments during the course of refining to ensure that the target will be reached satisfactorily. Using the missile analogy again, this type of control is like that in a guided missile where perturbations during the flight are corrected as the missile homes in on its target and any initial errors in launching are not carried forward.

For this purpose there are several alternative techniques. One technique developed by the Jones and Laughlin Co.[5] in the U.S.A. depends on the measurement of the rate of carbon removal. Carbon dioxide and carbon monoxide contents of the furnace waste gases are measured, and these, together with the measurement of the mass of waste gas flow, allow the carbon removal rate to be

Table 1   Static charge model input parameter accuracy

Variable	Desired accuracy of measurement to achieve $\pm 12°C$
Hot metal weight	$\frac{1}{2}\%$
Scrap	$\frac{1}{4}\%$
Lime	$\frac{1}{3}\%$
Oxygen	$100\ \text{ft}^3$
Silicon	0.04%
Carbon	0.01%
Hot metal temperature	$7°C$

calculated. Gas analysis is carried out by an accurate infrared analyser or mass spectrometer. The difficult part of the measurement is that associated with the measurement of mass flow. There is at present no satisfactory technique for this measurement, but a determination of mass flow rate can be carried out via a venturi or Dall tube, in conjunction with moisture measurement. The accuracy of this measurement technique has been discussed by West,[6] who has concluded that present techniques of waste gas measurement are only just accurate enough to permit a determination of carbon removal rate to meet the requirements of low-carbon steelmakers ($\pm 0.02\%$ carbon).

This rate measurement is used to determine end-point carbon in the following way. Fig. 3 illustrates a typical plot of dc/dt during a low-carbon blow. It has been established that there is a correlation between dc/dt and carbon

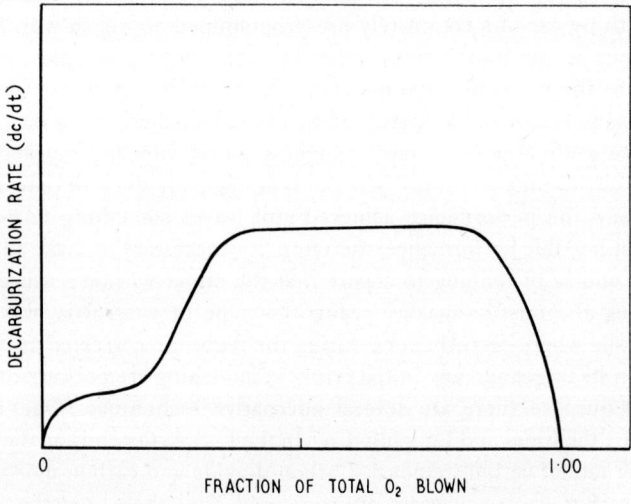

Fig. 3   Ideal BOS decarburization curve

during the last few minutes of the blow for a low-carbon steel. Coefficients in equations giving carbon as a function of dc/dt are determined experimentally and used to control future blows. The major disadvantage with this technique is that it determines carbon only, which is the less important of the two end-point target parameters. A further disadvantage is that it depends on having a reproducible decarburization curve, and some plants find this difficult to achieve. Finally, the technique can be used in the production of low-carbon steels only.

A much more satisfactory solution to end-point determination is the use of an auxiliary lance to determine carbon and temperature in the bath during the blow. A model can then be used to predict the further oxygen to be blown and any additional corrections that are needed. This technique is used in Japan and is under development in the U.S.A. and the United Kingdom. In the most common form of auxiliary lance, temperature is determined by an expendable thermocouple guided into the vessel down a water-cooled tube. The same expendable device contains a carbon sensor based on the liquids point technique.[7] Early, but unpublished, results from the U.S.A. showed how attractive this technique can be and indicated that a scheme based on it would produce substantial financial savings compared with current practice. It is interesting to speculate how oxygen furnace control will progress over the next few years. In the opinion of the authors, attention will be given to control of slag formation and to refining path control. Slag formation can be monitored, and controlled, by the use of sound-detecting equipment, and by microwave measurement of slag height. Refining path control has been practised by workers on the Continent,[8] who monitor the rate of oxidation of the melt via waste gas analysis and flow measurement. The oxidation rate is used to control blowing rate and lance height. This empirical technique will probably set the trend for blow bath control over the next few years, although some workers claim that monitoring dc/dt will give operators a more reliable guide to the progress of a heat. Looking further ahead, it is expected that refining path control will be achieved by the use of an on-line mathematical model of the process.

Conclusions

Compared with rolling mills, particularly strip mills, applied control is at a very early stage in the iron- and steelmaking areas of steel plants. This situation, however, is gradually being remedied, and there are already one or two outstanding examples of automatic control in the latter areas. It can be expected that, as more effort is devoted to these process areas, new control schemes and measuring techniques will be introduced and higher standards of performance will be achieved.

Looking still further ahead, the possibility of controlling sintering, iron- and steelmaking by a single integrated control system cannot be ruled out. This will probably be integrated into a production control and management information system and could be of special importance in the advent of new and continuous iron- and steelmaking processes.

Q

References

1. WHITE G. *et al*. The continual monitoring of sinter mixtures. *BISRA open Rep.* MG/D/589/68, 1968, 13 p.

2. CLAYTON C. G. Applications of radioisotope X-ray fluorescence analysis in geological assay, mining and mineral processing. In *Nuclear techniques and mineral resources* (Vienna: IAEA, 1969), 293–322. (*STI/TUB/198*)

3. LUCKERS J. *et al*. Relation automatique continue de la qualité d'un aggloméré sur une bande industrielle. In *International conference on iron and steelmaking automation* (Luxemburg: Centre de Recherches Métallurgiques, 1970), vol. 1, 53–63.

4. BESWICK A. A. McLEAN J. S. AND SHARP K. C. Blast furnace control by computer. *J. Iron Steel Inst.*, **207**, 1969, 743–59.

5. MAYER H. W. Oxygen steel making: its control and future. *J. Iron Steel Inst.*, **207,** 1969, 781–9.

6. WEST E. J. Consideration of the requirements of measurements instrumentation for on-line measurements of bath carbon. . . In *Determination of chemical composition* (London: Iron and Steel Institute, 1971), 106–15.

7. BOSWORTH C. J. A. Development of liquidus carbon and temperature sensors. In *Determination of chemical composition* (London: Iron and Steel Institute, 1971), 81–5.

8. NILLES P. *et al*. Le contrôle de l'affinage au procédé L.D. In *International conference on iron and steelmaking automation* (Luxemburg: Centre de Recherches Métallurgiques, 1970), vol. 1, 203–11.

Optimization of the standard tin-smelting circuit

P. A. Wright M.A., M.I.M.M.

Consolidated Tin Smelters, Ltd., London

669.012.5 : 669.631

Synopsis

The mass balance within the standard two-stage tin-smelting circuit is developed and the composition of intermediate products is deduced. The total metallurgical work to be done can then be calculated, and the introduction of the process unit costs leads, to a first approximation, to the direct costs of treatment. The variation of treatment cost with the disposable parameters of the circuit makes it possible to minimize this cost and so to optimize the circuit with respect to any given feed material. The costs so obtained break down into those attributable to the tin, iron and gangue of the feed.

Limitations of the model are pointed out, and certain corrections are indicated.

The basic two-stage smelting circuit used to treat high- and medium-grade concentrates consists of three unit process operations, which were described by Agricola.[1] These unit processes are (A) the smelting of concentrates to produce crude tin and a tin-rich slag; (D) drossing of the crude tin (furnace metal) to produce metal suitable for the market and an iron-bearing dross (the 'cakes' of Agricola); and (B) smelting the tin-rich slag to produce a 'final slag' and tin–iron alloy or hardhead.

Agricola's account does not state where intermediate products were returned to the circuit. This combination of processes effects the separation of tin from iron and irreducible gangue, reducible impurities such as lead, copper, bismuth, antimony and arsenic remaining in the metallic tin, although, as Agricola was aware, some of them may be removed by preliminary roasting of the concentrates. That the method is fundamentally sound is shown by the fact that about three-quarters of the world's tin is smelted in this way, but the high proportion of papers dealing with hardhead among the rather scanty published work on tin smelting suggests that the balance of the circuit has not been examined very carefully.

It is the main object of this paper to establish the mass balance and economics of the basic circuit and to draw attention to some of the consequences.

The basic circuit

The simplest tin-smelting circuit is that shown in Fig. 1, where the following symbols and notation are used.

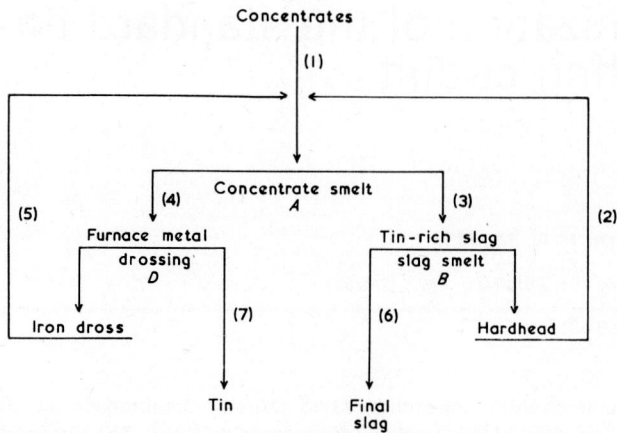

Fig. 1 Flowsheet of a two-stage tin-smelting circuit

(*a*) Each material is allotted a number: (1) concentrate feed; (2) hardhead; (3) tin-rich slag; (4) furnace metal (crude tin); (5) dross, iron-bearing; (6) final slag; and (7) tin, to market or further refining.

(*b*) Weight decimal fractions of tin, iron and irreducible gangue in each material i are designated by x_i, y_i and z_i, respectively.

(*c*) The weight of each material is designated W_i, and it is convenient to take $W_1 = 1$ (ton).

(*d*) The product $W_i x_i$, the weight of tin in material i, is denoted by X_i; similarly, the weights of iron and gangue in this material are Y_i and Z_i.

(*e*) The unit process operations are A, D and B as defined above. Fume arising from stages A and B is returned to A, and the relatively small transfer of tin from B to A by this route is ignored in this analysis, as is the small proportion of slag which is usually mixed with the hardhead.

(*f*) The tin/iron ratio in three materials is defined as

$$\alpha \text{ in the furnace metal } x_4/y_4$$
$$\beta \text{ in the hardhead } \quad x_2/y_2$$
$$\varepsilon \text{ in the dross} \qquad\quad x_5/y_5$$

Constraints

In the two smelting operations the proportions of tin and iron in the products are governed by the reversible reaction

$$\mathrm{SnO_{(sl)} + Fe_{(m)} \rightleftharpoons FeO_{(sl)} + Sn_{(m)}} \tag{1}$$

where the subscripts sl and m indicate the slag and liquid metallic phases, respectively. The equilibrium constant for this reaction, in terms of the activities of the species involved, is

$$K_T = \frac{\langle \mathrm{Sn} \rangle\, (\mathrm{FeO})}{\langle \mathrm{Fe} \rangle\, (\mathrm{SnO})}$$

This equation may be written in terms of weight percentages and activity coefficients

$$K_T = \left(\frac{\% \, \mathrm{Sn}}{\% \, \mathrm{Fe}}\right)_m \left(\frac{\% \, \mathrm{Fe}}{\% \, \mathrm{Sn}}\right)_{sl} \left[\frac{\gamma_{\mathrm{Sn}}}{\gamma_{\mathrm{Fe}}}\right]_m \left[\frac{\gamma_{\mathrm{FeO}}}{\gamma_{\mathrm{SnO}}}\right]_{sl}$$

or

$$C = \frac{K_T}{\left[\dfrac{\gamma_{\mathrm{Sn}}}{\gamma_{\mathrm{Fe}}}\right]\left[\dfrac{\gamma_{\mathrm{FeO}}}{\gamma_{\mathrm{SnO}}}\right]}$$

where

$$C = \left(\frac{\% \, \mathrm{Sn}}{\% \, \mathrm{Fe}}\right)_m \left(\frac{\% \, \mathrm{Fe}}{\% \, \mathrm{Sn}}\right)_{sl} \tag{2}$$

Our knowledge of the variation of the activity coefficient ratios in the two phases is still incomplete, but, as has been shown elsewhere,[2] the variation of C with the iron content of the metallic phase has the form shown in Fig. 2; there are two regions in which C is nearly constant. These two regions exist at iron contents below 1% and again at iron contents above 20%—conditions which

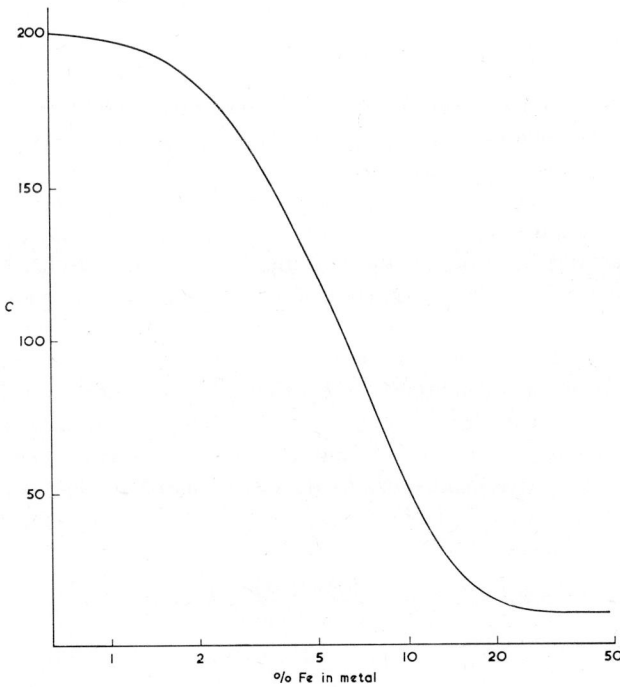

Fig. 2 Approximate relation between 'equilibrium constant' and iron content of metal

usually obtain in the concentrate-smelting stage A and slag-smelting stage B, respectively; we may therefore take the two values C_A and C_B as constants applicable to the equilibrium in these two processes.

Removal of iron is accomplished by cooling the liquid tin to a temperature close to the freezing point, where the solubility of iron in liquid tin is about 0.002% and iron is thrown out of solution as $FeSn_2$ (19% Fe). Much of the crystalline dross so formed can be dredged out of the kettle, but a fine suspension always remains in the tin, and this must be floated out by blowing air or steam through the liquid metal. The iron content of the dross dredged from the kettle is about 10%, and that of the floated dross about 5%; by liquating these drosses the iron content can be raised considerably, but at an increased cost of working.

If the dross is returned to the ore-smelting stage without liquation, the average iron content will be a little under 7%, giving a tin/iron ratio of $\varepsilon = 14$; a rough liquation may reduce ε to 7, and a really careful treatment should result in $\varepsilon = 4$. Whatever system is decided upon, ε (the tin/iron ratio of the dross) will be a constant of the plant; the value of liquation is discussed later.

The mass balance

Before proceeding to the algebraic development of the mass balance, it is worth considering the purpose served by cycling intermediate products.

Because of the position of equilibrium of the reaction represented by equation 1, we cannot obtain liquid tin of low iron content and slag of high iron and low tin content in contact with each other; we cannot therefore separate the tin and iron contents of the concentrates by any degree of partial reduction of the mixture, but we can improve the situation greatly by returning by-products to the concentrate smelt.

We know that the liquid tin from the concentrate smelt must contain some iron, so we add that iron in the form of dross in order to prevent iron of the concentrates from entering the metal. Similarly, we return hardhead in order to provide the major part of the tin content of the slag and so cause the maximum of tin from concentrates to report in the furnace metal; we then recover this 'buffering' tin as hardhead in the slag-smelting operation. Therefore, in a balanced circuit, two conditions are fulfilled: (1) iron entering in the concentrates is discarded in the final slag, $Y_6 = Y_1$; and (2) intermediate products remain at a steady level and are returned to the circuit as they are produced.

We shall now obtain expressions for the weight of each product W_i in terms of X_1 and Y_1. Starting with the final slag, whose iron content is defined as Y_1, we have from equation 2

$$C_B \frac{W_6 x_6}{W_6 y_6} = \frac{x_2}{y_2} = \beta$$

$$X_6 = Y_1 \beta / C_B \qquad (3)$$

where X_6 is the weight of tin discarded in the final slag.

In the balanced circuit the tin content of the tin-rich slag from the first operation (A) is made up of the tin content of the hardhead and of the tin which will be discarded in the final slag

$$X_3 = X_6 + X_2 = Y_1\beta/C_B + Y_2\beta$$

The iron content of this slag is that of the concentrates plus that of the hardhead

$$Y_3 = Y_1 + Y_2$$

From equation 2

$$C_A \frac{x_3}{y_3} = \frac{x_4}{y_4} = \alpha$$

whence

$$\frac{W_3 x_3}{W_3 y_3} = \frac{\alpha}{C_A} = \frac{X_3}{Y_3} = \frac{Y_1\beta/C_B + Y_2\beta}{Y_1 + Y_2}$$

$$W_2 = X_2 + Y_2 = Y_2(1+\beta)$$

$$= Y_1\left[\frac{\alpha C_B - \beta C_A}{\beta C_A - \alpha}\right]\left(\frac{1+\beta}{C_B}\right) \qquad (4)$$

Equation 4 gives the weight of cycling hardhead.

In the tin-rich slag

$$Y_3 = Y_1 + Y_2 = Y_1\left[\frac{\beta C_A \ (C_B - 1)}{C_B \ (\beta C_A - \alpha)}\right]$$

$$X_3 = Y_3 \frac{\alpha}{C_A}$$

and the combined tin and iron content is

$$X_3 + Y_3 = Y_3\left(1 + \frac{\alpha}{C_A}\right) = Y_1 \frac{\beta}{C_B}(C_A + \alpha)\frac{(C_B - 1)}{(\beta C_A - \alpha)}$$

Since the tin and iron contents are comparable, the factor 1·25 will give the corresponding weight of the oxides, and, by adding the weight of gangue from the concentrates Z_1 and that of fluxes and ash introduced in smelting Z_A, the total weight of tin-rich slag

$$W_3 = 1\cdot25\ Y_1\left[\frac{\beta}{C_B}\frac{(C_A + \alpha)(C_B - 1)}{\beta C_A - \alpha}\right] + Z_1 + Z_A \qquad (5)$$

In the final slag, where the tin content is much less than the iron content

$$W_6 = 1\cdot28\ Y_1\left[1 + \frac{\beta}{C_B}\right] + Z_1 + Z_A + Z_B \qquad (6)$$

where Z_B is the weight of flux and ash introduced in the slag-smelting stage B.

In the 'metal' side of the circuit

$$X_7 = X_1 - X_6$$

and

$$Y_7 = 0$$

Hence

$$Y_5 = Y_4$$

Now

$$\frac{X_4}{Y_4} = \frac{X_4}{Y_5} = \alpha$$

and

$$\frac{X_5}{Y_5} = \varepsilon$$

$$X_4 = X_1 - X_6 + X_5$$

$$\alpha Y_5 = X_1 - Y_1\beta/C_B + \varepsilon Y_5$$

$$Y_5 = \frac{X_1 - Y_1\beta/C_B}{\alpha - \varepsilon}$$

$$X_5 = \varepsilon\left[\frac{X_1 - Y_1\beta/C_B}{\alpha - \varepsilon}\right]$$

$$W_5 = \frac{1+\varepsilon}{\alpha - \varepsilon}[X_1 - Y_1\beta/C_B] \tag{7}$$

Equations 4, 5 and 7 give the weights of the cycling products, and equation 3 gives the weight of tin in the final slag; throughout these equations terms in X, Y and Z are separable.

The weight of charge to each operation is now shown by the sum of the various weights involved.

Concentrate smelting

$$W_1 + W_2 + W_5 + Z_A$$

Slag smelting

$$W_3 + Z_B$$

Drossing

$$W_5$$

Tin in final slag

$$Y_1\beta/C_B$$

To each of these operations we ascribe a cost or value; thus

Concentrate smelting	A units per ton smelted
Slag smelting	B units per ton smelted
Drossing	D units per ton removed and treated
Tin in final slag	V units per ton of tin

Since the terms in X, Y and Z are separable, we may divide the total cost up into three components, attributable to tin, iron and gangue, respectively, and these three equations will be referred to as the 'cost functions' since they show the cost of treating 1 ton of each of the three 'elements' in the circuit; it is assumed that tin and iron in concentrates are present as SnO_2 and Fe_2O_3; W_1 is therefore made up of

$$1 \cdot 27 X_1 + 1 \cdot 40 Y_1 + Z_1$$

The cost functions

The cost functions are then

$$\phi(X) = 1 \cdot 27 A + \frac{1+\varepsilon}{\alpha - \varepsilon}(A+D) \tag{8}$$

$$\phi(Y) = 1 \cdot 40 A + \left(\frac{1+\beta}{C_B}\right)\left[\frac{\alpha C_B - \beta C_A}{\beta C_A - \alpha}\right]A + \frac{\beta}{C_B}\left[-\frac{(C_B-1)(C_A+\alpha)}{\beta C_A - \alpha}\right]1 \cdot 25 B$$

$$- \frac{\beta}{C_B}\left(\frac{1+\varepsilon}{\alpha-\varepsilon}\right)(A+D) + \frac{\beta}{C_B}V \tag{9}$$

$$Z\phi(Z) = (Z_1 + Z_A)A + (Z_1 + Z_A + Z)B \tag{10}$$

The variables in the cost functions are α and β since, as was pointed out earlier, ε is a constant dependent on the treatment of the dross.

The cost function for irreducible gangue $Z\phi(Z)$ contains no variables and is therefore independent of the circuit conditions described by α and β. The only obvious constraint on the values of α and β is that

$$\alpha \frac{C_B}{C_A} > \beta > \frac{\alpha}{C_A}$$

necessary to maintain positive values in equations 4 and 5, but there is a closer relation, as the following argument will show.

Let us consider the effect of extreme values of β while α is maintained at a constant figure. If

$$\beta = \frac{\alpha C_B}{C_A}$$

the upper limit, the weight of hardhead cycled is zero, and the tin-rich slag is not smelted, so the minimum of metallurgical work is done and the value of the tin lost in final slag is $(\alpha/C_A)V$. At the other extreme, $\beta = \alpha/C_A$, the hardhead re-

Q*

cycled and slag smelted become infinite and, clearly, no amount of tin recovered will pay for the work done. There is therefore an optimum value of β (designated β') for any fixed value of α, and this is obtained by differentiating equation 9 with respect to β (α is constant).

$$C_A \beta' = \alpha + \sqrt{\frac{(A+1\cdot25B)(C_B-1)(\alpha^2+C_A\alpha)}{V-A-(A+D)\left(\dfrac{1+\varepsilon}{\alpha-\varepsilon}\right)}} \qquad (11)$$

The term in ε is less than A under any reasonable working conditions, so a constant value $V-3/2A$ may be taken for the denominator in this equation.

In principle, equation 11 could be used to substitute for β in the cost function (equation 9), but the resulting equation is unwieldy and it is more convenient in practice to tabulate values of β' over a range of values of α. Within the likely limits of α the relation is very nearly linear, and it is possible to write

$$\beta' \approx \frac{\alpha}{m}$$

where m is a constant.

By use of the approximation it can be seen that as α increases $\phi(X)$ diminishes and $\phi(Y)$ increases.

If we now consider one ton of concentrates at x_1'' Sn and y_1'' Fe, the sum

$$X_1\phi(X)+Y_1\phi(Y)$$

will have a minimum value for some particular value of α, and this corresponds to the optimum circuit conditions for that mixture of tin and iron; by adding $Z\phi(Z)$ to this minimum, we obtain the minimum total direct cost of treating this concentrate. We can also calculate two other important factors: (1) the total of cycling products to be moved (internal transport) by summing equations 4–7; and (2) the relative level of tin in cycling products, by summing X_2 and X_5 for two different concentrate feeds. This gives relative figures for the 'residence time' of tin in the plant.

$$\text{Residence time} = \frac{\text{Stock}}{\text{Output}}$$

Knowing the answer in one case, the relative figure for the unknown can be estimated; this is important in estimating the financial interest which will be incurred, and this item may well be comparable with direct costs.

It may well happen that the apparent optimum conditions are so far from the normal as to be unattainable, in which case the cost of working 'normally' can be calculated.

Examples

In order to show the working of the system some examples with figures averaged over a wide range of conditions are used. The costs are not representative of any particular plant, but the cost ratio $B = 2A$ and $D = 3A$ when $\varepsilon = 7$ is very common. The metallurgical parameters $C_A = 200$ and $C_B = 10$ are maintained throughout and, in order to estimate the effects of liquation of the iron-bearing dross, three situations are considered corresponding to those outlined earlier.

ε	14	7	4
'Cost' D	$1{\cdot}5A$	$3A$	$3A+10$

The value of tin is taken as $V = 1500$ throughout.

Fig. 3 shows the relation between β' and α for different basic cost structures characterized by the following levels of A:

Structure	I	II	III
A	10	7·5	5

Differences in β' due to the three possible levels of ε and D are in the third decimal place and are insignificant for practical purposes. For any chosen value of α the corresponding value of β' is reduced as the basic cost diminishes. In terms of the argument of the section *The cost functions* this means that as the cost of metallurgical work diminishes it pays to do more work and lose less tin. Table 1

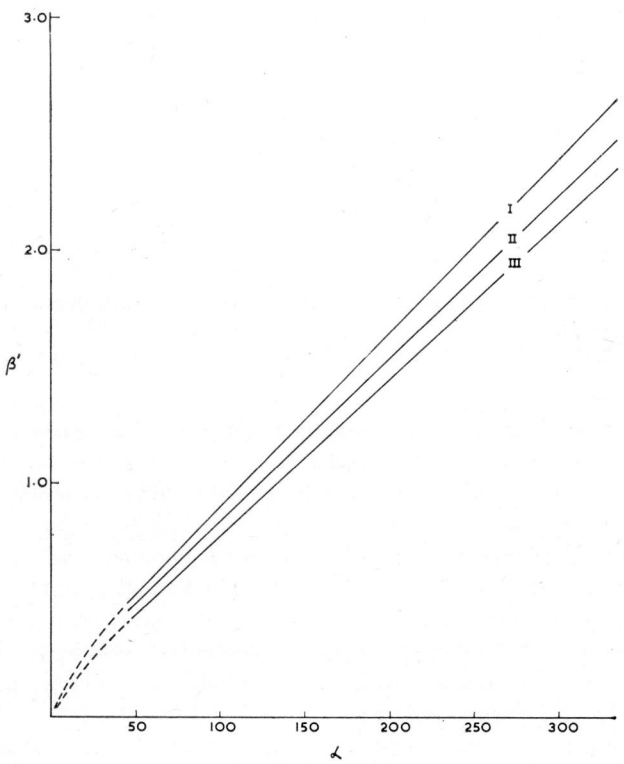

Fig. 3   Relation between β' and α for the three cost structures

Table 1   Cost functions for tin and iron under different circuit conditions (cost structure I)

Furnace metal, % Fe	α	Hardhead, β′	% Sn	$\phi(X)$ ε 14	7	4	$\phi(Y)$	L	α/C_A
0·3	333	2·63	72·5	13·88	13·68	13·31	624	395	1·67
0·5	200	1·65	62·3	14·72	14·36	13·72	409	247	1·0
0·8	125	1·09	52·1	16·08	15·41	14·35	286	163	0·625
1·0	100	0·90	47·3	17·06	16·17	14·78	243	134	0·500
1·5	66·7	0·64	39·1	19·82	18·07	15·89	186	96	0·333
2·0	50	0·51	33·7	23·12	20·14	17·05	157	76	0·25

shows the variation of the cost functions $\phi(X)$ and $\phi(Y)$ for cost structure I; $\phi(X)$ is tabulated for the three levels of ε and D and column L shows that part of $\phi(Y)$ which is attributable to the loss of tin in the final slag. Comparison between $\phi(X)$ and $\phi(Y)$ shows that the cost per ton of iron through the circuit varies from 5 to 46 times the cost per ton of tin at the extremes of the conditions encompassed by the tabulation, and that just over half the cost of iron is attributable to tin loss in the slag.

Fig. 4 shows the variation of total direct costs in cost structure I for a number of different tin and iron levels in concentrates; the estimation of the gangue cost is described in the Appendix. The full curves are for the conditions ε = 14, $D = 15$ and circles mark the minimum cost points; the minima for ε = 7 and $D = 30$ are marked by triangles and for ε = 4 and $D = 40$ by squares. Costs have been plotted against α/C_A, the tin/iron ratio in the tin-rich slag, since this is the parameter most readily available for control purposes; direct measurements of α are difficult to obtain.

The main feature of this set of curves is the rise in cost and shift of the optima towards higher iron contents in the furnace metal as the tin/iron ratio in the concentrates falls; it is also evident that the minimum is more pronounced in the lower-grade concentrates. Cost functions have not been carried beyond α = 50 (2% Fe in furnace metal), since it is questionable whether it is practicable to work at this level, and, moreover, the corresponding hardhead composition (34% Sn, 66% Fe) would require the slag-smelting operation to be carried out at high temperature, so partially annulling the lowering of other costs.

The relative costs of maintaining constant circuit conditions at α = 100 and β = 0·90 are shown by the intersection of the cost curves with the vertical line at $\alpha/C_A = 0·5$; the economy of constant circuit conditions is clearly justifiable at concentrate grades down to 60% Sn.

There is no obligation to use the 'least cost' value of β with the corresponding α; the two may be treated as independent variables and set at any convenient

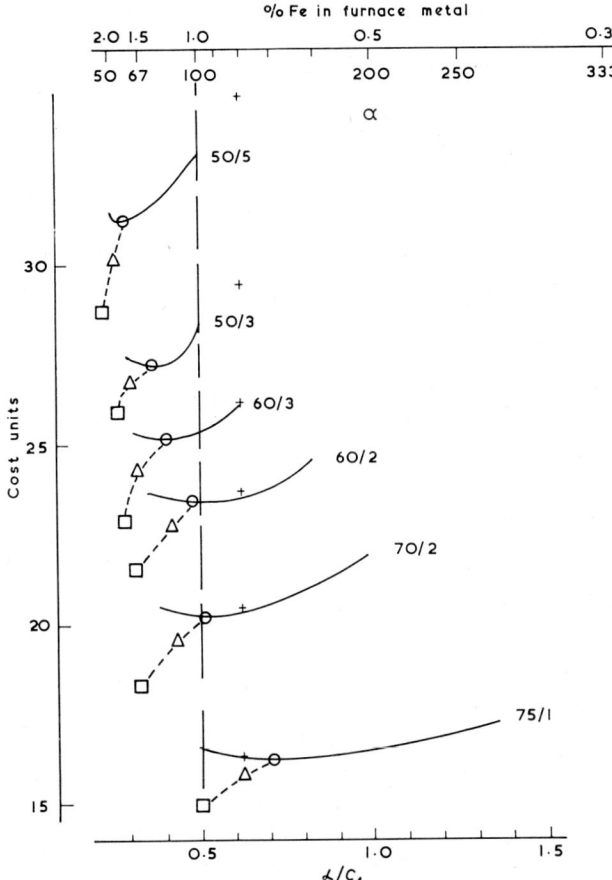

Fig. 4 Relative total direct treatment cost as a function of α for various concentrate grades: ○ minimum for $\varepsilon = 14$; △ minimum for $\varepsilon = 7$; □ minimum for $\varepsilon = 4$; + cost for $\alpha = 125$, $\beta = 1$

levels. Putting $\alpha = 125$ and $\beta = 1.0$ into equations 8 and 9, we obtain the constant cost functions

$$\phi(X) = 16.08$$
$$\phi(Y) = 289.2$$

These lead to total direct costs marked + along the vertical at $\alpha/C_A = 0.625$.

Liquation of the dross clearly lowers the cost and moves the optimum towards high iron contents of both furnace metal and hardhead; there is no significance in the path of the dotted lines joining the minima for each concentrate. In order to show the benefits of liquation the full curves for the treatment of a Sn 60%, Fe 2% concentrate under cost structures I and II and of a Sn 50%, Fe 10% concentrate under cost structure I are shown in Fig. 5. Under any circuit conditions there is some advantage in liquation, and this is greater in the higher cost circuit (I).

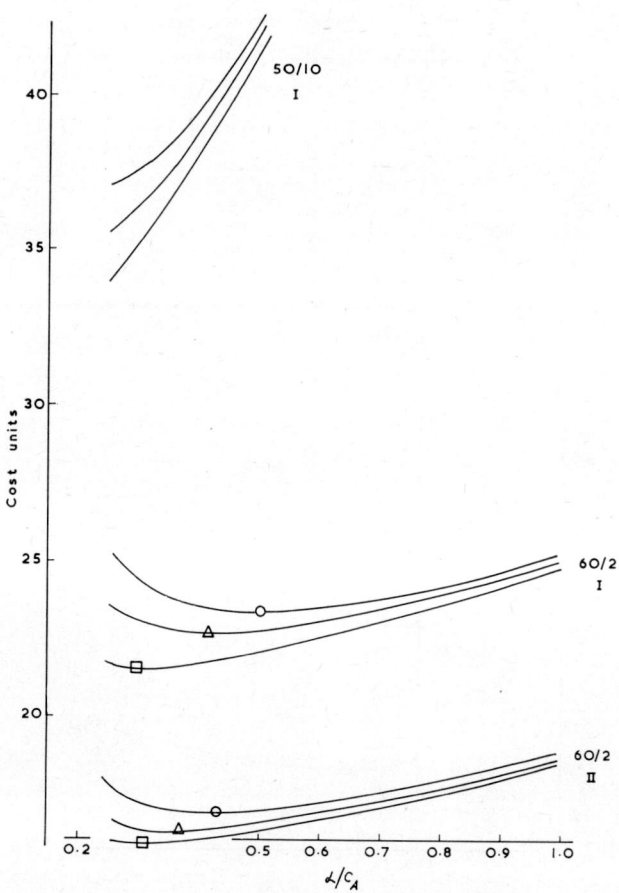

Fig. 5   Relative total direct treatment costs as a function of α for various concentrate grades. Full curves for each value of ε are drawn. Families I and II for Sn 60%, Fe 2% are calculated for cost structures I and II

'Stock lock-up'

Table 2 shows the weight of tin cycling in (*a*) furnace metal and dross and (*b*) tin-rich slag and hardhead as a percentage of the weight of concentrates smelted. These two figures are indicative of the level of stock lock-up, but they must be combined in the ratio of the residence time of each cycle, perhaps two days for (*a*) and two weeks for (*b*). On this basis the stock lock-up as a percentage of the tin in concentrates treated per day is shown as (*c*); if the lock-up is known for any one case tabulated, the lock-up in any other situation can be estimated and a suitable interest factor may be added to the direct cost already calculated.

Table 2

Concentrate grade, Sn/Fe	75/1			70/2			60/3		
(a) Dross treatment, ε	14	7	4	14	7	4	14	7	4
Sn in furnace metal and dross, % of conc. wt	8·2	4·5	3·1	10·8	6·1	4·5	13·4	7·1	4·7
(b) Sn in tin-rich slag and hardhead, % of conc. wt	1·4	1·2	0·9	2·0	1·6	1·1	2·0	1·7	1·3
(c) Sn in lock-up, % of tin production per day	156	87	60	221	126	93	320	172	114

Conclusions and comments

The mathematical model of a tin-smelting circuit developed in this paper shows the important part played by the cycling intermediate product loads and the means of calculating the optimum tin/iron ratios in these products. It is assumed that smelting rates and, hence, costs are not affected by the composition of the materials smelted—there is insufficient quantitative evidence on this point to make it possible to include this effect in a general treatment at this stage. The cycling fume load should also be taken into account, not so much for its effect on the metallurgical results as for its effect on the stock lock-up, but quantitative data are discordant.

It emerges from this study that the smelting of concentrates below 60% Sn content in a traditional two-stage circuit is expensive, owing to the choice between high tin loss in the final slag or difficult working conditions. Faced with concentrates of lower grades, it is clearly necessary to include a fuming furnace stage for the treatment of the final slags. The inclusion of this step radically changes the optimum conditions, since it is then possible to allow high tin contents in the slag (equation 6) produced from the slag smelt and to work in the region in which C_B is no longer a 'constant' but a function of β; the treatment of this situation remains to be worked out.

Acknowledgment

The author has to thank the Board of Directors of Consolidated Tin Smelters, Ltd., for permission to publish this paper.

References

1. AGRICOLA GEORGIUS. *De re metallica* Translated by HOOVER H. C. AND HOOVER L. H. (London: Mining Magazine, 1912), 637 p.
2. WRIGHT P. A. Activities in the tin–iron system. *Trans. Instn Min. Metall.* (*Sect. C: Mineral Process. Extr. Metall.*), **80,** 1971, C112–3.

Appendix

$Z\phi(Z)$

The cost attributable to gangue has been estimated in the following way. The irreducible gangue of the concentrates is

$$1 - 1 \cdot 27 X_1 - 1 \cdot 40 Y_1$$

and is subject to the cost $(A+B)$.

Limestone is added to produce a lime content of 20% CaO in the final slag, and is therefore

$$0 \cdot 25 \, (1 - 1 \cdot 27 X_1)$$

This is added in the proportions two-thirds to the concentrate smelt and one-third to the slag smelt; therefore the cost is

$$\left(\frac{2A}{3} + B \right)$$

The total is

$$Z\phi(Z) = (1 - 1 \cdot 27 X_1 - 1 \cdot 40 Y_1)(A+B) + 0 \cdot 25 \, (1 - 1 \cdot 27 X_1)\left(\frac{2A}{3} + B \right)$$

The corresponding value of this function is added to $X_1\phi(X) + Y_1\phi(Y)$ in calculating total direct costs.

DISCUSSION

Dr. P. J. Bowles, in introducing his joint paper, said that a method was described for the determination of small concentrations of heavy metal dissolved in fused silicate melts, which was intended for use in industrial calcium aluminosilicate slags. The electroanalytical method used was that of voltammetry, of which the well known technique of dropping-electrode polarography was a special case. The method involved measurement of the current passing between a working and a secondary electrode immersed in an electrolyte—in the present case an oxyanion melt. The current was a function of a linearly varying voltage, which was applied between the working electrode and a third unpolarized reference electrode. If a species capable of being reduced or oxidized were present in the electrolyte, then an increase in the current passing through the cell was observed at a potential determined by the Gibbs free energy of the reduction or oxidation reaction. A rotating-disc electrode was chosen as the working electrode in the study since a dropping-metal electrode would be inapplicable to the type of on-line analytical system envisaged in the final application of the work.

A model system was used initially to test the rotating-electrode system—the reduction of silver and copper in a nitrate eutectic at temperatures up to 350°C. Current–voltage curves of the form required for quantitative analysis were obtained for both solutes (Figs. 1 and 2, p. 440). A rigid mathematical expression for the limiting diffusion current at a rotating disc electrode had been derived by Levich, and analysis of the results obtained in the nitrate melt showed good agreement with the Levich relationship both with regard to proportionality to the square root of the electrode rotational velocity (Fig. 3, p. 442) and direct proportionality to the solute concentration (Figs. 4 and 5, pp. 442 and 443).

The next step involved work in a simple sodium silicate melt at temperatures of 1000 and 1200°C, with solutes of the type encountered in the calcium aluminosilicate slags used in the secondary copper blast-furnace. Because of the high viscosity of the sodium silicate melts current–voltage curves exhibiting a limiting diffusion current were not obtained, but rather curves exhibiting a maximum corresponding to the reduction of the solute cations studied—copper, tin, zinc and iron. Current voltage curves of that type were observed at stationary electrodes when the rate of charge of the linearly varying applied voltage was high, and a relationship had been derived, independently, by J. E. B. Randles and A. Sevcik, relating the maximum or peak current observed to the solute concentration, and to the square root of the voltage scan rate. The direct proportionality between peak current and concentration could be seen for the reduction of copper at 1000°C in Fig 6 (p. 444) and the relationship between peak current and the square root of the voltage scan rate was shown for a number of solutes at 1200°C (Fig. 9, p. 446). Although one could use platinum as an electrode material in nitrate melts, that was not possible in silicate melts containing heavy metal ions at 1000–1200°C because platinum alloyed rapidly with the reduced metals and the electrode surface became pitted. The use of tungsten as an electrode material, although satisfactory in that no surface attack occurred, created a more fundamental problem, in that, when deposited metals were insoluble in the electrode surface, it might be shown theoretically that the peak potential for a given solute varied with the solute concentration.

Experimental results were in agreement with theoretical predictions for the case of copper in silicate melts (Fig. 7, p. 444). If it were assumed that the same relationship existed for other solutes, difficulties were inherent in that peak potentials for two solutes at different concentrations could overlap, thereby making the voltammetric technique less useful as a slag analysis method. The reduction of heavy metals from silicate melts had also been shown in the present study to be an irreversible process, since theory predicted that the peak potential would then be proportional to the logarithm of the voltage scan rate (Fig. 10, p. 447). That presented less of a problem from the viewpoint of slag analysis, however, since all determinations could be performed at a given voltage sweep rate.

Future work in the development of the slag electroanalytical technique would be concentrated, initially, on finding an electrode material where the reduction potential of heavy metals was independent of concentration. If that problem could be solved, the method must then be adapted, first, to on-site industrial operation, taking samples of slag from the furnace, and, subsequently, to on-line operation, possibly in a flowing slag system.

Dr. R. V. Williams, in introducing his joint paper, emphasized that control was only necessary because of the presence of disturbances and that, in assessing the control needs of a plant, it was essential to quantify the variations occurring in raw materials, plant characteristics and operating requirements. He then went on to describe the various stages in the steelmaking process, dealing first with the sinter plant. The sinter plant had long time-delays and difficult measurement problems and, until recently, it had received little attention compared with the later processes. That situation was being remedied and a number of sensors and control techniques were being developed for sinter plant. Next followed a description of the blast-furnace and the control system that was being implemented at a B.S.C. plant in South Wales. That made use of an on-line mathematical model which could be used to predict the future behaviour of the furnace.

The basic oxygen furnace was a batch process compared with the previously discussed continuous processes. Results were quoted for the necessary accuracy of measurement at the plant to achieve a specified accuracy in the steel cast from the vessel. Alternative control strategies for that process were compared and the use of a temperature-sensing auxiliary lance was advocated. He concluded by saying that control in the early stages of the steelmaking process was at an early stage compared with the rolling and finishing areas, but that that situation was gradually being remedied.

P. A. Wright, in introducing his paper, said that tin smelting was an ancient art whose object was to produce tin without producing iron; and, although it appeared to be a well developed art, it was clear that it had not yet reached a quantitative state in respect of the weight and analysis of drosses and hardhead which were cycled. It was the feeling that that question must have a quantitative answer that prompted the present exercise.

The first stage was to build up the mass balance in terms of the composition of the feed material and a number of parameters which defined the smelting operation. There was nothing elaborate in the algebra involved, but it took several weeks of work to avoid arriving at results such as $0 = 0$ or $1 = 1$, and therefore seemed worth reporting in order to save others from that trouble; there remained a number of approximations which would have to be removed before the results could be considered definitive.

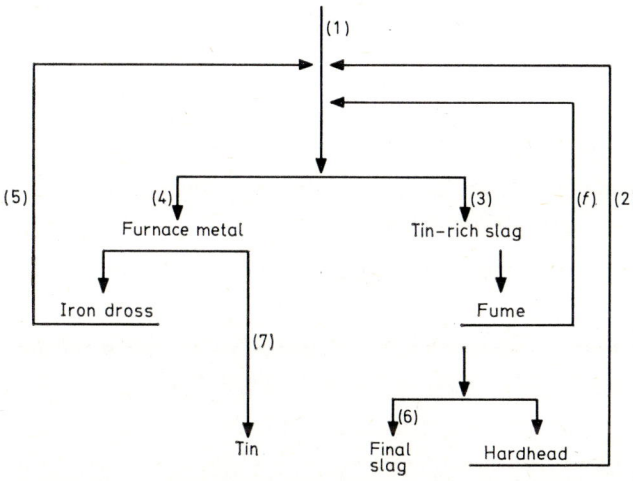

Fig. 1   Modified flowsheet

The transfer of tin from the slag-smelting stage (B) to the concentrate smelt (A) by fume produced in slag smelting could best be accounted for by imagining the slag smelting to take place in two steps: first, a proportion of the tin was fumed off, and then the remaining tin and iron were equilibrated between the hardhead and the final slag; the modified flowsheet was shown in Fig. 1. If, following T. R. A. Davey, they assumed that the tin fumed was a constant fraction (f) of the tin content of the tin-rich slag (3)

$$X_f = (f)X_3$$

and the new equation for X_3 (see p. 471) became

$$X_3 = (f)X_3 + X_6 + X_2$$

$$X_3(1-(f)) = Y_1\frac{\beta}{C_B} + Y_2\beta$$

and

$$W_2 = Y_1 \left[\frac{\{1-(f)\}\alpha C_B - \beta C_A}{\beta C_A - \{1-(f)\}\alpha} \right] \left(\frac{1+\beta}{C_B} \right)$$

$$W_3 = 1 \cdot 25 \, Y_1 \left[\frac{\beta(C_A + \alpha) \ (C_B - 1)}{C_B \ \beta C_A - \{1-(f)\}\alpha} \right] + Z_1 + Z_A$$

W_6 remained unchanged.

The effect on the optimum condition was to move β to a lower value, and therefore diminish, in particular, the tin content of the final slag. With that modification the mass balance in terms of the smelting parameters was substantially correct. The choice of those parameters was more difficult: it was obvious from Fig. 2 (p. 469) that C was related to the tin/iron ratio in the metallic phase; thus, C_A was related to α and C_B to β, but he did not wish to discuss that subject at present. Suffice it to say that no obvious relationship between C_B and β could be found on surveying a large number of results.

The relation between treatment cost and composition of slags could perhaps be estimated from the proposition that

Time of treatment = time to melt charge + time of reaction of molten charge with carbon

If the cost of treatment were related directly to the time of treatment and carbon added, then

Cost = constant + cost of reductant + a factor × reductant

Such an expression could be substituted for B in equations 9 and 10 (p. 473).

Clearly, anyone who used that method of calculation must use the parameters which accorded with his experience, and if the results suggested a serious change in composition, that new composition should be approached slowly and the calculation should be repeated with new parameters as the trend of those emerged. When the relations between parameters, and clearcut cost-composition data, were available, those might be put into the equations derived; no doubt they would become so cumbersome that it would be necessary to write a computer program for their solution; until that state was reached, he would hesitate to use a computer because of the awe with which computer results were accepted.

Professor T. R. A. Davey* then summarized the joint contributed remarks which appear on pages 487–501.

A. G. Moncrieff† said that Wright had quoted typical ranges of the 'direct costs' for each of the three basic stages of tin smelting. He would be interested

* Colorado School of Mines, Golden, Colorado, U.S.A.
† Consolidated Gold Fields, Ltd., London.

to know what had been included in such 'direct costs', e.g. did they include salaries, assaying, maintenance? He suggested that, for the purposes of calculating the optimum conditions in an existing smelter, only 'variable' costs should be included, but he had the impression that the figures given included some 'fixed' costs as well.

In the same context, the author had taken the costs of primary smelting as being proportional to total feed (i.e. concentrates plus dross plus hardhead). Would not the amount of reducing agent required be proportional to the amount of tin and iron reduced in that stage, and would not recycled hardhead actually reduce the amount of anthracite needed as it acted as a reducing agent?

Figs. 4 and 5 (pp. 477 and 478) showed clearly how, with increasing iron content in concentrates, the optimum conditions required lower values of α and thus also of β. He thought, however, that there must be a minimum value of β below which it was not practical to operate, and thus a smelter treating such concentrates might not be able to operate under the 'optimum' conditions as calculated by the author. That might arise because of the high melting point of hardhead with a high iron content, or because of the corrosive nature of the primary slag if its iron content were too high. What was the lowest practical value of β?

In his final paragraph the author referred to slag fuming, and he hoped that, one day, he would be able to give them further information on that subject and its effect on the economics of tin smelting. In the meantime he would be interested to know if the author considered it feasible to fume the primary slag, so eliminating the slag-smelting stage and the formation of hardhead.

W. Drummond,[*] commenting on the Wright paper, asked if the author could state whether he had tried to fume slag direct from the first-stage smelter, thereby cutting out the second-stage smelter. Although recognizing that a differently sized or more frequently rapped baghouse or electrostatic precipitator might be required, he felt that direct fuming of the slag would be more economical in first cost, running costs and fuel costs.

J. L. Leroy[†] said that Winter and Bowles were to be congratulated on developing a technique for the continuous determination of metal values in slags. Experience with other continuous analytical methods proved that there was need for those new methods and that industry should not regard them as too complicated for practical application in fabrication processes.

In that regard a good example resulting from close work between university and industry—including Professor F. D. Richardson, Professor C. M. Diaz and others at Imperial College, London, R.S.T. International Metals, Ltd., and Metallurgie Hoboken-Overpelt—was the 'Oxycell'. From early laboratory work at the university, development in actual plant operations followed, with the

[*] Babcock and Wilcox, Ltd., London.
[†] Metallurgie Hoboken–Overpelt, Belgium.

result that a workable tool was made available to industry for the continuous determination of oxygen in molten copper.

He wished the authors further success in their work and hoped that a practical method of analysis of metal values in slags for use in industry would be the outcome of their research.

Dr. D. Inman,* commenting on the paper by Winter and Bowles, asked the authors why they did not consider the electrochemical technique, chrono-potentiometry, for the *in situ* analysis of molten salt–slag streams. That was a very rapid technique, so, in principle, it would be possible to monitor quite rapidly moving streams. It could be used in the derivative form for better delineation of the transition times and a reverse pulse could be used to return the layer of solution immediately adjacent to the electrode to its original form immediately after the initial pulse.

Although he agreed that the hydrodynamic flow pattern at the rotating-disc electrode was very well defined and amenable to mathematical analysis, it was necessary to use a linear sweep voltammetric technique, and, thus, peaks rather than limiting currents as the quantitative measure of the concentrations of the ions in the melt. In that case, at short times, the use of a rotating-disc electrode was not necessary as concentration depletion took place in the thin stationary layer of solution immediately adjacent to the electrode surface. A further point was that the resolving power of linear sweep voltammetry was no better than that of derivative chronopotentiometry, although he agreed that if a mixture of ions were being analysed, the 'staircase' on a conventional electrode potential–current plot would be slightly easier to resolve than the 'staircase' on the electrode potential–time trace of chronopotentiometry.

Dr. H. K. Worner,† commenting, first, on the paper by Leigh and Williams, congratulated the authors on their valuable review. Because of his particular interest in continuous steelmaking he was hopeful that they would soon have a reliable method for analysing continuously for carbon. Perhaps the authors would indicate how the important work on that subject was progressing at BISRA.

In that connexion he would mention briefly an idea put forward by Professor Thonvald Engh of Trondheim Technical University while he was collaborating in the WORCRA steelmaking work at Luleå. Engh proposed jetting a cold inert gas at a portion of the clean stream of steel and measuring with an optical pyrometer the temperature at which the 'tail' of temporarily frozen alloy became fully liquid again. That temperature should be directly related to the carbon content of the steel. He had suggested to Professor Engh that it might be desirable to entrain a little powdered pure iron in the cold gas stream to assist in nucleating crystallization under the gentle jet. Some preliminary laboratory experiments

* Department of Metallurgy, Imperial College, London.
† Conzinc Riotinto of Australia, Ltd., Melbourne, Australia.

indicated that that approach to continuous carbon determination had possibilities.

He and his colleagues were keenly interested in work such as that described by Bowles and Winter. Any system that would measure and record continuously the copper content of the slag in the quiescent slag well of a WORCRA copper furnace would indeed be valuable. He would point out that in practice the small amount of copper in the slag continuously flowing from the furnace existed as fine prills of matte as well as in solution in the fayalite-type slag.

Contributed remarks

Optimization of tin smelting by use of a computer

Professor T. R. A. Davey* and M. V. Ginatta* Since Davey and Floyd's[1] 1966 paper it has been possible for tin smelters to optimize their classical two-stage smelting operations along the lines of Wright's treatment, but this is the first published account known to the writers.

Wright's metallurgical balance follows generally the treatment of Davey and Floyd, although he has altered the reaction constants somewhat, and added the drossing stage to their simple two-stage process. The addition of the drossing stage actually simplifies, rather than complicates, the mathematics, so a simple analytical solution is possible, instead of the successive approximations method used by Davey and Floyd at that time. Any further additions to the flowsheet greatly complicate matters, and warrant the introduction of computer methods.

In the example following we have considered fume recirculation as well as dross recirculation, and it is quite a simple matter to add further stages (e.g. a slag-fuming operation) and to consider the retreatment of refining drosses as well, if desired. As already reported,[2] a program was written for the optimization of two stages of smelting followed by a slag-fuming stage, in Oruro, in March, 1970. All stages were performed in rotary furnaces, and it was shown that the second-stage smelting, to hardhead, is superfluous for low-grade concentrates.

The slag-fuming stage is governed by kinetic rather than equilibrium considerations, but its inclusion in the computer program is very simple. In fact, the program presented here is a simplification of an actual plant program, which included a slag-fuming stage, removed here for the sake of simplicity.

COMPUTER PROGRAM

This contribution is based on a class exercise used in a graduate class in pyrometallurgical processes at the Colorado School of Mines.

The flowsheet of the smelter concerned is shown in Fig. 2. It includes two smelting stages and a drossing process, from which it is assumed that marketable tin is produced. Refining steps for impurities other than iron can easily be introduced with a little extra complication, but without any new principles being involved.

* Colorado School of Mines, Golden, Colorado, U.S.A.

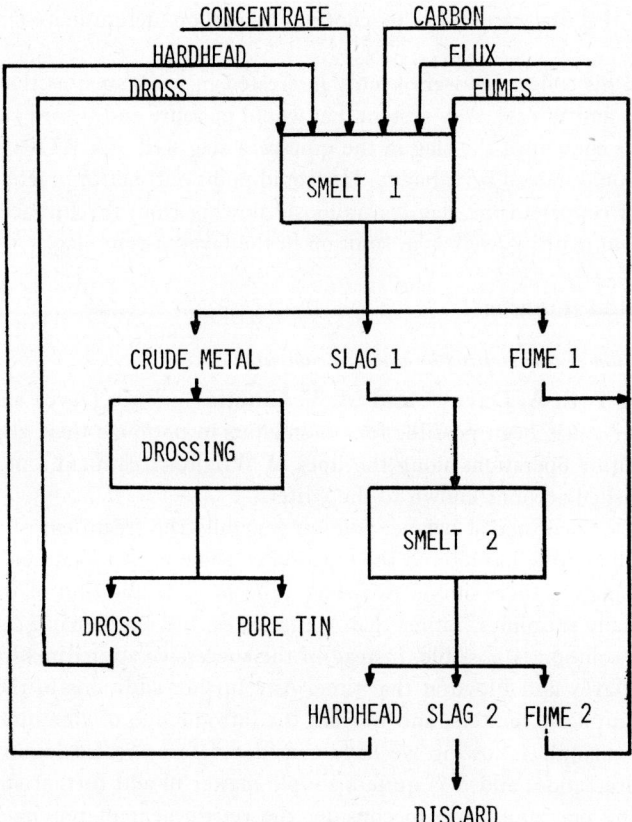

Fig. 2 Flowsheet

The cost factors and operating parameters taken apply to conditions at Oruro, Bolivia (chosen because a significant number of students at Colorado School of Mines are Bolivians), and both smelts are conducted in rotary furnaces. The results of smelting are governed by equilibrium between slag and metal phases, and smelting time is not treated as a variable. (If a final stage of fuming tin from slag were included, as this is a first-order reaction with respect to tin content of slag, the time of fuming is the determining factor for tin elimination.)

The governing factors for the flowsheet shown are the amounts of carbon added to both first and second stages of smelting. It has already been shown[1] that optimum results are obtained when just sufficient reduction is done in the second stage to produce a tin–iron alloy (hardhead) of miscibility gap composition (80% Sn, 20% Fe) with only an infinitesimal amount of the conjugate solution at 50% Sn, 50% Fe. In this case, therefore, one has only the amount of reduction performed in the first stage smelt to vary, and this is chosen so as to minimize costs for the whole smelter.

The main assumptions, operating parameters and cost factors involved are listed below, together with the definition of the symbols used.

Assumptions There are no unaccounted losses; all iron and other materials introduced appear in final slag; all tin introduced appears as tin metal production or final slag loss.

Fumes are resmelted in the first smelting stage, as is hardhead produced in the second smelt. Limestone (at 50% CaO) is added to the first stage to equal the iron content of the slag—this is the only flux.

In the first smelting stage the equilibrium between tin and iron in slag and metal is characterized by K values of 300 or 200, and in the second stage of 50 or 40.

15% of the oxidized tin fed to the first smelting stage is fumed off, and the iron/tin ratio in this fume is 4%, and other constituents in the fume are 5% of the tin content.

30% of the tin fed to the second smelting stage is fumed off, and the iron/tin ratio in this fume is 10%, and other constituents in the fume are 25% of the tin content.

Tin occurs in slag as the stannous form, SnO, and in fumes or concentrates as stannic, SnO_2; iron occurs in slag as FeO, and in fumes or concentrate as Fe_2O_3.

The carbon is consumed by the reaction

$$C + (O) = CO$$

and 50% excess is required for the first, and 100% excess for the second, smelting stage.

Iron is drossed from tin metal as a dross containing 10% Fe, 90% Sn.

A charge of 3 tons is smelted in 9 h (stage 1) or 7 h (stage 2), consuming 60 l/h of oil, costing $0·025/l. Cost of labour, electricity, water, etc., is $70 per furnace-day. Costs of coke and limestone are $75 and $10 per ton, respectively. A furnace campaign lasts 60 days, requiring one complete reline, plus three replacements of bricks around the furnace openings, in this time. Cost of bricks is $2200, and labour $500—a total of $2700 maintenance for 60 days' production. These figures relate to a 2·5-m short rotary furnace.

No account has been taken of capital charges for plant or for tin held up in the process.

Nomenclature In the two-letter symbols the first letter represents: S = Sn, F = Fe, X = other material; and the second letter represents: C = concentrate, S = slag, F = fume, M = crude metal, P = Product metal, D = dross, H = hardhead; 1 = first-stage smelt, 2 = second-stage smelt

OF1,2 = oxygen combined with Sn and Fe fumed from slags 1, 2 (stannous and ferrous forms)

OF3,4 = oxygen combined with Sn and Fe in fume collected from stages 1, 2, respectively (stannic and ferric forms)

EL = limestone flux (added in stage 1 only)

C1,2 = carbon added to stages 1, 2
CL = cost of limestone
CO1,2 = carbon monoxide evolved in stages 1, 2
E1,2 = factor for excess carbon required in stages 1, 2
T1,2 = time required to smelt one ton of charge in stages 1, 2
CHAR1,2 = total charge to stages 1, 2
CHF = cost of handling fumes
CC1,2 = cost of carbon for stages 1, 2
OIL1,2 = cost of oil for stages 1, 2
SER1,2 = cost of services (labour, electricity, water) for stages 1, 2
AIN1,2 = cost of maintenance for stages 1, 2
WOST = value of tin lost in final slag ($ for 1000 tons of concentrate)
OPTIM = optimum total cost
TOT1,2 = cost of smelting 1000 tons of concentrate in stages 1, 2
ALFA = Wright's α = SM/FM

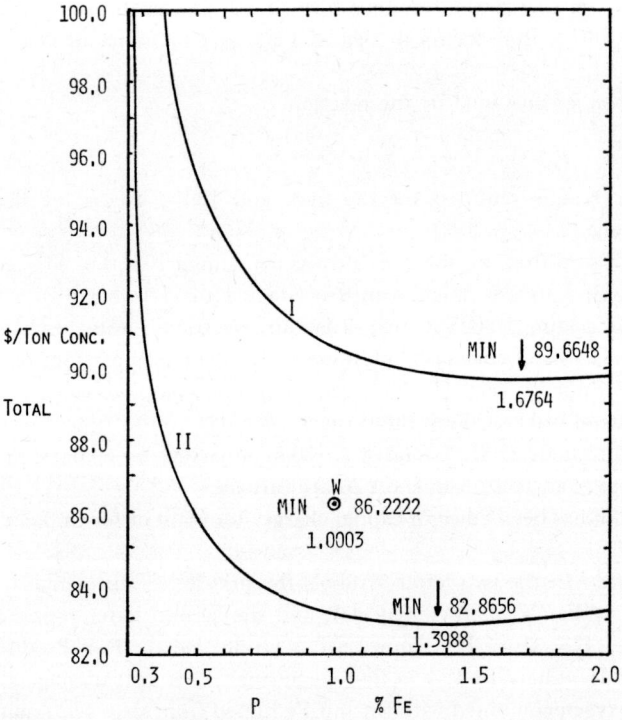

Fig. 3 Cost variation for concentrate containing 60% Sn, 10% Fe by use of (I), K_1 = 200, K_2 = 40; (II), K_1 = 300, K_2 = 50; (W) (Wright), K_1 = 200, K_2 = 10; 60% Sn, 3% Fe

Equations The equations used are based on materials balances, either overall or for a single stage, and on the equilibrium attained in each stage. For a given concentrate composition (i.e. given values of FC and SC) the metallurgical balance sheet is calculated for various values of P, the percentage iron in crude tin metal produced in the first smelt. The total cost of the operation is then calculated for each set of conditions, and this cost is plotted against P, when the minimum cost can readily be seen, and the value of P at which this occurs. Figs. 3 and 4 show graphs for two concentrates: 70% Sn, 4% Fe, and 60% Sn, 10% Fe, and two sets of equilibrium constants.

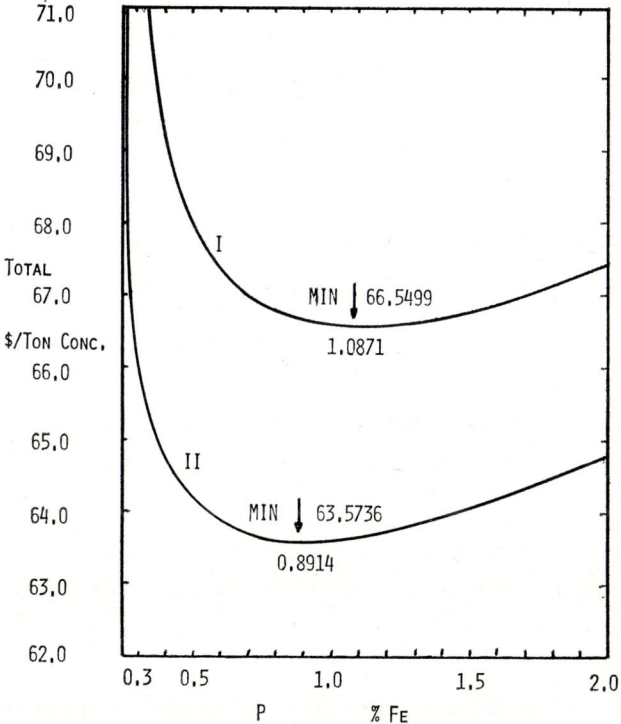

Fig. 4 Cost variation for concentrate containing 70% Sn, 4% Fe by use of (I), $K_1 = 200$, $K_2 = 40$; (II), $K_1 = 300$, $K_2 = 50$

The following equations, after rearrangement and substitution as necessary, were used to solve for all the variables:

$$
\begin{aligned}
\text{XC} &= 1000 - 1\cdot2696\ \text{SC} - 1\cdot4296\ \text{FC} \\
\text{SC} &= \text{SP} + \text{SS2} \\
\text{SP} &= \text{SM} - \text{SD} \\
\text{SD} &= 9*\text{FM} \\
\text{FC} &= \text{FS2}
\end{aligned}
$$

P   = 100*FM/(SM + FM)
SS1   = SH + SS2 + SF2
SF2   = 0·30*SS1
SF1   = 0·15* (SC + SF1 + SF2)
FF1   = 0·04*SF1
XF1   = 0·05*SF1
FF2   = 0·10*SF2
XF2   = 0·25*SF2
FS1   = FH + FS2 + FF2
SH   = 4*FH
K1   = SM*FS1/(FM*SS1)
K2   = SH*FS2/(FH*SS2)
K1   = 200
K2   = 40
OS1   = 0·1348*SS1 + 0·2864*FS1
OS2   = 0·1348*SS2 + 0·2864*FS2
OF1   = 0·1348*SF1 + 0·2864*FF1
OF2   = 0·1348*SF2 + 0·2864*FF2
OF3   = 0·2696*SF1 + 0·4296*FF1
OF4   = 0·2696*SF2 + 0·4296*FF2
OC   = 0·2696*SC + 0·4296*FC
CO1   = (28/16)* (OC + OF3 + OF4 − OS1 − OF1)
CO2   = (28/16)* (OS1 − OS2 − OF2)
C1   = (12/28)*CO1*E1
C2   = (12/28)*CO2*E2
E1   = 1·50
E2   = 2·0
EL   = 2·0*FS1
CC1   = 75*C1
CC2   = 75*C1
CL   = 10*EL
WOST   = 3000*SS2
CHF   = 12·5* (SF1 + FF1 + OF3 + SF2 + FF2 + OF4 + XF1 + XF2)
CHAR1   = 1000 + C1 + EL + SF1 + FF1 + OF3 + XF1 + SF2
           + FF2 + OF4 + XF2 + SH + FH + SD + FM
T1   = CHAR1* (9/3)
OIL1   = 1·5*T1
SER1   = (70/24)*T1
AIN1   = (2700/(60*24))*T1
TOT1   = (CC1 + CHF + CL1 + OIL1 + SER1 + AIN1)/1000
CHAR2   = SS1 + FS1 + OS1 + XC + EL + C2
T2   = (7/3)*CHAR2
OIL2   = 1·5*T2
SER2   = (70/24)*T2

AIN2   = (2700/(60*24))*T2
TOT2   = (CC2+OIL2+SER2+AIN2+WOST)/1000
TOTAL = TOT1+TOT2

CONCLUSIONS

Some results of this class exercise are shown in Figs. 3–6. A higher iron content of first metal should be aimed for when lower-tin, higher-iron concentrates are smelted.

If one were using a similar program in practice, one would simply print out values corresponding to the optimum conditions, and these would preferably be in the form of working instructions for the plant, e.g. charge composition for one furnace charge.

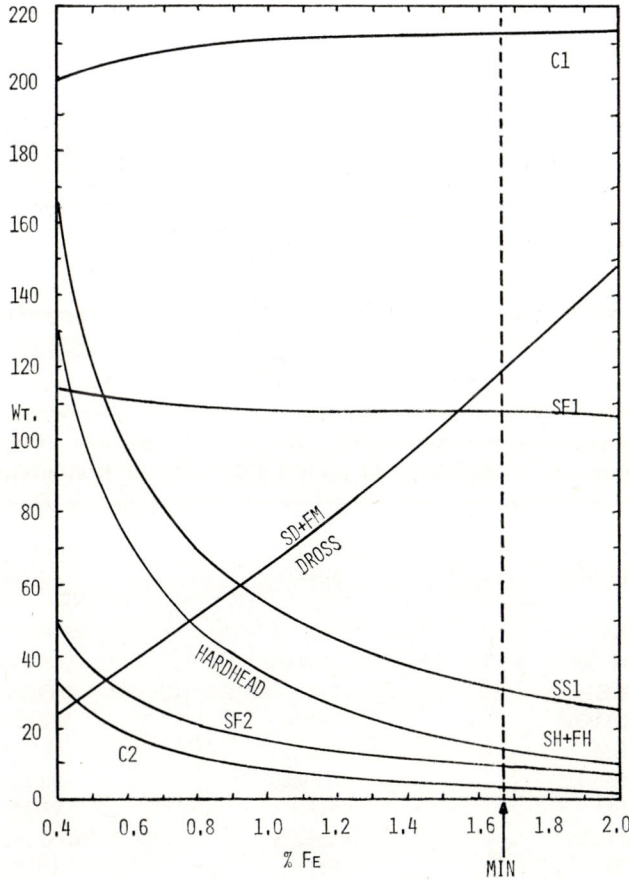

Fig. 5 Variation of metallurgical values with iron in first metal: concentrate 60% Sn, 10% Fe; $K_1 = 200$, $K_2 = 40$

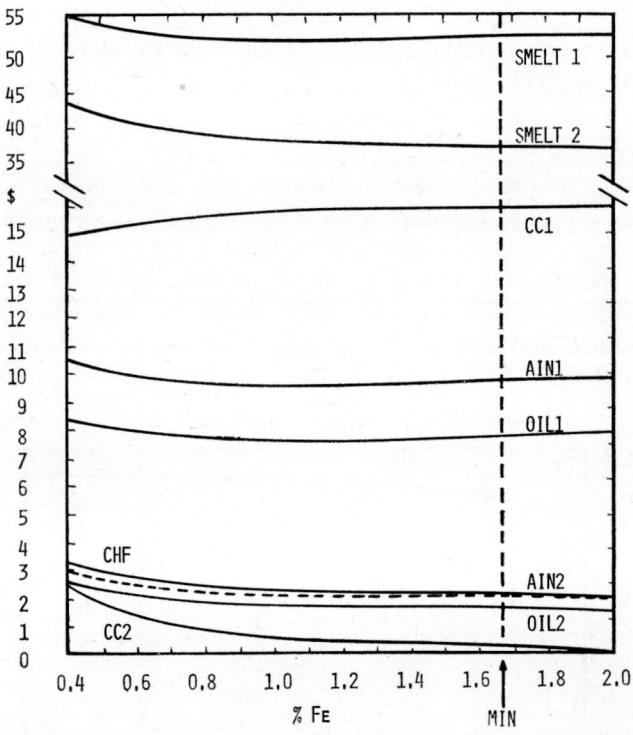

Fig. 6 Variation of partial costs with iron in first metal: concentrate 60% Sn, 10% Fe; $K_1 = 200$, $K_2 = 40$

Table 1   Flowsheet values for optimum cost of treating a concentrate containing 60% Sn, 10% Fe, by use of the values $K_1 = 200$, $K_2 = 40$ with 1·6764% Fe in first metal

TOTAL COST	SMELT 1	SMELT 2
89·6648	52·4407	37·2241
K1	K2	P
200·0000	40·0000	1·6764
SC	FC	OC
600·0000	100·0000	204·7200
SM	FM	XC
696·9451	11·8828	95·2800
SH	FH	WOST
11·2951	2·8238	30000·0001
SP	SD	CHF
590·0000	106·9451	2039·5976

Continued on next page

SHN	SHD	EL
51·7148	4·5785	207·4728
SS1	SS2	FS1
30·4216	10·0000	103·7364
FS2	SF1	SF2
100·0000	107·4929	9·1265
FF1	FF2	OF1
4·2997	0·9126	15·7215
OF2	OF3	OF4
1·4916	30·8272	2·8526
C1	C2	CO1
212·4758	3·4970	330·5179
CO2	XF1	XF2
4·0798	5·3746	2·2816
OS1	OS2	CHAR1
33·8109	29·9880	1716·0632
T1	CHAR2	T2
5148·1897	474·2187	1106·5103
OIL1	OIL2	SER1
7722·2845	1659·7655	15015·5531
SER2	CC1	CC2
3227·3217	15935·6862	262·2719
AIN1	AIN2	CL
9652·8556	2074·7069	2074·7284
OPTIM	ALFA	
89·6648	58·6516	

Plant operation instructions: Case 1
Stage 1, furnace 1, 3-ton charge

Concentrate	1748·1873 kg
Limestone	362·7014 kg
Carbon	371·4475 kg
Hardhead	24·6824 kg
Dross	207·7335 kg
Fumes from furnace 1	258·7221 kg
Fumes from furnace 2	26·5258 kg

Stage 2, furnace 2, 3-ton charge

Slag from furnace 1	2977·8775 kg
Carbon	22·1224 kg

Tables 1–4 show typical printouts for all materials in the metallurgical flow-sheet, plus treatment times, costs, etc., for the optimum working conditions for two concentrates (60% Sn, 10% Fe, or 70% Sn, 4% Fe) and two sets of equilibrium constants ($K_1 = 200$ and $K_2 = 40$, or $K_1 = 300$ and $K_2 = 50$; the latter pair are more likely to be achieved in a rotary furnace, which approaches equilibrium more closely than a stationary reverberatory.)

Each table also shows a printout of the charge composition for an individual furnace charge, for each of the optima shown in Tables 1–4, i.e. actual furnace working instructions.

Table 2 Flowsheet values for optimum cost of treating a concentrate containing 60% Sn, 10% Fe, by use of the values $K_1 = 300$, $K_2 = 50$ with 1·3988% Fe in first metal

TOTAL COST	SMELT 1	SMELT 2
82·8656	51·8483	31·0172
K1	K2	P
300·0000	50·0000	1·3988
SC	FC	OC
600·0000	100·0000	204·7200
SM	FM	XC
678·6484	9·6276	95·2800
SH	FH	WOST
8·9344	2·2336	24000·0000
SP	SD	CHF
592·0000	86·6484	1995·0828
SHN	SHD	EL
51·7036	5·7870	205·9187
SS1	SS2	FS1
24·1920	8·0000	102·9594
FS2	SF1	SF2
100·0000	107·1631	7·2576
FF1	FF2	OF1
4·2865	0·7258	15·6732
OF2	OF3	OF4
1·1862	30·7327	2·2684
C1	C2	CO1
212·9616	2·7661	331·2736
CO2	XF1	XF2
3·2271	5·3582	1·8144
OS1	OS2	CHAR1
32·7486	29·7184	1685·9310
T1	CHAR2	T2
5057·7930	463·8648	1082·3511
OIL1	OIL2	SER1
7586·6895	1623·5266	14751·8963
SER2	CC1	CC2
3156·8573	15972·1211	207·4563
AIN1	AIN2	CL
9483·3618	2029·4083	2059·1871
OPTIM	ALFA	
82·8656	70·4898	

Continued on next page

Plant operation instructions: Case 2
   Stage 1, furnace 1, 3-ton charge

Concentrate	1779·4322 kg
Limestone	366·4184 kg
Carbon	378·9508 kg
Hardhead	19·8726 kg
Dross	171·3167 kg
Fumes from furnace 1	262·5382 kg
Fumes from furnace 2	21·4709 kg

   Stage 2, furnace 2, 3-ton charge

Slag from furnace 1	2982·1106 kg
Carbon	17·8894 kg

Table 3   Flowsheet values for optimum cost of treating a concentrate containing 70% Sn, 4% Fe, by use of the values $K_1 = 200$, $K_2 = 40$ with 1·0871% Fe in first metal

TOTAL COST	SMELT 1	SMELT 2
66·5499	51·0854	15·4645
K1	K2	P
200·0000	40·0000	1·0871
SC	FC	OC
700·0000	40·0000	205·9040
SM	FM	XC
772·4016	8·4891	54·0960
SH	FH	WOST
9·6973	2·4243	12000·0000
SP	SD	CHF
696·0000	76·4016	2265·7404
SHN	SHD	EL
27·6109	2·8473	86·0227
SS1	SS2	FS1
19·5676	4·0000	43·0113
FS2	SF1	SF2
40·0000	124·5653	5·8703
FF1	FF2	OF1
4·9826	0·5870	18·2184
OF2	OF3	OF4
0·9594	35·7233	1·8348
C1	C2	CO1
236·5735	3·0023	368·0032
CO2	XF1	XF2
3·5027	6·2283	1·4676
OS1	OS2	CHAR1
14,9562	11·9952	1600·8677

Continued on next page

R

T1	CHAR2	T2
4802·6030	220·6560	514·8641
OIL1	OIL2	SER1
7203·9045	772·2961	14007·5922
SER2	CC1	CC2
1501·6869	17743·0136	225·1710
AIN1	AIN2	CL
9004·8806	965·3702	860·2270
OPTIM	ALFA	
66·5499	90·9879	

Plant operation instructions: Case 3
Stage 1, furnace 1, 3-ton charge

Concentrate	1873·9837 kg
Limestone	161·2051 kg
Carbon	443·3349 kg
Hardhead	22·7157 kg
Dross	159·0836 kg
Fumes from furnace 1	321·3874 kg
Fumes from furnace 2	18·2895 kg

Stage 2, furnace 2, 3-ton charge

Slag from furnace 1	2959·1816 kg
Carbon	40·8185 kg

Table 4 Flowsheet values for optimum cost of treating a concentrate containing 70% Sn, 4% Fe, by use of the values $K_1 = 300$, $K_2 = 50$ with 0·8914% Fe in first metal

TOTAL COST	SMELT 1	SMELT 2
63·5736	50·6540	12·9196
K1	K2	P
300·0000	50·0000	0·8914
SC	FC	OC
700·0000	40·0000	205·9040
SM	FM	XC
758·1722	6·8191	54·0960
SH	FH	WOST
7·8057	1·9514	9600·0000
SP	SD	CHF
696·8000	61·3722	2238·2643
SHN	SHD	EL
27·8023	3·5618	84·8462
SS1	SS2	FS1
15·7224	3·2000	42·4231
FS2	SF1	SF2
40·0000	124·3618	4·7167

Continued on next page

FF1	FF2	OF1
4·9745	0·4717	18·1887
OF2	OF3	OF4
0·7709	35·6650	1·4743
C1	C2	CO1
236·9084	2·4166	368·5241
CO2	XF1	XF2
2·8194	6·2181	1·1792
OS1	OS2	CHAR1
14·2694	11·8874	1578·7642
T1	CHAR2	T2
4736·2925	213·7738	498·8054
OIL1	OIL2	SER1
7104·4388	748·2081	13814·1865
SER2	CC1	CC2
1454·8491	17768·1271	181·2485
AIN1	AIN2	CL
8880·5485	935·2602	848·4620
OPTIM	ALFA	
63·5736	111·1831	

Plant operation instructions: Case 4
  Stage 1, furnace 1, 3-ton charge
    Concentrate   1900·2204 kg
    Limestone   161·2265 kg
    Carbon   450·1781 kg
    Hardhead   18·5407 kg
    Dross   129·5786 kg
    Fumes from furnace 1   325·3544 kg
    Fumes from furnace 2   14·9012 kg
  Stage 2, furnace 2, 3-ton charge
    Slag from furnace 1   2966,0859 kg
    Carbon   33·9141 kg

In comparing our results with those of Wright, we find a remarkable similarity, despite considerable variations in cost factors. We would draw attention, however, to the following differences.

(1) We have taken it for granted that the optimum hardhead composition is 80:20 Sn/Fe. We do not believe that it is economical to produce hardhead of a lower Sn/Fe ratio than this, at any rate from low-grade tin concentrates. Certainly, because of the Sn–Fe miscibility gap, no additional tin is removed from the slag, although considerably more carbon is consumed, in making 50:50 Sn/Fe hardhead. Fig. 4 (p. 477) is, we believe, slightly in error, which accounts for the author's finding of optimal β' values different from our constant value of about 4.

Fig. 7 shows the relation of Harris and Hallett,[3] together with Wright's Fig. 4. It is preferable to plot log C versus linear concentration of iron in metal, rather than linear C versus log concentration of iron, since then a slightly curved line results. Harris and Hallett's data relate to experimental equilibrium results, confirmed by many plant measurements when equilibrium could be attained. Further, more detailed discussion of Fig. 4 (which, incidentally, is rather different from the source quoted[4]) will be reserved for another occasion. Here it is simply noted that, when the metal produced in the first stage contains around 1·5% Fe, then K_1 is somewhat greater than 200—about 230 according to Fig. 7. In a

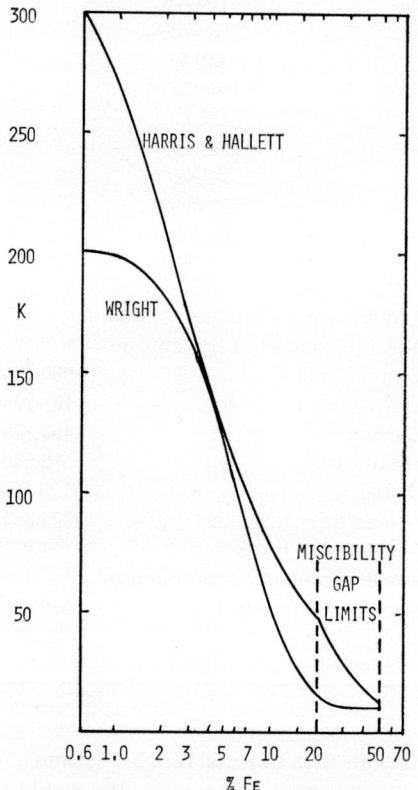

Fig. 7 $K = (Fe/Sn)_{Slag} \times (Sn/Fe)_{Metal}$ as function of Fe in metal

complete program K_1 would be expressed as a function of FM, the Fe content of the metal. Figs. 3 and 4 illustrate the effect of changes in K_1 and K_2 on the optimization program. Although the effect is marked on the total smelting costs, the optimum FM to aim at is not so greatly affected.

(2) We have assumed that the cheapest way of liquating the tin–iron dross is to feed it to the first smelting stage rather than to use a separate liquation furnace. It seems to us that the correct comparison is between the *total* cost of

operating a liquation furnace and the *incremental* cost of first-stage smelting. By use of this comparison we believe that, under any conceivable cost levels, a separate liquation process does not pay.

Our treatment is a graduate class exercise, designed to illustrate the principles of optimizing a complete metallurgical plant, without introducing too many complications. It is, therefore, far from complete and cannot be applied directly to any specific plant. It suffers from one serious shortcoming (also shared by Wright's treatment) that the costs of smelting one ton of any material are assumed to be independent of its composition. This assumption is certainly not true, but we do not at present have the data necessary to correct it. It is a very simple matter to modify the program to incorporate such data when they become available.

The computer routine technique possesses many advantages over the method used by Wright, some of which have been mentioned already. One great advantage is that we do not have to assume (which is patently false) that cost factors entering into the expression differentiated in equation 11 (p. 474) remain constant. Variations in these can lead to considerable inaccuracies in the estimation of optimum values.

References

1. DAVEY T. R. A. AND FLOYD J. M. Slag–metal equilibria in tin smelting. *Proc. Australas. Inst. Min. Metall.* no. 219, 1966, 1–10.
2. DAVEY T. R. A. AND FLOSSBACH F. J. Tin smelting in rotary furnaces. *J. Metals, N.Y.*, to be published.
3. HARRIS J. H. AND HALLETT G. D. Discussion of reference 1. *Proc. Australas. Inst. Min. Metall.* no. 223, 1967, 75–7.
4. WRIGHT P. A. Activities in the tin–iron system. *Trans. Instn Min. Metall. (Sect. C: Mineral Process. Extr. Metall.)*, **80**, 1971, C112–3.

AUTHORS' REPLIES

D. G. Winter and Dr. P. J. Bowles In reply to the comments by Dr. D. Inman (p. 486), chronopotentiometry was not used for slag analysis since we have found this technique in fused salts less reliable than voltammetry. The voltage–time curves obtained have been irreproducible due to solute depletion effects, even when current reversal has been used to strip deposited metal from the working electrode. We consider that in any electroanalytical technique, either galvanostatic or potentiodynamic, operated over a very short time-interval in viscous oxyanion melts, phenomena will be recorded which are due partly to non-Faradaic processes like double layer charging and partly to the reduction of solute ions. Discontinuities in the curves recorded are not then amenable to mathematical analysis, making these 'fast' techniques less useful in practical slag analysis.

In reply to Dr. H. K. Worner's comments (pp. 486–7) on the problem of determining copper in suspension as fine matte prills in metallurgical slags, the voltammetric technique will not determine this material, and we would offer, as a first suggestion only, the possibility of settling out the prills in suspension in the slag by the application of a voltage higher than that used in a purely electrochemical determination, when the molten matte droplets will separate out under forces caused by the electrocapillary effect.

Dr. J. R. Leigh and Dr. R. V. Williams We appreciate the interest shown by Dr. H. K. Worner and his collaborators in the continuous analysis of steels for carbon, and we are happy to say that the first full-scale trials of this equipment at a works are scheduled for the spring of 1972. At the same time we are discussing the commercial availability of the equipment with instrument companies competent to manufacture it.

P. A. Wright Mr. A. G. Moncrieff (pp. 484–5) is not quite right in assuming that the costs which I have used are typical; I would say that they are possible, but that only the ratio is typical. I have taken the costs of all stages as proportional to the feed and have thus based my optimum on throughput, which is usually the deciding factor. The total amount of reducing agent needed for any concentrate is theoretically that required for the reaction

$$a\mathrm{SnO_2} + b\mathrm{Fe_2O_3} + (2a+b)\mathrm{C} = a\mathrm{Sn} + 2b\mathrm{FeO} + (2a+b)\,\mathrm{CO}$$

because, as Mr. Moncrieff remarks, iron reduced into the hardhead by carbon acts as reductant when added to the ore smelt. It is only because the efficiency of carbon utilization is lower in slag smelting than in ore smelting that there is any change in total carbon consumption when the proportion of work done by carbon in the two stages is altered. The change in total carbon consumption is therefore a second-order correction, unless the disparity in carbon utilization is very great between the two stages.

I think that my remarks on p. 476 cover his third point; I should not like to run β lower than 3/4—hence my conclusion that the standard circuit cannot be used for concentrates containing less than 60% Sn, assuming, of course, that %Fe increases as %Sn goes down.

Both Mr. Moncrieff and Mr. W. Drummond (p. 485) ask the reasonable question 'why not fume the tin from the first slag?' This is clearly the ultimate solution, but it is not done in the standard circuit which I set out to discuss. It is done in the ENAF smelter in Oruro and is, I believe, planned at the Ikuno smelter in Japan, but it places the most stringent requirements on the capacity and efficiency of the gas filtration system and, because a sulphidizing agent such as pyrites must be used in greater quantity, gives rise to a greater emission of $\mathrm{SO_2}$ than the normal process. The evolution of fume is directly proportional to the tin content of the slag being treated. Suppose that a filter is designed to operate with a furnace fed with 2% Sn slag and that the tin content is reduced to 0·2% in 2 h and that a fume loss of 0·5% is acceptable (filter efficiency 99·5%). If this furnace is charged with a 10% Sn slag, the filter has to cope with a fivefold increase in fume burden, and if the same absolute loss is to be maintained, the efficiency must be raised to 99·9%; this probably means an eightfold increase in the size of the filter. Now the time taken to get from 10% Sn to 0·2% Sn in the slag will be 3·4 hours, so seven-eighths of the filter is really effective for only 40% of the time. This rough calculation shows that the problem must have a 'least bad' answer.

The contribution by Professor T. R. A. Davey and Mr. M. V. Ginatta (pp. 487–501) rests on four principal points: (1) the minimum treatment cost corresponds to the minimum carbon consumption; (2) the equilibrium constants are known and are represented by the results of Harris and Hallett; (3) a close approach to equilibrium is obtained in a rotary furnace; and (4) the optimum result is automatically obtained by taking the slag-smelting step to equilibrium with 80% Sn: 20% Fe hardhead.

In reply to Mr. Moncrieff I have pointed out that carbon consumption for a given ore is theoretically constant and it is only the difference in the excess requirement in the two stages that gives rise to a variation in total carbon consumption. Davey and Ginatta's optimum is therefore critically dependent on the choice of excess factors (50% in the ore smelt and 100% in the slag smelt), and these factors are not very reliable, particularly in a rotary furnace.

The second and third points might have been supported by the work of Davey and Flossbach, but the evidence is scanty. The ore smelt is described as producing metal with 97% Sn, 1–2% Fe and slags with 10–14% Sn; the iron content of the slag is not stated, but I calculate that it was about 17%. Taking the mean values we obtain

$$K = \frac{97}{1 \cdot 5} \times \frac{17}{12} \approx 100$$

compared with the value of about 250 to be expected from the results of Harris and Hallet reproduced in Fig. 7. The only information concerning the slag smelt is that the hardhead was about 80%Sn/20%Fe and that the slags contained several per cent Sn. It appears that the rotary furnace did not attain the expected equilibria.

Since the standard tin-smelting circuit does not include a fuming stage, and slags containing several per cent Sn cannot be rejected, it is clear that reduction of the slag must be taken beyond equilibrium with 80/20 hardhead, and the economics of doing this are the subject of my enquiry. My paper is intended not so much for students as for smelters, who, having their own ideas about the actual figures, can estimate the possible improvement in performance which might be expected from changes in practice.

It seems to have been forgotten that in the nineteenth century* and even as late as 1954† computers were people paid to do arithmetic and that they worked to programs. The validity of the results depended then, as it does now, on the validity of the program.

* Darwin G. H. *The tides and kindred phenomena in the solar system* (London and San Francisco, 1962), 378 p. (p. 215)
† Sutton *Sir* G. *Mathematics in action* (London: Bell, 1954), 266 p. (p. 83)

Session 8

New and improved techniques

Chairman
Dr. J. E. Hughes

R*

Alcan (U.K.), Ltd., smelter, Lynemouth, Northumberland

E. M. Strachan
C. Chamberland

Both of Alcan (U.K.), Ltd., Lynemouth, Northumberland

669.713(428.2)

Synopsis
The new Alcan aluminium smelter at Lynemouth, Northumberland, will produce some 120 000 tons per annum—about one-third of the total production of the three new United Kingdom aluminium smelters.

The advantages of the Alcan smelter site are noted, and port handling and storage facilities are outlined. It will be possible to accommodate ships of up to 35 000-ton capacity.

Descriptions are given of the carbon plant, the pot rooms, including the ventilation and pot gas cleaning arrangements, and the casting plant.

Until very recently the United Kingdom was one of the few advanced countries not possessing a sizable primary aluminium industry. In the space of a very few years the aluminium industry in this country will increase from approximately 30 000 to 360 000 tons per annum—as a result of three new, separate, aluminium smelters now either under construction or at the early stages of production. The effect will be that from being a large importer of aluminium the United Kingdom will very shortly be virtually self-sufficient in this metal. Alcan's smelter at Lynemouth will yield 120 000 tons of this increase in capacity.

The building, design and operation of a new smelter offer the opportunity of trying out new ideas and also of combining the best methods from other associated plants throughout the world. It consists of a complex of processes, each distinct, but totally interdependent. These processes are a carbon plant, in which the anodes and the cathodes for the electrolytic cells are fabricated; the pot rooms, in which the actual reduction of alumina to aluminium takes place; and a casting plant, in which the molten aluminium is purified, necessary alloying elements are added and casting of suitable shapes and sizes for further fabrication ensues; pollution control facilities, which, at the present time, are as complex as any individual process itself, are also required. In addition, facilities for the unloading and storage of bulk raw materials are required.

Site

The Alcan smelter is located near the village of Lynemouth, some 20 miles north of Newcastle upon Tyne. The site was chosen as it fulfils most of the pre-

Fig. 1

requisites for an aluminium industry. Coal for power generation is close at hand, and is provided by the National Coal Board from collieries with many years of reserves. A deep-sea port is already in existence at Blyth, some 8 miles away, limiting the length of relatively expensive rail haulage of high-volume bulk materials. Flat land not underlain by coal mining operations was chosen and as distinct from many new aluminium smelters a labour force already familiar with heavy industry can be recruited from local areas.

Port handling and storage facilities

Land was purchased on the north side of the Blyth harbour, and a concrete quay, large enough to handle vessels of up to 625 ft long, was constructed to accommodate alumina and coke vessels. The ship unloader is of high-speed design, and incorporates a clamshell capable of hoisting about 10 tons at a time. As alumina is a fine powdering material, dusting can present problems when it is being dumped into hoppers. The open side of the unloader tower is therefore equipped with an 'air curtain', which comprises both a pressure air supply and a suction air system across the width of the opening. Belt conveyors take the materials to steel storage silos—two 15 000-ton silos for alumina and one 7500-ton silo for calcined coke. Dust collectors at transfer points are designed to minimize losses, and they ensure good working conditions in the conveyor galleries. From the point where the clam discharges into the unloader hopper all other equipment, i.e. conveyors, dust collectors, etc., are electrically interlocked. Reclaiming of materials is by means of conveyors beneath the storage silos, air slides being used for alumina and a belt conveyor for coke. Separate loading stations are installed for the two materials, which are elevated to small bins above the railway tracks. Rail wagons

Fig. 2

are top-loaded from four pipe connexions to matching hatches. Equipment is installed to allow for an automatic cutoff when the 30-ton payload is reached for each wagon. Subsequent wagons are then moved into position by mechanical means and spotted accurately for the next fill. Eighteen loaded wagons will form the train—14 for alumina and 4 for coke—and the total payload will be some 540 tons.

Alumina will be supplied by an Alcan subsidiary, Alcanore, which is based in the Caribbean. The alumina will be carried in ships averaging about 20 000 tons. The berth has been dredged to a depth of 36 ft to accommodate ships of up to 35 000 tons, should this prove necessary in the future.

Calcined coke is supplied from a United Kingdom source, the coke being produced from Libyan crude, which is particularly low in metallics and in sulphur. This material will be shipped to Blyth in coastal vessels with a maximum capacity of 5000 tons. If large ships should become available, space exists for the construction of a second coke silo.

Carbon plant

The electrolytic reduction process relies heavily for its economy and efficiency on the correlated processes that produce the anodes and the cathodes. The refinements are specially important in the classification of particle sizes of petroleum coke and pitch materials in the paste plant and the method of controlled proportioning by weight for the production of anodes.

Anode mix consists of a mixture of petroleum coke and hard pitch. Their precise classification of particle sizes and their subsequent proportioning add greatly to the effectiveness of the finished anode and the electrolytic process. Petroleum coke is crushed then conveyed and screened into six fraction tanks. The sizes are divided into uniform descending ranges from $\frac{5}{8}$ in down to the finest dust fraction (-200 mesh). The feed of these materials is by gravity in totally enclosed duct work, thus minimizing maintenance and dust problems.

Hard pitch in pencil form is pneumatically conveyed from storage into a fraction tank above a Howe Richardson scale.

Fig. 3

From the tanks exact proportions of material are weighed out and mixed in Sigmablade mixers for a period of 30 min. This mixture is heated to 160°C and then conveyed to two vibratory formers. This unique method of forming has many advantages over more conventional methods, such as pressing—the prime advantage being capital cost, which is approximately 10% of that of a hydraulic press.

Although this system involves batch mixers, the plant is so integrated as to give continuous feed to the vibrators at a rate of 24 ton/h, and, in terms of anodes, is equivalent to 33- to 1610-lb anodes measuring 26 in × 56 in × 20 in high. These anodes are automatically pushed on to transporting pallets and cooled *en route* to the carbon baking furnaces. On arrival at the furnace the anodes again are automatically up-ended and loaded into the furnace, five at a time, by overhead cranes.

After the anodes have been packed with granular coke, the materials are indirectly heated through the hollow flues alongside the pits to about 1200°C. This cures the anodes, turning the pitch into coke, and greatly improving the electrical conductivity of the anode; thus, 21 days later, the anodes are removed from the furnace, cleaned and conveyed to the rodding plant.

In the rodding building the anodes are attached to the anode rods by a technique known as mix rodding, rather than by the more conventional cast iron rodding.

The high degree of automation, the use of the vibrator as a means of anode forming and mix rodding in the rodding building have enabled a substantial reduction to be made in capital cost, as well as keeping operating manpower requirements low—for example, the total plant will only require 16 operators per shift.

Pot rooms

336 cells, each some 30 ft long and 14 ft wide, are located in four buildings, each approximately one-third of a mile long and 78 ft wide. A two-storey structure of the semi-basement type is employed, the upper floor being the main working floor and the lower floor being used to assist ventilation and cooling and also to provide access to the busbar on the underside of the reduction cells. With extensive use of floor grills there is a direct flow of fresh air around the working areas. The type of cell selected for Lynemouth is an end-to-end pre-bake cell completely enclosed with hoods. The pre-bake type was chosen as hooding to collect fumes is simpler and more effective than the slightly cheaper Soderberg type.

As power represents a major cost factor, every attempt has been made to produce a cell with low energy consumption. Careful attention has been paid to busbar sizing and current densities have been optimized. The cathode, which consists of a steel shell lined with carbon blocks, has been very heavily insulated with both protective fire-brick and insulating brick and the steel shell itself has been given additional rigidity by being held in heavy steel cradles. A further feature of the cathode is the method by which current is passed from cell to cell. As very heavy currents are employed, magnetic effects can be very severe. Busbar connexions are therefore organized so that offsetting currents are created to give maximum magnetic stability; as a result of all these features a power efficiency well below 7 kWh/lb is expected.

Fig. 4

The pots will be serviced by high-speed dc cranes for anode replacement and for transportation of hot metal crucibles, and these same cranes can be employed for the removal of failed cathodes. End-to-end cells allow easy servicing by custom-built, floor-mounted machines, employed for the addition of alumina, crust breaking and anode effect suppression. Emphasis has been on speed of operation to limit the time the reduction cells are open to atmosphere.

A total of 22 anodes are installed in each cell, and the anode panel is controlled by computer—the object being to maintain the distance between the anode and the cathode at the optimum for high current efficiency and minimum voltage. Information on this and other process variables is continuously monitored to a centrally located control room. This permits close control to be maintained and corrective action to be taken quickly. The computer system has been extensively and successfully employed in other Alcan smelters.

Power for the processes is provided from the company's own power station, located half a mile away. It enters the plant at 24 000 V. Six rectiformers lower the voltage to a maximum of 840 V dc at the line amperage of 142 000. Normally, five rectiformers will be in operation, the sixth serving as a spare.

Pot room ventilation and pot gas cleaning

Air at the rate of 25 000 Sft^3/min per pot is pulled into the open basements and through the pot room floor grills by banks of fans located periodically along the pot room buildings. A plenum in the apex of the roof of each pot room building serves as a collection point for the air, which is then exhausted through four 22-ft

Fig. 5

diameter concrete stacks for each pot line. Each stack is 250 ft high above the pot room floor level.

All residual pot emissions not caught under the pot hoods are dispersed at 250 ft, thus ensuring that the infrequent inversion conditions caused by night cooling, sea fogs, etc., do not cause a 'lid effect' on the emissions. Experience has shown that the majority of inversion conditions on this part of the Northumberland coast range from ground level to about 200 ft. Higher-level inversions than this are so rare to be almost negligible. The low gamma-level concentrations of fluoride which result from such conditions are completely innocuous. The cleaned pot exhaust gas is also exhausted through these stacks. The result is ground level concentrations of fluoride which are completely innocuous.

Every pot is individually hooded and operations are so arranged that these hoods, or sections of them, are opened only for essential operations, which amount to less than 5% of the time. Great care will be taken to ensure good alumina coverage on the operation pots. The pot exhaust gases consist, essentially, of indrawn air, with minor amounts of carbon dioxide and sulphur dioxide and trace amounts of gaseous and particulate fluorides. The rate of hood exhaust is 3500 Sft^3/min per pot, i.e. about 4350 ft^3/min at operating temperature, which, under normal operation, is sufficient to entrap all pot emissions when the hoods are closed.

The pot exhaust is drawn off at both ends of each pot and conducted by means of connecting ducts into the centre courtyard for each pot line to the gas cleaning plants, which are set up to clean the gas from groups of 24 pots. In the first pot line the gas cleaning plant is the Alcan patented floating-bed wet scrubber, sea water being used as the scrubbing medium. The pot gas is cleaned in a counter-current flow to the sea water at an efficiency of greater than 98% on the phytoxic gaseous fluorides. On particulate fluorides the cleaning efficiency depends on the number of stages and the pressure drop across them. The scrubber effluent is then bled off harmlessly to sea, at a controlled rate of about 350 gal/min, to be diluted by the power station cooling water system, which will operate at 120 000 gal/min.

Preceding each scrubber will be a multi-cyclone, which will remove the larger solids from the gas stream so that they can be recovered.

In the second pot line a very recently developed Alcan-type dry gas cleaning system is used. The normal production alumina is continuously fed into a series of baghouses at a very high rate. The efficiency of this system, based on extensive work and prototype units, is expected to be 98% on gaseous fluorides and, being a bag filter, better than 99% on particulate fluorides. In this way all the entrapped fluorides are returned to the reduction process, thus reducing the consumption of these expensive materials.

The cleaned air from the gas cleaning plants in each pot line is then exhausted through the same 250-ft stacks as is the ventilation air.

Casting plant

The casting plant is designed to convert the whole output of the smelter to ingots for extrusion, rolling and remelting. The alloys made will be mainly pure metal types Al–Mg–Si types. The heart of the plant is a furnace/casting machine complex, which consists of three large holding furnaces, a vertical D.C. casting machine and a remelt ingot-casting machine.

The furnaces each hold 57 tons of metal, are fired by natural gas, tilt for pouring and have doors along the whole length of one long side to facilitate charging of scrap and alloy additions, and stirring and skimming the charge. Hot metal will be transferred to the furnaces by siphon. Metal can be transferred from any of the furnaces direct to the casting machine, or to any of the other furnaces. Two of the furnaces can be used to feed the remelt ingot-casting machine. Transfer to the D.C. casting machine, or to other furnaces, will be by water-cooled re-fractory-lined troughs. Transfer to the remelt ingot-casting machine will be by uncooled refractory-lined troughs.

Generally, all metal cast will be fluxed with a mixture of chlorine and nitrogen, chosen to give adequate degassing and cleaning of the metal while minimizing chlorine emissions to atmosphere.

It is expected that the bulk of the production will be made on the casting machine: this has a pit which is about 120 in × 108 in in cross-section, and ingots up to 270 in long can be cast. At all times the maximum number of moulds that can be incorporated will be used in order to maximize productivity on this machine. The remelt ingot-casting machine has water-cooled cast iron moulds mounted on an endless chain, and produces ingots weighing about 50 lb.

In addition to the above, there is a panning centre at which metal can be poured direct from crucibles into pans, each holding about 3500 lb. This centre is, however, primarily intended to allow either high- or low-grade metal from the pot rooms to be segregated for later internal use. Panned metal will not normally be sold.

After casting, ingots will be removed from the pit with a 20-ton capacity crane. Rolling ingots will be cast to length and shipped in this condition to other Alcan-affiliated plants for rolling. Extrusion ingot will be inspected after casting and then homogenized. The homogenizing furnace is radiant-tube, natural gas fired, and has a load capacity of 90 tons of ingot. The ingots will be homogenized in full cast lengths. After homogenizing, extrusion ingot will be sawn to length by use of a high-speed saw, which is designed to automatically cut ingots from 3- to 12-in diameter and to stamp and rack the cut lengths for bundling and weighing. It is expected that ingots will be shipped from Lynemouth by road.

Generally, movement of metal in the plant will be by forklift trucks with capacities ranging from 7000 to 25 000 lb. These trucks will also be used, where possible, for charging, skimming, stirring and cleaning furnaces.

The Magnetherm process, Marignac, France

F. Trocmé

Société Générale du Magnésium, Paris, France

669.721.34

Synopsis

A general summary is presented of the Magnetherm process for the production of magnesium. The treatment of dolomite, bauxite and ferrosilicon is outlined, together with the reduction of dolomite in magnesium. A brief description of the foundry operation is given.

Description of the process

General outline

Magnesium is obtained by the reduction, by ferrosilicon, of calcined dolomite

$$MgO, CaO + (Fe)Si \rightarrow SiO_2, 2CaO + Mg \nearrow + (Fe)$$

This reaction being endothermic, calories are provided by an electrical furnace. The reaction takes place under vacuum, at temperatures of 1500–1600°C. The magnesium is produced in the gaseous form, becoming liquid at about 800°C on the walls of an air-cooled condenser. At start-up, or in the event of any stoppage, the condenser can be brought back to this temperature by a heater.

Magnesium trickling from the walls of the condenser is recovered in a water-cooled crucible, situated beneath the condenser, where it solidifies at a temperature below 650°C. The by-product lime silicates have a high melting point (> 2000°C). The addition of calcined alumina yields a double silicate of lime and alumina, melting at a lower temperature (1500–1600°C), and its use avoids secondary reactions detrimental to the proper working of the condenser, which would reduce output.

Iron in the ferrosilicon at 75% Si used for the reduction passes to the slag as ferrosilicon at 22% Si (a greater amount would cause an increase in the energy consumption).

Raw magnesium, solidified in the crucible, contains impurities (magnesia, nitrates) which are eliminated in the foundry. Refining is carried out in the reaction crucible heated in a gas furnace in a SO_2 atmosphere with various fluxes. The magnesium is cast as 99.8% Mg ingots.

517

The particularly noteworthy aspect of the Magnetherm process lies in the reaction taking place in the liquid phase, the electrode being immersed in liquid slag transmitting the heat necessary to the various elements combined in the reaction. A flowsheet of the process is given in Fig. 1. Heating of the bath is by the Joule effect.

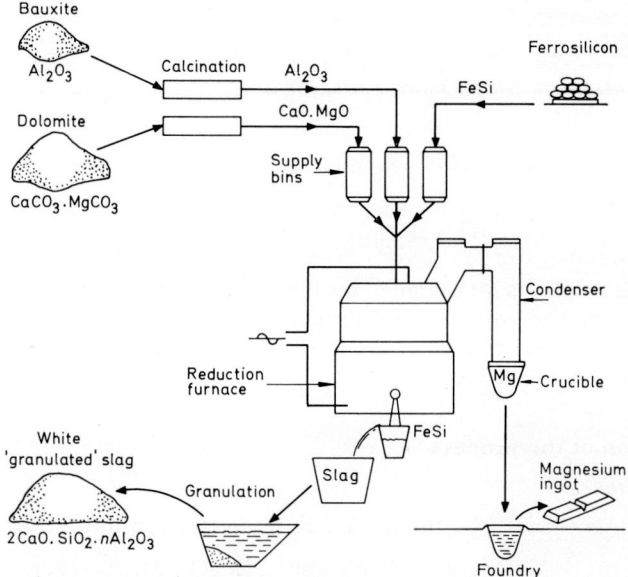

Fig. 1

Description of the installation

Reception and treatment of raw materials

DOLOMITE

Raw dolomite is a double lime and magnesia carbonate. To obtain CaO–MgO containing about 39% MgO, the carbonates must be reduced by heat in a revolving calcination furnace. The decarbonization reaction is

$$CO_3Mg, \; CO_3Ca \rightarrow 2CO_2 + MgO, \; CaO$$

The raw dolomite, stockpiled in a natural bunker near the furnace, is picked up at the bottom of the bunker by a conveyor belt and directed to the washer (washing is intended to eliminate fines which disturb the operation in the revolving furnace and cause, in the electric furnace, dust flows toward the condenser). It is then picked up by the same conveyor and delivered to a hopper on top of the calcination oven, the level of the dolomite in the hopper starting or stopping the conveyor.

A vibrating distributor, at the bottom of the hopper, feeds a scale with a moving hopper, emptying being controlled by a time switch. The quantity of dolomite introduced to the hopper is predetermined by an attachment to the scale. When this quantity is reached, the vibrating distributor is stopped. The time switch regulates the frequency of the emptying cycles.

The dolomite then goes to the revolving furnace, which is heated by natural gas or oil. After roasting, it emerges at a temperature of 900°C and falls into lagged containers (in this way the dolomite is kept warm until it reaches the reduction furnace, thus enabling savings in electrical energy and a lessening of the humidity of the calcined product; as raw materials are introduced into the reduction furnace under vacuum, it is necessary to keep heat loss to a minimum).

Dust swept off by the gases burned in the calcination furnace is recovered in a dust chamber and a multi-cyclone and discarded.

BAUXITE

Bauxite is dried in a calcination furnace to eliminate crystallization water. It is fed to the furnace in the same way as the dolomite. The heating, control and de-dusting are the same for the two furnaces. The calcined bauxite is emptied continuously at about 600–700°C in heated containers.

FERROSILICON

Granulated ferrosilicon 75% Si is used for the reduction. It is kept in special containers.

Reduction of dolomite in magnesium

Operation in the reduction furnace is almost continuous, with one operation every 24 h. Twice a day, in the middle and at the end of the operation, the feeding of raw materials is stopped, power to the furnace is reduced to just enough to maintain the oven temperature, the oven is returned to atmospheric pressure under argon so that excess slag can be discarded, together with the residual ferrosilicon. Once a day, at the end of the operation, the whole apparatus, the movable condenser-crucible containing the magnesium produced, is taken from the furnace and replaced by another assembly—empty, clean and preheated to the correct temperature.

The crucible containing the magnesium is emptied in the smelter, the condenser and heater then being taken for cleaning. All raw materials are introduced under vacuum to the furnace. Dolomite and bauxite, kept hot in the containers, are introduced to the furnace periodically, but ferrosilicon is introduced continuously, their flow being controlled by vibrating distributors.

The introduction of raw materials takes place according to a theoretical programme which corresponds to the working of the furnace. The setting and control of the feed are carried out by an electrical apparatus which operates on the basis of constant weighing of the dolomite, bauxite and ferrosilicon containers, which rest on electronic weighing machines.

The reduction furnace is, essentially, a cylinder made of soldered steel sheets, with a bottom and a lid. The junction between the two constituent parts (the bucket and the roof) is watertight. The bucket is lined inside with a foundation plate made of carbon blocks to ensure good electrical conductivity and heat and chemical resistance to the slag. The foundation plate is separated from the bucket steel sheet by a refractory and insulating lining. The carbon foundation plate constitutes one of the electrodes of the furnace and has four copper leads.

The roof is lined inside by a refractory concrete lining and outside by in-sulating bricks. It has several openings—one to let in the second electrode; one, a large one, to let magnesium vapours into the condenser; and two for raw materials to pass into the furnace.

Each oven has a condensation chamber, its principal components being a condenser, in which the magnesium condenses partly in the liquid state, and the steel crucible, in which the magnesium solidifies; it is cooled by a water jet. Ancillary components include vacuum pumps with connecting pipes and a water-cooling circuit for the crucible, the electrode and the various parts of the furnace (lining, joints, etc.). The installation also has two moving cranes—one to move the raw materials containers and the other to move the whole condenser–heater–crucible assembly and the slag tank.

At the furnace exit the slag (silico-aluminate of lime) is melted in cascade into two tanks. The residual ferrosilicon accumulates in the first, and the slag over-flows into the second. The slag is poured in the liquid state into a granulation installation by water jet. After collection of the residual ferrosilicon and granula-tion of the slag, the tanks and the hoppers still contain a little slag, which fuses and breaks up on contact with air. They are easily dealt with at the cleaning installation.

Foundry

The foundry aims, essentially, to refine the metal by eliminating dirt and calcium by refusion and flux treatment; to get the metal to the desired standard—if necessary by appropriate additions to yield the alloys required; and to melt it in ingots or sheets to facilitate its transport.

The solidified magnesium contained in the crucible is remelted in a furnace heated by natural gas; it is maintained under flux during the whole process to avoid burning as it comes into contact with air.

When the metal is completely melted, the bath is mixed by a mechanical mixer and decanted. Dross falls to the bottom of the crucible. After refining, the metal is fed by a pump to an ingot casting machine, flow taking place in an atmosphere of SO_2 in moulds preheated by gas burners.

Treatment of zinc leach plant residues by the jarosite process

G. Steintveit

Det Norske Zinkkompani, A/S, Odda, Norway

669.536.221

Synopsis

The jarosite process enables iron to be precipitated in acid solutions as crystalline compounds, which have been identified as being similar to naturally occurring carphosiderite and jarosite minerals. The process was developed to meet the requirement of hydrometallurgical residue treatment in electrolytic zinc plants.

A description is given of the jarosite process, together with operating flowsheets and test results. Modifications of the process are indicated.

In the hydrometallurgy of zinc, as practised up to recent times, zinc leach plant residue is defined as the insoluble part of the roasted zinc ore remaining after the zinc oxide and zinc sulphate components have been dissolved. This residue contains practically all the iron, from 8 to 20% of the zinc, from 30 to 40% of the copper and cadmium, and all the lead and silver present in the calcine.

The reason for leaving so much zinc, copper and cadmium in this leach residue is that the acidities and temperature during the leaching stages must be sufficiently low to avoid breaking up the zinc ferrites formed during the roasting process. Greater quantities of iron could be dissolved if a practical separation process of iron from zinc sulphate solutions were available. The presence of zinc ferrites reduces the leaching efficiencies of zinc, copper and cadmium, but the formation of these low-solubility iron compounds during roasting is, nevertheless, inevitable in the traditional hydrometallurgical zinc process.

The resulting leach plant residue with 18–24% zinc and 20–25% iron has been, in the past, sent to tailing ponds for storage, or has been treated by pyrometallurgical processes, such as slag fuming, Waelz processes or sulphation roasting, to recover the greater part of the remaining valuable components.

The main raw material for zinc production is marmatite, where FeS replaces ZnS isomorphically. The orebodies are also often very complex, containing iron minerals such as pyrites, marcasite or pyrrhotite, separation even by use of sophisticated flotation techniques being difficult. The zinc metallurgist must, therefore, in most cases, be prepared to treat flotation concentrates with iron contents averaging between 7 and 14%.

The loss of valuable metals in the residue has therefore been more or less proportional to the iron in the ore—hence, residue treatment has become of vital importance.

The capital expenditure of pyrometallurgical plants for residue treatment has always been high, and could not be generally justified at electrolytic zinc plants. With steadily rising production costs, particularly for pyrometallurgical operations, it became quite clear that, for electrolytic zinc plants, hydrometallurgical residue treatment would represent the key to profitable operation, and the ideal procedure would be one that eventually might be completely integral within the leaching circuit, thereby simplifying the entire production process.

The jarosite process

The writer's company, to meet these requirements, has made use of the *jarosite process*,[3] by which it is possible to precipitate iron in acid solutions as crystalline compounds, identified as similar in structure to the carphosiderite and jarosite minerals found in nature.

By this separation process it became a practical proposition to separate large quantities of iron from zinc in solutions, and it was no longer necessary to limit the acid strength and the temperature during the leaching of zinc calcine. We are now in the position to dissolve the ferrites, obtain high extraction efficiencies of zinc, copper and cadmium, and separate the truly insoluble compounds of the zinc ore from the soluble zinc, copper, cadmium and iron in a residue where the lead and silver values may be concentrated. The residue obtained after this new high-acidity, high-temperature leach is essentially a quite different type of residue with such a high enrichment of the valuable elements Pb and Ag in the calcine that it may be economic to process it to recover these metals. This is an additional benefit of the hydrometallurgical residue process.

The analysis of the residue from the hot acid leaching is, of course, dependent on the calcine composition. Typical figures of the residue for lead–silver bearing residues would be Zn, 2–5%; Fe, 10–20%; Pb, 10–30%; Ag, 500–1500 g/t; SiO_2, 10–25%; and SO_4, 15–25%.

Easy control of sulphate balance in the leaching circuit is also attained through the precipitation of the complex basic iron sulphates.

The chemical reactions which may take place during the hydrolysis of iron are summarized below.

$$3Fe_2(SO_4)_3 + 6H_2O = 6Fe(OH)SO_4 + 3H_2SO_4 \qquad (1)$$
$$4Fe(OH)SO_4 + 4H_2O = 2Fe_2(OH)_4SO_4 + 2H_2SO_4 \qquad (2)$$
$$2Fe(OH)SO_4 + 2Fe_2(OH)_4\ SO_4 + 2NH_4OH = (NH_4)_2\ Fe_6(SO_4)_4(OH)_{12} \qquad (3)$$
$$2Fe(OH)SO_4 + 2Fe_2(OH)_4\ SO_4 + Na_2SO_4 + 2H_2O =$$
$$Na_2Fe_6(SO_4)_4(OH)_{12} + H_2SO_4 \qquad (4)$$
$$2Fe(OH)SO_4 + 2Fe_2(OH)_4SO_4 + 4H_2O = (H_3O)_2\ Fe_6(SO_4)_4(OH)_{12} \qquad (5)$$
$$(1) + (2) + (3):$$
$$3Fe_2(SO_4)_3 + 10\ H_2O + 2NH_4OH = (NH_4)_2\ Fe_6(SO_4)_4(OH)_{12} + 5H_2SO_4 \qquad (6)$$
$$\text{(Ammonium jarosite)}$$

(1)+(2)+(4):
$$3Fe_2(SO_4)_3 + 12\,H_2O + Na_2SO_4 = Na_2Fe_6(SO_4)_4(OH)_{12} + 6H_2SO_4 \quad (7)$$
(Sodium jarosite)

(1)+(2)+(5):
$$3Fe_2(SO_4)_3 + 14\,H_2O = (H_3O)_2Fe_6(SO_4)_4(OH)_{12} + 5H_2SO_4 \quad (8)$$
(Carphosiderite)
$$ZnO + H_2SO_4 = ZnSO_4 + H_2O \quad (9)$$
$$Fe_2O_3 + 3H_2SO_4 = Fe_2(SO_4)_3 + 3H_2O \quad (10)$$

(6)+5(9):
$$3Fe_2(SO_4)_3 + 5\,ZnO + 2NH_4OH + 5H_2O =$$
$$(NH_4)_2\,Fe_6(SO_4)_4(OH)_{12} + 5ZnSO_4 \quad (11)$$

3 . (6)+5 . (10):
$$4Fe_2(SO_4)_3 + 5Fe_2O_3 + 6NH_4OH + 15\,H_2O = 3(NH_4)_2Fe_6(SO_4)_4(OH)_{12} \quad (12)$$
(Ammonium jarosite)

The progress of the iron precipitation at pH 1·5 and in the presence of the ions NH_4^+, Na^+ follows the pattern of the curve shown in Fig. 1 for a batch operation. After an initial period of about one hour, precipitation follows quite rapidly during the next 2 h.

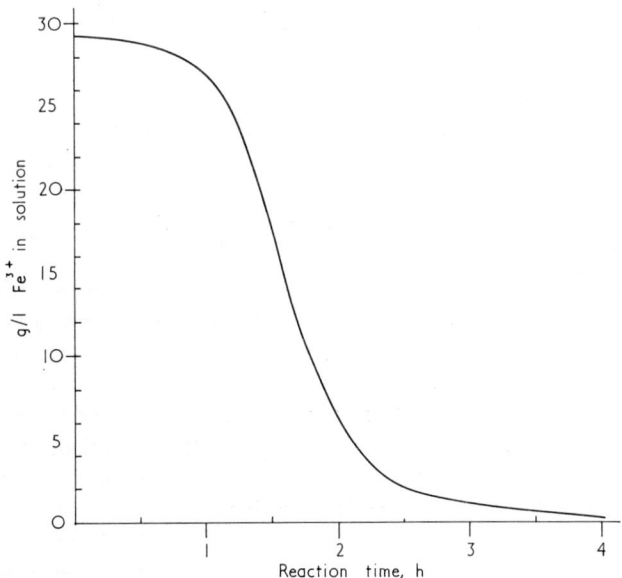

Fig. 1 Progress of precipitation of iron as jarosite. Solution: 29·1 g/l Fe^{3+}, 45 g/l H_2SO_4

In a continuous operation the same precipitation is effected by use of at least three stages, keeping to the optimum pH in each stage.

The jarosite process was developed in Norway by Det Norske Zinkkompani and in Tasmania by Electrolytic Zinc Co. of Australasia virtually at the same time: it results from numerous experiments, carried out over many years, on the problem of iron precipitation; curiously, the investigations were independent of each other.

The Spanish zinc plant, Asturiana de Zinc, designed by Det Norske Zinkkompani in 1958–60, faced an expansion programme in 1963. The only desulphurized raw material then available was, however, zinc sinter from a newly erected Robson sinter machine. Most of the iron in the sinter is present as soluble oxides, as this material does not contain any ferrites. The sinter is therefore not a suitable material for the hydrometallurgy of zinc, unless the separation of the dissolved iron is fully controlled.

Det Norske Zinkkompani was a consultant for this company, and introduced the new iron precipitation process at the Spanish zinc plant in April, 1964. Full-scale plant tests could be carried out subsequently with sinter and flash-roasted calcine as raw materials, the normal zinc leach plant residue being treated at the same time.

Asturiana de Zinc was thus the first plant to be given the right to adopt the jarosite process: operation has been quite successful there, and the Spanish sinter has proved to be an excellent neutralization material for the hydrolysis of the iron.

Gradually, a number of electrolytic zinc plants have shown interest in the process, which is in use or under consideration in the following zinc plants: Canadian Electrolytic Zinc, Canada; Ruhr Zinc GmbH, Germany; Weser Zink GmbH, Germany; Ecstall Mining Co., Canada; Société Prayon, Belgium; Met-Mex-Penoles, Mexico; Kempensche Zink, Holland; Outokumpu Oy, Finland; and Asarco Mexicana, Mexico.

The Risdon residue treatment plant, described recently,[1] is a typical example of a residue plant added to the main flowsheet of the leaching plant.

At Det Norske Zinkkompani we have integrated the treatment of the residue into the leaching circuit, a description of the plant having been given earlier.[2] The flowsheet of the operation is given in Fig. 2. The system consists of a neutral leach (I), dissolution of about 80% of the soluble zinc in the calcine being aimed at. At the same time minor quantities of iron and other impurities are precipitated to produce a neutral solution. After separation, the residue is subjected to hot acid leaching (II) at temperatures of 90–95°C and acidities of 40–80 g/l H_2SO_4 to dissolve the remaining zinc.

Different calcines may have different solubilities, and it is necessary to have the exact acidity to attain optimum extraction. Concentrated H_2SO_4 is added corresponding to the general sulphate balance. The insoluble Pb–Ag residue, normally amounting to 10–12% of the calcine added to the neutral leach, is separated, and in the remaining zinc–iron solution iron is precipitated as jarosite (IV).

At the acidities maintained during the hydrolysis of iron (pH about 1·5) only the acid-soluble zinc and iron contents of this calcine will be dissolved; the zinc ferrite present will not be decomposed. This does not influence iron precipitation, but less extraction is possible from this part of the roasted ore, which will affect the overall leaching efficiencies.

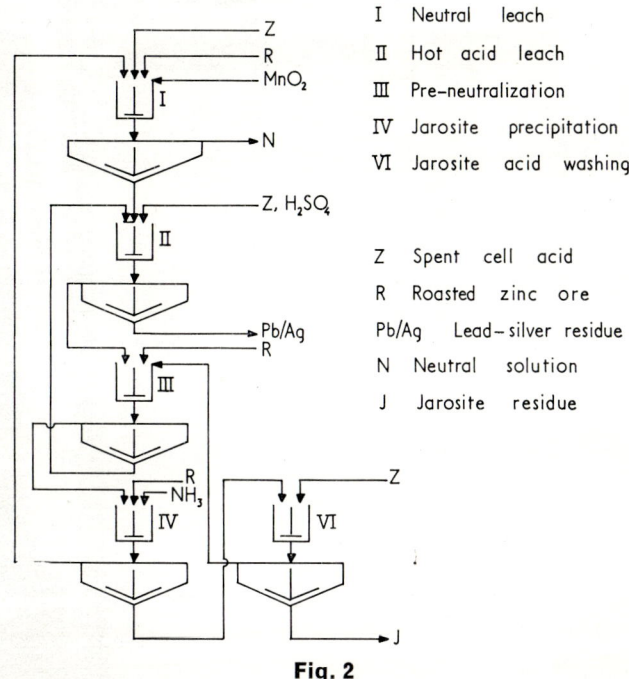

I   Neutral   leach

II   Hot   acid   leach

III   Pre-neutralization

IV   Jarosite   precipitation

VI   Jarosite   acid   washing

Z   Spent   cell   acid

R   Roasted   zinc   ore

Pb/Ag   Lead–silver residue

N   Neutral   solution

J   Jarosite   residue

Fig. 2

See Fig 4

To reduce the quantity of calcine in this process step an intermediate pre-neutralization stage has been introduced (III). The thickened residue from this stage is returned to hot acid leaching. A further introduction is that of acid washing of the jarosite residue (VI).

The acidities and temperatures are about the same as for hot acid leaching, whereby the ferrites are broken up, whereas the jarosite residue itself, being insoluble, is left unchanged. The resolution of impurities by acid treatment of the residue does not exceed tolerable limits.

Practical experience with acid washing in plant operation has shown that the insoluble zinc content in the final jarosite residue is lowered to 2–3% zinc. The final residue will be pure yellow, the natural colour of the jarosites (Fig. 3). The extraction efficiencies of zinc, taking into account losses in the acid-washed residue, reach 98·5%.

Some of the new zinc plants mentioned above have been constructed along the lines of the process flowsheet described, and some operating plants currently adopting the jarosite process will convert their operations along similar lines.

Other plants, which are well established with regard to batch operations, will follow the system presented in Fig. 4. This system also has the jarosite process

Fig. 3

integrated in it, but instead of starting with a neutral leach with excess calcine
addition, hot acid leaching is the first leaching stage (II). In the simpler version
iron precipitation (IV) follows immediately without separation of the insoluble
residue, and the last traces of iron and other impurities are removed by a final
neutralization at pH 4·5–5·0 (V). The neutral solution for the zinc dust purification is then separated from the residue. The batch plants have already obtained

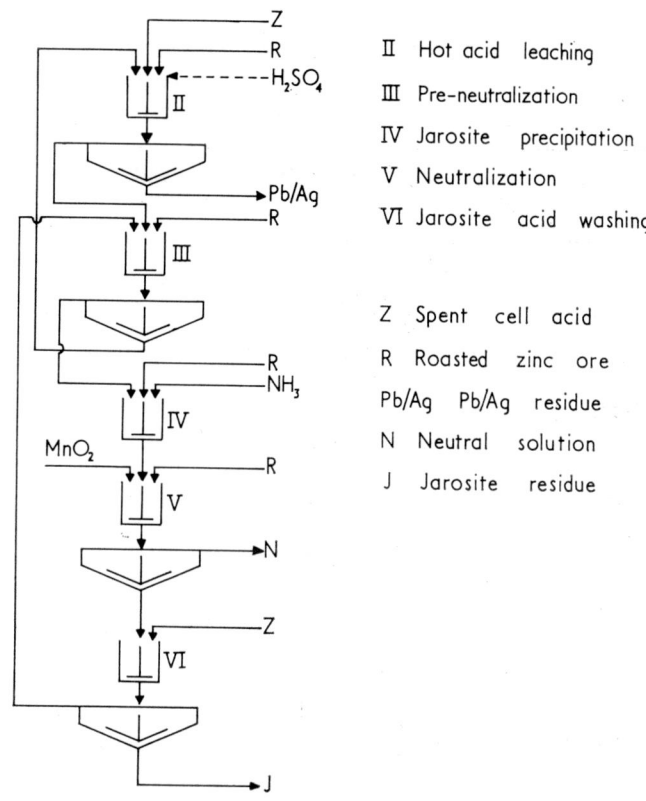

II   Hot acid leaching

III   Pre-neutralization

IV   Jarosite precipitation

V   Neutralization

VI   Jarosite acid washing

Z   Spent cell acid

R   Roasted zinc ore

Pb/Ag   Pb/Ag residue

N   Neutral solution

J   Jarosite residue

Fig. 4

increased metal recoveries by making minor modifications to convert their operation to the simple version described, and without separation of the different stages. Depending on the raw material composition and local conditions, it may be justifiable to separate the Pb–Ag residue and include pre-neutralization and/or jarosite acid-washing stages.

To evaluate the different possibilities and process parameters we use standard tests in a pilot plant, and further calculations from these data indicate the optimum system. Results of some leaching tests carried out recently with a calcine of the composition Zn 58·9%, Fe 11·5%, Cu 0·44%, Cd 0·15%, Pb 0·40% and Ag 0·005% are presented in Table 1.

The extraction efficiencies of Zn, Cu and Cd are given for the simple direct leaching procedure, for the more elaborate system (1.1–1.4), and for the system starting with the neutral leach (2.1–2.3). It should be emphasized that the simple procedure with neutral leach (2.1) gives a considerably better extraction than simple direct leaching (1.1). The results are, however, comparable when sufficient process stages are added.

The arrangement of a continuous system starting with a Neutral Leach is con-

Table 1

Process		Extraction efficiency, %		
		Zn	Cu	Cd
1.1 Direct leaching	Stages (II), (IV) and (V) combined	93·1	27·1	81·1
1.2 Direct leaching	Stages (II) and (IV) combined; stage (V) separated and residue returned to (II)	97·0	77·3	80·0
1.3 Direct leaching	Stages (II), (III), (IV) and (V) all separated; residue stage (V) returned to (II)	97·9	80·7	86·2
1.4 Direct leaching	Stage (II), (IV) and (V) combined; residue treated in stage (V)	98·0	91·0	91·1
2.1 With neutral leach	Stage (I), (II) and (IV) all separated	96·9	83·7	85·0
2.2 With neutral leach	Stage (I), (II), (III) and (IV) all separated	97·9	84·2	87·1
2.3 With neutral leach	Stage (I), (II), (IV) and (VI) all separated	98·2	91·1	91·4

Stage (I), neutral leach; stage (II), hot acid leach; stage (III), pre-neutralization; stage (IV), jarosite precipitation; stage (V), neutralization; state (VI), jarosite acid washing.

sidered more economic with regard to equipment, and may therefore be preferable for new plants.

References

1. HAIGH C. J. AND PICKERING R. W. The treatment of zinc plant residue at the Risdon Works of the Electrolytic Zinc Company of Australasia Limited. In *AIME World symp. on mining and metallurgy of lead & zinc* COTTERILL C. H. AND CIGAN J. M. eds (New York: AIME, 1970), vol. 2, 423–48.
2. STEINTVEIT G. Electrolytic zinc plant and residue recovery Det Norske Zinkkompani A/S. In *AIME World symp. on mining and metallurgy of lead & zinc* COTTERILL C. H. AND CIGAN J. M. eds (New York: AIME, 1970), vol. 2, 223–46.
3. STEINTVEIT G. Jarosittprosessen. *Tidsskr. Kjemi Bergv. Metall.*, **31,** April 1971, 18–20.

High-temperature reduction of sulphur dioxide gases with pulverized coal

R. Malmström Dr. Sc.
T. Tuominen Dr. Sc.

Both of Outokumpu Oy, Pori, Finland

661.21:669.015.7(471.17)

Synopsis

In the smelting of non-ferrous sulphide ores the large amounts of sulphur dioxide produced raise pollution problems if no market exists near the smelter for sulphuric acid or liquid SO_2. In such cases a process by which sulphur could be recovered directly in elemental form would be particularly attractive.

Outokumpu Oy has investigated the possible reduction of copper or nickel flash-smelting gases with pulverized coal and the adaptation of its experience of sulphur gas handling to the reduced gases. Studies have led to a process in which SO_2 gas reduction is carried out in the furnace uptake at 1300–1350°C. In addition to the SO_2 reduction reaction, various side reactions take place, so the gases, after passing through a waste-heat boiler for cooling and an electrostatic precipitator for cleaning, are catalysed to convert the sulphur compounds into elemental sulphur, which is condensed by cooling.

The SO_2 reduction process described is based on the use of pulverized coal as the reductant, but the use of light virgin naphtha, as employed for reducing smelter gases at the Kokkola plant, can also be considered.

The reduction process was run in a pilot system having a gas flow of 3000 Nm^3/h: 85–90% of the sulphur in the gas could be converted into elemental form. The same high-temperature reduction process has been found to be suitable for the reduction of roaster gases.

In the pyrometallurgical treatment of non-ferrous sulphide ores, e.g. copper, nickel, lead and zinc sulphides, the large yields of sulphur dioxide can be used for the production of either sulphuric acid or liquid SO_2. If, however, no market exists near the smelter, difficulties may arise. A process by which sulphur can be recovered directly in elemental form would be most attractive. In fact, numerous patents have been granted for processes designed to recover elemental sulphur from smelter gases by use of gaseous, liquid or solid reductants, but only some of these methods have been worked on a large scale. These applications include some processes based on the use of an incandescent coke bed for reduction of

S 529

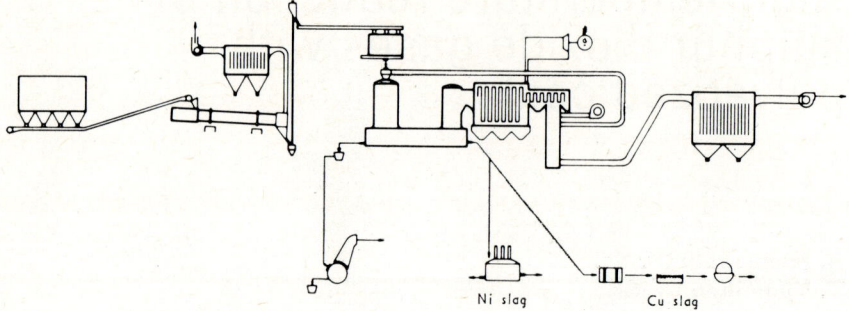

Fig. 1 Copper and nickel flash-smelter

sulphur dioxide directly[1–4] or after concentration,[3–6] and some which employ
natural gas as the high-temperature reductant[7] or for catalytic reduction of
SO_2.[8, 9]

In the Outokumpu flash-smelting method[10, 11, 12] (see Fig. 1), when processing copper or nickel concentrates to 60–80% matte, about 80% of the sulphur
content in the feed is oxidized to sulphur dioxide, the furnace gases having a
uniform flow and, without oxygen enrichment, a sulphur dioxide concentration
of about 10–15 vol per cent. The gases are normally used for the production
of sulphuric acid, but they could also, because of the high SO_2 concentration
and low oxygen content, be an ideal feed for a direct reduction process.

In the Outokumpu sulphur process[12, 13, 14] (see Fig. 2), when processing pyrite

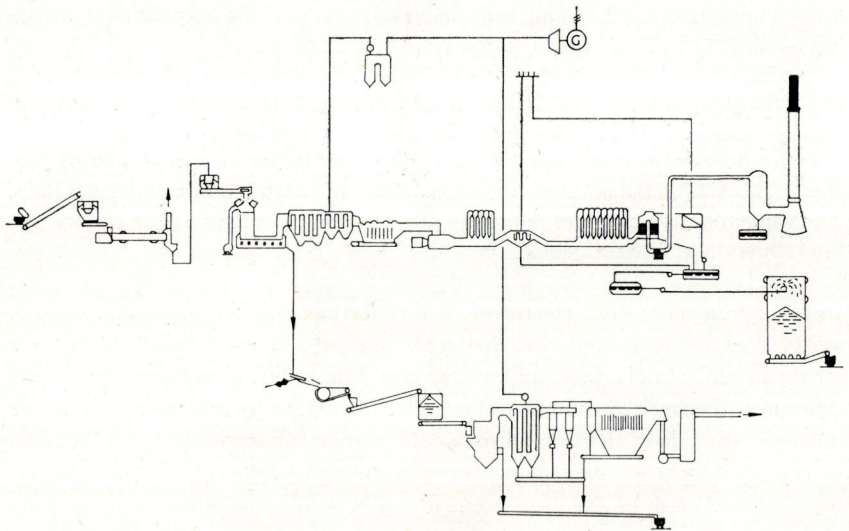

Fig. 2 Outokumpu sulphur plant

concentrates the furnace gases containing sulphur and sulphur compounds are cooled, cleaned and catalysed and the sulphur vapour is condensed to give elemental sulphur, the recovery being about 90% of the sulphur content in the gases.

It is quite understandable that Outokumpu Oy should, in recent years, have investigated the possibilities of reducing copper or nickel flash-smelting gases with a suitable reductant, and to adopt the existing 'knowhow' in sulphur gas handling on the reduced gases. This can be achieved by a process in which the SO_2 gas reduction is carried out in suspension in the flash-smelting furnace uptake at 1300–1350°C with pulverized coal.[15] Because of various side reactions that take place during the reduction, the gases, after passing through a waste-heat boiler for cooling and an electrostatic precipitator for cleaning, are catalysed to convert the sulphur compounds into elemental sulphur, which is then condensed by cooling.

Reduction reactions and equilibria

The reduction of sulphur dioxide to elemental sulphur by carbon takes place according to the overall reaction

$$SO_2 + C = \tfrac{1}{2}S_2 + CO_2 \qquad (1)$$

It is evident, however, that sulphur dioxide cannot be reduced by means of carbon at any temperature without simultaneous reduction of a part of the carbon dioxide, the consecutive reduction reactions being

$$CO_2 + C = 2CO \qquad (2)$$
$$SO_2 + 2CO = 2CO_2 + \tfrac{1}{2}S_2 \qquad (3)$$

Simultaneously, there are several side reactions forming carbon disulphide and carbon oxysulphide:

$$CO + \tfrac{1}{2}S_2 = COS \qquad (4)$$
$$2COS = CO_2 + CS_2 \qquad (5)$$

From thermodynamic calculations it appears that the complete reduction of sulphur dioxide by solid carbon will, theoretically, take place at any temperature. Results actually obtained, however, will depend on reaction rates. According to Lepsoe,[6] the reduction rate is, at lower temperatures, controlled by the chemical reaction rate, but above 1200°C the rate appears to be controlled by the gas diffusion rate. For high-temperature reduction it may therefore be concluded that the reduction rate will be the same for any type of carbon, provided that the same amount of surface is exposed in each case.

When reducing sulphur dioxide by liquid or gaseous hydrocarbons, the reactions are more complicated, due to the hydrogen-containing species in equilibria. For example, with natural gas or methane the overall reduction reaction can be written

$$2SO_2 + CH_4 = 2H_2O + CO_2 + S_2 \qquad (6)$$

Also, in this case, the side reactions are generating CO, COS and CS_2, but they are also forming hydrogen-containing compounds:

$$SO_2 + CH_4 = H_2S + CO + H_2O \qquad (7)$$
$$2H_2O + \tfrac{1}{2}S_2 = 2H_2 + SO_2 \qquad (8)$$

Thermodynamic calculations show that the reduction with hydrocarbons is less complete than the reduction with carbon due to the effect of water vapour on elemental sulphur according to the reaction

$$2H_2O + 1\tfrac{1}{2}S_2 = 2H_2S + SO_2 \qquad (9)$$

which decreases the conversion efficiency during catalysis of the reduced gases. Another difficulty with the use of hydrocarbons is the possibility of cracking the resultant soot, causing the produced sulphur to be 'off colour'. Fleming and Fitt,[7] for example, found that to avoid cracking with natural gas the reduction temperature should be at least 1250°C.

In order to obtain an efficient conversion of all the produced sulphur compounds to elemental sulphur, two conversion stages are necessary in all sulphur dioxide reduction processes. The first step at higher temperatures is for the purpose of reacting the carbon compounds and hydrogen with sulphur dioxide, according to reactions 10–12, and the second step at lower temperature for the reaction between hydrogen sulphide and sulphur dioxide, according to reaction 13:

$$2CO + SO_2 = \tfrac{1}{2}S_2 + 2CO_2 \qquad (10)$$
$$2COS + SO_2 = 1\tfrac{1}{2}S_2 + 2CO_2 \qquad (11)$$
$$2H_2 + SO_2 = \tfrac{1}{2}S_2 + 2H_2O \qquad (12)$$
$$2H_2S + SO_2 = 1\tfrac{1}{2}S_2 + 2H_2O \qquad (13)$$

From these reactions it is clear that to obtain maximum conversion of sulphur compounds to elemental sulphur the gases after reduction should contain reducing components, i.e. CO, COS, H_2 and H_2S twice the amount of SO_2 by volume, this optimum reduction ratio

$$\frac{CO + COS + H_2 + H_2S}{SO_2} = \frac{2}{1} \qquad (14)$$

thus giving the highest overall recovery of sulphur.

Outokumpu high-temperature reduction process

The high-temperature reduction of sulphur dioxide gases comprises the reduction of flash-smelting gases in the furnace uptake (or immediately after it) at a temperature of at least 1300°C by means of pulverized coal evenly suspended in the gas stream with distributors. The reduced gases are then cooled, cleaned and catalysed to convert all sulphur compounds into elemental sulphur, which is condensed by cooling.

A relatively large amount of laboratory and pilot-plant development work for the reduction process was done at the Outokumpu Metallurgical Research Centre at Pori. The process was tested during the period 1968–70 on the pilot-plant scale with all the units necessary for a complete process, the sulphur content of the flash-smelting gases being equal to a sulphur production capacity of about 5–6 t/day. The flowsheet of the pilot plant is shown in Fig. 3.

Pilot-plant equipment

FLASH-SMELTING

The pilot furnace comprises a vertical reaction shaft of 1·5-m internal diameter and 3·3-m height, a horizontal settling section with a bath area of 7·2 m^2 and a height of 1·2 m, and an uptake modified for reduction purposes. The length and the volume of the modified uptake are, respectively, 7·5 m and 8·6 m^3. The reaction shaft and settler are lined with magnesite brick backed by fireclay insulating brick. The uptake is lined with chrome–magnesite and magnesite brick backed by fireclay insulating brick. The dried concentrate from a gas-fired rotary kiln dryer, flux and air preheated to about 500°C are fed into the reaction shaft through a concentrate burner, where thorough mixing takes place.

The copper concentrate was smelted at a rate of 750 kg/h; to this were usually added flux materials at about 100 kg/h. The smelting products, matte and slag, were tapped into a sand bed. A typical analysis of the materials is given in Table 1.

Table 1   Typical analysis of concentrate and flash-smelting products

| | Analysis, % | | | | | |
	Cu	Fe	S	O	SiO$_2$	Fe^{3+}
Concentrate	10·7	39·5	42·8		5·7	
Matte	57·5	17·8	23·1	1·1	0·13	
Slag	1·0	46·4	0·5	13·6	26·5	8·6
Flue dust	13·6	26·6	24·0		12·0	

To balance the relatively large heat losses, auxiliary butane burners were situated in the settler roof and in the connexion point of the settler and reduction shaft (uptake).

SULPHUR DIOXIDE REDUCTION

The gases leaving the settler contained about 11–14% SO_2 and less than 0·5% O_2, the gas temperature being about 1250°C. Because the temperature required for reduction is higher, the gas temperature was increased to 1350°C by burning butane or pulverized coal before feeding the reductant.

Pulverized coal was dried in a fluidized-bed dryer by use of warm air at 60°C.

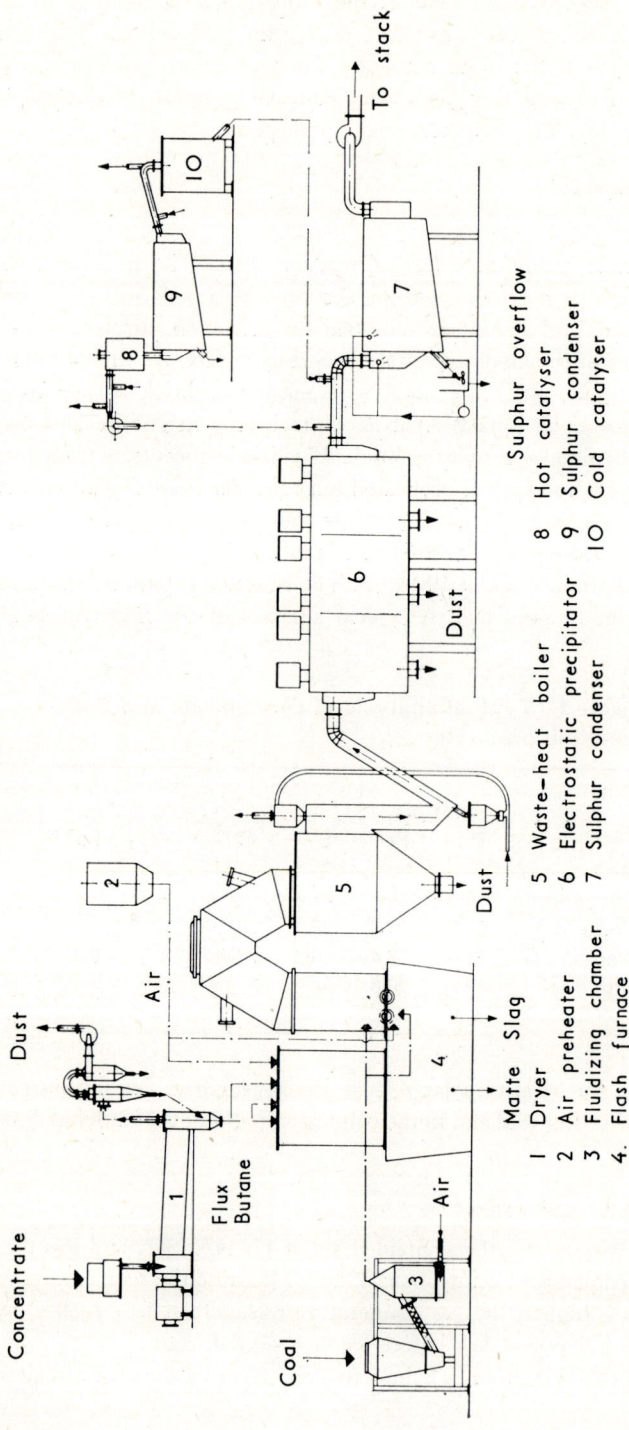

Fig. 3 Pilot-plant equipment

1 Dryer
2 Air preheater
3 Fluidizing chamber
4. Flash furnace
5 Waste–heat boiler
6 Electrostatic precipitator
7 Sulphur condenser
8 Hot catalyser
9 Sulphur condenser
10 Cold catalyser

Dried coal, containing about 2% moisture, was fed to the reduction shaft by an injection system connected to four tuyères. The coal feed rate was regulated automatically and a fairly uniform distribution was accomplished by use of individual injection lines to each of the four tuyères. The coal feed was about 200 kg/h, the coal feed–injection air ratio being about 12 kg coal/Nm^3 air.

GAS COOLING AND CLEANING

The reduced gases from the reduction shaft were first cooled in a waste-heat boiler. This boiler consists of a water-walled radiation section, cooling the gases from about 1250 to 600°C, followed by a convection section with horizontal tube banks to bring the temperature down to 350–300°C. The radiation section is cleaned with steam lances, and the convection section by shot cleaning. The boiler generates saturated steam at 40 atm pressure.

From the waste-heat boiler the gases were led through an electrostatic precipitator, the mean dust-collecting efficiency of which was found to be about 99·5%. The temperature of the cleaned sulphur gases was about 250–320°C.

From the electrostatic precipitator the main gas flow passes to a sulphur condenser—a low-pressure water-tube boiler generating steam at 4·5 atm pressure. Sulphur condenses and flows out from the bottom of the boiler. The desulphurized gases are led to the stack at a temperature of 140°C.

THE CATALYSIS SECTION

Part of the gases from the electrostatic precipitator outlet can be drawn off by a fan and passed through a catalysis train, which consists of a heater to raise the gas temperature to 420–440°C for high-temperature catalysis, a high-temperature catalyst chamber, a waste-heat boiler to cool the gases to 150°C, whereby the sulphur formed is condensed, a second heater to reheat the gases to 200–220°C for low-temperature catalysis and a low-temperature catalyst chamber. The gases are then led back to the main gas flow. In both catalyst chambers alumina-based catalyst was used.

Test results

RETENTION TIME

The effect of the retention time of the gases on the completeness of reduction reactions in the reduction shaft was determined by taking gas samples from various levels of the shaft and analysing the samples for H_2, H_2S, CO, CO_2, COS, SO_2, $O_2 + Ar$ and N_2 (CS_2 was never detected) by a gas chromatograph. From these values the reduction ratio mentioned above, the ratio of reducing gas components to sulphur dioxide content, was calculated. Some reduction ratio–retention time curves are presented in Fig. 4(a): at temperatures of about 1350°C the reactions are completed, i.e. the reduction ratio has reached the value 2, in about 2 sec. Lower temperatures resulted in much slower reduction reactions and, hence, incomplete reduction.

Fig. 5 shows the effect of temperature on equilibrium gas composition at the optimum reduction ratio in a typical reduction test, and Fig. 6 the effect of temperature and coal feed on the reduction ratio, showing the importance of reducing the gases to the reduction ratio 2, thus keeping the sulphur losses in off-gases to a minimum.

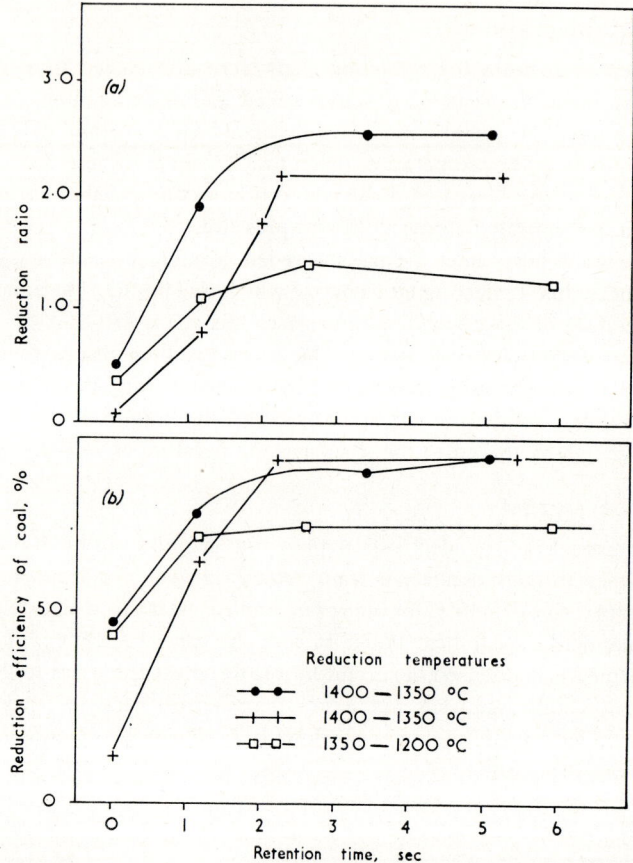

Fig. 4 Reduction ratio and reduction efficiency of coal versus retention time

COAL EFFICIENCY

In the reduction tests two types of pulverized coal were studied to ascertain their suitability for the reduction process. From their chemical and grain size analyses (Table 2) it is apparent that coal A is somewhat finer than coal B. In reduction tests, however, it was found that the reactivity of both coals was of the same order, reduction efficiencies calculated on the basis of the material balance as well as on that of gas analysis being always about 85–90% if the temperature was approximately 1350°C (see Fig. 4(b)). The reduction efficiency of the coal remains constant even if the reduction ratio varies from about 1·0 to 2·5.

In the reduction tests it was concluded that, in addition to fineness, other qualities are required of the coal in order to optimize the reduction process, e.g. high carbon content and relatively low hydrogen content to minimize side reactions in the catalysis section, low ash content and sufficiently high ash fusion temperature to avoid problems with ash adhering to the waste-heat boiler tubes.

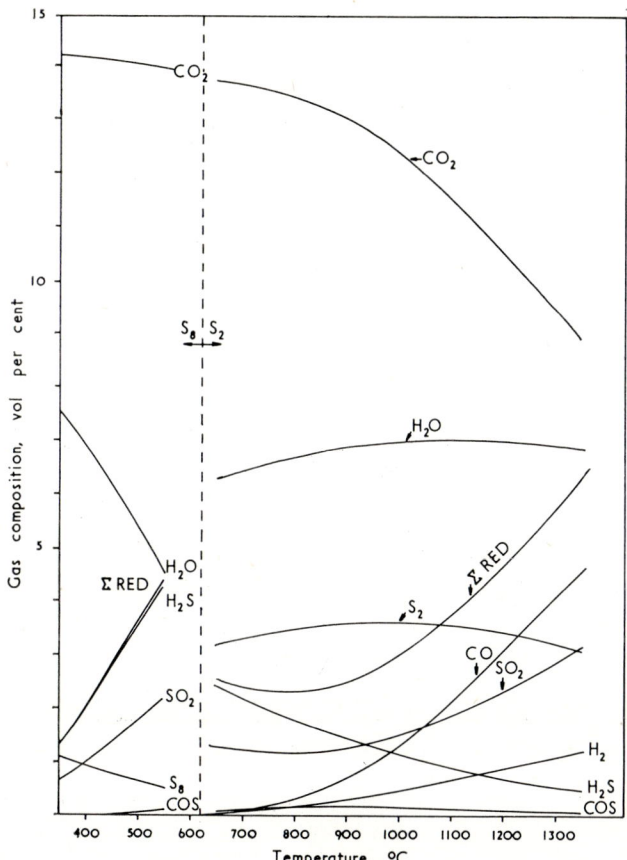

Fig. 5 Equilibrium gas composition for reduction of sulphur dioxide with pulverized coal ($\Sigma RED = CO + COS + H_2 + H_2S$)

FLUE DUSTS

In a normal oxidizing flash-smelting the flue dust is in oxide or sulphate form, but when SO_2 gases are reduced in the reduction shaft the dust is converted to sulphides as a result of the high sulphur pressure in the gases after reduction. In the reduction process the dust then contains copper and iron sulphides from smelting, and slag from completely combusted coal, as well as unreacted coal

s*

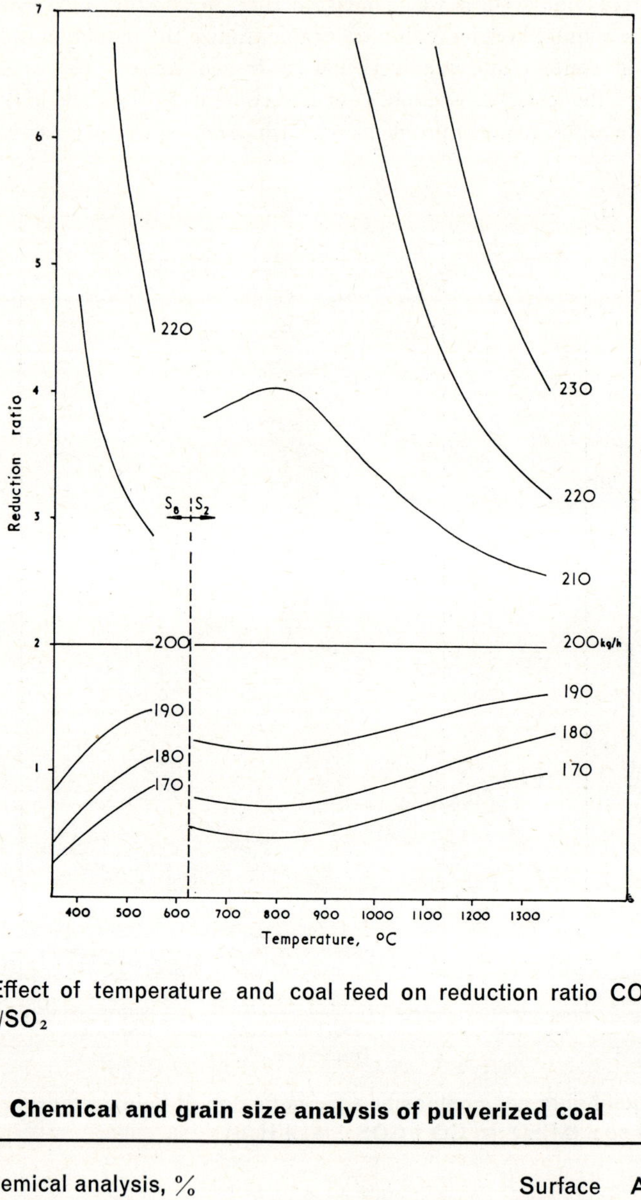

Fig. 6 Effect of temperature and coal feed on reduction ratio $COS+CO+H_2+H_2S/SO_2$

Table 2 Chemical and grain size analysis of pulverized coal

Coal	Chemical analysis, % C_{tot}	C_{fix}	H	O	S	N	Ash	Volatile matter	Surface area, cm^2/g	Average grain size, μm
A	71·5	56·0	2·8	9·9	0·85	8	11	28·7	38·000	~30
B	71·0	50·0	3·4	12·5	1·3	5	13	32·8	27·000	~40

Table 3 Chemical analysis of flue dusts from separate sections of electrostatic precipitator

Section no.	Dust quantity, %	Chemical analysis, %					
		Cu	Fe	S	Zn	SiO$_2$	C
1	95·4	13·5	26·7	24·0	3·6	12·0	14·0
2	3·8	14·5	25·3	23·2	5·2	11·4	13·0
3	0·8	13·8	23·3	24·4	6·2	11·5	12·0

particles. All these solid impurities have to be removed before sulphur condensing.

In the flash-smelting processes an electrostatic precipitator is used, and this was also found to be very suitable for the removal of unreacted carbon (Table 3). This can be seen in Fig. 7, where the mean dust-collection efficiency is compared with the carbon-collection efficiency during a test period, the average collection efficiencies for total dust and carbon being 99·5 and 99·6%, respectively. The reason for this easy removal of unreacted carbon compared with the difficulties associated with the elimination of soot formed by cracking of hydrocarbons lies in the larger grain size of the coal.

VOLATILE IMPURITIES

In flash-smelting some impurities are vaporized to a greater or lesser extent, and most are recovered in the flue dust. Some, nevertheless, pass through the whole

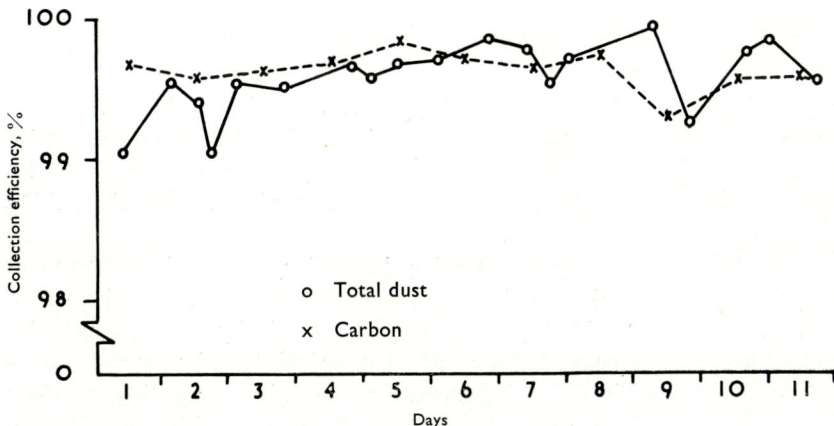

Fig. 7 Mean dust and carbon collection efficiencies of electrostatic precipitator during a test period

gas-handling equipment in a gaseous state and are recovered together with elemental sulphur. The distribution of arsenic and selenium in the reduction process (Table 4) shows that about 85% of the arsenic will be in elemental sulphur, whereas selenium and tellurium are to a greater part found in matte or slag, only 20–30% being in sulphur.

Special features

Coal injection and mixing

The dimensions of the uptake in production furnaces will be much larger than in the pilot plant because of the high gas volumes and the reduction retention times required. The larger cross-sectional area of the uptake also increases the difficulty of attaining rapid and complete mixing, and the reaction time necessary for coal reduction demands a higher uptake than in normal flash-smelting units. Because of the mixing problem it is essential to take into account the

Table 4 Distribution of volatile impurities

| | Distribution, % | | |
	As	Se	Te
In			
Concentrate	100	100	100
Out			
Matte	8	46	51
Slag	2	13	15
Flue dust	5	11	14
Crude sulphur	85	30	20

penetration characteristics of the coal jet. It was therefore decided to conduct model tests on the penetration and the mixing of coal in the uptakes with different configurations. Coal was injected through different types of nozzles with different coal–air ratios. The tests were carried out in a model flash-smelting furnace and in the pilot furnace.

On the basis of these tests the following observations were made. (1) For small coal–air ratios the coal injected into the furnace is analogous to a gas jet, whose penetration decreases with decreasing quantity and velocity of the gas and with increasing spreading angle. (2) For large coal–air ratios the jet has the characteristics of a liquid jet which is penetrating as a rather narrow jet, spreading only when its velocity is so low that the main gas flow can disintegrate it. This point approximately corresponds to maximum penetration. (3) For reduction large coal–air ratios are preferred because of the better penetration depth and more even total distribution of the coal in the reduction shaft. This also makes it possible to keep the excess air to a minimum.

Conclusions

The pilot tests confirmed the feasibility of reducing sulphur dioxide gases by pulverized coal in the uptake of a flash-smelting furnace. The temperature required for reduction has to be about 1350°C and the retention time for gases in the reduction shaft about 2 sec. The reduction efficiency of the coal varied between 85 and 90%. In addition to pulverized coal, liquid reductants have been investigated. Heavy oil has been tested, the only difficulty arising from soot formation due to cracking, which places considerable burdens on the gas-cleaning system. Light virgin naphtha, on the other hand, has for some years been used in the Outokumpu sulphur process at Kokkola for the reduction of the sulphur dioxide containing gases, the gas volumes handled being about 100 000 Nm^3/h.

The production of elemental sulphur from sulphur dioxide gases originating from other sources by the process is also possible. Roaster gases usually contain free oxygen, which has to be removed by combustion before reduction of sulphur dioxide. The reduction of roaster gases, too, has been proved on the pilot-plant scale, the results being comparable with those from the reduction of flash-smelting gases. In the pilot-plant tests it has been found that the sulphur gas handling system used in the Outokumpu sulphur process is suitable for the gases from the high-temperature reduction process.

The process would be particularly attractive as an efficient procedure to avoid pollution problems at sites where no market exists for sulphuric acid or liquid sulphur dioxide. High-temperature reduction with pulverized coal has been developed to the extent that the first commercial plant to handle flash-smelting gases is now under construction.

References

1. POTTS H. R. AND LAWFORD E. G. Recovery of sulphur from smelter gases by the Orkla Process at Rio Tinto. *Trans. Instn Min. Metall.*, **58,** 1948–49, 427–62.
2. KIAER T. Smelter gases yield elemental sulphur at Orkla-Grube plant in Norway. *Engng Min. J.*, **155,** July 1954, 88–90.
3. APPLEBEY M. P. The recovery of sulfur from smelter gases. *Trans. Soc. chem. Ind.*, **56,** 1937, 139T–46T.
4. KATZ M. AND COLE R. J. Recovery of sulfur compounds from atmospheric contaminants. *Ind. Engng Chem.*, **42,** 1950, 2258–69.
5. KING R. A. Economic utilization of sulfur dioxide from metallurgical gases. *Ind. Engng Chem.*, **42,** 1950, 2241–8.
6. LEPSOE R. Chemistry of sulfur dioxide reduction. Thermodynamics; kinetics. *Ind. Engng Chem.*, **30,** 1938, 92–100; **32,** 1940, 910–8.
7. FLEMING E. P. AND FITT T. C. High purity sulfur from smelter gases. *Ind. Engng Chem.*, **42,** 1950, 2249–53.
8. QUENEAU P. BRACKEN E. H. AND KELLY D. High-grade iron ore at Copper Cliff, Ontario. *J. Metals, N.Y.*, **10,** 1958, 527–32.
9. New facility will produce iron–nickel pellets and elemental sulphur. *Engng Min. J.*, **169,** March 1968, 168; 170.
10. BRYK P. *et al.* Flash smelting copper concentrates. *J. Metals, N.Y.*, **10,** 1958, 395–400.

11. Toivanen T. and Grönqvist P. O. Nickel refining in Finland. *Can. Min. Metall. Bull.*, **57,** 1964, 653–8.

12. Seeste R. and Härkki S. Das Outokumpu-Schwebeschmelzverfahren für Nickelkonzentrate. In *Symposium nickel, Wiesbaden 1970* (Clausthal-Zellerfeld: Gesellschaft Deutscher Metallhütten- und Bergleute, 1970), 65–70.

13. Outokumpu process for the production of elemental sulphur from pyrites. *Sulphur* no. 50, 1964, 33–8.

14. Argall G. O. Jr. Outokumpu adds second catalyzer to raise pyrite-to-sulphur conversion to 91 percent. *World Min.*, **20,** March 1967, 42–6.

15. Bryk P. B. *et al.* Canadian Patent 867 269, 1971.

DISCUSSION

C. Chamberland introduced his joint paper briefly, summarizing its principal contents.

F. Roberts* said that the authors had laid stress on saving capital, e.g. by use of a vibratory method of compaction in producing carbon electrodes rather than a conventional press. But they had, nevertheless, expended an enormous amount of capital in having their own power station. Would it not have been better to go for a cheap-tariff electricity supply from the public corporation, who could achieve economies of large-scale power generation? Also, the small power station seemed to be harnessed to the economics of the adjacent coal mine.

He asked if the authors were satisfied that there would be no problems in the long term in obtaining good-quality supplies of coke for electrode manufacture to a satisfactory specification, with stable, not rising, prices. At Harwell they had had experience of carbon artefact manufacturing technology and it was possible that the smelter might run into anode production problems related to raw material supplies if that situation were not watched carefully.

H. G. Trevor Busby† said that on page 514 the authors gave the expected efficiency of the Alcan dry-type (baghouse) gas cleaning system as 98.0% on gaseous fluorides, and better than 99% on particulate fluorides. That system was installed on the second pot line, the first pot line being fitted with the Alcan floating-bed wet scrubber; the inference was that a considerable economic advantage would ensue from the dry system. That implied a relatively low efficiency for the floating-bed scrubber. Perhaps the authors would indicate the efficiency of that system for comparison with the dry system.

Dr. E. F. Emley,‡ in introducing the Trocmé paper in the absence of the author, summarized its principal contents. He said that it was of particular significance, bearing in mind present-day conditions, that no pollution problems arose from use of the Magnetherm process: dust emissions from the various operations were readily controlled. Pollution problems emanated solely from the production of ferrosilicon.

J. H. Versteegh§ asked the author to indicate the present production of one Magnetherm furnace (tons magnesium per day) and if he foresaw any increase in capacity.

* A.E.R.E., Harwell, Berkshire.
† Lodge–Cottrell, Ltd., Birmingham.
‡ British Aluminium Co., Ltd., Gerrards Cross, Buckinghamshire.
§ Shell International Petroleum Mij., N.V., The Hague, Holland.

Information on the total energy consumption (kWh/kg magnesium produced), including the energy consumed in producing the required ferrosilicon, would also be welcomed—as would a note of the percentage of the total direct plant capital which could be allocated to ferrosilicon production, dolomite and bauxite calcination and the Magnetherm furnace itself.

Dr. J. H. E. Jeffes* said that it appeared that the heating of the charge was by a single-phase electricity supply between one electrode immersed in the slag and the case of the furnace. It seemed unlikely that a 4-MW furnace would operate on a single-phase supply. It would be interesting to have further information on the internal arrangements of the furnace.

The silicon efficiency of the process was indicated by the composition of the metal leaving the furnace, but there was no indication of the extent to which the magnesium was eliminated from the slag. Perhaps the author would give some information of that subject.

A. W. Fletcher† said that the by-products of the reaction, calcium aluminate slag and excess iron, looked interesting. He asked if credits for the sale of those materials were included in the process economics.

G. Steintveit introduced his paper briefly, summarizing its principal contents.

A. G. Moncrieff‡ asked what effect the jarosite process had on the amount of deleterious impurities taken into solution, e.g. germanium, tellurium, arsenic, antimony, etc., and if it increased the amount of magnesia dissolved. The author had mentioned that the process helped the control of sulphate in the circuit. In the normal leach circuit the only way to control that (other than by roasting conditions) was to bleed off electrolyte. In some operations, however, the amount of bleed required might be controlled more by the build-up of magnesia in the circuit than of sulphate.

Other processes had been developed to increase the recovery of zinc by hydrometallurgical methods: for example, the American Zinc and Vieille Montagne processes. As in the jarosite process, those dissolved the zinc ferrite by use of high acidities and temperatures, but they differed in their method of iron precipitation. He would be interested to have the author's views on why the jarosite process had proved commercially more successful, particularly as the cost of reagents in the American Zinc process would appear to be considerably less than in the jarosite process. Perhaps there was some fundamental advantage in the jarosite process, or perhaps it was just that the originators in Norway and

* Department of Metallurgy, Imperial College, London.
† Warren Spring Laboratory, Department of Trade and Industry, Stevenage, Hertford-shire.
‡ Consolidated Gold Fields, Ltd., London.

Tasmania had successfully developed it on their own plants and so proved its worth in commercial operation more conclusively.

Professor G. Björling* said that he presumed that the jarosite precipitate was toxic, and therefore harmful to nature: he asked how it was intended to dispose of it. As it was not completely insoluble, there must be some dissipation from a dump into the groundwater; clearly, attention must be paid to that problem in the not too distant future.

A. W. Fletcher said that the hydrometallurgist had waited a long time for a satisfactory solution to the problem of iron removal from process liquors, and the author's company and the Electrolytic Zinc Co. of Australasia were to be congratulated on the simultaneous discovery of the jarosite process. So far, only a limited amount of information had been made available on the mechanism of the reaction, but from the equations given it could be concluded that jarosite was precipitated after a series of complex reactions. In fact, because the process was more complex than might at first appear, a certain amount of mystery had been built up around the technique. He therefore made a plea for more technical details. For example, the result given in Fig. 1 (p. 523) was not very meaningful without the temperature at which the precipitation was carried out and the initial and final iron content, pH, etc., of the solution. Some indication of solution analyses in Figs. 2 and 4 (pp. 525 and 527) would also be helpful— in particular, the ammonium ion concentration.

He asked if jarosite were formed by reaction between precipitated basic ferric sulphate or ferric hydroxide and alkali ions in solution. In what way did the process used by Det Norske Zinkkompani differ from that used at Risdon?

Dr. T. Tuominen introduced his joint paper briefly, summarizing its principal contents.

Dr. H. K. Worner† said that the work described promised to become yet another notable contribution to improved pyrometallurgy from Outokumpu Oy. It was of particular relevance to WORCRA copper or nickel smelting–converting because their gases were expected to leave commercial-scale furnaces at between 1200 and 1250°C, with more than 10% SO_2 and only 0·5–1·5% oxygen. Presumably, the desirable 1300–1350°C could be achieved by reacting such residual oxygen with the fine injected coal.

On page 537 it was stated that the coal used should have a high carbon content and relatively low hydrogen. Table 2 (p. 538) showed that the coals used in the best work contained 2·8 and 3·4% hydrogen. What was the upper limit of hydrogen in coals suitable for the high-temperature SO_2 reduction process?

* Royal Institute of Technology, Stockholm, Sweden.
† Conzinc Riotinto of Australia, Ltd., Melbourne, Australia.

AUTHORS' REPLIES

E. M. Strachan and C. Chamberland   In reply to Mr. F. Roberts (p. 543), the logic in using a vibratory method for producing carbon electrodes applied equally to the decision in having our own power station—it was all a question of economics. Despite a very high load factor, it was not possible for public power rates to compete with the equivalent cost of power from our totally owned power station, even including the capital.

The basic raw materials for the production of electrodes are petroleum coke and high-quality pitch. Britain is well served in its supplies of pitch and exports to other countries. Petroleum coke is also produced in Britain from imported crude oil. Supplies of good-quality coke have, so far, not been a problem and are not expected to be. However, as this is a basic commodity, the supply situation is under constant review.

In reply to Mr. H. G. Trevor Busby (p. 543), a very high degree of efficiency on gaseous hydrogen fluoride is achieved by the Alcan floating-bed wet scrubber (98–99%). The question of efficiency on particulate fluoride is harder to answer as it is a function of the nature of the particulates themselves, which is, in turn, a function of the manner in which the electrolytic process is operated. The recovery of the particulates is, however, definitely inferior to that of the dry system. The form in which they are recovered, i.e. a liquid, is not so amenable for reuse in the process and generally requires a cryolite recovery plant for their regeneration. The inference that the dry scrubbing process has considerable economic advantages is therefore absolutely true and has been correctly interpreted by the questioner.

F. Trocmé   The present production of a Magnetherm furnace, queried by Mr. J. H. Versteegh (pp. 543–4), is 7 tonnes per day. This represents an increase in that the first furnaces built at Marignac produced only 3·5 t/day, and the Beaudéan pilot-plant furnace yielded no more than 2 t/day. Eventually, an increase to 14 t/day can be envisaged—in a triphase furnace.

Total energy consumption is some 19 kWh/kg (10·5 kWh/kg for thermic reduction and 8·5 kWh/kg for ferrosilicon production—1 kg FeSi is needed for an equivalent amount of Mg).

An approximate (percentage) statement of costs, which will vary from site to site, would be: ferrosilicon production, 20; dolomite–bauxite calcining, 15; reduction of roast dolomite, 60; and buildings and cranes, 5.

In reply to Dr. J. H. E. Jeffes (p. 544), the reduction furnace is effectively a single-phase vertical furnace. This furnace takes in a plunging electrode, the lower end of which is immersed in the slag, and a foundation plate made of carbon blocks in which the leads are embedded. The side walls and the top of the furnace are refractory lined on the inside.

The slag composition (%) is approximately as follows: CaO, 54–56; SiO_2,

546

24–26; Al_2O_3, 14–16; and MgO, 4–6. The non-elimination of magnesium in the slag is deliberate in that dolomite is of negligible economic importance and the slag composition represents optimum operating conditions.

In reply to Mr. A. W. Fletcher (p. 544), the slag is sold to manufacturers of cement and the by-product to steelworks. Full account is taken of these sales in the process economics.

G. Steintveit   In reply to Mr. A. G. Moncrieff (pp. 544–5), the intense hot acid leaching, which is part of the new hydrometallurgical process, increases the extraction efficiency of valuable and harmful constituents of the zinc ore. In the subsequent precipitation of the complex basic iron sulphate, however, the greater part of the deleterious impurities germanium, tellurium, arsenic, antimony, etc., are removed. If an excessive quantity of magnesia is present in the ore, this might call for a bleed of electrolyte to control the build-up.

In new plants based on the leaching of fluid-bed calcine with a high content of sulphate sulphur, the jarosite process has been a highly successful procedure to control the build-up of the sulphate. This is a valuable feature of the process in addition to the benefit of higher metal recoveries. In newer plant practice the build-up of magnesia has thus not been the determining factor for bleed-off of electrolyte.

In my view the success of the jarosite process is due to the very easily controlled iron precipitation taking place at relatively high acidities. At these conditions iron can be precipitated without excess of calcine. The reagent costs are normally more than paid for by the higher extraction yields compared to other processes.

In reply to Professor G. Björling (p. 545), in principle, it should not be more difficult to dispose of the jarosite precipitate than normal tailings from the electrolytic zinc industry and other hydrometallurgical processes. The jarosite residue, produced at high acid conditions, is insoluble and cannot be considered harmful. The pure precipitate is identical to the mineral jarosite found in nature. Minor amounts of entrained electrolyte from incomplete washing of the filter cake, however, may call for neutralization if some dissipation is expected from the dump into the groundwater.

In reply to Mr. A. W. Fletcher (p. 545), the chemistry of the hydrolysis and precipitation of iron is very complex and there might indeed be a need for fundamental scientific investigations in this field. The intermediate complexes formed at acid conditions (pH maximum 1·5–1·7) and at high temperatures (90–100°C) are of primary importance for the precipitation.

The time factor to allow for the formation of these complexes and the reactions between them is important for the initiation of precipitation. The precipitation takes place in the presence of alkali ions, and the consumption of these ions, when they are present in excess, is in accordance with the formula

$$M[Fe_6(SO_4)_4(OH)_{12}]$$

where M is K, Na or NH_4. H_3O^+ may replace the alkali ions if the amount present is below the stoichiometrically required quantity.

The precipitation of the complex basic ferric complexes is, in principle, identical at DNZ and at EZ, Risdon. In Norway, however, the process is more integrated into the leaching system than in Tasmania, where they simultaneously treat a stockpile of old residue in addition to the residue from current production.

Dr. R. Malmström and Dr. T. Tuominen   The temperature of gases from WORCRA copper or nickel smelting–converting is the same as the temperature of normal flash-smelting gases, and in both cases it has to be increased by about 100–150°C for high-temperature reduction. The upper limit of residual oxygen mentioned by Dr. H. K. Worner (p. 545) will presumably suffice, considering that the pulverized coal is fed into the furnace with a certain amount of injection air.

The coal suited for reduction has no upper limit of hydrogen—reduction can also be carried out by use of light naphtha with a much higher hydrogen content— but with higher hydrogen the recovery of elemental sulphur is decreased due to the effect of the resultant water vapour on elemental sulphur according to the reaction

$$2H_2O + 1\tfrac{1}{2}S_2 = 2H_2S + SO_2$$

Session 9

Recovery of values

Chairman
Professor A. V. Bradshaw

Recovery of non-ferrous metals from secondary copper smelter slags

C. C. Banks B.Sc.

Mineral Science and Technology Division, Warren Spring Laboratory, Department of Trade and Industry, Stevenage, Hertfordshire

669.2/.6:669.3.054.8

Synopsis

A process was examined in which molten secondary copper blast-furnace slag, normally discarded, was subjected to a further reduction stage by being contacted with a carbonaceous reductant. Laboratory crucible tests, followed by field tests with a 650-kVA arc furnace, demonstrated that substantial quantities of copper, nickel and tin could be recovered as a metal product and zinc recovered as a fume. Parameters which were shown to influence metal recovery included the residence time of the slag in the furnace, the type of coke used and the initial slag composition.

In the United Kingdom about 40% of the copper used by industry is obtained from scrap or secondary sources. High-grade copper scrap containing more than 60% Cu is generally melted in either rotary or reverberatory furnaces, and is refined by conventional methods, such as oxidation and selective slagging of impurities. Low-grade secondary feed sources—residues, slag and miscellaneous copper-bearing materials—are usually smelted in a blast-furnace to produce 'black copper' containing about 80% Cu.

Apart from flue dust, the major waste product from the blast-furnace is the slag, which contains, in addition to 1–2% Cu, appreciable quantities of zinc, nickel and tin. It has been estimated that nearly 50 000 tonnes of secondary copper blast-furnace slag is produced each year in the United Kingdom. The major portion of this slag is used for grit-blasting; but, assuming an average copper content of 1·5%, approximately 750 t of copper is lost each year.

General considerations

In order to make a preliminary assessment of the effectiveness of various techniques for recovering copper from secondary copper blast-furnace slags it would be useful to have information on the occurrence of copper and associated metals in the slag system. Unfortunately, details of the physico-chemical proper-

551

ties of the slag systems used in secondary copper refining are scarce. A large number of papers have, however, been published on the physical chemistry of slag–matte systems employed in the smelting of copper concentrates. The work of Ruddle, Taylor and Bates[1] showed that appreciable quantities of copper in slags can be held in solid solution, and it is not unreasonable to conclude that these results also apply to the non-sulphidic systems occurring in secondary copper smelting practice. Mineralogical examination of chilled samples of secondary copper blast-furnace slag has shown that only a small proportion of the total copper is present as metallics. The paucity of appreciable quantities of metallics in these slags indicates, therefore, that in order to obtain worthwhile recoveries of copper and associated metals techniques other than a simple settling process must be employed.

In recent years details of several techniques for the recovery of copper from slag by use of both physical and chemical methods have been published. In particular, the carbothermic reduction process has been examined with considerable success.[2, 3] For example, Drobchenko and co-workers[4] described tests with both carbon and pyrite for the treatment of copper-containing slags in a 1000-kVA arc furnace. It was claimed that by settling slags under a coke layer 50–65% of the copper could be reduced to metal from a slag feed containing 0·8–1·2% Cu; the remaining slag assayed 0·34–0·49% Cu. By making an addition of pyrite to this treated slag the copper content could be reduced still further (to 0·16–0·31% Cu). From this two-stage process a matte grade of 9·17% Cu was obtained. The applicability of carbothermic reduction to the treatment of non-sulphidic smelting slags has been described in a Polish patent.[5] This patent referred to the treatment of liquid slags from a shaft furnace where the slag contained 2·7% Cu, 1·8% Sn and 13% Zn. The slag was transferred to an arc furnace, where it was reduced for approximately 2 h by the addition of 5–6% coke of particle size 3–10 mm. The final products from the test were a metal alloy assaying 55% Cu, 18% Sn and 8% Fe, and a slag assaying 0·3% Cu, 0·2% Sn and 3% Zn. References to carbothermic reduction tests by use of rotary furnaces[6] and tower furnaces[7] have also been noted, but the preferred vessel for such an operation appears to be an arc furnace.

Alternative techniques for the recovery of copper from slags include flotation, acid leaching and magnetic separation. The operation of a flotation plant by Outokumpu Oy,[8] treating 18 t/h of flash-smelter slag, is sufficient evidence of the effectiveness of the flotation technique for the recovery of copper from slags. This technique, however, is only suitable if the copper is present in the slag as discrete particles which can be readily liberated by crushing and grinding. Unfortunately, existing evidence suggests that the copper in chilled secondary copper blast-furnace slags does not occur in this form and, therefore, flotation techniques are unlikely to be effective—indeed, because of the complex occurrence of copper in these slags, it is improbable that recovery processes based on either leaching or magnetic separation techniques will be effective. Thus, in implementing a programme of work on the recovery of copper and other valuable metals from secondary copper blast-furnace slags, the effort at Warren Spring Laboratory has been concentrated on the carbothermic reduction technique. The laboratory's slag treatment programme has progressed successfully from laboratory-scale tests to pilot-scale operations. In this paper the initial laboratory studies are mentioned briefly, but the results from the pilot-scale tests are considered in more detail.

Preliminary laboratory investigations on the carbothermic reduction of blast-furnace slag

A test programme was initiated to evaluate the applicability of either carbothermic or pyritic smelting methods to the copper blast-furnace slags produced by United Kingdom smelting works. Preliminary work was carried out on the laboratory scale, and crushed slags were smelted with various additions of finely divided coke or pyrite. Although it was recognized that this laboratory technique differed from any envisaged commercial process for treating molten slag, it was considered that information obtained on the relationships between reagent addition (either coke or pyrite), grades of metal or matte produced and the sequence of reduction of metals from the slag would indicate the amenability of secondary copper slags to treatment with either carbon or pyrites.

Summarizing the laboratory work to date, it has been shown that when slags from the major United Kingdom producers are heated to 1350°C with 5% by weight of -100-mesh coke, 54–86% of the copper, 35–70% of the tin, 30–48% of the nickel and 6–44% of the iron is recovered as a metallic phase. Smaller amounts of coke result in less reduction to the metallic state, but in no test was it found possible to achieve selective reduction to copper without some contamination by iron. Laboratory tests also indicated that up to 60% of the copper in the blast-furnace slag could be removed by the addition of 60% by weight of marcasite (FeS_2), but the matte grades obtained were low at about 2% Cu for a single treatment.

In view of these encouraging results it was desirable that the process should be examined further on the pilot scale, preferably with a molten slag feed to a furnace of a type suitable for a commercial operation. The results of the laboratory-scale tests were discussed with operating personnel and an agreement was reached with James Bridge Copper, Ltd., for Warren Spring Laboratory staff to conduct pilot-scale reduction tests on molten blast-furnace slag by use of a 650-kVA arc furnace.

Pilot-scale operation of slag treatment process

Description of pilot plant and ancillary equipment

The 650-kVA arc furnace used for the pilot-scale test work was originally purchased for stainless steel melting and refining, and was therefore not entirely suitable for processing slags, for which different electrical characteristics are desirable. The furnace consisted basically of a cylindrical steel shell, with a dished bottom, and was fitted with a detachable roof. The walls and roof of the furnace were lined with chrome–magnesite bricks and the hearth consisted of a layer of chrome–magnesite brick onto which was rammed a monolithic refractory lining. The tilting mechanism comprised rocker trunnions fitted with teeth and operated manually through a worm gear. The slagging or charging door, also refractory-lined, was situated opposite the refractory-lined pouring spout.

The three 10-cm diameter graphite electrodes entered the furnace roof vertically through water-cooled glands. Power to the furnace was supplied by a transformer–reactor with a tapped stepwise output varying from 85 to 156 V. Power input stability was maintained through an electrical monitoring system which automatically raised or lowered the electrodes as required.

Fume emitted from the charge passed through the electrode orifices in the furnace roof into a mild steel ducting, which led to a 200 m^3/min baghouse fitted with terylene bags. A shaking mechanism facilitated the dumping of fume product from the bags into sacks sealed to discharge chutes. Because of the long ducting run to the baghouse, only a small quantity of fume was collected. A metallurgical balance for zinc could not, therefore, be calculated.

Operating procedure

For all tests molten blast-furnace slag was transported in slag pots to the arc furnace building and the contents were weighed before and after charging the furnace.

Coke was used as a reductant in all tests, and the coke sizing and addition rate were examined as variables. In most tests a proportion of the coke was added to the furnace prior to charging slag, and the remainder, based on slag weights, was added after the slag had been charged.

During the tests slag samples were periodically removed from the furnace by use of sampling spoons; analyses of these samples enabled the sequence and rate of extraction of metals from the slag to be determined. Slag frothing occurred after about 10 min of operation and, therefore, in most tests the application of power was regulated to a 10-min on–10-min off cycle.

On completion of each test the furnace was tilted and the reduction products were cast into a preheated slag pot of known weight. Metal produced during the reduction operation generally settled from the slag on casting. In several tests, however, erosion of the furnace hearth prevented complete extraction of metal and slag. A depression was formed in the hearth and, because of the limited tilting angle of the furnace, a 'heel' of metal and slag remained after the casting operation. When the furnace had cooled, the metal and residual slag were extracted by hand.

Results

Summarized results and details of the principal operating parameters for individual tests are shown in Table 1. The copper, zinc and iron assays of individual slag samples taken during several tests are presented graphically in Figs. 1, 2 and 3, and a mass balance for one test is shown in Table 2.

Test no.		1	2	3	4	5	6	7	8
Refractory material in furnace hearth		Magnesite	Magnesite	Magnesite	Magnesite	Magnesite	Magnesite	Silica + 20% anthracite	Silica
Weight of slag charged to furnace, kg		346	377	331	280	255	268	254	245
% Coke addition		1·3	1·2	3·3*	Nil	2·7	2·6	2·5	2·9
Type of coke		Medium gas (−50 mm)	Coarse met. (−150 mm)	Breeze	Nil	Breeze	Breeze	Breeze	Breeze
Residence time of slag in furnace after coke addition, min		155	60	88	86	59	60	60	60
Total time during which power was supplied to furnace, min		116	38	42	29	35	35	37	40
Power consumption, kWh/t		n.d.	584	967	n.d.	824	709	551	694
Assay of slag charged to furnace	%Cu	1·49	0·95	1·47	1·21	1·65	2·19	1·78	1·23
	%Sn	0·44	0·13	0·50	0·36	0·46	0·56	0·88	0·55
	%Zn	7·43	4·78	5·53	4·08	5·5	8·0	7·2	6·3
	%Fe	32	38	35	41	39	40	26	38
Assay of slag after 60-min furnace residence time	%Cu	0·65†	0·86	0·40	0·95†	0·61	0·92	0·52	0·60
	%Sn	0·15†	0·14	0·16	0·20†	0·13	0·25	0·30	0·26
	%Zn	1·0†	2·06	0·79	2·0†	1·2	2·9	1·98	0·86
	%Fe	33†	40	36	40†	40	44	27	31
Assay of metal product at completion of test	%Cu	14·6	69	8·8	No metal produced	29	32	42	26
	%Sn	3·1	9·9	2·1		4·5	5·1	16	8·8
	%Ni	4·9	8·4	1·0		4·6	5·0	7·9	4·0
	%Fe	72	3·2	88		60	56	27	61

* Additional coke added after 79 min to give total coke addition equivalent to 4·7% of slag input.
† Estimated assays from Figs. 1, 2 and 3.

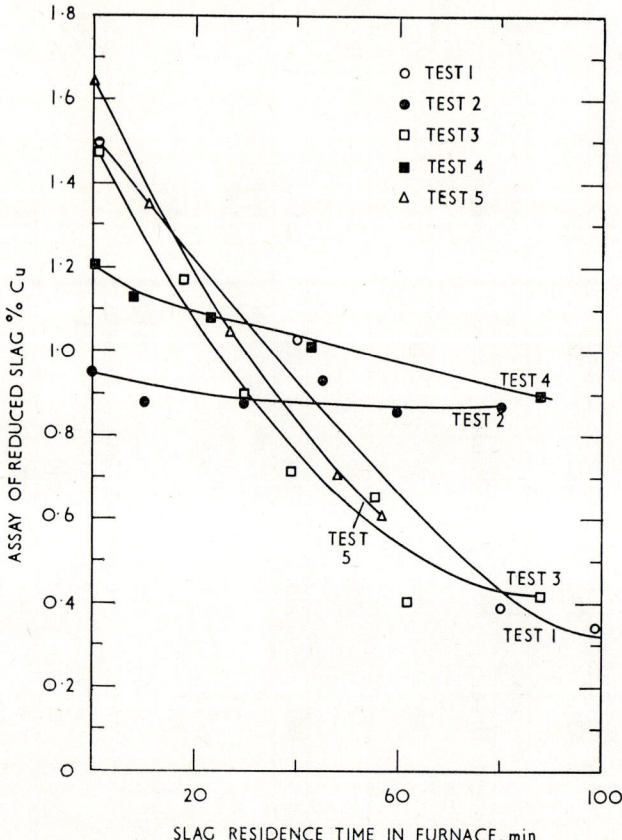

Fig. 1   Slag residence time in furnace: copper assay of reduced slag

The progressive decrease in copper, tin and zinc assays of slag during the tests show that appreciable recovery of non-ferrous metals from blast-furnace slag can be obtained by the carbothermic reduction technique. Based on initial and final slag assays, the recovery of copper into a metal phase varied from 50 to 70% for a slag residence time in the furnace of 60 min. Recoveries of tin and nickel were generally slightly lower than that for copper. Up to 10% of the iron in the original slag also reported in the metal fraction. The elimination of zinc as a fume product assaying 65% Zn was in excess of 70%.

Analysis of the results shows that the recovery of metal from slags is largely controlled by the residence time of the slag in the furnace and the type of reductant used. The laboratory-scale tests, however, suggested that the extent of metal recovery was also influenced by the iron content of the slag. Unfortunately, the variations in iron content of the slags tested during the pilot-scale work were insufficient for this effect to be fully investigated; nevertheless, it was evident that the variations in iron content did affect several other aspects of the process—

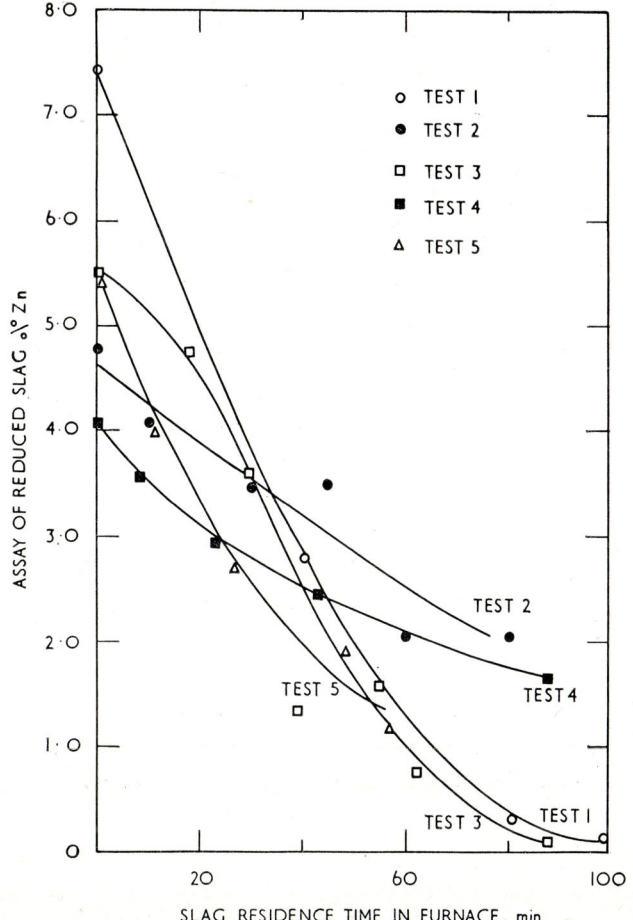

Fig. 2   Slag residence time in furnace: zinc assay of reduced slag

in particular, the assay of the metal product and the conductivity of the slag. Furthermore, it is believed that the high iron content of the slags was responsible for the rapid erosion of the magnesite refractory used for the furnace hearth in tests 1–6.

Discussion

Effect of slag residence time in the furnace

The relationships between the slag residence time in the furnace and copper and zinc assays in slag for tests with coke breeze or gas coke as the reductant follow a similar trend (see Figs. 1 and 2). A fairly sharp decrease in copper and zinc concentration during the first 60 min of the test is followed by a more gradual fall in concentration. Equilibrium appears to be achieved after approximately

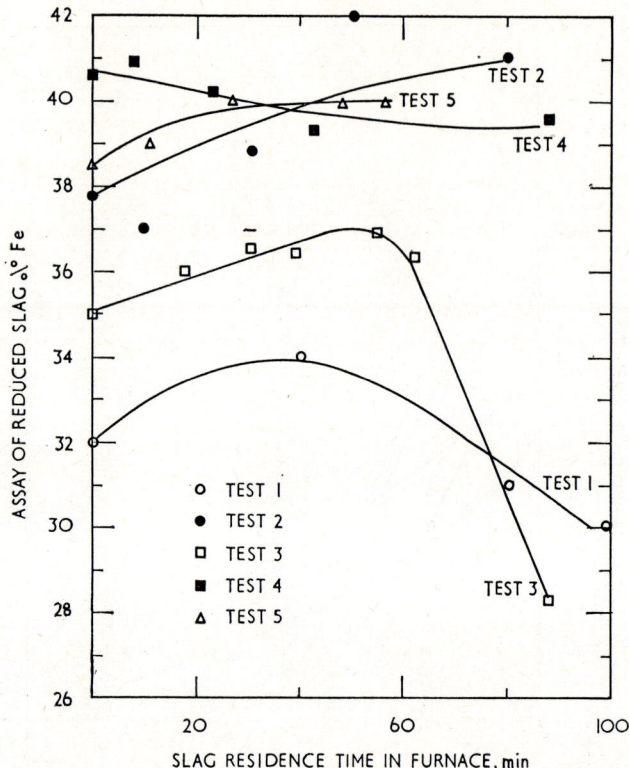

Fig. 3 Slag residence time in furnace: iron assay of reduced slag

80 min. The iron concentration in slag, however (Fig. 3), followed a different relationship. An initial increase in the iron content of the slag is followed by a decrease, the maximum concentration occurring at a slag residence time in the furnace of between 40 and 60 min. Clearly, the increase is due to the decreasing weight of slag as extraction of the more noble metals proceeds. The subsequent decrease in iron content is associated with the commencement of appreciable iron extraction. The cause of the delay before significant extraction of iron occurs is not clear; but, undoubtedly, the reaction sequences are complex and may involve various metal–metal oxide interactions. It is considered significant that the onset of appreciable iron extraction from the slag coincides with the rapid decrease in the rate of extraction of copper and zinc.

The delay before substantial iron extraction occurs is extremely important because it permits the production of an alloy which is not grossly debased by iron. Thus, by limiting the slag residence time in the furnace to 60 min, as in tests 5, 6 and 8, metal assaying approximately 30% Cu and 60% Fe was produced, whereas for a slag residence time of 88 min (test 3) the metal product assayed only 8·8% Cu but 88% Fe. Despite the shorter residence time, the copper

Table 2 Materials balance for test 7

Fraction	Wt, kg	Copper Assay, %	Wt, kg	Distribution, %	Tin Assay, %	Wt, kg	Distribution, %	Nickel Assay, %	Wt, kg	Distribution, %	Iron Assay, %	Wt, kg	Distribution, %	Silica (SiO_2) Assay, %	Wt, kg	Distribution, %
Slag to arc furnace	254	1·78	4·52		0·88	2·24		0·43	1·09		26	66·0		22	55·9	
Cast slag after reduction	165	0·52	0·86	17·7	0·30	0·50	25·9	0·17	0·28	25·5	27	44·6	80·1	27	44·6	82·4
Slag remaining in arc furnace	35	4·3	1·51	31·1	1·4	0·49	25·4	1·0	0·35	31·8	27	9·5	17·1	27	9·5	17·6
Metal	5·9	42	2·48	51·2	16	0·94	48·7	7·9	0·47	42·7	27	1·6	2·8	Nil		
Total recovered			4·85	100		1·93	100		1·10	100		55·7	100		54·1	100

recoveries were not appreciably lower, as is apparent from the copper assays of the final slag samples.

Effect of reductant

Three types of coke were used in the pilot-scale tests—(a) medium gas coke (−50 mm), (b) metallurgical coke (−150 mm) and (c) coke breeze (−15 mm). The effects of these various types of reductant on the rate and degree of extraction of copper, zinc and iron from the blast-furnace slags can be seen in Figs. 1, 2 and 3. The lack of significant extraction during test 2 shows that coarse metallurgical coke is completely unsuitable for the type of process under investigation. Indeed the rate of copper extraction during test 2 is similar to that obtained in test 4— indicating that the metallurgical coke had a negligible reducing effect on the slag. Moreover, the assay of the small amount of metal produced during this test (Table 1) approximates to that of 'black copper', suggesting that the material was entrained metal which settled out during the test.

In tests with coke breeze and gas coke similar results were obtained: for example, in tests 1, 3 and 5 the differences between the rates of copper and zinc extraction are marginal. The ready availability of coke breeze, however, makes it the preferred reductant.

Blast-furnace slag composition

From thermodynamic considerations it will be evident that the recovery of copper and other non-ferrous metals from secondary copper blast-furnace slags by the carbothermic reduction technique will be dependent on the activities of the metal-bearing species in the slag melt. The relationships between the activities of metal oxides and the concentration of various components which, combined, make up the slag systems found in industry have been investigated by several workers. For example, Davenport and Samis[9] have examined the activity of ZnO in slags similar to those used in the slag fuming process. Although the data available are not directly applicable to slag systems used in the secondary copper smelting industry, it can be inferred from the results of these studies that the extent of metal recovery achieved during the smelting of waste slags will be affected by the overall slag composition and, in particular, the lime, silica and iron oxide contents. The present studies were not primarily intended to investigate this aspect of slag technology, but it is interesting to note that the results from the preliminary laboratory tests suggest that non-ferrous metal recovery was highly dependent on the iron content of the original slag. For a given treatment time, carbon addition and reaction temperature the recovery of copper from slags with low iron contents ($<20\%$ Fe) was greater than for slags with much higher iron contents.

Another feature of the results obtained in the present test work which can be related to the initial slag composition is the composition of the metal product. Table 3 shows the iron and copper contents of the metal product and the iron content of the slag charged to the arc furnace for three tests carried out with similar reducing conditions. Results from laboratory tests, which, unlike the arc furnace trials, were carried out on slags of widely differing compositions, are also included.

Table 3 Effect of slag composition on metal assay

	%Fe in slag to furnace	Metal assay %Fe	%Cu	Cu:Fe in metal
Test 7	26	27	42	1·56
Test 5	39	60	29	0·48
Test 8	38	61	26	0·43
Laboratory-	14	48	44	0·92
scale	20	63	35	0·56
tests	24	77	19	0·25
	30	86	10	0·12

Although the magnitude of the iron and copper assays in the metal product differs between the laboratory- and pilot-scale tests for a given iron content in slag, it is apparent that the Cu:Fe ratio in the metal product increases as the iron content of the slag decreases in both sets of results. This relationship is probably associated with the increase in copper extraction achieved with slags having low iron contents. The precise mechanism of the reduction reaction and possible interactions between iron and non-ferrous metals has, however, not been established, although a preliminary theoretical assessment of the present results suggests that the equilibrium distribution of copper and iron between metal and slag phases is largely governed by the reaction

$$Fe_{(m)} + Cu_2O_{(s)} = 2Cu_{(m)} + FeO_{(s)}$$

Studies on this aspect of the carbothermic reduction techniques as applied to complex slag systems are now being undertaken. It is expected that the results obtained will provide a method of computing slag compositions which will enable optimum recovery of values into a metal phase to be achieved in addition to forming a metal product having satisfactory properties for further treatment by recycling through the existing smelter operations.

Electrical power consumption

It will be appreciated that the largest single operating cost in a commercial slag cleaning operation with an electric furnace will almost certainly be the power cost. Slag conductivity is therefore an important parameter, and some measure of control is desirable. No actual conductivity measurements were

T

carried out during the test work described; for a given electrode voltage, however, it was observed that some slags permitted submerged electrode operation, whereas other slags had such a high conductivity that open-arc operation occurred. There was an indication that slag conductivity was directly related to the iron concentration in the slag, and comments in the literature[10] substantiate this observation.

Reductions in power consumption resulted when submerged electrode operation was possible. For example, in test 7 the power consumption was 551 kWh/t of slag treated, whereas in test 6, with open-arc operation, and for which similar reducing conditions applied, 709 kWh/t was consumed. In addition to lowering the power consumption, operation of the furnace with submerged electrodes improved the slag handling characteristics. With open-arc operation it is suspected that steep thermal gradients were present in the slag bath owing to the poor heat-transfer properties inherent in this mode of operation, especially with a material such as slag. Under these conditions the lower temperatures present in the slag close to the furnace hearth would increase slag viscosity and, hence, hinder the tapping of slag from the furnace.

It is apparent from the above observations that in the design of a commercial furnace used for carbothermic reduction of slags considerable latitude must be allowed in its electrical characteristics so that adjustments can be made to compensate for changes in slag conductivity.

Furnace hearth refractory

A rammed magnesite refractory was used for the furnace hearth in tests 1–6. Slag attack on this material was severe. Considerable dissolution of refractory in the slag was indicated by the increase in MgO content of the treated slag from less than 2% at the commencement of a test to greater than 4% after a 60-min slag residence time. On completion of each test the furnace was cleaned out and samples from the refractory–slag interface region were obtained. Mineralogical examination of a sample consisting of unattacked refractory and slag with an intimate mixture of slag and refractory in between suggested that slag attack was similar to the intergranular attack described by Chesters;[11] after breakdown of the ceramic bond, the magnesite grains become surrounded by the iron-rich slag. Assimilation of the grains into the slag occurs with the formation of magnesio-ferrite.

The considerable problems encountered with the magnesite hearth necessitated the testing of other materials. Although a siliceous hearth proved to be equally unsuitable, the addition of anthracite to the siliceous ramming mix did give more encouraging results. On completion of test 7, during which this material was used, a visual inspection of the hearth suggested that slag attack on the refractory was minimal. This conclusion is corroborated by the results of the silica balance recorded in Table 2; moreover, the metal and small weight of slag remaining in the furnace after this test were easily removed by virtue of the absence of any appreciable wetting of the hearth refractory by the slag.

Conclusions

The work carried out so far on the treatment of waste slags has demonstrated that substantial amounts of copper, nickel, tin and zinc can be recovered from secondary copper blast-furnace slags. Pilot-scale test work has shown that between 50 and 70% of the copper contained in a blast-furnace slag could be recovered by the addition of coke breeze to the slag while it was maintained in a molten condition in an arc furnace. The copper was recovered as a metal phase assaying between 30 and 40% Cu and 30–60% Fe. The extraction of zinc was in excess of 70% and reported as a fume product assaying 65% Zn.

The concentration of iron in the original blast-furnace slag dramatically affected the assay of the metal product and, to a more limited extent, the degree of non-ferrous metal recovery. The relationship between the concentration of various components of the slag, product composition and metal recovery are not yet completely understood, but studies in progress should enable the optimum conditions for slag cleaning to be predicted.

Refractory attack was severe in the early stages of the work. A siliceous ramming refractory containing anthracite proved to have suitable properties for resisting attack from the high iron slags used in the current work.

Although electric power costs were moderately high in the pilot-scale tests, it is expected that power consumption can be drastically reduced by use of equipment designed specifically for slag treatment.

Acknowledgment

The author wishes to thank the management of James Bridge Copper, Ltd., for placing their facilities at the disposal of Warren Spring Laboratory, and also the members of the staff of both organizations, without whose assistance the work could not have been accomplished. In particular, the support and encouragement received from Mr. J. S. Jacobi are acknowledged.

References

1. RUDDLE R. W. TAYLOR B. AND BATES A. P. The solubility of copper in iron silicate slags. *Trans. Instn Min. Metall. (Sect. C: Mineral Process. Extr. Metall.)*, **75**, 1966, C1–12.
2. COMMONWEALTH COMMITTEE ON MINERAL PROCESSING. Decopperization of reverberatory slags. *Commonw. Miner. Process. News* no. 7, Aug. 1967, p. 33. (Restricted)
3. SMIRNOV V. I. *et al.* Complex treatment of copper production discard slags. *Tsvet. Metally, Mosk.*, **31**, no. 10 1961, 46–50; *Tsvet. Metally, N.Y.*, **2**, no. 10 1961, 49–53.
4. DROBCHENKO A. T. *et al.* Impoverishment of smelting slags from secondary copper-containing raw material. *Tsvet. Metally, Mosk.*, **37**, no. 12 1964, 23–5; *Tsvet. Metally, N.Y.*, **5**, no. 12 1964, 25–6.
5. SOSIN J. *et al.* Polish Patent 55 475, 1968.
6. KIRYANOV A. K. *et al.* Impoverishment of slags in a tubular rotary furnace. *Tsvet. Metally, Mosk.*, **36**, no. 9 1963, 29–32; *Tsvet. Metally, N.Y.*, **6**, no. 9 1963, 31–4.
7. WARNER J. P. U.S. Patent 2 820 705, 1958.
8. LUKKARINEN T. Copper slag treatment by Outokumpu. *Vuoritsbergs.*, **25**, no. 1 1967, 19–27. (Finnish text)
9. DAVENPORT W. G. AND SAMIS C. S. Activity of zinc oxide in $ZnO–CaO–FeO–SiO_2$ slags. Paper presented at annual meeting of the Metallurgical Society of AIME, New York, Feb. 1962.

10. Denisov S. I. Degtyarev V. S. and Reznichenko V. A. Electrical conductivity of melts during the reductive smelting of titanium concentrates. *Izv. Akad. Nauk SSSR, Metally*, no. 1 1970, 80–2. (Russian text)

11. Chesters J. H. *Steelplant refractories* (Sheffield: United Steel Co., Ltd., 1944), 509 p. (p. 91)

Influence of raw material composition on the zinc–lead blast-furnace

C. J. G. Evans M.A., A.I.M., C.Eng., A.M.I.M.M.

Imperial Smelting Corporation (N.S.C.), Ltd., Avonmouth

P. M. J. Gray B.Sc., A.R.S.M., C.Eng., M.I.M.M.

*Formerly Imperial Smelting Processes, Ltd., Avonmouth;
now Power Gas, Ltd., London*

669.012.22:669.531.7
622.785:622.7–344.1:669.531.7

Synopsis

The Imperial Smelting zinc–lead blast-furnace has been an established production process since 1960 and there are now ten furnaces in operation in nine
different countries. The range of raw materials fed to the smelter plants has
broadened continuously throughout the period since 1960, and it can now be said
that almost all known zinc or lead primary or secondary materials (other than
metal scrap) have been used at some time or other. Analyses of ores, concentrates and secondary materials used are tabulated. Operating data from eleven
furnaces have been used in the preparation of the paper, together with experimental data, where available.

To a large extent, the type and combinations of raw materials fed to the smelter
are dictated by economic selection rather than technical considerations. Variations in day-to-day operation can rarely be associated with changes in raw
material feed. In this respect the Imperial Smelting Furnace differs from other
zinc-producing processes. Raw material values and smelter economics are,
however, founded on the metallurgical response of the process to raw material
composition, and raw material procurement is bounded by the basic technology:
this basic technology of the sintering process and the blast-furnace is the subject
of this paper.

The sintering process

The updraught zinc–lead sintering process used in conjunction with the Imperial
Smelting Furnace (ISF) has been described in earlier publications.[1, 2, 3] Much
investigational work into sintering has been done at Avonmouth[4, 5, 7, 8] and at the
Cockle Creek works of Sulphide Corporation Pty., Ltd., in Australia,[6] but every
one of the eleven sinter plants associated with operating ISFs has contributed to
the state of knowledge. Analyses of ores, concentrates and secondary materials
that have been used in ISF operations are given in Table 1.

Table 1   Analyses of concentrates used by ISF smelters
Zinc concentrates—sulphides

Type	Zn	Pb	Cu	Cd	As	Sn	Fe	Bi	SiO$_2$	CaO	Ag, g/t	MgO	Al$_2$O$_3$	S (total)
1	55·55	0·03	0·4	0·2	—	—	7·9	—	0·9	0·25	20	0·39	0·91	32·86
2	50·04	2·28	0·57	0·19	0·23	—	10·05	0·0008	0·32	0·77	108	0·31	0·69	31·15
3	50·66	2·19	0·1	0·25	0·007	—	7·0	0·0003	1·43	1·07	116	0·45	0·27	32·33
4	51·56	0·15	0·56	0·12	0·025	—	12·05	0·0002	1·8	0·17	47	0·56	0·42	32·23
5	50·61	2·27	0·05	0·04	0·09	—	8·3	0·0004	1·39	0·09	12	0·08	0·54	34·52
6	57·01	0·68	0·22	0·09	0·25	—	4·75	0·0007	1·92	0·30	158	0·16	0·65	30·52
7	49·16	0·24	0·61	0·12	0·002	—	14·05	0·0009	0·16	0·18	25	0·22	0·57	33·65
8	56·74	4·23	0·2	0·2	0·2	—	0·68	0·006	5·6	2·45	28	0·05	0·23	29·35
9	54·5	0·6	0·08	0·18	0·07	0·0014	8·65	—	1·0	0·3	16	0·05	0·25	32·0
10	52·6	1·15	0·2	—	—	—	9·86	—	1·2	0·2	—	—	0·4	30·1
11	50·6	0·11	0·96	—	—	—	9·37	—	0·9	0·83	—	—	0·25	30·5
12	53·4	1·52	0·22	—	—	—	5·67	—	2·6	1·3	—	—	0·6	29·5
13	55·4	4·83	0·57	—	—	—	2·84	—	0·18	0·16	—	—	0·2	—
14	51·9	6·4	0·16	—	—	—	3·75	—	3·7	0·03	—	—	0·66	—
15	41·1	0·83	5·82	—	—	—	11·6	—	3·7	0·16	—	—	0·5	—
16	45·3	3·4	2·37	0·13	—	—	—	—	3·75	1·6	—	—	—	30·51
17	51·11	0·35	0·45	0·24	—	—	—	—	2·5	1·2	—	—	—	31·39
18	50·56	1·6	0·22	0·14	—	—	—	—	2·11	0·79	—	—	—	31·45
19	50·94	2·24	0·43	0·37	—	—	—	—	5·26	0·04	—	—	—	31·40
20	49·77	2·35	0·78	0·14	—	—	—	—	2·54	1·91	—	—	—	30·98
21	49·37	0·74	0·36	0·24	—	—	—	—	2·11	0·43	—	—	—	31·59
22	55·15	0·75	0·11	0·28	—	—	—	—	3·23	0·73	—	—	—	31·4
23	53·01	2·19	1·81	0·44	—	—	—	—	2·28	1·29	—	—	—	28·81
24	53·3	1·9	0·6	0·24	—	—	—	—	1·6	0·45	—	—	—	31·81
25	47·47	0·9	0·75	—	—	—	—	—	—	—	—	—	—	32·8
26	51·19	1·2	0·71	—	—	—	—	—	—	—	—	—	—	33·1
27	52·56	0·8	0·84	—	—	—	—	—	—	—	—	—	—	32·3
28	45·5	0·78	0·74	—	—	—	—	—	—	—	—	—	—	34·22

Table 1 (*continued*)
Mixed concentrates—sulphides

Type	Zn	Pb	Cu	Cd	As	Sn	Fe	Bi	SiO$_2$	CaO	Ag, g/t	MgO	Al$_2$O$_3$	S (total)
1	10·0	49·0	1·71	0·06	0·9	0·008	9·85	0·05	1·9	0·07	2100	0·2	0·32	23·0
2	17·35	57·7	0·67	0·04	—	—	2·6	0·073	0·2	0·4	790	0·04	—	19·8
3	8·00	48·0	4·0	0·03	0·03	0·03	14·0	0·09	1·3	0·03	700	0·08	0·2	24·0
4	28·2	28·3	0·72	0·29	0·2	0·002	4·5	0·002	4·4	0·3	2900	0·034	1·06	23·5
5	10·9	63·0	0·04	0·08	0·05	—	0·6	—	1·2	4·8	—	0·04	—	15·0
6	31·8	8·7	5·72	0·15	0·13	—	13·6	—	1·9	0·23	—	0·19	—	32·4
7	45·2	17·1	0·2	0·14	0·049	—	0·8	—	3·4	2·05	—	0·9	—	20·0
8	30·0	29·0	—	—	—	—	3·6	—	2·2	0·2	—	—	—	24·2
9	24·2	30·5	—	—	—	—	4·6	—	0·6	5·7	—	—	—	19·2
10	19·0	37·0	—	—	—	—	10·0	—	0·4	0·2	—	—	—	26·0
11	35·5	14·6	—	—	—	—	14·7	—	0·2	0·2	—	—	—	33·0
12	45·3	5·58	3·05	0·11	—	—	—	—	3·01	0·41	—	—	—	30·65
13	14·96	53·4	3·07	0·04	—	—	—	—	0·9	0·7	—	—	—	20·2
14	17·78	54·8	0·71	0·1	—	—	—	—	0·24	0·09	—	—	—	17·97
15	9·42	48·2	5·46	0·04	—	—	—	—	0·3	0·04	—	—	—	25·0
16	11·27	58·7	2·43	0·03	—	—	—	—	2·02	0·10	—	—	—	18·95
17	52·4	6·02	0·31	0·27	0·14	—	3·57	—	5·0	0·1	—	0·05	0·5	28·1
18	42·1	7·93	0·95	0·05	0·041	—	0·53	—	9·6	1·48	—	0·35	1·56	22·7
19	17·5	58·3	0·75	0·04	0·07	—	3·0	—	0·23	0·08	—	0·04	0·06	20·0
20	25·1	36·7	2·45	0·095	0·64	—	4·21	—	2·2	0·32	—	0·11	0·73	23·0
21	18·2	56·5	0·54	0·55	0·077	—	2·8	—	0·22	0·04	—	0·04	0·51	19·5
22	35·6	15·3	2·5	—	—	—	10·2	—	2·28	0·83	—	—	2·0	26·9
23	32·8	16·3	1·3	—	—	—	7·47	—	6·73	0·81	—	—	2·2	27·6
24	22·5	36·0	0·6	—	—	—	5·62	—	3·22	1·0	—	—	1·6	22·7
25	29·3	21·2	1·7	—	—	—	18·1	—	3·5	1·2	—	—	1·8	21·2
26	23·1	6·4	4·8	0·06	—	—	32·5	—	2·4	1·5	—	—	3·1	36·2

Table 1 *(continued)*
Lead concentrates—sulphides

Type	Zn	Pb	Cu	Cd	As	Sn	Fe	Bi	SiO$_2$	CaO	Ag, g/t	MgO	Al$_2$O$_3$	S (total)
1	13·35	58·14	2·7	0·05	0·06	—	4·6	0·0135	0·71	0·03	603	tr.	0·15	20·44
2	7·6	49·17	4·51	0·02	0·05	—	13·4	0·0976	0·85	0·34	720	0·028	0·23	22·93
3	8·23	61·24	1·38	0·09	0·37	—	3·6	0·0803	1·41	0·21	399	0·084	0·97	17·15
4	8·14	57·82	1·6	0·04	1·05	—	tr.	0·1235	tr.	tr.	2710	tr.	tr.	19·81
5	3·6	76·5	0·8	0·01	0·05	—	1·5	0·011	0·75	0·25	606	0·03	0·1	14·7
6	2·36	53·65	—	0·01	—	—	—	—	0·27	1·05	—	0·5	0·38	22·53
7	3·75	74·8	1·08	0·014	—	—	2·06	—	0·81	0·21	—	—	0·18	14·8
8	18·4	57·6	0·6	0·050	—	—	2·13	—	0·07	0·01	—	—	0·1	19·5
9	7·0	59·7	1·21	0·02	—	—	6·7	—	2·13	0·03	—	—	0·57	16·4
10	6·9	65·4	2·5	0·037	—	—	4·4	—	0·25	0·03	—	—	0·1	17·6
11	6·25	53·0	4·1	0·03	—	—	0·36	—	1·0	0·05	—	—	0·09	19·8
12	15·26	55·52	2·35	0·04	—	—	—	—	0·9	0·95	—	—	—	21·51
13	3·51	76·08	0·94	0·01	—	—	—	—	1·2	0·38	—	—	—	15·2
14	15·2	57·24	3·28	0·11	—	—	—	—	0·83	0·01	—	—	—	20·77
15	17·93	57·28	0·59	0·04	—	—	—	—	0·09	0·01	—	—	—	20·41
16	8·7	45·54	5·67	0·28	—	—	—	—	0·68	0·83	—	—	—	9·63
17	5·77	53·99	4·91	—	—	—	—	—	—	—	—	—	—	21·9
18	4·65	55·27	2·51	—	—	—	—	—	—	—	—	—	—	21·75
19	4·0	45·0	2·5	—	—	—	—	—	—	—	—	—	—	20·5
20	9·0	65·0	—	—	0·02	0·006	—	—	1·96	—	855	0·08	—	—

Table 1 (continued)
Mixed oxidized ores

Type	Zn	Pb	Cu	Cd	As	Fe	SiO$_2$	CaO	MgO	Al$_2$O$_3$	S (total)
Zn ash residue	74·0	0·5	—	—	—	0·7	0·1	0·1	—	—	2·1
Electroprecipitation residue	21·0	5·0	—	—	—	30·2	6·2	0·6	—	—	4·2
Zn silicate residue	49·0	0·5	—	—	—	1·3	24·0	2·7	—	—	0·2
Waelz oxide	58·0	10·0	—	—	—	—	—	—	—	—	2·0
Ore 1	54·1	12·8	0·03	0·85	0·51	2·1	7·2	0·3	0·17	0·4	7·19
Ore 2	62·1	5·18	0·08	0·016	0·008	1·0	2·3	0·15	0·05	1·23	3·23
Ore 3	45·0	6·13	0·23	0·16	0·013	3·06	0·39	0·27	0·14	0·34	5·61
Ore 4	27·0	5·2	0·21	0·77	0·021	21·4	2·59	1·48	2·85	1·05	5·2
Ore 5	36·0	26·4	0·90	0·30	0·078	6·4	0·09	0·01	0·11	0·07	6·0
Ore 6	41·06	15·12	—	—	—	13·3	—	—	—	—	—
Ore 7	20·8	22·8	—	—	—	14·6	10·8	3·3	2·5	2·6	—
Ore 8	29·6	23·6	—	—	—	10·6	3·6	2·5	1·1	1·3	—

T*

ISF requirements in respect of sinter quality are (*a*) small variation in chemical composition; (*b*) hardness—to minimize the quantity of −15-mm material entering the furnace shaft; (*c*) low total and sulphate sulphur content; (*d*) high porosity; and (*e*) minimum size range.

It is proposed to examine the influence of raw material chemical and physical composition on the ability of the sintering process to achieve the desired objectives of burden preparation for the blast-furnace.

Effect of particle size

The 'as-mined' ore has to be crushed to fine sizing before it is subjected to flotation separation. The fineness of grind has a bearing on the sizing of the resulting concentrate, and there is evidence to suggest that this, in turn, can influence the performance of the sinter plant—this was particularly evident at the Cockle Creek works of Sulphide Corporation Pty., Ltd., during 1969. Up to that time the plant had been operating on concentrates from the Broken Hill mines. Those concentrates became unavailable and the plant was operated for a period with Mount Isa zinc concentrates as a proportion of the charge. The respective sizings were Broken Hill zinc concentrates, 30% − 300 mesh; Mount Isa zinc concentrates, 90% − 300 mesh. As a result of this change in concentrates the new feed rate to the sinter machine could be increased from 18 to 24 ton/h.

Subsequent changes in the feed preparation section of the plant and method of plant operation have led to increased production rates with the coarser Broken Hill material, and there is no doubt that the coarse materials can be sintered successfully. It is felt, however, that the finer concentrates will coat more uniformly over the inert returns' nuclei—thereby promoting more even sintering. This results in a harder, more porous sinter and greater sulphur elimination from the sinter machine—leading to higher productivity.

The phenomenon encountered at Cockle Creek was investigated in the laboratory at Avonmouth. Under the more ideal mixing conditions prevailing in the laboratory no difference was observed between fine and coarse concentrates. Plant mixing conditions are never as efficient as those attained in the laboratory, and it is therefore to be expected that some effect of coarse concentrates is always likely to be apparent in plant practice. Flotation concentrates are, however, seldom as coarse as those from Broken Hill.

Mineralogy

Experimental work to assess the effect of different mineral forms on the sintering process is very sparse, but operating plants have shown some interesting indications.

At Kabwe, Zambia, ignition proceeds with an extraordinary ease atypical of zinc sintering, and the desulphurization rate is high, rates of more than 2·0 t/m² having been obtained—despite the coarse nature of the main sulphide sulphur-bearing material, which is a run-of-mine mixed deslimed fines −6-mm product, and in direct contrast to the performance obtained at Cockle Creek with the relatively coarse Broken Hill zinc concentrate. This comparison suggests that the mineralogical form of the sulphides may be important in affecting burning rates; at Kabwe the mineral is sphalerite, whereas at Broken Hill it is marmatite. It is also interesting to note that at Mount Isa the zinc material is also sphalerite and, hence, the sizing effect referred to earlier could be aided by the mineralogical nature of the concentrates.

Fuel

In most plants the sulphide sulphur present in the concentrates provides the fuel for the sinter process. For process reasons the sulphur content of sinter machine feed must be carefully controlled. This is achieved by use of varying quantities of recirculated undersize or crushed lump sinter. Under normal operating conditions the lump recovery is more than adequate, and insufficient undersize is produced to maintain a balance in the recirculated material. To achieve a balance it becomes necessary to crush lump sinter which would otherwise be acceptable to the blast-furnace.

As an alternative to returns there is an increasing tendency to use oxidized ores, i.e. silicates or carbonates, or Waelz oxides to minimize the recirculating load and the new sulphur loading to the sinter machine. The nature of the oxide has some bearing on the quantity which can be assimilated in the mix, and current operating experience indicates a maximum of 20% of new mix to be the limit for fine Waelz-type oxide additions. Experimental work indicates, however, that this proportion can be exceeded, and the plant under construction in Sardinia has been designed on the basis of a 27% Waelz oxide addition.

The incorporation of more granular oxidized material, i.e. in the range 1–6 mm, presents no problems. This material is very similar physically to sinter returns and can replace them provided that adequate mixing and conditioning equipment is installed.

As oxide additions are increased, the amount of recirculated sinter required to effect the necessary sulphur dilution diminishes until a balance point is reached. Any oxide addition beyond this point will result in a deficiency of fuel in the form of sulphur. In such a case coke breeze may be added to make up the deficiency, the requirement being approximately 1% of coke breeze to every 1·5% new sulphur below 5%.

Mixed sulphide–coke sintering does create difficulties with acid plant operation because of the low SO_2 strength gas produced, and for this reason it is preferable to operate either with sulphide fuel or coke fuel and to avoid the mixed sintering. The plant at Miasteczko in Poland has operated successfully on the following new mix: fine Waelz oxide, 45%; clinkered Waelz oxide, 34%; lead concentrates, 15%; returned furnace secondaries, 3·5%; limestone, 1·5%; and iron pyrites concentrates, 1·0%. A coke breeze addition of about 3·5–4·0% was used, and the waste gas was discharged to atmosphere after fume removal.

Lead

Lead has a major influence on sinter strength and hardness, and this factor alone, in practice, excludes the Imperial Smelting Process (ISP) from being used as a pure zinc smelter. If the raw materials are too low in lead content, sufficient sinter hardness can only be achieved by the use of extra silica; the furnace slag make is then increased and the zinc productivity and recovery thereby reduced. For acceptable sinter the comparable lead and silica levels are as shown in Table 2. In practice, it is rarely economically attractive to operate with less than 15% lead in sinter.

Table 2   Lead and silica requirements

% Pb in sinter	Minimum % SiO_2 in sinter
20	2·5
15	4·5
10	7·5

Sinter strength is related to the degree of fusion that takes place at the interfaces between the granules in the sinter bed. Lead silicate is a convenient bond since it has a melting point below that of the peak bed temperature normally achieved (1200–1300°C). In the absence of lead it is necessary to rely on the bonding action of other silicates (e.g. zinc silicate or ferric silicate) with higher melting points. Fortunately, as the lead tenor decreases the peak bed temperature increases because of the greater heat release in oxidizing zinc or iron sulphides.

Although the ability to smelt zinc and lead simultaneously is undoubtedly a merit of the ISP, equally, the commercial viability of the process is dependent on lead because of its role in the sintering process. Other means than sintering could be used to agglomerate the feed for the furnace, e.g. pelletizing or briquetting, but no other means of desulphurizing lead-containing sulphides than a sinter strand are known because of the self-agglomerating characteristics of lead silicate at temperatures well below the roasting temperatures. Fluid-bed or flash roasting followed by pelletizing or briquetting might be possible for a consistently low (say, less than 5%) lead feed, but this would impose a penalty against smelting lead in the ISF. A process for desulphurizing lead-rich sulphides without self-agglomeration is required which would make it possible to use the ISP for any level of lead at will, hence gaining the versatility which at present it lacks.

Gangue constituents

As has already been discussed above, the presence of a certain amount of silica, depending on the lead level, is necessary for the desired strength and hardness of sinter to be attained. If the natural silica level of raw materials exceeds the amount required, the excess is a net penalty to the process because of the extra furnace slag produced. Every unit of silica in raw materials above that required to produce satisfactory sinter actually means an additional two or three units of slag because it has to be fluxed with lime added to the sinter mix or to the furnace charge. The natural lime content of raw materials is very rarely sufficient to form a self-fluxing sinter, so flux additions are almost directly related to the silica content of the feed.

Besides affecting the slag make in the furnace, increasing amounts of lime flux added to the sinter mix increase the sulphate sulphur content of sinter. Calcium sulphate has a high decomposition temperature (1253°C in equilibrium with 1% SO_2) and, in any case, the endothermic decomposition of calcium carbonate reduces the peak bed temperatures during sintering.[4] The overall recovery of sulphur in the acid plant is thus diminished, and the sulphur input to the furnace unnecessarily increased.

The iron content of sinter varies from 6 to 18%, depending on the concentrates used. If concentrates with iron contents less then 5% are available, it may be necessary to add iron to the feed in order to bring the FeO in furnace slag within the 25–50% range—this is rarely required.

It has been found in laboratory tests that there is no significant difference between sintering parameters and iron level when the iron level is below 10%.[8]

The hardness of high-iron sinter (7·5–15% Fe) is profoundly influenced by the chemical combination in which iron is added to the mix; when iron is added as sulphide, there is a moderate decline in hardness with increasing iron content; but when iron is added as oxide, the decline is more marked and extremely low hardness values are obtained at higher iron levels.

As the content of pyritic iron in raw materials increases, the ratio of sulphur to zinc increases. The sintering and acid plant capacity required for a given zinc throughput is thus more. There is therefore a relationship between installed capital cost of a smelter complex and pyrite in the raw materials. Alternatively, an increase of pyrite in raw feed on a plant already working to full capacity will force a reduction in zinc production.

Alumina is normally a minor constituent of sinter, the typical level being 0·5%; it has no perceptible influence on sintering.[8] Magnesia, likewise, is a minor constituent, but it may be as high as 1·5%. The level of magnesia in sinter is more important from its effect on the furnace slag than on sinter, but it would appear that increasing magnesia content results in decreasing hardness. It has little or no effect on the sulphur in sinter or the peak bed temperature.

In current practice, with materials as listed in Table 1, gangue constituents have a negligible effect on the sintering requirements.

Chlorine and fluorine

Chlorine and fluorine occur in most concentrates, but the amount is usually less than 0·05% and often less then 0·01%. Under these conditions no serious effects have been noted. These elements pass over with the rich gas stream and, in the case of chlorine, the volatilization of lead in the form of lead chloride is enhanced at higher chlorine levels. This can occur if materials such as galvanizer's dross are added to the sinter machine feed which may contain as much as 0·15% Cl. The higher lead volatilization is undesirable in that it leads to increased hand-ling and handling losses and also that the fume produced tends to be sticky and can build up on fans and in gas mains—with consequent operational difficulties. High chlorine drosses are more suitable to add direct to the furnace.

A high fluorine content of sinter machine feed will result in fluorine attack on the materials of construction used in the gas-cleaning and cooling section between the sinter plant and associated acid plant. This can be overcome by use of a carbon brick lining and by the provision of a suitable water bleed from the system to prevent the fluorine in circulating liquors from building up to too high a level. A fluorine content of sinter machine feed of 0·06% has been successfully handled.

Cadmium

Cadmium occurs in almost all zinc-containing raw materials (see Table 1). It has no effect on the sintering process, but it is a valuable by-product which is largely recovered from the sintering circuit rather than through the ISF circuit.

The usual method of cadmium recovery is to dissolve cadmium oxide and sulphate out of the fume volatilized from the sinter machine before it is returned to the sinter mix. Soluble cadmium is recovered by direct chemical precipitation or by use of ion exchange to separate it from arsenic, followed by chemical precipitation. A typical cadmium circuit and flowsheet has been described by Baker and Munro.[9]

Theoretically, all cadmium should be recovered either via fume leaching or from the zinc metal product of the furnace. In practice, cadmium losses on the treatment circuits are often high (40–50% of the total cadmium in input raw materials is not unusual). The losses arise because cadmium and its compounds are very volatile and recirculating loads are several hundred per cent of the net cadmium throughput. To minimize the loss of cadmium it is desirable to maximize the rate of one-pass cadmium volatilization on the sinter machine and also to maximize the proportion of cadmium present in the fume in readily soluble form; cadmium oxide and sulphate are soluble, but cadmium sulphide is not. Unfortunately, as has been demonstrated by laboratory work at Avonmouth, cadmium sulphide is more volatile than the oxide or sulphate, and the two requirements are thus incompatible. Typical operating practice is to volatilize 65–80% of the total cadmium fed on to the sinter machine, of which 45–55% is dissolved out of the fume. Recovery from solution is better than 95%. Variations in cadmium recovery from one raw material to another have been observed, but no practical method has been found of influencing volatilization rates or leach recoveries.

A typical analysis of sinter plant fume is as follows: Zn, 1·0–1·5%; Pb, 60·0–65·0%; Cd, 2·5–3·0%; and S (as SO_4), 10%.

On one sinter plant (Belledune, Canada) the fume is collected dry and returned directly to the sinter mix without leaching; cadmium is recovered only by refining of zinc metal. Such a system is only possible where the total zinc output is refined; it does result in even more recirculation of cadmium than in the more usual circuit.

The efficiency with which cadmium is recovered is a factor of how much capital and operating expenditure is devoted to the collection and handling of cadmium-containing fumes and liquid effluents.

Other volatile elements—As, Hg

Normally, 10–15% of the arsenic in raw materials is volatilized in sintering, almost all being recycled to the sinter mix with the lead fume. Its presence in the fume is a potential hazard if the fume is leached with dilute acid to recover cadmium, as arsine is generated. Few raw materials contain so little arsenic that this hazard can be ignored. The only bleed of arsenic from the whole smelter circuit is in slag and speiss from the furnace bottom.

Information relating to the behaviour of mercury is sparse—probably because little trouble has been encountered. There is some danger of attack of lead gas mains and at Noyelles-Godault build-up of mercuric sulphate has occurred in the heat exchangers and on catalyst trays from which mercury has been recovered. The normal acceptable limit in concentrates is 0·03%.

Other elements—Cu, Ag, Au, Sn, Tl

None of these elements has any marked effect on the sintering process at the levels normally encountered. Copper, with its high affinity for sulphur, can lead to marginally higher sulphide sulphur analyses of sinter, but, with the possible exception of the Copşa Mică plant, where the Cu in sinter has been up to the 2·7% level, the effect is not noticeable.

Copper, silver, gold and tin are not volatilized during sintering and they report in the product sinter. Thallium, however, is volatilized, and it follows cadmium, being separated from it during the cadmium-refining process.

General

The sintering process is extremely flexible and can handle a wide variety of ores and concentrates with equal facility. The sinter plants operating on a custom basis work with up to eleven different metalliferous raw materials at any one time, and they may use up to fifty in any one year. Typical number of concentrates recently used at the different smelters in any one month are:

Avonmouth No. 4 (United Kingdom)	11
Belledune (Canada)	2 (Tied to mine)
Cockle Creek (Australia)	3
Copşa Mică (Rumania)	3
Duisburg (West Germany)	14
Hachinohe (Japan)	8
Harima (Japan)	15
Kabwe (Zambia)	3 (Tied to mine)
Miasteczko (Poland)	4
Noyelles-Godault (France)	8
Swansea Vale (United Kingdom)	8

Table 3 Typical ISF sinter compositions

	Zn	Pb	Cu	Cd	FeO	CaO	SiO$_2$	Al$_2$O$_3$	MgO	S (total)
Avonmouth	42·5	20·5	0·5	0·09	9·0	5·6	3·5	0·3	0·3	1·0
Belledune	31·0	20·0	0·8	—	21·0	7·5	5·5	0·6	—	1·2
Cockle Creek	46·0	20·0	0·3	0·07	10·0	4·0	2·5	—	—	0·6
Copşa Mică	38·0	18·0	1·9	0·13	12·0	8·0	5·5	1·3	0·5	1·2
Duisburg	46·0	18·5	0·7	0·03	10·0	4·0	3·0	1·44	0·2	0·7
Hachinohe	44·5	20·0	1·1	0·09	10·5	4·0	3·0	—	—	0·7
Harima	47·5	16·0	0·6	0·07	9·5	5·0	3·0	0·8	—	0·7
Kabwe	27·0	22·0	—	—	15·5	12·0	7·5	1·0	1·4	0·9
Miasteczko	42·5	20·5	—	0·05	9·0	6·5	6·0	—	—	1·0
Noyelles-Godault	46·0	17·5	0·4	0·06	11·0	4·5	3·5	1·3	0·6	0·9
Swansea Vale	45·0	19·0	0·35	0·04	9·5	5·0	3·5	—	—	1·1

Because of the varying nature of the raw materials available at the different smelters, typical analyses of the sinters produced are widely different (Table 3).

The ISF

Mineralogy

Very little is known about the mineralogy of sinter, and even less about how it is related to the mineralogy of the raw materials from which it is made. Oxidized zinc can, presumably, be present in sinter as the simple oxide or as more complex minerals such as silicates, ferrites or aluminates; the more complex minerals have slightly higher heats of formation than zinc oxide and should therefore, in theory, demand more fuel for their reduction to zinc metal. In practice, however, no variations in fuel:zinc ratio requirements have been observed which can be traced to the mineralogy of the sinter or concentrates, and the working assumption is made that sinters of identical chemical composition made from different mixes of raw materials would behave identically.

Lead

Lead is readily smelted in the ISF shaft and, as the reduction of lead oxide by carbon monoxide or zinc vapour is exothermic, imposes no extra energy demand on the process.

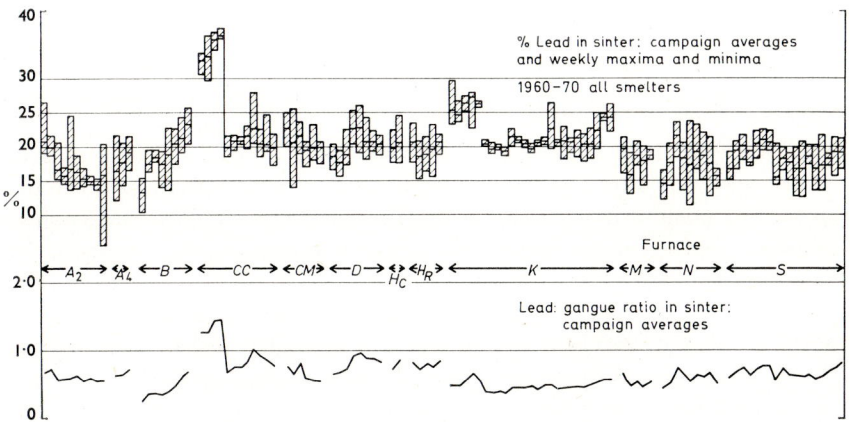

Fig. 1 Lead in sinter

In Fig. 1 the practice at all smelters operating between 1960 and 1970 is illustrated. Furnaces have operated with lead contents of sinter ranging from 5 to 36%, but the bulk of experience is with lead in sinter in the range 15–22%. Although the choice of lead level is, to some extent, determined by economic circumstances, as has already been discussed by Morgan and Greenwood,[10] metallurgical considerations also play some part.

As was mentioned earlier, it is desirable to employ a certain amount of lead to obtain satisfactory cold sinter strength without excessive use of inert hardening agents such as silica. Primarily, therefore, it is the sintering process which determines the lower economic limit for lead in feed materials. The question of how an ISF shaft would operate in the total absence of lead has never been tested since, even in the absence of lead in raw materials, the sinter would still contain 4–5% of lead, which is derived from recirculated drosses from the ISF lead splash condenser. It is possible that, with very low lead contents of charge, there would be some effect on the shaft performance, since lead probably contributes significantly to the transfer of heat from the combustion zone to the upper shaft by vapour. Lead sulphide has a very high vapour pressure in the tuyère zone and is, at these temperatures, more stable than zinc sulphide. Appreciable cycling of lead via PbS volatilization and condensation or lower temperature decomposition with zinc vapour must occur, and experimental evidence indicates that gases in the tuyère zone contain at least 2–3% sulphur (v/v). The vapour pressure of metallic lead is less than that of PbS, but lead is present at unit activity, and, from published evidence,[11] a significant amount of heat transference by lead vapour would also be expected. Indicative evidence for the volatilization of lead vapour in the shaft is given by analysis of the relative quantities of lead and sulphur leaving the charge level at 850–900°C.

Under equilibrium conditions Pb and S should be present in a weight ratio of about 7:1; actual ratios can often be 10 or more, especially at higher levels of lead in charge. No operating evidence clearly shows that shaft reactions can be adversely affected by a deficiency of lead vapour, but the possible role of lead as a heat-transfer medium cannot be overlooked.

As the lead content of sinter increases, the cold strength increases due to the formation of a well fused lead silicate bond. At high (+25%) lead contents of sinter, however, the hot strength of sinter decreases. This may be due either to the ease with which the lead oxide bond is reduced in the furnace gas or to the low melting point of lead silicate. Which mechanism predominates under shaft conditions depends on the relative rates of heat and mass transfer into the sinter lump, and the two effects cannot, in practice, easily be distinguished. The breakdown of the sizing of the sinter charge and the stickiness of the sinter caused by these mechanisms can be highly detrimental to shaft performance. The effects are more pronounced in sinters made from high-grade raw materials, where, presumably, the sinter bond is almost entirely lead silicate or even lead oxide. For high-lead charges the ratio of lead to gangue in the sinter is thus important, and this ratio is shown in Fig. 1. Operation with Pb in sinter of 25% and a Pb:gangue ratio of 0·7 or less has not generally been difficult. One period of operation on a furnace with more than 30% Pb in sinter and a lead:gangue ratio of 1·2–1·4 was exceedingly difficult.

Gangue

Raw material gangue ultimately forms slag in the furnace, together with coke ash and any fluxes added at the sinter plant or furnace. ISFs have operated with slag:zinc ratios as low as 0·5 and as high as 3·03, and no metallurgical limitations can be ascribed to the quantity of slag produced. In theory, the furnace could smelt raw materials free of gangue or of very low metal content; in practice, the limitations are economic.

Heat is required to melt slag, and the more heat required the less is available for zinc oxide reduction. The practical equivalence of heat demand for slag melting and zinc oxide reduction is expressed empirically by the ISP Carbon Estimation, which defines the carbon requirement as

$$\text{Carbon requirement} = (0·936 \times \text{zinc volatilized} + 0·2173 \times \text{slag weight}) \times K$$

Thus, an additional ton of slag will reduce the amount of zinc that can be produced from a given amount of carbon by

$$\frac{0·2173}{0·936} = 0·232 \text{ tons}$$

This formula has been found to agree with practice over many years, and it enables the bulk value of gangue to be assessed with some precision. Increasing gangue weight also reduces the overall zinc recovery if the concentration of zinc in slag remains unaltered.

The relationship between gangue compositions and zinc and lead recovery is more complex. For almost all raw materials and cokes the natural slag formed in the furnace would be essentially an $FeO–SiO_2–Al_2O_3$ melt, with FeO ranging from possibly $+60\%$ for ores of the massive pyrite type to as low as 10–15% FeO for oxidic silicate ores. In practice, fluxes are added to modify the slag to an $FeO–SiO_2–CaO–Al_2O_3$ type of a more limited range. Some lime addition is invariably used, and sometimes silica and iron oxide are added as well. In Table 4 average slag compositions over six-month periods in 1968 and 1970 are listed for all smelters in operation.

Two distinct mechanisms for dezincing of the charge in the furnace can be recognized. For most of the shaft height the charge is descending countercurrent to the gas flow, and at the lower end of this region the sinter gangue melts to form a free-flowing slag. Zinc oxide reduction is favoured thermodynamically and kinetically by increasing temperature, and, to delay the onset of formation of a free-running slag which rapidly escapes from the region of countercurrent contact with the hot reducing gas, it is normal practice to raise the slag melting point. This is done by adding lime to the sinter. The free-running slag will contain zinc oxide in solution at levels up to the saturation point, which is usually equivalent to 15–20% zinc.

When the slag collects in the hearth, further dezincing takes place to an extent that is controlled by the efficiency of heat transfer between the combustion zone above the hearth and contact between slag and a reducing agent (either hot carbon monoxide or lumps of coke immersed in the slag). A high slag melting point should favour dezincing, as should also a slag composition which enhances zinc oxide activity coefficients. Of great importance also is the length of time for which

Table 4 Average slag analyses, all smelters, 1968 and 1970*

Furnace	Zn 1968	Zn 1970	Pb 1968	Pb 1970	FeO 1968	FeO 1970	CaO 1968	CaO 1970	SiO₂ 1968	SiO₂ 1970	Al₂O₃ 1968	Al₂O₃ 1970	CaO/SiO₂ 1968	CaO/SiO₂ 1970	FeO/SiO₂ 1968	FeO/SiO₂ 1970
Avonmouth	7·86	9·46	0·84	1·07	42·18	39·62	27·25	24·39	22·43	17·85	5·94	5·41	1·215	1·367	1·970	2·220
Belledune	10·63	6·77	1·27	1·33	45·10	48·56	24·59	19·33	19·21	18·42	—	6·35	1·278	1·049	2·346	2·636
Cockle Creek	8·31	7·15	0·71	0·69	36·72	35·58	29·53	29·39	17·13	18·94	8·20	8·23	1·724	1·552	2·147	1·878
Copşa Mică	8·42	7·28	0·78	0·71	39·10	44·19	21·07	18·35	17·38	17·58	4·92	6·18	1·213	1·044	2·249	2·514
Duisburg	5·61	6·47	0·97	0·90	35·30	36·62	23·52	20·80	17·24	18·04	6·31	7·15	1·365	1·154	2·048	2·031
Hachinohe	—	6·02	—	0·79	—	42·08	—	21·27	—	20·32	—	9·05	—	1·047	—	2·071
Harima	7·17	8·17	0·37	0·76	37·60	37·92	23·32	16·05	23·22	21·30	10·13	11·35	1·005	0·753	1·624	1·781
Kabwe	9·35	8·70	0·85	0·75	37·77	34·20	25·98	27·10	23·46	22·61	6·46	7·07	1·105	1·199	1·610	1·514
Miasteczko	—	6·49	—	1·51	—	24·83	—	24·63	—	25·32	—	10·62	—	0·973	—	0·981
Noyelles-Godault	6·83	7·65	1·56	1·05	37·25	40·55	21·92	16·20	20·22	23·40	8·98	8·54	1·086	0·692	1·846	1·733
Swansea Vale	8·25	6·68	0·85	1·36	38·32	37·03	23·35	22·45	19·18	19·20	—	6·23	1·217	1·169	1·999	1·928

* All analyses (except Zn) are corrected to a zinc-free basis.

the slag is held in the hearth before tapping. This suggests that heat-transfer conditions are dominant. The greatly different rates at which ISF slags can be dezinced has recently been strikingly demonstrated under laboratory conditions by Henrard and co-workers.[12] The practical relationship between time and residual zinc in slag resembles that normally found in slag fuming operations.

The trend now in ISF operation is to make increasing use of hearth pool dezincing and less of flux additions to produce high melting point slags. This trend is shown in Table 4 and illustrated in Fig. 2. It can be seen that the con-

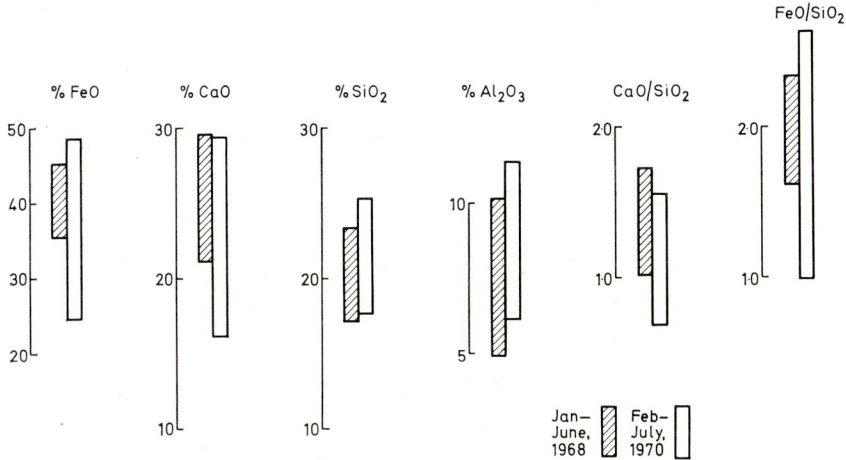

Fig. 2 ISF slag composition ranges: all smelters, 1968–70

centrations of CaO in slag and CaO : SiO$_2$ ratios are decreasing with the use of less flux and the increasing concentration of naturally occurring gangue constituents (FeO, SiO$_2$ and Al$_2$O$_3$). The increase in the operating band of FeO : SiO$_2$ ratio is also most noteworthy. Despite the broadening of the operating range of slag composition, the level of zinc in slag has actually declined (Table 4). This trend is quite recent, and it is hoped that it will continue further so that furnace slags move closer to the natural compositions and slag : zinc ratios are consequently further reduced.

For a custom smelter the natural gangue composition of the raw materials changes constantly. A typical situation is illustrated in Fig. 3, which is compiled from data from 26 consecutive weeks' operation on one custom ISF in 1970. The FeO : SiO$_2$ ratio is particularly sensitive to raw material gangue, and this varies widely and frequently. Very little operating trouble is associated with these variations.

A minor component of the gangue in some raw materials is magnesia. ISF slags have been operated with up to 6% MgO, but usually it does not exceed 3%. Magnesia increases the solidus and liquidus temperatures of the slags, and with levels above 6% there could be a problem in obtaining fully molten slag.

Alumina is a minor component of raw materials and the main contributor of alumina to the slag is usually coke ash. The Al_2O_3 content of slags ranges from 4 to 12%. The high-alumina slags are usually easier to handle from the furnace, and alumina cannot therefore be regarded as in any way an objectionable component of raw material gangue.

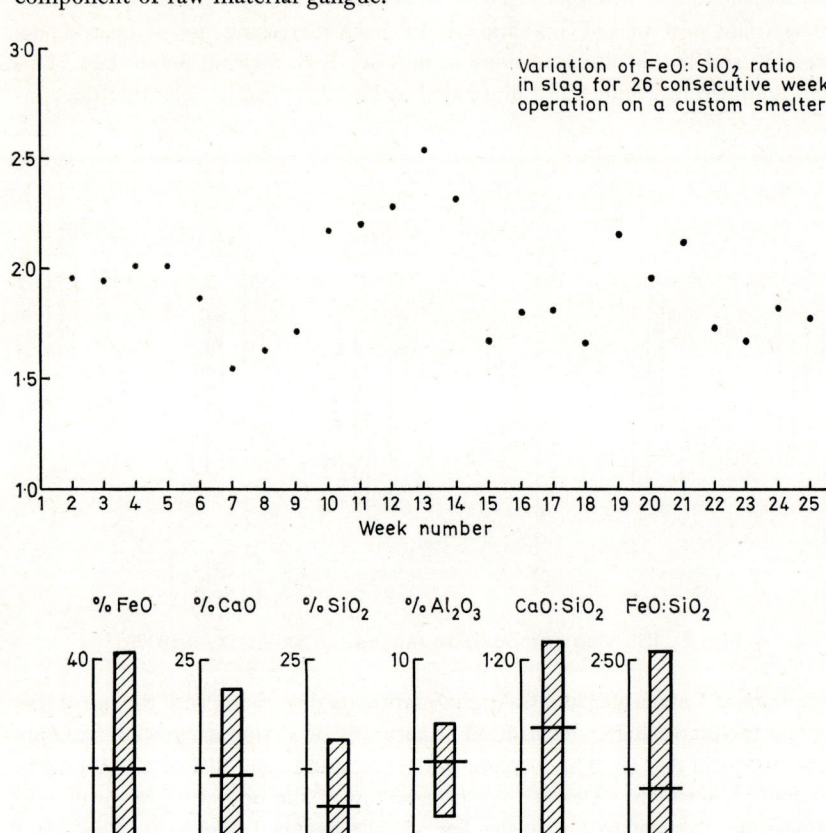

Variation of FeO: SiO_2 ratio in slag for 26 consecutive weeks' operation on a custom smelter

Mean and range of variation of slag composition in 26 consecutive weeks' operation for a custom smelter, 1970

Fig. 3   Variation of slag composition of an ISF custom smelter

It will be noted from Table 4 that lead in slag figures vary considerably. The level of lead in slag does not seem to bear any relation to slag composition and is, as yet, a largely unexplained phenomenon.

Copper

The metallurgy of copper in the ISF has been fully described by Bryson and Gray.[13]

Copper in the charge is collected either by the lead bullion or by the slag. Matte is not formed with normal levels of sulphur input. At the temperatures attained in the hearth of the furnace, the alloy of lead and copper formed is readily molten and is tapped from the furnace without difficulty. It is likely that this would still be true even if no lead at all were present and 'black' copper were tapped.

The loss of copper in the slag is controlled by the activity of lead in the bullion and the ratio of slag to copper. Slag:copper ratios are very much higher than in a conventional copper smelter, and copper recoveries in an ISF cannot therefore compete with them. The ISF can, however, recover copper present in lead or zinc raw materials at efficiencies, in some instances, of up to 90%.

Copper presents no metallurgical problems and it does, in fact, materially assist in the reduction of some problems arising from arsenic and sulphur in the charge. The volatilization of arsenic from the shaft to the condenser, where it forms dross, is significantly suppressed by copper due to the formation of the stable compound Cu_3As. In practice, it has been found that as little as 0·5% Cu in sinter is sufficient to suppress arsenic volatilization to very low levels.

Accretion builds up in the lower part of the shaft due to the precipitation of zinc sulphide, and this interferes with smelting operations and must be periodically removed with explosives. Copper competes with the zinc for the sulphur and forms a lower melting point phase which will be absorbed by the slag. It has been observed that, in the presence of copper, the growth of sulphide accretion is much reduced—with a consequent beneficial effect on smelting and continuity of operation. The effect is most marked when the Cu is 2·0% or more in the sinter.

The ISP cannot compete with conventional copper smelters in recovery of copper from copper concentrates, but the level of recovery achieved in the ISF, together with the absence of deleterious side-effects, may permit a higher overall recovery from orebody to metal than is possible with conventional smelters.

Other metals

SILVER AND GOLD

Silver and gold are collected by the lead and may be recovered from the bullion by normal refining methods.

BISMUTH

Bismuth is also collected by the lead bullion—with an efficiency of better than 95%.

ANTIMONY

Experience with antimony is limited as no operations have used more than 0·12% Sb in sinter. The antimony is largely collected by the lead and, in the bottom of the furnace, is distributed between bullion and speiss in a ratio of about 3:1. As speiss is not normally collected and treated in ISF practice, the antimony content is lost.

A small amount of antimony is carried over from the shaft to the condenser, probably in association with lead. Most of the volatilized antimony enters condenser drosses and blue powder which recycle to the sinter plant. About 15% of the volatilized antimony enters the zinc metal and, if the concentration exceeds metal sales specifications, it must be removed by addition of metallic sodium together with the arsenic in the zinc. In Table 5 a typical antimony balance for a furnace operating with sinter containing 0·05% Sb is given.

Table 5   Antimony balance

Input	Distribution, %
Sinter at 0·05% Sb	100·0
Output	
Bullion	60·0
Speiss	20·0
Slag	11·0
Condenser drosses	7·5
Zinc output	1·5
	100·0

Cadmium

With a very similar chemistry to that of zinc, but a higher vapour pressure, cadmium is more readily eliminated from the charge in the shaft; but it is less efficiently absorbed in the lead splash condenser. Thus, much of the cadmium which enters the furnace in sinter is recycled to the sinter plant. Cadmium which enters the zinc can be separated by fractional distillation. In the main, the cadmium content of zinc will be related to the cadmium content of sinter, about 60% of the input cadmium reporting in the zinc; only small fluctuations in this ratio occur due to changes in absorption efficiency in the condenser. A typical cadmium balance is given in Table 6.

Table 6   Distribution of cadmium

Input	Distribution, %
Sinter at 0·1% Cd	100·0
Output	
Cadmium in output zinc	57·2
Cadmium in drosses	2·6
Cadmium in blue powder	40·0
Cadmium in slag	0·2
	100·0

Irrecoverable losses of cadmium in the ISF plant should be very small.

Tin

The presence of even quite small amounts of tin in concentrates has serious practical implications for the ISF. For most uses of zinc an upper limit of about 0·02% Sn in metal is imposed, and, as can be seen from Fig. 4, this is exceeded at

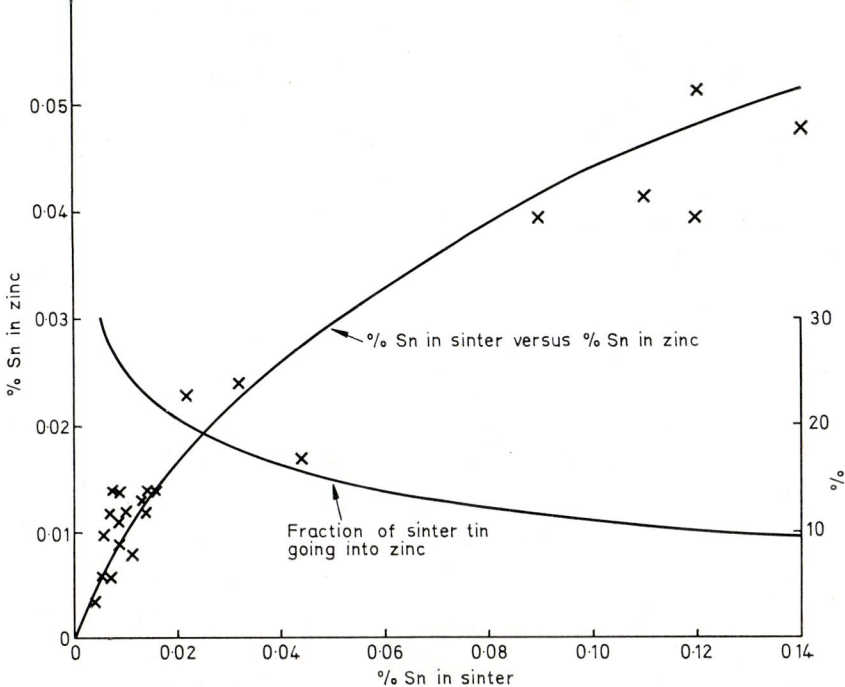

Fig. 4 Operating relationship for distribution of tin in the ISF

low levels of tin in sinter. If more than the tolerable amount of tin is present, all the zinc output must be refined by distillation in a refluxer column or in a vacuum dezincing unit. As the operating data given in Fig. 4 show, the relationship between tin in raw materials and tin in zinc is fairly predictable, and no operating

Table 7 Tin distribution

Input	Distribution, %
Sinter at 0·035% Sn	100·0
Output	
Tin in output zinc	16·7
Tin in condenser drosses	9·9
Tin in Pb bullion	68·9
Tin in slag	4·5
	100·0

practice has been found for influencing the relationship significantly. Typical tin distributions are given in Table 7.

The behaviour of tin is somewhat unexpected, since any tin compounds in the charge should be readily reduced and the metal absorbed into the lead. With the low concentrations of tin in lead, the partial pressure of tin would be extremely low and insufficient to account for the volatilization rate experienced. It is presumed that some tin is volatilized from the charge as SnS or SnO before gas–solid reduction is complete. For tin to be incorporated in the zinc product, complete reduction of the volatile compounds must occur somewhere in the condenser system, but the efficiency with which tin carried over from shaft to condenser is absorbed in the condenser lead is more characteristic of a volatile component of the gas than it is of fine suspended particles of non-volatile liquid or solid. Copper, for example, is carried over from the furnace to the condenser in similar amounts to tin, but is not absorbed by the lead splash condenser nearly so readily. Thus, the contamination of zinc by tin in raw materials is a consequence of two successive mechanisms which are thermodynamically unexpected.

Tin in raw materials for the ISF does therefore impose a restraint which can only be overcome by the refining of zinc.

Chlorine

It is sometimes convenient to feed drosses in lump or briquette form into the shaft together with the sinter. Some of these drosses contain up to 10% chlorine. The chlorine readily volatilizes from the shaft to the condenser. The effect of chlorine in the condenser is beneficial since low melting point chlorides flux oxides and assist the recovery of metallics entrained in the dross. The effect is significant on the quantity of lead entrained in the condenser drosses.

Fluorine in drosses is similarly volatilized and lost in the gas-cooling wash water.

Arsenic

Very few zinc-containing raw materials are free of arsenic, and some have appreciable arsenic content. Very little arsenic is eliminated in the sintering process and virtually all enters the furnace in the sinter.

As was mentioned above, the arsenic volatilization rate from the shaft to the condenser is very much influenced by the copper content of the charge—more so than it is by the arsenic content of charge.

Volatilized arsenic, like tin, is largely absorbed by the lead in the condenser. Unlike tin, however, most of the absorbed arsenic is precipitated out of the lead on cooling, as zinc arsenide, and only a small quantity goes into the zinc. The residual arsenic content of zinc is readily and cheaply removed by the addition of sodium metal. The precipitation of zinc arsenide, however, results in drossing of zinc, and, hence, a loss of productive capacity of the process. Arsenical drosses can also create hygiene problems by generating arsine in contact with water.

The economic and hygiene problems created by arsenic in the condenser system are relatively minor if there is 0·5% or more copper in the sinter to suppress arsenic volatilization.

The only bleed for arsenic from the whole system is in the furnace bottom products of lead bullion, slag and speiss. Most of the arsenic forms speiss which, typically, contains about 15% arsenic and 60–65% iron. Speiss also contains 6–7% of copper, so there is a loss of copper which is proportional to the arsenic content of the charge. It is therefore necessary for the smelter to impose some penalty on arsenic which is related to the loss of copper value that it will cause.

Conclusion

From the technical point of view the ISF has shown itself to be capable of treating a wide range of zinc and lead raw materials in varying proportions and with frequent changes of mix. The ability to recover zinc, lead, copper, silver, gold, cadmium, antimony and bismuth from the process means that there is no technical need to separate minerals of these metals ahead of the smelter. The economic considerations as to whether it is better to produce separate concentrates from a single orebody for treatment in separate smelters or a single bulk concentrate for the ISF are much more complex and can only be evaluated for each raw material. The economics of the different treatment routes are dictated by the relative influences on recovery and smelting capacity of the components of the raw materials associated with the payable values. Because the effective penalties differ between processes, it is essential to evaluate the optimum treatment route from ore deposit to metal, taking into account the possibilities in mining and concentrating.

How single-pass metal recoveries are related to concentration practice is shown in the Appendix by a simplified and hypothetical example.

Acknowledgment

The authors wish to thank Imperial Smelting Corporation for permission to publish this paper and their many colleagues in I.S.C. and associated companies who have contributed information.

References

1. BROAD A. V. AND SHUTT D. A. Sintering practice at the Avonmouth works of Imperial Smelting Corporation Limited. In *Sintering symposium, Port Pirie, 1958* (Melbourne: Australasian Institute of Mining and Metallurgy, 1958), 219–59.
2. PETRAITIS P. AND GREEN A. D. M. Updraught sintering—Cockle Creek. *Proc. Australas. Inst. Min. Metall.* no. 212, Dec. 1964, 1–39.
3. SELLWOOD R. M. No. 4 I.S.F. smelter complex of Imperial Smelting Corp., Ltd., Avonmouth, England. In *Lead and zinc, vol. 2: Extractive metallurgy of lead and zinc*, COTTERILL C. H. and CIGAN J. M. eds (New York: A.I.M.E., 1970), 581–618.
4. WOODS S. E. AND HARRIS C. F. Factors in zinc–lead sinter production. In *Sintering symposium, Port Pirie, 1958* (Melbourne: Australasian Institute of Mining and Metallurgy, 1958), 193–218.
5. SELLWOOD R. M. Up draught zinc–lead sintering. *Min. J., Lond.*, **254**, 1960, 434–5.

6. Green A. D. M. and Andrews B. S. Sintering developments—Cockle Creek. *Proc. Australas. Inst. Min. Metall.* no. 212, Dec. 1964, 41–59.

7. Woods S. E. and Harris C. F. Heat transfer in sinter roasting. In *Chemical engineering in the metallurgical industries* (London: Institution of Chemical Engineers, 1963), 77–86.

8. Harris C. F. Bryson J. L. and Sarkar K. M. Effect of compositional variations on the quality of zinc–lead sinters. *Trans. Instn Min. Metall. (Sect. C: Mineral Process. Extr. Metall.)*, **76**, 1967, C12–7; discussion, **77**, 1968, C44, C111.

9. Baker F. H. and Munro J. G. Cadmium recovery by ion exchange. *J. Metals, N.Y.*, **17**, 1965, 255–60.

10. Morgan S. W. K. and Greenwood D. A. The metallurgical and economic behavior of lead in the Imperial Smelting Furnace. *J. Metals, N.Y.*, **20**, Dec. 1968, 31–5.

11. Mackey P. J. and Warner N. A. Studies in the vaporization of mercury in irrigated packed columns. Paper presented at AIME Centennial Meeting, New York, March, 1971.

12. Henrard R. P. W. Howat D. D. and Jochens P. R. Factors affecting the elimination of zinc from slags associated with the Imperial Smelting blast-furnace. In press.

13. Bryson J. L. and Gray P. M. J. Recovery of copper in the Imperial Smelting Furnace. *Trans. Instn Min. Metall. (Sect. C: Mineral Process. Extr. Metall.)*, **77**, 1968 C72–84; discussion **77**, 1968, C176.

Appendix

A process that can recover a number of metals simultaneously in a single pass has some advantages to offer over a combination of processes, each of which recovers only one or two metals. Quantifying the advantage is difficult because there are such a wide number of process combinations* and systems for valuing concentrates that can be used. One has, therefore, to simplify the possibilities at the risk of some distortion.

In the following example it is assumed that an ore has the following analysis:

Zn,%	Pb,%	Cu,%	Cd,%	Sb,%	Bi,%	Ag, oz/ton	Au, oz/ton
10	5	0·7	0·05	0·01	0·0075	2·5	0·1

Such an ore might be milled to produce separate zinc and lead concentrates or to produce a bulk zinc–lead concentrate. Depending on the complexity of the mineralogy, the proportions of zinc in the lead concentrate and lead in the zinc concentrate will differ. Other assumptions that have been made are that (1) the loss of values into the tailings is the same whether bulk or separate concentrates are produced; (2) Pb, Cu, Ag, Au, Sb, Bi are paid for in the lead concentrate; Sb and Bi are not always paid for in concentrates; (3) Zn and Cd are paid for in the zinc concentrate; (4) Cd minerals are wholly associated with zinc; Ag, Au, Sb and Bi are wholly associated with Pb; Cu minerals split 75% with the lead and 25% with the zinc; (5) overall recoveries are 80% for zinc and cadmium, 85% for Pb, Ag, Au, Sb and Bi and 60% for Cu; and (6) relative values for metals are taken in the relationship (ton of contained metal) Zn, 1·0; Pb,1·5; Cu, 6·3; Cd, 25·0; Sb, 10·0; Bi, 70·0; Ag, 0·0118/oz; and Au, 0·259/oz.

If clean zinc and lead concentrates are produced, the advantages of going to bulk concentrates are small unless bulk flotation happens also to increase the

*Temple D. A. and John G. O. The treatment of complex zinc–lead–copper ores in the Imperial Smelting Process. *CIM Trans.*, **74**, 1971, 52–60.

Table 1

	Distribution of zinc between zinc concentrates and lead concentrates	Distribution of lead between lead concentrates and zinc concentrates	Relative value index
Bulk concentrates	—	—	100
Separate concentrates	95:5	95:5	93
	95:5	85:15	87
	95:5	75:25	82
	85:15	95:5	89
	85:15	85:15	83
	85:15	75:25	78
	75:25	95:5	85
	75:25	85:15	80
	75:25	75:25	74

overall recovery. With less good separation between zinc and lead the advantages of bulk flotation become appreciable—particularly in the case of lead going into zinc concentrates because of the number of side values associated with lead for which a zinc smelter will not pay.

In this simplified example allowance has neither been made for changes in returning charges nor for the effect of concentrate grade. Nor has allowance been made for the possible effect of higher recovery into bulk concentrates (possibly because there is no need to use depressants), for saving in reagent costs or for savings in mill capital costs.

Heat recovery in metallurgical processes and applications within the Outokumpu Company

Kauko Kaasila
Eero Löytymäki

Both of Outokumpu Oy, Helsinki, Finland

662.99:669.332.21(471.17)

Synopsis

The various methods of waste-heat recovery in pyrometallurgical processes used by Outokumpu are described. Examples of waste-heat recovery have been taken from the flash-smelters and roasting plants at the Harjavalta and Kokkola works of the Outokumpu Company.

The flash-smelting process used at Harjavalta for both copper and nickel concentrates is described. An illustration of the present waste-heat recovery systems applied in the smelter is given, the modifications necessitated by the oxygen plant under construction being considered.

The Kokkola works, comprising a pyrite smelter and FeS matte roaster, a cobalt plant, a zinc plant and a power plant, are considered, in particular, from the point of view of heat-recovery systems.

The design basis and special features of the waste-heat boiler in connexion with the processes used are described, and a comparison of the economics of the flash-smelting process, including either sulphuric acid or elemental sulphur production, is also made.

The cooling of structures (for example, a smelting furnace), gases and solids (for example, calcines) is essential to the continuity of a metallurgical process. Heat recovery in connexion with cooling may be effected in different ways, the method chosen generally being dependent on technical and economic conditions relating to each particular case, besides any limitations imposed by the process itself.

Examples and flowsheets illustrate various methods of waste-heat recovery in metallurgical processes used by Outokumpu. There are 15 waste-heat boilers and other heat-recovery systems of different types in use at the present time. Examples of waste-heat recovery methods have been taken from the flash-smelters and roasting plants at the Harjavalta and Kokkola works, and the waste-heat boiler for the flash-smelting furnace is considered in greater detail. The

591

feasibility of waste-heat recovery is treated in connexion with a 1200 t/day copper flash-smelter.

Applications of waste-heat recovery at the copper and nickel smelters at Harjavalta

The Outokumpu flash-smelting process is a continuous process which combines the three stages of conventional copper smelting—roasting, smelting and a part of converting, all three stages being carried out in the flash-smelting furnace. Heat generated by the exothermic oxidation reactions is utilized for smelting, and, hence, only a small amount of additional fuel is needed. The flash-smelting furnace consists of three sections—a reaction shaft, a settler and an uptake. The oxidation reactions and smelting are effected in the vertical reaction shaft: for this purpose, the dried, fine-grained concentrate and flux are fed into one or

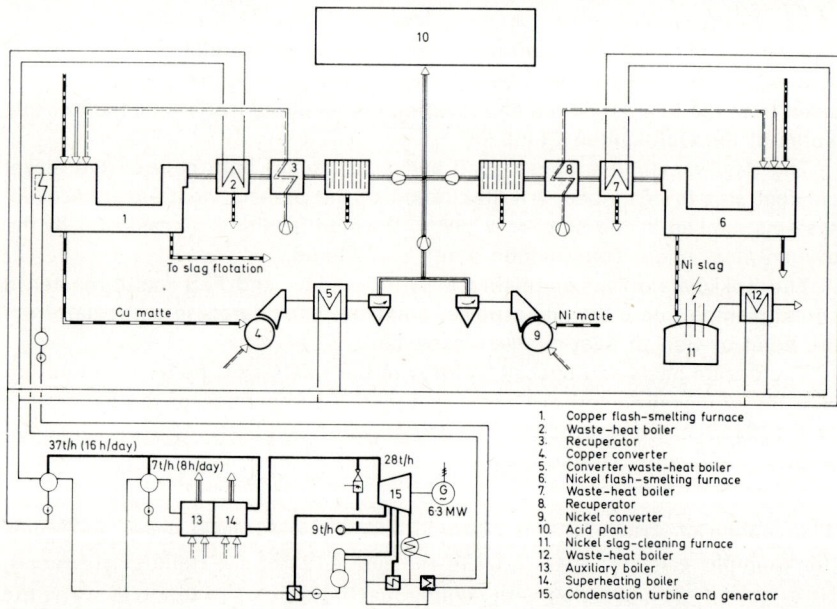

Fig. 1 Flash-smelter at Harjavalta: present flowsheet of waste-heat recovery and power generation

several concentrate burners at the top of the shaft. The preheated air or oxygen-enriched air is also led into the concentrate burner; the air and concentrate feed mix and form a suspension which is blown into the reaction shaft. The heat developed by the oxidation reactions and the additional fuel raise the temperature above the fusion point of the reaction products.

Fig. 1 shows waste-heat recovery and power generation at the Harjavalta copper and nickel flash-smelters.

Cooling of the SO_2-bearing gases of the copper flash-smelting furnace takes place in a 40 atm pressure waste-heat boiler. In the existing system a recuperator is employed to preheat the process air for the flash-smelting furnace and, simultaneously, to cool the furnace exhaust gases from 600°C at the boiler outlet to approximately 300°C. The temperature of the preheated process air is about 400°C. An equivalent system has also been adopted to cool the SO_2-containing gases from the nickel flash-smelting furnace. Exhaust gases from the copper converters are also cooled in a waste-heat boiler.

Saturated steam from various sources is superheated to 400°C in the power plant before being led to a 6·3-MW condensation turbine. At the power plant there is a boiler divided into two sections—one to superheat the steam and the other to produce saturated steam. This boiler balances fluctuations in the process steam production, which are mainly caused by the converter boiler, so that electric power generation can be maintained constant, if required.

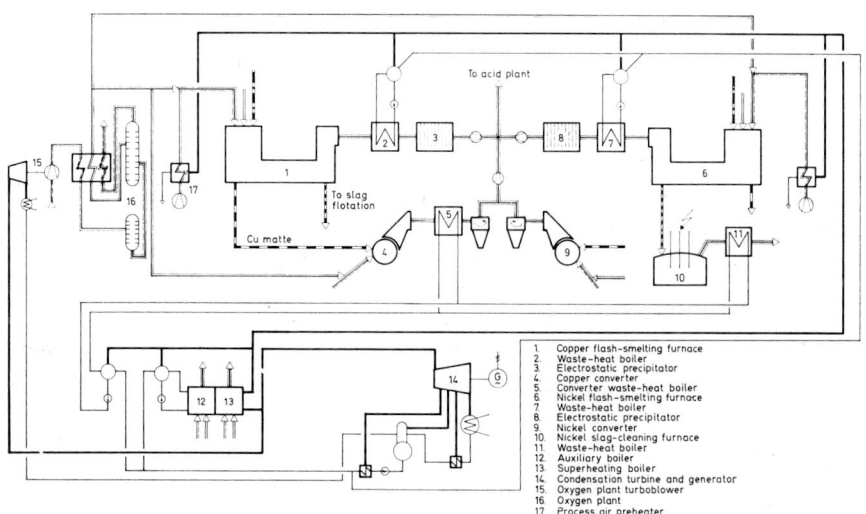

Fig. 2 Flash-smelter at Harjavalta: flowsheet of waste-heat recovery and power generation with future oxygen plant included

An expansion programme is currently being carried out at the Harjavalta works to increase the copper and nickel smelter output by enriching the process air with oxygen in the flash-smelting furnaces and converters. The oxygen plant under construction will have a capacity of 7200 Nm^3 of oxygen per hour. The basic intention is to increase the capacity of the smelter without increasing the gas volume. Both present waste-heat boiler–recuperator combinations will

U

soon be replaced by new waste-heat boilers to cool the gases to 350°C. These changes have been necessitated by the high repair and maintenance costs of the recuperator, as well as by the need to replace the waste-heat boilers. Fig. 2 shows the proposed flowsheet and waste-heat recovery system.

Applications of waste-heat recovery at the Kokkola works

Pyrite smelting and sulphur recovery plant

The most advanced cooling systems are at the Kokkola pyrite smelter, the maximum waste heat being recovered there. The process used has been developed by the Outokumpu Company and is based on the thermal decomposition of the pyrites. On heating to 1200–1300°C pyrite decomposes:

$$FeS_2 \rightarrow FeS_{(l)} + \tfrac{1}{2}S_{2(g)}$$

Under these conditions FeS matte is molten and the sulphur is gaseous. The heat required for the reaction is mainly generated by fuel oil. The sulphur-bearing gases are cooled, cleaned in an electrostatic precipitator, and then led to the catalysis and sulphur condensation stages. FeS matte produced in the furnace is granulated in water jets and conveyed to the roasting plant. Fig. 3 shows the main equipment employed and the recovery of heat at various stages.

COOLING OF FLASH-SMELTING FURNACE

The high temperatures generated necessitate a cooling system in the reaction shaft. This cooling system consists of three parts. The roof and oil burners are cooled by circulating pressurized water, the heat being recovered for process air preheating. The upper part of the reaction shaft walls is cooled by evaporation cooling through vertical channels welded to the shell, and separate evaporation cooling coils are positioned in the brickwork of the lower part of the reaction shaft and the front of the settler. All the cooling elements are in a forced-circulation system under a pressure of 4·5 atm.

Process air for the furnace is preheated in two stages: in the first stage the circulating water from the furnace cooling system is used to preheat the process air; the second stage is by means of an oil-fired preheater. The exhaust gases of the preheater at 450°C are utilized to dry the concentrate.

COOLING OF GASES

The gases from the smelting furnace, containing sulphur and sulphur components, are first cooled from 1200°C to 350°C in a 70 atm waste-heat boiler. The saturated steam is superheated in a separate boiler to a temperature of 500°C at the power plant. The exhaust gases from the superheating boiler are used to heat the boiler feed water.

The gases are reheated to 420°C before hot catalysis, where the temperature of the gases rises to 470°C. After catalysis, the gases are again cooled to 250°C by a 4·5 atm forced-circulation boiler. Part of the 4·5 atmosphere steam

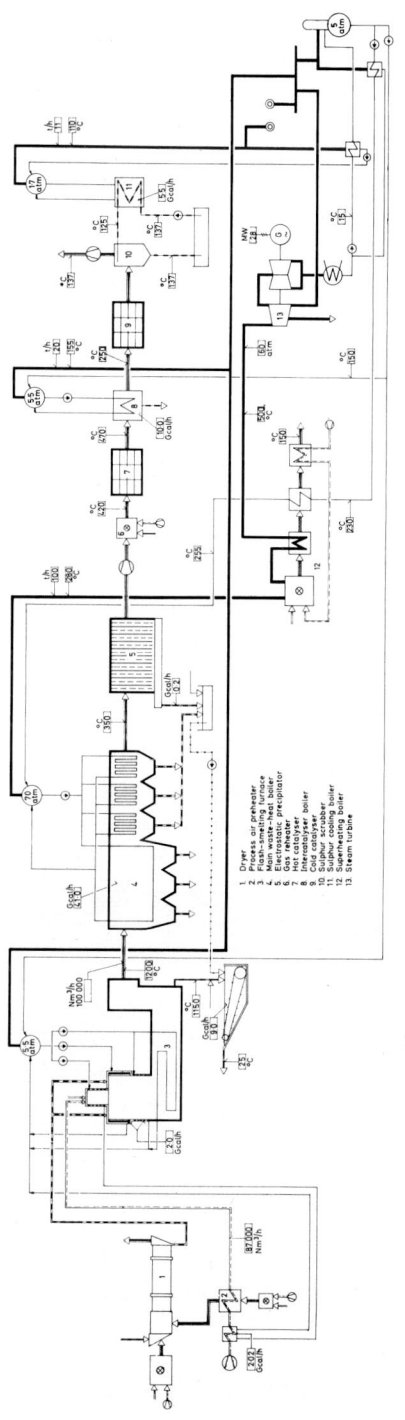

Fig. 3 Pyrite flash-smelter: cooling systems and heat recovery

1. Dryer
2. Process air preheater
3. Flash-smelting furnace
4. Main waste-heat boiler
5. Electrostatic precipitator
6. Gas reheater
7. Hot catalyser
8. Intermediate boiler
9. Cold catalyser
10. Cold catalyser
11. Sulphur scrubber
12. Sulphur cooling boiler
13. Superheating boiler
13. Steam turbine

is used as process steam, but the main part is used to preheat feed water in the deaerator at the power plant.

The final cooling stage in the pyrite smelting process is that of the gases to approximately 135°C for sulphur condensation with circulating liquid sulphur in a scrubber. The cooling of circulating sulphur again takes place in three natural-circulation boilers. The generated low-pressure steam (0·5 atm) is also used in the power plant—either to preheat the condensate or the make-up water.

The power plant has two 60-MW condensation turbines. The pyrite smelter has an hourly feed rate of 65 tons of pyrites and gives 28 MW.

Roasting of FeS matte produced in pyrite smelter

The roasting plant has four production lines, each line having the following cooling and heat-recovery systems: fluidized-bed cooling, gas cooling and calcine cooling.

In roasting processes there is usually excess heat in the fluidized bed in the roaster itself. In the Kokkola plant this is recovered by the cooling elements. High-pressure (70 atm) steam is generated in these elements, which are connected to a common drum with the waste-heat boiler. Fig. 4 shows the present cooling and heat-recovery systems at the Kokkola roasting plant.

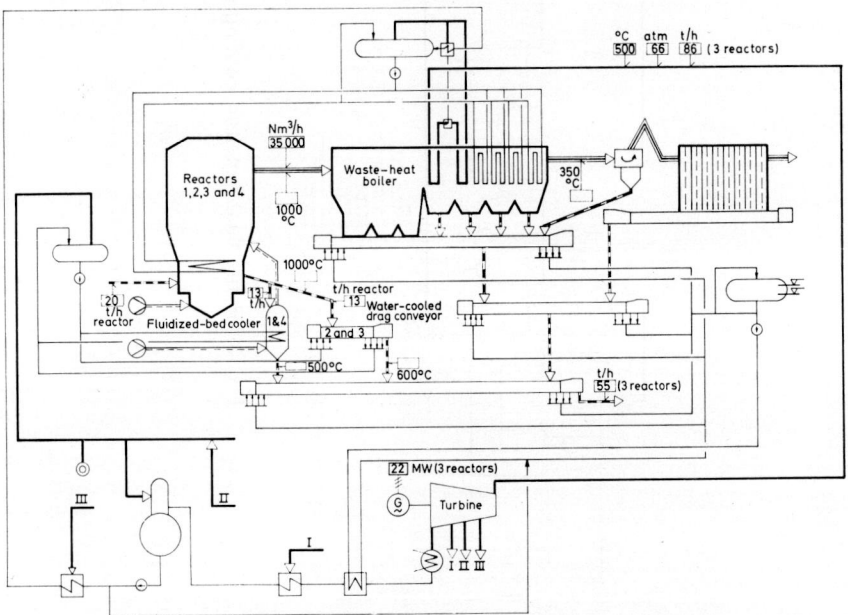

Fig. 4 Cooling and heat recovery at the roasting plant for iron sulphide matte

The two boilers initially erected are natural-circulation boilers of the vertical type, the gas flow being diverted up and down several times; the other two boilers are forced-circulation boilers of the horizontal gas-flow type. This latter type was adopted because of heavy erosion in the vertical-type boilers—caused by high gas velocities in the upper and lower parts of the boiler where the gas flow is diverted.

In the waste-heat boilers steam is superheated to a temperature of 500°C. The steam generated is directly led into the two 60-MW turbines at the power plant. The electric power generated by the FeS roasting plant is 22 MW when three roasting furnaces are in operation.

Coarse calcines from the roasting furnace are cooled indirectly from 1000°C to 150°C by conveyors and coolers, the heat being recovered partly as steam (4·5 atm) (cooling of the calcines from 1000°C to approximately 500°C) and partly as hot water at a temperature of 90°C (the temperature of the calcines dropping to 150°C). The hot calcines from the boilers, cyclones and electrostatic precipitators are cooled in water-cooled drag conveyors, the heat recovered being used to preheat the turbine condensate.

Two kinds of equipment have been developed for the cooling of hot calcines—a drag conveyor and a fluidized-bed cooler; both produce 4·5 atm steam.

Zinc and cobalt plants

The cooling systems in the zinc roasting plant are similar to those employed in the FeS roasting plant, except that heat is not recovered from the calcines

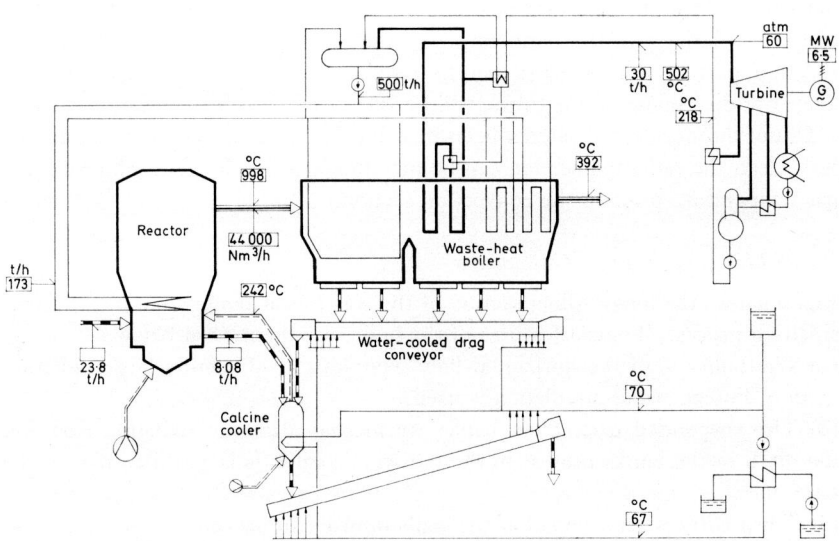

Fig. 5 Cooling and heat recovery at the zinc roasting plant

(Fig. 5). In the cobalt plant there are two sulphatizing roasting furnaces, each with a waste-heat boiler.

Design of waste-heat boiler for flash-smelting process

General

Smelter gases are cooled by a waste-heat boiler with a radiation section and a convection section. The purpose of the radiation section is to cool the gases so that the molten particles in the gases solidify and the temperature drops below the sintering point before they enter the convection section of the boiler. Particles striking the convection tubes are therefore in the solid state and do not stick to the tubes. The radiation section should be sufficiently long, the velocity of the gases low and the flow through the boiler should preferably be horizontal. The cross-section of the radiation section in proportion to the inlet opening should be large enough for a relatively cold layer of gas to be maintained close to the walls, thereby preventing the hot semi-molten dust particles from reaching them.

Influence of flue dust characteristics on boiler design

The sintering temperature of the flue dust particles is dependent on their composition. If the particles contain considerable amounts of lead or zinc, for example, their sintering temperature is relatively low, and, consequently, they easily sinter to the cooling surfaces. To ensure that the flue dust particles are solid when they contact the cooling surface, the radiation section of the boiler should be designed with full consideration of the sintering temperature of the dust particles and the temperature difference between the gases and dust particles. Thus, if the sintering temperature of the dust particles is $950°C$, and the difference in the temperature of the particles and gases is $250°C$, the radiation part has to be sized so that the gas temperature, in operating conditions, a layer of dust being on the tubes, will be $700°C$ prior to the convection section.

One of the most complicated aspects in sizing the radiation section is to estimate how clean the radiation section can be maintained—which again influences the gas temperature prior to the convection section.

Waste-heat boiler used by Outokumpu

Fig. 6 shows the longitudinal section of the waste-heat boiler used in the flash-smelting process. Typical features of the boiler are mentioned below.
(1) The boiler is of the horizontal-flow type with a sufficiently large radiation section. Forced-water circulation is used.
(2) The suspended convection banks are located after the radiation part and the pitch in the banks nearest to the radiation section is larger than that in the later ones.
(3) Sharp corners are avoided at the walls in order to prevent the accumulation of dust. For the same reason, the walls of the dust hoppers are steep.
(4) The boiler is located as near to the furnace as possible, and the distance of the edges of the boiler inlet opening from the walls and roof is of sufficient length.
(5) Forced-water circulation has been selected for the following reasons. (a) Forced circulation gives the boiler designer freedom to select the best shape for

the boiler. (*b*) A forced-circulation boiler can be started rapidly, the water circulation being little influenced by rapid changes in gas flow. (*c*) In forced-circulation boilers tubes of small diameter (approximately 1-in internal diameter) are

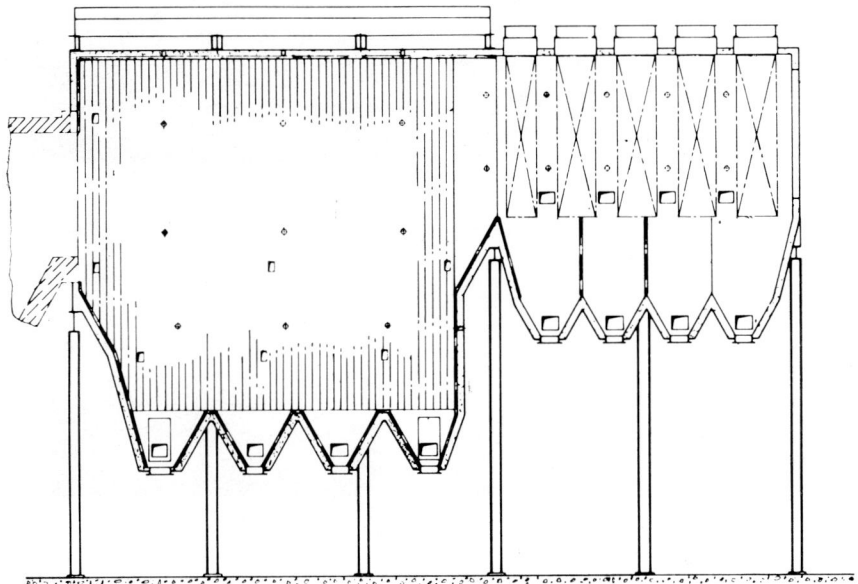

Fig. 6 Waste-heat boiler: 40 000 Nm³/h; 76 atm

generally used. Small tubes with a large wall thickness are mechanically strong enough in the radiation part of the boiler, where large, hard lumps may fall on the tubes. Any leaks in the tubes would not cause great damage, as water flow through the tubes is limited by the small tube diameter and distribution nozzle. In addition, the free space between the convection parts enables repairs to be made rapidly.

(6) It is essential that the process boilers be gastight: to achieve this, welded membrane walls are used.

(7) Steam or compressed air is generally used for soot blowing. Mechanical rapping may also be applied to clean the convection part of the boiler.

(8) In general, the inclusion of a superheater in the waste-heat boiler built subsequent to the flash-smelting furnace is not recommended, especially if the furnace feed contains higher amounts of such volatile components as zinc and lead.

Model tests on waste-heat boiler

As the waste-heat boiler is an essential item of equipment in pyrometallurgical plants, the Outokumpu Company has devoted considerable time and effort in model tests on boilers (Fig. 7).

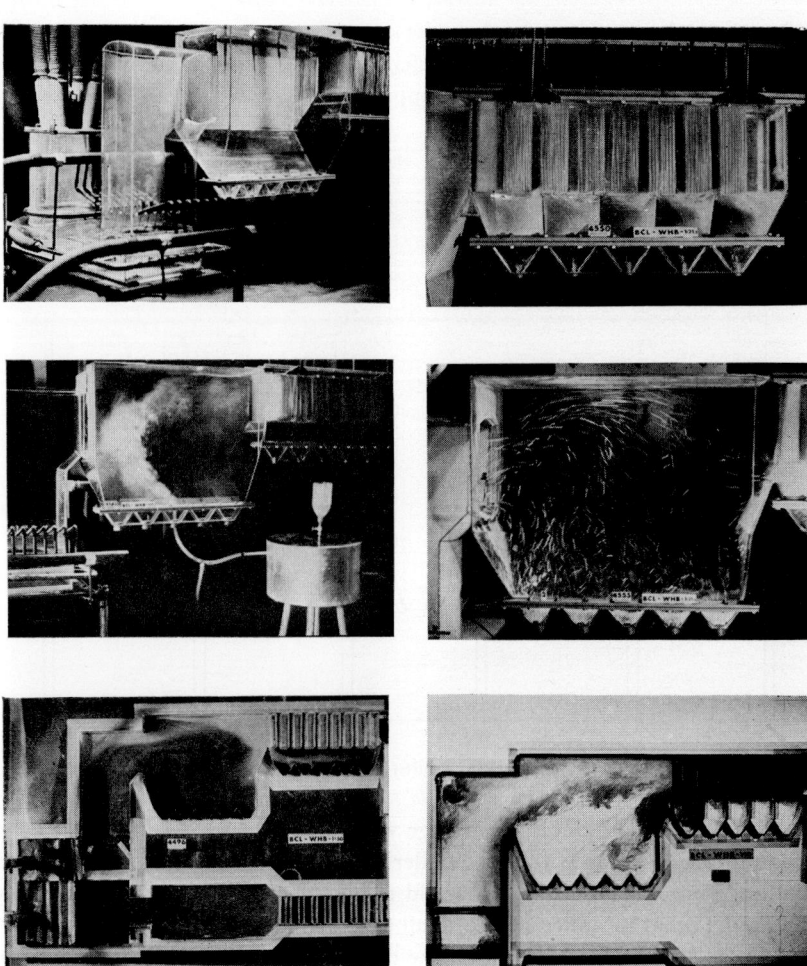

Fig. 7 Model tests. Three-dimensional air-flow model of flash-smelting furnace and waste-heat boiler *(top left)*. Air-flow model of convection section *(top right)*. Air-flow model and small generators *(centre left)*. Two-dimensional water-flow model (1 : 50) *(centre right)*. Water-flow model: flow pattern (sawdust) *(bottom left)*. Water-flow model: flow pattern (colouring agent) *(bottom right)*

Waste-heat recovery at a 1200 t/day copper flash-smelter

Conversion of SO_2 gases to sulphuric acid

Fig. 8 shows the plant flowsheet and basic process data. Steam is generated as follows: flash-smelting furnace waste-heat boiler, 46 t/h; converter waste-heat boiler (operating a 15-h day), 15 t/h. When the converter is not blowing, the auxiliary boiler generates steam at the rate of 15 t/h.

The combined steam produced, 61 t/h, when superheated in a separate superheating boiler, enables the condensing turbine to generate 13·8 MW of electric power. Thus, the average electric power consumption (the consumption of the smelter plus that of the sulphuric acid plant) is maintained in balance with the power supply by use of a converter waste-heat boiler.

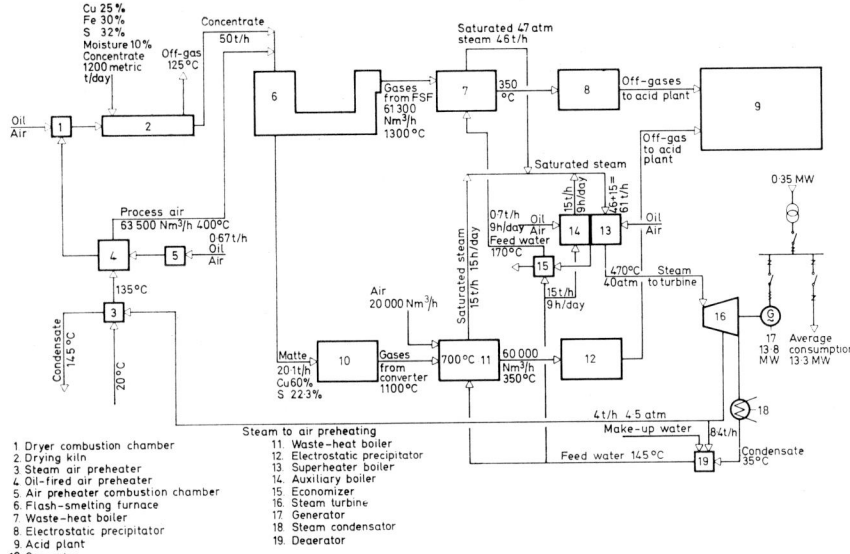

1. Dryer combustion chamber
2. Drying kiln
3. Steam air preheater
4. Oil-fired air preheater
5. Air preheater combustion chamber
6. Flash-smelting furnace
7. Waste-heat boiler
8. Electrostatic precipitator
9. Acid plant
10. Converter
11. Waste-heat boiler
12. Electrostatic precipitator
13. Superheater boiler
14. Auxiliary boiler
15. Economizer
16. Steam turbine
17. Generator
18. Steam condensator
19. Deaerator

Fig. 8 Flowsheet of waste-heat recovery in a flash-smelting process with sulphuric acid production

In any assessment of the economy of the power plant investment account must be taken of the fact that the cooling of the gases by generating high-pressure steam requires a dump condenser, equipment for cooling water, feed water treatment and feed water pumps with auxiliaries. The rest of the equipment necessary for the power plant should therefore be considered as an expenditure on power generation.

The economics of the power plant investment is, in any case, primarily dependent on the price of the electricity to be purchased.

Sulphur dioxide reduction from flash-smelting furnace gases with pulverized coal to elemental sulphur

The SO_2 reduction plant flowsheet is shown in Fig. 9, together with operating data; and comparative figures for the two processes are given in Table 1.

Summary

Applications of heat recovery at the metallurgical plants of the Outokumpu Company emphasize its importance to their troublefree and economical operation.

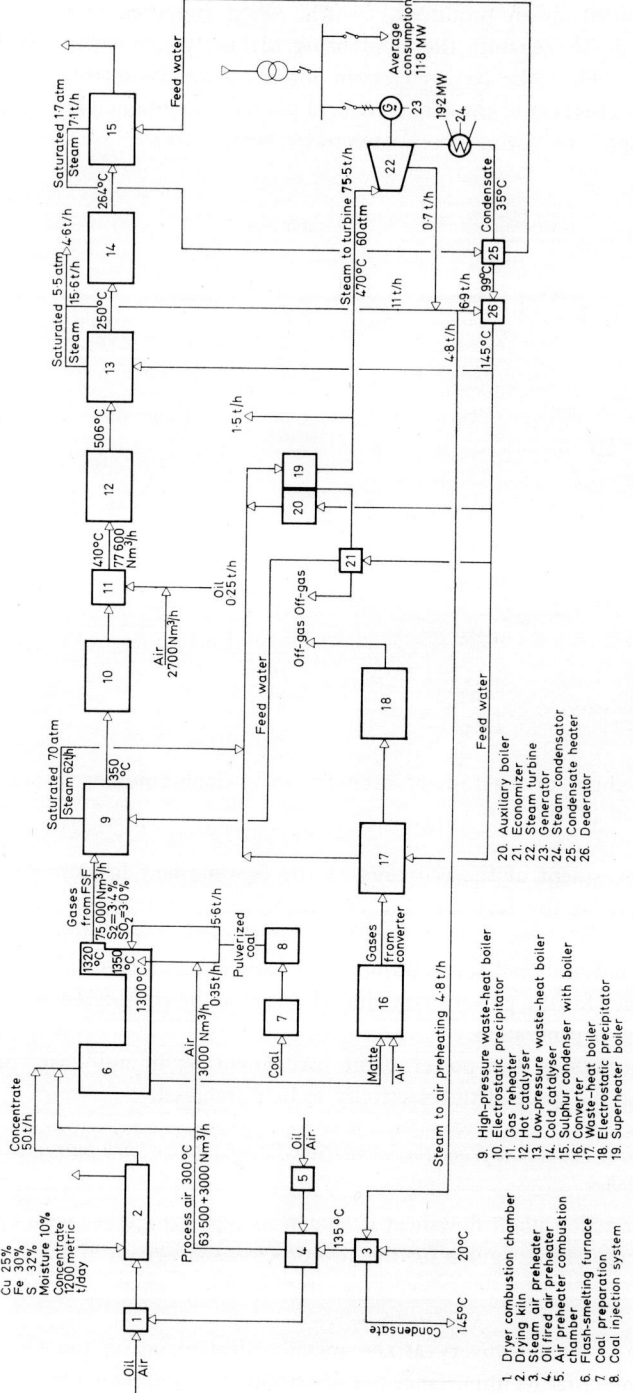

Fig. 9 Flowsheet of waste-heat recovery in a flash-smelting process with coal reduction of SO_2

1. Dryer combustion chamber
2. Drying kiln
3. Steam air preheater
4. Oil fired air preheater
5. Air preheater combustion chamber
6. Flash-smelting furnace
7. Coal preparation
8. Coal injection system

9. High-pressure waste-heat boiler
10. Electrostatic precipitator
11. Gas reheater
12. Hot catalyser
13. Low-pressure waste-heat boiler
14. Cold catalyser
15. Sulphur condenser with boiler
16. Converter
17. Waste-heat boiler
18. Electrostatic precipitator
19. Superheater boiler

20. Auxiliary boiler
21. Economizer
22. Steam turbine
23. Generator
24. Steam condensator
25. Condensate heater
26. Deaerator

Table 1   Comparative operating data for waste-heat recovery and power generation of flash-smelting process with and without reduction of sulphur dioxide

	Flash-smelting	Flash-smelting+SO_2 reduction and converting
Capacity, t/day	1200	1200
Flash-smelting furnace		
Copper concentrate, t/h	50	50
Exhaust gas from flash-smelting furnace, Nm³	61 300	75 800
High-pressure steam		
70 atm, t/h	—	62
47 atm, t/h	46	—
4·5 atm steam, t/h	—	15·6
0·7 atm steam, t/h	—	7·1
Fuel oil, t/h, for superheating of high-pressure steam from waste-heat boiler of flash-smelting furnace	0·73	1·0
Fuel oil, t/h, for gas reheating	—	0·25
Converter		
High-pressure steam, t/h, from converter waste-heat boiler 15 t/day	15	15
Fuel oil, t/h, for superheating of high-pressure steam from converter waste-heat boiler, 15 t/day	0·24	0·24
Fuel oil, t/h, for generating and superheating of saturated steam, 9 t/day (constant power generation)	(0·9+0·24 = 1·14)	(1·14)
Electric power generated		
Flash-smelting furnace, MW	10·4	15·8
Converters, MW	3·4	3·4
Total	13·8	19·2

The economics of heat recovery should be judged on the basis of electric power consumption, cost of purchased electric power, fuel and capital costs. Moreover, it is essential that the equipment selected for cooling and heat-recovery purposes, particularly in connexion with pyrometallurgical processes, be reliable. The waste-heat boiler should be designed so that the undisturbed continuous operation of the whole plant is ensured. If required, it should be possible to operate the boiler at a sufficient overload.

The importance of the methods of cooling and heat recovery dictates that they should be considered in the initial design of a new plant.

DISCUSSION

C. C. Banks, in introducing his paper, said that the work on the treatment of secondary copper smelting slags formed part of a basic research programme which the Metals Extraction Division of Warren Spring Laboratory was currently undertaking on the chemical treatment of secondary materials. The paper dealt specifically with the treatment of secondary copper blast-furnace slags, and even though the copper content of those slags was only between 1 and 2%, the annual loss of copper to the nation was still approximately 750 tons. It was that significant loss which had provided the stimulus for examining possible methods of recovery. In the initial stages of the investigation both carbothermic and matte smelting techniques had been investigated. The results from the matte smelting tests had not been encouraging, but, to some extent that was not a disappointment as matte smelting could have been a retrograde step in terms of pollution, especially as the secondary copper smelting operations, as carried out in the United Kingdom, were largely devoid of sulphur-bearing materials.

Effort had therefore been concentrated on the carbon reduction route. Initially, laboratory-scale tests were carried out on slag samples provided by the four major copper smelters in the United Kingdom. The results showed great promise and, following consultations with various members of the secondary copper industry, an agreement was reached with James Bridge Copper, Ltd., for the use of an arc furnace at their smelter, and a supply of molten blast-furnace slag.

The pilot-scale studies provided much practical information, especially for quantifying the parameters required for the design of a future commercial operation. The analytical data from that phase of the work had also given much food for thought, although at the present stage only the results of the laboratory-scale tests had been used in a theoretical analysis of the carbothermic reduction technique, principally because of the wider variation in composition of the slags tested in the latter work. In those studies the effect of the initial iron content of the slag on the copper–iron distribution between metal product and reduced slag had been examined in some detail. The logarithm of an equilibrium constant for the reaction

$$Fe_{(m)} + Cu_2O_{(s)} \rightleftharpoons 2Cu_{(m)} + FeO_{(s)}$$

where (m) and (s) referred to metal and slag phases, respectively, had been calculated and plotted against a function of the mole fraction of iron in the metal (Fig. 1). In order to arrive at that relationship several assumptions had been made, such as ignoring any possible interaction effects of nickel and tin on the copper and iron activities in the metal. Furthermore, the laboratory tests were exploratory in nature and some of the necessary thermodynamic data for those calculations were not available; thus, in addition to the assumptions, several factors had had to be extrapolated from the literature. Despite those problems, the relationship showed a reasonable linear correlation between the two func-

604

tions, and the line depicted had been determined by regression analysis of results for 'slags *A–D*' and the 'converter slag'. By use of the slope of that line a free energy value of −17 000 cal at 1350°C had been obtained for the reduction reaction of cuprous oxide by iron (literature value, −23 000 cal). That appeared to be fair agreement, considering the nature of the test work and the assumptions

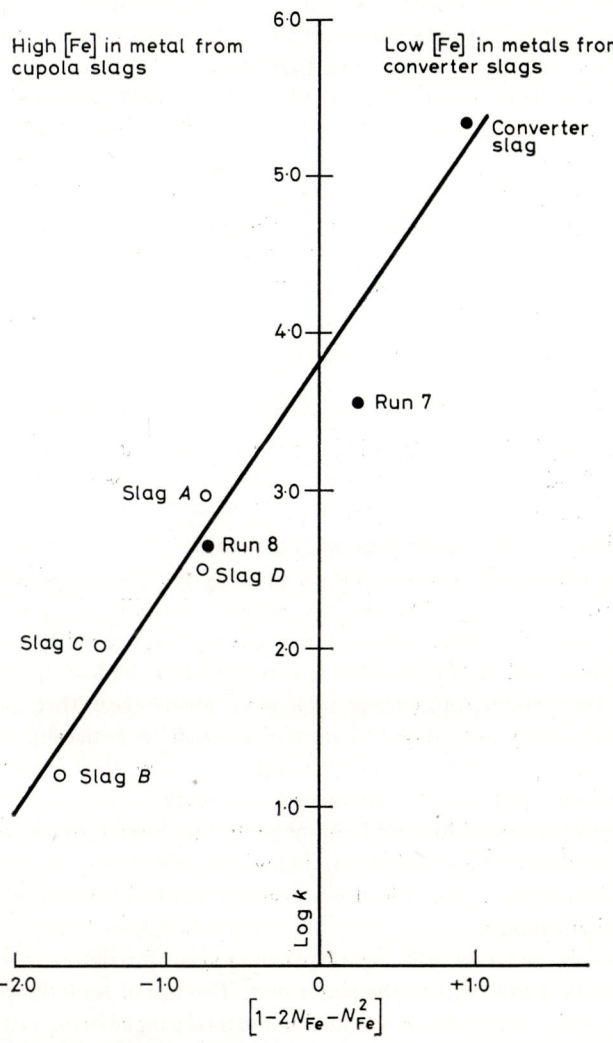

Fig. 1 Graphical solution of

$$\log k = \log \left[\frac{K.M_{Cu}}{2_s} \right] + \beta \left[1 - 2N_{Fe} - N^2_{Fe} \right]$$

or the small-scale tests of cupola slags *A–D*

X

made. The equilibrium constant had also been calculated for pilot-scale runs 7 and 8 (see Fig. 1). The proximity of those results to the relationship determined for the laboratory-scale work was interesting, and suggested that, despite the differences in scale, the chemical control of the reduction process was similar for both sets of tests.

Obviously, there still remained much to be examined, especially in terms of the kinetics of the process, which, of course, were most important—in particular, because the pilot-scale tests suggested that the reduction of the various metallic elements proceeded at different rates. Exploitation of that fact might enable the composition of the resultant metal product to be selected. More detailed studies aimed at examining the kinetics of the process were now being carried out under closely controlled laboratory conditions.

In conclusion, even though studies on the fundamental principles of the carbothermic reduction reactions were continuing, most of the practical problems associated with the process had been identified and explored, and there was now little cause for doubt that, technologically, a commercial operation would be successful. The implementation of the process would therefore appear to be dependent on satisfactory economic conditions prevailing.

C. J. G. Evans, in introducing his joint paper, said that they had outlined the behaviour of individual elements or compounds in the operations utilized in the production of zinc and lead by the Imperial Smelting Process. Their influence on the viability of the process was also discussed.

A comprehensive list of materials smelted by the ISF was given in Table 1 (pp. 566–9): that, he felt, illustrated the extreme flexibility the process enjoyed. To amplify that point, at Avonmouth, they used up to ten metal-bearing materials in any one mix, and in 1971 (to October) they had smelted 25 different concentrates. A major sinter mix change took place about every three weeks and a minor change every 7–10 days. Those changes had no noticeable effect on the operation, and 2240 long tons of zinc and more than 1000 long tons of lead bullion had been produced by the furnace in a week.

With regard to individual feed components, the blast-furnace had been developed originally as a method of producing zinc, but during the mid-1950s the ability of the process to smelt lead was realized and had since been exploited to commercial advantage.

Lead had the property of being a hardening agent for sinter—a role formerly fulfilled by silica additions to the sinter mix. The use of lead allowed the silica content to be decreased, thereby reducing the total gangue being introduced into the circuit.

Table 2 (p. 572) illustrated the lead and silica requirements, and it must be remembered that each ton of silica required about 1·5 tons of lime for fluxing. 2·5% SiO_2 was approaching the natural SiO_2 level normally experienced. Lead, however, was not restricted to a 20% maximum.

Additional lead promoted high gold, silver and copper recovery, and was itself recovered at high efficiency.

Reduction of the gangue input also reduced the slag:zinc ratio in the sinter charged to the blast-furnace. Furnaces had been operated successfully with that ratio as low as 0·5 and as high as 3·03, no metallurgical problems being revealed. The lower the ratio, however, the greater was the quantity of zinc which could be produced with a fixed weight of carbon. That factor had encouraged the current tendency to make increasing use of hearth pool dezincing, since that avoided the use of flux additions necessary for high melting point slags and so minimized slag volume. The economic implications of reduced gangue content of sinter mix were therefore very considerable. More zinc was volatilized and less zinc was lost in slag.

Cadmium did not play a significant role in the metallurgy of an ISF operation, but it constituted a valuable by-product. Recovery was generally via the fume volatilized from the sinter machine, although there was an increasing tendency for a proportion to be recovered from zinc refining. With good process control recoveries of 90% could be achieved.

At the levels normally encountered copper had no effect on the sintering process. In the furnace the copper reported in the bottom products, dividing itself between the bullion and the slag. The copper loss was dependent on the copper:gangue and copper:lead ratios in sinter, but marginal recoveries could be up to 90%. It was felt that overall recovery from ore to metal could be competitive with the conventional copper smelter if the advantages of bulk flotation were fully exploited.

The range of acceptable slag compositions had increased considerably in recent years. That had extended the flexibility in choosing raw materials, and the acceptable range was far wider than for the conventional zinc or lead smelter. Suitable raw material blending in the sinter plant permitted the use of materials high in magnesia, manganese, chlorine or fluorine, which might otherwise be untreatable.

That brought him back to Table 1.

K. Kaasila introduced his joint paper briefly, summarizing its principal contents.

G. B. Harris,[*] commenting on the paper by Banks, said that with reference to the increase in iron assay of the slag as the reduction proceeded (Fig. 3, p. 558), it was stated (p. 558): 'Clearly, the increase is due to the decreasing weight of slag as extraction of the more noble metals proceeds'. He asked if that reduction in the weight of the slag might not be due to the volatilization of zinc and the removal of oxygen, as ferric iron was reduced to ferrous, rather than the extraction of the noble metals. Secondary smelting slags contained of the order of 5–6% zinc oxide, which was readily reduced and volatilized at very low oxygen pressures. Those

[*] Department of Minerals Engineering, University of Birmingham.

slags also contained appreciable quantities of ferric iron, since they were the result of an oxidation process. When magnetite was reduced to ferrous oxide, there was a 7% reduction in weight of the iron compounds, and that loss, allied to that of zinc, would account for the reduction in weight of the slag and, thus, the increase in iron assay.

The equilibrium distribution of copper and iron contents between metal and slag phases was suggested (p. 561) as being governed by the reaction

$$Fe_{(m)} + Cu_2O_{(s)} = 2Cu_{(m)} + FeO_{(s)}$$

Because of its variable oxidation state, iron acted as an oxygen carrier and was instrumental in the dissolution of copper in iron silicate slags. Fig. 1 confirmed work in the Department of Minerals Engineering that copper was related to the iron content of the slag. In the absence of data on slag structure and the kinetics of copper dissolution, however, it might be an oversimplification to combine those two facts to propose that equation as the controlling mechanism.

Dr. J. H. E. Jeffes,[*] commenting on the paper by Banks, said that the author was to be congratulated on the interesting results he had described. From the point of view of making a thermodynamic analysis of the results obtained it would be of interest to know the oxygen content of the metal at various stages during the recovery process. Perhaps in any subsequent work such measurements could be included.

The sampling of the metal in the furnace could best be carried out by means of a silica tube dipped into the metal through the slag and connected to a vacuum line. For oxygen analysis it would be necessary for the tube to be purged with an inert gas during insertion.

C. F. Harris,[†] commenting on the paper by Evans and Gray, said that the authors gave the impression that there might be a relationship between the mineralogy of sinter and the materials from which it was made. In his view only a very tenuous link could be envisaged. It had been demonstrated by Beveridge[‡] that, in a sinter bed, a large proportion of zinc sulphide was oxidized in the vapour phase, thus completely destroying the original mineralogical form.

The actual mineralogy of sinter had been the subject of two studies, but those had never been carried through to a state warranting publication, due to evidence that performance of sinter in the furnace was independent of mineralogy. Unlike the iron blast-furnace, in which there was a large proportion of direct reduction of iron oxides by carbon relatively high in the shaft, zinc reduction occurred, for the most part, low in the blast-furnace shaft. In that region the mineralogical form of sinter was being destroyed by melting.

* Department of Metallurgy, Imperial College, London.
† Imperial Smelting Corporation, Ltd., Avonmouth.
‡ BEVERIDGE G. S. G. The oxidation rates of zinc sulfide spheres. In *Agglomeration*, KNEPPER W. A. ed. (New York: Wiley, 1962), 303–44.

The presence of zinc oxide, zinc ferrite, zinc silicate and zinc aluminate, lead oxide, mellilite and other complex phases had been identified by X-ray diffraction techniques. Both metallic lead and lime had been identified visually in some samples. Lead silicate normally formed a glass which was not easily identifiable by X-ray diffraction techniques.

J. S. Jacobi* said that he had been closely following the development described by Banks—mainly from the sidelines, but occasionally entering the arena as a sort of referee. He had been impressed throughout with the excellence of the experimental approach and the soundness of the underlying thinking. On behalf of the United Kingdom based copper smelting industry he thanked Warren Spring Laboratory for their unfailing help that they extended to them whenever they were in technical difficulties—which was most of the time!

The pilot-scale work described should be considered as a beginning only; proposals for further investigations were now being formulated. In his view that slag cleaning method was feasible provided that it could be operated as a continuous in-line system and at a power cost not exceeding 250 kWh/ton of slag or thereabouts. A similar approach to slag cleaning had recently been reported from Japan, and he believed that a fairly large in-line slag cleaning arc furnace was being planned in at least one North American installation. An iron/copper ratio of 3:1 in the product would not worry them very much since they had to contend with far worse in their raw materials. On the other hand, slag fuming as such, with the emphasis on zinc recovery, would not be economic under their conditions; nor would any non-continuous system.

A wide variation in slag compositions had been mentioned. That, he believed, referred to the laboratory examinations, where slags from different smelters were examined, because the slags used in the pilot trials were remarkably consistent, although in the wrong direction. They were too high in iron because that was the nature of the scrap they processed. They were too high in magnetite because the slag was produced in a small blast-furnace, which was driven hard on a low coke ratio. They were far too high in alumina because they could not keep aluminium out of the arisings which they processed. They were low in lime to enhance hardness, which was required for the industrial utilization of the slag. They were, consequently, low in silica and much higher than they would like to see in copper, nickel and tin.

Lest his friends in the primary copper smelting industry wonder why they tolerated discard slags containing up to 1·5% Cu, might he just record the above limitations plus the fact that there was no matte formation at all in most secondary copper smelting systems.

Professor T. R. A. Davey† said that some years ago there was a general belief at Avonmouth that tin in an ISF charge caused the zinc dust to become

* IMI Refiners, Ltd., Walsall, Staffordshire.
† Colorado School of Mines, Golden, Colorado, U.S.A.

pyrophoric, but he understood that that came to be doubted some time later. He asked if it were now known definitely whether tin in the charge really had that effect or not, as it was rather difficult to understand.

I. D. Vassilev,* commenting on the paper by Evans and Gray, enquired the maximum copper content in the concentrates that would still permit the process to be operated normally. He had in mind lead–zinc–copper concentrates with high copper contents—6–7% and above.

W. Drummond† said that Outokumpu Oy had clearly shown that waste-heat boilers need not be the *bête noire* of the smelting world, provided that they were properly designed and adequately sized. Indeed, if clean air conditions were to be maintained by economical acid or sulphur manufacture, a boiler was almost a necessity. It was good to see the extensive use of modelling and, if that technique could not solve all the problems, it went a long way towards understanding the flow patterns in full-size units. In that respect intuition was usually wrong!

The use of superheaters was going out of fashion in flash-smelting boilers— could the authors report fully on why that was so? Was it because of fouling or metallurgical troubles, and did the authors know of any research work on the corrosion of sulphurous gases and gaseous sulphur on carbon steel and low-alloy steels?

Contributed remarks

A. Vega‡ What would be the recommended minimum capacity for the flash-smelting process with regard to heat and metal recovery? The authors' comments on fuel consumption per ton of metal and personnel requirements would be welcomed.

M. A. T. Cocquerel§ Because of the great importance of power consumption in the electric slag cleaning operation, it is felt that the following observations will be of use to potential users in any preliminary assessment of the process considered by Banks.

The reference to Outokumpu slag milling practice refers to the present-day operation at the Harjavalta smelter; prior to the introduction of the milling process, electric furnace slag cleaning was employed.

Flash furnace slag for cleaning contains approximately 45% Fe, 30% SiO_2 and 1–2% Cu. The discard slag, which was granulated, contained 0·6–0·7% Cu. Converter slags containing 5–6% Cu were also cleaned in the electric furnace. Approximately 20 t/h of slag was treated, with a quoted power consumption of 90 kWh/t.

---

* State Committee for Science and Technology, Sofia, Bulgaria.
† Babcock and Wilcox, Ltd., London.
‡ Ministry of Mining and Metallurgy, Havana, Cuba.
§ Engineering Division, Selection Trust, Ltd., London.

An electric furnace at the Ashio smelter in Japan is used for slag cleaning, the reported power consumption being somewhat lower than that of Outokumpu.

Nickel flash-smelting slags require reduction under coke in an electric furnace, the required power consumption being within the range of 120–180 kWh/t of slag, depending on the desired degree of contained cobalt recovery.

It would appear from these data that, in accordance with Banks's closing observations, significantly lower power consumption would be required for blast-furnace slag cleaning in a large-scale purpose-built furnace.

G. J. Brittingham* It is notable that copper and other non-ferrous metals are reduced from the slag by carbothermic reduction at an appreciable rate over the initial period of treatment, approximating 60 min in duration. During the same period the iron concentration increases, but, when treatment is continued further, it is slowly reduced.

All such industrially produced slags would be in a highly oxidized condition initially, and so the early reduction period would be expected to lower the oxygen potential, i.e. some of the ferric iron present in the slag will be reduced to the ferrous condition. As this occurs, the protective oxygen of the ferric oxide, which has provided solubility for the non-ferrous metals present, is lowered, and, as a result, the metals must appear as the conjugate which would exist in contact with slag of that composition. When the slag oxygen potential has been lowered to its minimum value, any oxygen-induced solubility for non-ferrous metals will have been reduced to a level consistent with the coexistence of a small proportion of ferric oxide, ferrous oxide and the incipient presence of metallic iron. From here on any further reducing action must result in the chemical reduction of iron oxide to metal as well as any other reduction processes occurring, and this is confirmed both by the slowing of the rate of reduction of the non-ferrous metals and the appearance of iron in the metallic product.

A similar effect is to be observed in the mineral dressing treatment of some smelter and converter slags; high copper tenor slags yield a sulphide concentrate and a tailing of 0·4% copper. All the copper rejected from solution above the ternary eutectic temperature has the opportunity to diffuse through the slag and form droplets of a size amenable to concentration by flotation. But the remaining copper, soluble in the ternary eutectic because of its remaining oxygen potential due to the fact that ferric oxide still remains as a component, must precipitate in so fine a state of subdivision that it is quite irrecoverable by mineral dressing techniques.

If it is desired to recover the remaining non-ferrous components of the slag, it will clearly be necessary to introduce another phase which can maintain a higher concentration of non-ferrous metals than occurs in the slag in equilibrium with it. A sulphide phase, for instance, would enable the copper in slag to be reduced to 0·1%.

* Independent Metallurgical Consultant, Broadbeach, Queensland, Australia.

AUTHORS' REPLIES

C. C. Banks Unfortunately, we still do not have a reliable method for determining the ferric iron content in copper slag systems typical of industrial smelting operations. I feel, therefore, that the significance of the suggestion put forward by Mr. G. B. Harris (pp. 607–8), whereby a portion of the weight loss in slag may be due to reduction of ferric to ferrous iron, with the consequent decrease in oxygen content, must remain a matter for conjecture. I certainly concur with Mr. Harris when he notes that the zinc elimination from the slag contributes significantly to the decrease in slag weight. This aspect is readily apparent in Fig. 2 (p. 557), from which it can be shown that the loss of ZnO from the slag during carbothermic reduction will be equivalent to at least a 7% loss in weight over a period of 60 min.

With reference to Mr. Harris's comments on the mechanism for copper reduction in the system, it may be significant that a free energy calculation similar to that outlined in the presentation of the paper (for which I am indebted to my colleagues M. A. Hughes* and D. G. Winter†), but based on the reaction

$$FeO_{(s)} + Cu_2O_{(s)} \rightleftharpoons 2Cu_{(m)} + Fe_3O_{4(s)}$$

produced results differing widely from published data. This could imply that iron in its higher oxidation state plays only a minor role in the system.

The comments by Dr. J. H. E. Jeffes (p. 608) on metal sampling are most welcome and earnest consideration will be given to his suggestions when further test work is carried out.

I would like to thank Mr. J. S. Jacobi (p. 609) for his enthusiastic and encouraging remarks. The wide variations in slag composition mentioned in the introductory statement do indeed refer to laboratory studies, in which slags from several secondary copper smelters were examined. These slags differed essentially in the quantity of the major slag-forming constituents, such as silica, lime and total iron. It was because of these differences, however, that the results proved so useful in identifying factors affecting metal reduction during carbothermic smelting.

The comments by Mr. G. J. Brittingham (p. 611) on the necessity of introducing an alternative phase for the collection of non-ferrous metals if very low levels of copper in treated slag are required, were confirmed in initial studies on secondary copper slag systems at Warren Spring Laboratory. Blast-furnace slags were smelted with pyrites and the residual slags contained <0·15% Cu. The matte grade in these tests, however, was only about 2–2·5% Cu and the work was not pursued.

C. J. G. Evans and P. M. J. Gray Mr. C. F. Harris is thanked for the contribution (pp. 608–9) on the mineralogy of sinter.

---

* Chemical Engineering Department, University of Bradford.
† Warren Spring Laboratory, Department of Trade and Industry, Stevenage, Hertfordshire.

In reply to Professor T. R. A. Davey (p. 609–10), we are unaware of any recent incident of pyrophoric zinc dust being produced from an ISF due to the presence of tin. The presence of tin in the furnace is so detrimental to slab zinc quality that the relationship between tin and the pyrophoric nature of zinc dust had not seemed worth separate study.

In reply to Mr. I. D. Vassilev (p. 610), we would refer him to the paper on copper in the ISF.* The upper limit for copper in concentrates is not known, but available evidence suggests that it is probable that a level of 6–7% Cu could be handled successfully by the process.

Kauko Kaasila and Eero Löytymäki   In reply to Mr. W. Drummond (p. 610), if the flash-smelter gases are used to produce elemental sulphur, the use of a superheater is out of the question because, besides elemental sulphur, the waste gases then contain hydrogen sulphide, which causes corrosion on common carbon steels, even at temperatures above 350°C. By increasing the chromium content of the steel, it has become possible to raise the operating temperature to about 450–480°C; however, the surface temperature of the superheater tube in waste-heat boilers normally exceeds 450°C.

As far as the process is concerned where the gases are used for producing sulphuric acid, it has been clearly proved that zinc, lead, bismuth, arsenic and other dust components with a low melting point stick rather to the hot super-heater tubes than to tubes generating saturated steam. For this reason a super-heater in the waste-heat boiler is not recommended in general.

If the required superheating degree is relatively low, the use of a superheater in the waste-heat boiler may be considered in some cases as far as the production of sulphuric acid is concerned. A condition for this arrangement is that the flash-smelter exhaust gases contain only minor amounts of zinc, lead and other low-melting dust components and that the cleaning of the superheater be properly arranged.

It is difficult to give any recommendations for a minimum capacity, queried by Mr. A. Vega (p. 610). At the metallurgical research plant of Outokumpu Oy the furnace capacity is one ton of concentrate per hour. The smallest flash-smelting furnaces designed as commercial units are capable of smelting approximately 200–240 tons of concentrate per day. A furnace small in size is, of course, not so advantageous with regard to heat economy as a large one. As an example, it can be mentioned that with the same concentrate and under equal circumstances the fuel consumption per ton of concentrate for a 50 t/h concentrate feed is roughly half of that for a feed of 10 t/h. The operating labour requirement in the whole smelter will be reduced in the same proportion.

---

* See reference 13 on page 588.

x*

Closing speeches

Chairman
Professor M. G. Fleming

Dr. D. A. Temple   As Chairman of the Organizing Committee, I appreciate the opportunity to make some closing remarks on behalf of the Committee, and would first like to comment on the papers presented and the ensuing discussion.

We have been encouraged to see the large spread of papers from so many metallurgical centres in 13 countries, but many of us will regret that the paper from the U.S.S.R. on the Kivcet process did not materialize.

The Organizing Committee originally requested that cost data on operations should be indicated, where appropriate, and we have been most gratified to find that so many authors have presented an appreciable amount of economic information in their papers. The inclusion of such data, when correctly interpreted, makes so much more sense in the profit-orientated society in which we live.

I know only too well that it can be unwise to make comparisons, but it has been interesting to note the proportion of papers featuring high-temperature techniques with those which involve hydrometallurgy. In this Symposium the ratio is more than 5:1 (about 2:1 for the 1967 meeting). At the end of the last metallurgical Symposium both Mr. M. J. Cahalan and Dr. K. W. Downes drew attention to the increasing interest and role of the chemical engineer and, especially, the organic chemist in extractive metallurgy.* I hope that this change in the proportion of papers submitted does not mean that specialists in the metallurgical industry following these disciplines are submitting papers on their advanced work to other professional bodies in preference to this Institution—this would be very regrettable.

Another possible explanation that I have heard, admittedly by one who perhaps hankers after fusion in one form or other, is that the punditry may possibly be wrong when they predict that we will all be 'in solution' by the next generation.

It is my personal belief that, when the next IMM metallurgy symposium is held, much more attention will need to be paid to the treatment of secondary metals and waste materials containing metals. The Committee tried to obtain more papers on this important subject, but, clearly, improved rapport with the secondary metal industry is necessary so that the subject can be jointly considered with this Institution. This will, I think, be in the interests of national and international conservation, because specialists in the minerals industry, as represented in this Institution, can apply useful skills for the recovery of metal values. Again, comparing these last three days with the 1967 meeting, there is a larger number of papers dealing with different aspects of copper metallurgy—illustrating the scope and incentive of this metal for the development of improved techniques. Many other metals are considered in the papers to varying extents; zinc and lead, in fact, tie for second place in attention given. There are some exceptions, of course, but perhaps the lack of papers on nickel this year will be remedied in the future. These comments on hydrometallurgy, secondary metals and nickel indicate a period of rapid change in the extractive industry.

* *Advances in extractive metallurgy* (London: Institution of Mining and Metallurgy, 1968), 993–4.

Another impression gained during the last three days is that the established specialists have contributed again to the Symposium; at least four authors or co-authors have submitted papers on both occasions. The Institution is proud to have been chosen by them to present their papers. For example, we have heard again from Dr. Walsh of the Mines Branch, Ottawa, about the concern in Canada for energy supplies in the ferrous industry. The Australians have told us of the latest progress in continuous copper metallurgy; on this occasion the paper by Dr. Worner and his colleagues was supplemented by papers from Canada and Czechoslovakia (incidentally, the discussion of the relative merits of the Noranda and WORCRA processes can be judged to be a draw!). We have heard again from Monsieur Lenoir and his colleagues about further aspects of Hoboken copper–lead practice, and the extensive studies made by Warren Spring Laboratory on the electrochemistry of metals have been described further by Dr. Bowles and his colleague.

The major innovation at the Symposium has been the introduction of an informal discussion meeting on environmental pollution (see pp. xi–xv). The Committee felt that the opportunity should be taken to discuss this topical and important subject when there was present together such a representative gathering from the world's smelting and refining industries. We were most fortunate in having Sir Frederick Warner—a Past-President of the Institution of Chemical Engineers and Visiting Professor in Environmental Studies at University College, London—as Chairman. The excellent introductions to the subject by Mr. E. C. Mantle and Mr. D. G. Fowler were followed by contributions which were both interesting and authoritative. I feel that this meeting could usefully have continued for a longer time, and perhaps the Institution may consider how best this subject can be adequately discussed in the future.

On behalf of the Institution and the Organizing Committee, I would like to express thanks to all those people who have contributed and helped to make the Symposium a success.

To the authors—your efforts in producing stimulating papers are much appreciated; we acknowledge the many hours spent in their preparation.

To the contributors to the discussions—your comments have helped greatly to make the Symposium a lively meeting.

To the referees—your patience and judgment played so large a part in structuring the programme.

To the sessional chairmen—you have conducted the proceedings with great aplomb, maintaining the fine balance between the clock and the eager questioner.

To the registrants—The Institution appreciates the compliment paid to it by your attendance—often from distant parts of the world.

We must also acknowledge the support provided by the organizations which sponsor so many of us present.

The excellent teamwork by the secretariat of the Institution has enabled the administration to proceed smoothly. It is difficult to single out particular tributes, but the fine work of the Editorial Department must not pass without acknowledgment. I am sure that Michael Jones now has an aim to improve on the speed with which the 1967 Symposium volume was published.

In conclusion, I would like to express our appreciation to the Institution of Electrical Engineers for making available to us this Conference Hall, which has proved to be ideally suited to the requirements of our Symposium.

Dr. Howard K. Worner and **Dr. A. W. Schlechten** then expressed their thanks to the Organizing Committee and to the Institution staff for the considerable effort expended to guarantee the high standard of papers presented and the smooth running of the Symposium.

The Chairman thanked Dr. Temple, Dr. Worner and Dr. Schlechten for their remarks. The Institution was very gratified that so many distinguished registrants had arranged to attend the Symposium, the success of which was due in large part to their presence.

He then declared the Symposium formally closed.

Author index

Subject index

Printed in Great Britain by
Alden & Mowbray Ltd
at the Alden Press, Oxford